Readings in the
ECONOMICS OF AGRICULTURE

The Series of
Republished Articles on
Economics
VOLUME XIII

Readings in the

Selected by a Committee of
The American Economic Association

The participation of the American Economic Association in the presentation of this series consists in the appointment of a committee to determine the subjects of the volumes and of special committees to select the articles for each volume.

ECONOMICS OF AGRICULTURE

Selection Committee for This Volume

KARL A. FOX
D. GALE JOHNSON

1969 • *Published for the Association by*

RICHARD D. IRWIN, INC., Homewood, Illinois

IRWIN-DORSEY LIMITED, Georgetown, Ontario

First Printing, June, 1969

Library of Congress Catalog Card No. 69-15543

Printed in the United States of America

Dedicated to
HENRY C. TAYLOR
1873–1969
Pioneer in applying the
methods of economics to
the study of agriculture

Acknowledgments

All of the articles in this volume were first published in professional journals or symposium volumes, as noted at the beginning of each contribution. We appreciate the prompt and cordial responses of all the editors, publishers, and authors in permitting us to reproduce these articles without charge. The places of original publication include the *Journal of Farm Economics* (renamed the *American Journal of Agricultural Economics* in 1968), the *American Economic Review,* the *Journal of Political Economy, Econometrica,* the *Economic Journal,* the *Australian Journal of Agricultural Economics, Agricultural Economics Research,* and a symposium volume issued by the Iowa State University Press.

We wish to thank also the many agricultural economists who responded to our October 1965 requests for suggestions as to appropriate articles for the volume. Their advice was most helpful; we of course accept full responsibility for our selections. Our criteria are described in the Editors' Introduction.

The two editors were equally involved in searching the literature, evaluating suggestions, and making the final selection of articles. Manuscript preparation, proofreading, and related production activities were handled at Iowa State University under the supervision of Karl A. Fox. Dr. B. C. Sanyal monitored the permission letters to authors and publishers and the changes supplied by some authors. Charlotte Latta gave invaluable help in correcting the galleys and page proofs. Rhea Barron prepared the index of names. Juanita Adams, Helen M. Brown, Rita Bauman, and Karen Skilbred all helped at various stages with typing, correspondence, and duplicating. The surviving errors are, we hope, minor ones.

The merit of the volume lies in the contributions of the individual authors. It has been a pleasure to review the work of many leading contributors to the 1945–66 literature of agricultural economics. Our decision to cluster articles relating to a limited number of topics, together with the limitation on total length, means that some outstanding research workers could not be represented here. The literature contains many other articles (not to mention technical bulletins and books) of quality and importance comparable to those included; the reader should recognize that he is getting some of the best but by no means all of it.

Ames, Iowa
Chicago, Illinois
May, 1969

KARL A. FOX
D. GALE JOHNSON

Table of Contents

PART V. AGGREGATE ANALYSIS OF PRODUCTION AND SUPPLY

PART VI. ECONOMIC DEVELOPMENT

PART VII. AGRICULTURAL POLICY

INDEX OF NAMES

Editors' Introduction

This is one of a series of volumes of readings in various fields of economics sponsored by the American Economic Association. We believe the present collection will be useful to graduate students and professional economists who wish to have a general overview of the major analytical problems tackled and methods used by leading agricultural economists in the period subsequent to World War II.

Agricultural economics does not have a unique body of theory and methods. Agricultural economics research involves the application of economic theory and appropriate (usually quantitative) methods to problems arising in or related to the agricultural sector. In this volume we have attempted to achieve some degree of focus in terms of subject matter content of the articles; we have by no means covered the range of topics that individuals who consider themselves to be agricultural economists have in fact dealt with. In a number of instances, some of the most important articles written by authors whose articles are included in the volume have been excluded because of the limitations imposed by the particular major topics that we have emphasized. The topics selected for inclusion are those that are either unique to the agricultural sector or appear there in distinctly different forms than in other sectors. We have arbitrarily limited the range of publication dates to 1945–66. This limitation was not an easy one to accept since it meant that some of the classic articles in agricultural economics had to be excluded. However, the need to keep the volume within a reasonable size limit required restraint with respect to both the time period covered and the range of topics.

Since this volume has been prepared, at least in part, to meet the interests of economists generally rather than primarily for agricultural economists, we hope we will be excused if we briefly outline the areas of economic research in which the work of agricultural economists has been of a pioneering nature.

Perhaps the most important contribution of agricultural economics to economic research has been due to the relatively early and sustained application of quantitative methods to the analysis of economic problems and issues. The innovators were not agricultural economists in all cases; among them were Henry L. Moore (Columbia University) and Henry Schultz (University of Chicago), men primarily interested in econometric method; and Sewall Wright, a brilliant geneticist whose statistical concepts influenced the thinking of Mordecai Ezekiel and some other agricultural economists.

The immediate source of inspiration and method for the development of numerous demand and supply studies during the 1920's was Henry L. Moore, one of the few American economists of his generation who was strongly influenced by Walras and Pareto. As the Walras-Pareto tradition in economic theory became the dominant one in the United States after World War II, some of the work influenced by Moore seems surprisingly modern in outlook. Mordecai Ezekiel, Frederick V. Waugh, Holbrook Working, and Elmer J. Working did work on the theory, methodology, and implementation of statistical demand analysis in the 1920's that has stood the test of time. The work of these men and others was undertaken about the same time that Henry Schultz, a student of Moore, was doing his demand studies for numerous agricultural products. During the 1920's there was also a great deal of attention to the empirical estimation of supply curves for agricultural products, an interest that may also be attributed to Henry Moore, whose *Forecasting the Yield and Price of Cotton* had appeared in 1917. Foster F. Elliott, Louis H. Bean, and Bradford B. Smith were leading contributors in this field.

It should be noted, too, that one of the early appliers of correlation and regression analysis to supply and demand problems in the 1920's was Henry A. Wallace, who served as Secretary of Agriculture from 1933 to 1941. While Henry Wallace during the 1920's was an editor and not associated with any college or university, he had close ties to the economists and statisticians at Iowa State College (now University) and with George Snedecor wrote *Correlation and Machine Calculation* which was published in 1925 and was the source of inspiration, instruction, and frustration for scores of agricultural economists.

The development of statistical demand and supply analysis marked the beginning of cumulative work in applied econometrics in the United States. It was a young man's field; Ezekiel, Waugh, and the two Workings made major contributions, both empirical and methodological, in their mid-twenties. These men were just a few years older than Tinbergen, Leontief, and others who came to dominate the new field of econometrics in the 1930's; the publications of Ezekiel, Holbrook Working, Waugh, Henry Schultz and E. J. Working during 1922–29 were widely known in Europe and were emulated by a number of young economists there. Moore, Schultz, Ezekiel, Waugh, Holbrook Working and E. J. Working became Fellows of the Econometric Society soon after this distinction was inaugurated; several of them contributed articles to the first volume of *Econometrica* (1933).

A second major area in which agricultural economists made pioneering applications and contributions was production economics. John D. Black in his *Introduction to Production Economics* (1926) summarized and codified and built upon the work of agricultural economists for the previous quarter century. Major contributions to the study of production and the firm had been made by Henry C. Taylor, George F. Warren, and William J. Spillman. The work on the firm and production had included the study of input-output relations, the empirical estimation of diminishing returns functions, the development of farm budgets (which could have served as a precursor for linear programming), the analysis of specialization and comparative advantage, and the evaluation of success of farmers in the maximization of income from given or accessible resources.

The third area in which agricultural economists have made substantial contributions has been in the study of governmental policy. The agricultural situation in the 1880's and 1890's aroused much concern and activity among farmers and political leaders. Extension of the railroads across the prairies and Great Plains and the improvement of farm machinery had led to a vast increase in production of wheat, corn, hogs, and cattle and to prices which brought distress to farmers in both new and old farming areas of the United States. (Railroads on other continents had similar though smaller effects, and the depression in prices of agricultural staples was worldwide.) Continued low prices caused farmer-leaders in the early 1890's to advocate government intervention on behalf of farmers along a number of lines, many of which were pursued in subsequent decades.

This economic distress and political ferment made a great impression on Henry C. Taylor (1873–1969), who did more than any one other person to shape the development of agricultural economics during the first quarter of the present century. Many other farm youths who entered this field were no doubt impressed by the same circumstances, in which individual farmers were left to cope as best they might with a disequilibrium situation of worldwide scope. By the time Taylor, Benjamin H. Hibbard, and others of their generation had completed their graduate studies, the price situation was improving and selective reforms (as in the farm credit system) rather than massive intervention provided the agenda for farm policy during the early 1900's. World War I led to a new expansion of wheat production, a short-lived inflation in farm prices and land values, and a disastrous deflation commencing in 1920.

The task of interpreting this situation and contributing to the design and evaluation of remedies fell to a new generation of agricultural economists, most notably John D. Black, Joseph S. Davis, and Edwin G. Nourse. As the Great Depression of the 1930's superseded the "agricultural depression" of the 1920's, still another generation, including a number of the young demand and supply analysts, became involved in program development and appraisal under the new Secretary of Agriculture, Henry A. Wallace. Wallace could and did go over the multiple regression analyses and scatter diagrams which underlay the conclusions of his economic advisers (Ezekiel, L. H. Bean, H. R. Tolley, F. F. Elliott, O. V. Wells, and several other quantitative economists occupied such roles formally or informally at various periods during 1933–41); he was no doubt one of the few cabinet officers in our history who was so nearly up-to-date in the modes of economic analysis relevant to his policy domain.

Most of Wallace's economic advisers (including the program development staff of the Agricultural Adjustment Administration under the direction of H. R. Tolley) had previously served in the U.S. Bureau of Agricultural Economics and had won recognition for their published research. In the AAA and the Office of the Secretary most of their work was anonymous, though not necessarily unpublished; some outstanding reports were issued (as seems appropriate in our political system) as institutional products signed by the Secretary of Agriculture or the AAA Administrator.

From 1933 into the 1960's, the U.S. Department of Agriculture's capacity to perform "in-house" analyses of complex economic programs on short notice has been almost unique among federal agencies. During the 1940's and early 1950's, USDA economists pioneered in the quantitative analysis and comparison of alternative farm price support policies under alternative assumptions concerning general economic conditions. Some of these analyses involved the use of quantitative relationships equivalent to approximately 100 simultaneous equations. Leaders in this type of analysis included O. V. Wells, James P. Cavin, Willard W. Cochrane, Nathan M. Koffsky, Rex F. Daly, C. Kyle Randall, Harold F. Breimyer, and Karl A. Fox. This work built upon the tradition of demand and supply analysis already mentioned, and is reflected to a limited extent in the articles by Fox and by Cochrane in the present volume.

In 1961, George E. Brandow (Pennsylvania State University) synthesized much of the earlier work on demand and supply functions into a completely integrated model of interrelationships of demand and supply for agricultural commodities in the United States at the level of about 25 major crop and livestock commodities and groups. A central feature of Brandow's model was a complete matrix of own-price and cross-price elasticities and income elasticities of consumer demand for all food products, meeting the consistency requirements specified in the pure theory of consumer demand. This model has been further modified and developed for a new generation of computerized "in-house" analyses of the kind alluded to in Cochrane's paper.

A fourth area in which agricultural economists have made significant contributions during the past 20 years has been in the analysis of economic development. While it is true that this work has not yet resulted in a general theory of economic growth, agricultural economists have added to our knowledge of important elements of growth. Attempts to explain the rapid increase in productivity in U.S. agriculture which could not be explained in terms of conventional inputs led to some of the earliest and most effective attempts to estimate the economic values of agricultural research and education. Agricultural economists have also emphasized the structural changes in an economy that occur with economic growth. As these contributions have been made for the most part since 1950, a number of them (by T. W. Schultz, William H. Nicholls, Zvi Griliches, Bruce Johnston, John Mellor, and others) are included in this volume.

The first and second distinctive areas mentioned, demand and supply analysis and production economics, are represented in the present collection. Unfortunately, the quantitative analyses of the effects of alternative price support programs are too voluminous, and in some particulars too dated in terms of the particular programs being compared, to be represented here. Instead, we have included a set of articles on agricultural policy which emphasize basic principles and the institutional and political aspects of policy determination and implementation relating to food and agriculture. References to some of the earlier published work in demand and supply analysis, production economics, and agricultural policy are listed at the end of this introduction.

In some respects, the tradition of quantitative empirical research in agricultural economics can be traced back to the 1880's, when federal funds were first appropriated to help support the establishment of agricultural experiment stations in the land-grant universities. (In the 1880's, of course, most of these institutions were essentially "colleges of agriculture and mechanic arts.") Administratively, agricultural economists in the land-grant colleges reported to the same research director as did the agronomists, agricultural engineers, animal scientists, and food technologists. Hence, agricultural economists benefited from the realization that empirical research required office space, equipment, research assistants, and clerical and computing help in addition to a specific allocation of the faculty members' time for research. The U.S. Bureau of Agricultural Economics (founded in 1922, though some of its constituent groups went as far back as 1910 or earlier) was a thoroughly professional research organization, with good equipment and ample clerical, stenographic, technical, and junior professional personnel to carry out the research plans of the senior agricultural economists.

Comparable facilities for quantitative and empirical research in other fields of economics were quite rare until the 1950's. The concentration and professionalization of computing facilities and skills in central university installations, beginning in the 1950's, have permitted economists in other fields to undertake quantitative research without making large investments in departmental clerical and computing pools.

Broadly speaking, the comparative advantage of agricultural economists in funds, supporting personnel, and facilities for quantitative economic research was still pronounced during the 1945–55 decade. From 1955 on, high-speed computers have become increasingly available to economists and agricultural economists alike; the National Science Foundation and many federal action agencies in addition to the U.S. Department of Agriculture have become interested in quantitative economic research; and expertise in econometrics and statistics is no longer a basis for distinguishing between agricultural and other economists.

We have described our intended readership, our time period, our scope, and, in general terms, our rationale for emphasizing certain fields of agricultural economics in this volume. We were also guided by additional constraints, some but not all of which were self-imposed:

1. The American Economic Association Committee on Research and Publications urged us to keep the total length below 500 or at most 550 pages;
2. We decided to select only one article by any one author, but did in the end decide to violate this criterion to include two articles each by T. W. Schultz and Frederick V. Waugh;
3. We have included only articles which were published in English;
4. We have included only journal articles or articles published in conference or symposium volumes; this meant that we excluded many excellent technical bulletins published by the U.S. Department of Agriculture or the State Agricultural Experiment Stations, not on principle, but because bulletins are normally considerably longer than journal articles; and
5. We have selected clusters of two or more articles which would be internally complementary and coherent.

The decision to emphasize a limited number of topics resulted in the exclusion of a number of areas in which agricultural economists have specialized. Among the more important fields that have been excluded are farm credit, rural taxation, land tenure and land economics, farm labor, and international trade.

While we take full responsibility for our selections, we have not been capricious. In October, 1965, we sent letters to more than 40 agricultural economists, located in many different universities and in several U.S. Department of Agriculture agencies, requesting them to list articles which we should consider for the proposed book of readings. We received replies from a substantial proportion of them, some recommending articles in a particular specialty and others presenting rather extensive lists. We have given consideration to all of these suggestions.

Since 1947, the American Farm Economic Association (renamed the American Agricultural Economics Association in January, 1968) has given annual awards for outstanding research publications. The basis of the awards has undergone some modifications during this period. However, the typical pattern has been that three awards have been given each year for outstanding, published, agricultural economics research by economists under the age of 41. The awards have been made for journal articles, technical bulletins, and books. In addition, the association has given one award each year for the best article published in the *Journal of Farm Economics*, without regard to the author's age.

Many of the articles and bulletins honored by the American Farm Economic Association had been read by us at the time of publication or shortly thereafter. We reexamined all of the journal articles and articles in symposium volumes which had received awards from the American Farm Economic Association. Several articles in the present volume have been drawn from this group.

In addition, we searched all the issues of the *Journal of Farm Economics* from 1945 through 1966 for suitable articles by highly regarded agricultural economists who had received research awards for bulletins or books but not for journal articles. In some cases, we reluctantly concluded that none of their JFE articles was suitable for the purposes of our book. It should be noted that the AFEA awards to agricultural economists under 41 were frequently based on articles published in such journals as *Econometrica, American Economic Review*, *Journal of Political Economy*, *Agricultural Economics Research*, and occasionally in journals published in other English-speaking countries. Finally, we examined lists of members of the American Farm Economic Association, listed by states and by fields of primary professional interests, to see if we had inadvertently omitted outstanding contributors to areas of high research productivity in the 1945–66 period.

We cannot claim optimality for our selection at either the level of individual articles or the level of clusters. For example, it is possible that a cluster of articles on bargaining power in agriculture might have been drawn together and substituted for some other cluster.

Some aspects of the results of our selection are as follows:

1. Of the 27 articles, 16 were published in the *Journal of Farm Economics*; 3 more were published in journals or symposium volumes intended primarily for agricultural economists; and the remaining 8 were published in the *American Economic Review* (3), the *Journal of Political Economy* (2), *Econometrica* (2), and the *Economic Journal* (1).

2. As of April, 1968, the authors of the articles were located at 16 different universities. One author (formerly with the U.S. Department of Agriculture) was deceased. Some of the authors had served at two or more universities, and several authors now located at universities had spent substantial portions of their careers in the U.S. Department of Agriculture. One or two authors were located on or near land-grant university campuses but were employed by the U.S. Department of Agriculture. The authors with current or past USDA connections include Brewster, Waugh, Breimyer, Fox, Cochrane, Day, Nerlove and Tyner; this list is probably not exhaustive.

For the reader who wishes to see the agricultural economics literature of 1945–66 in a historical perspective, the following comments may be helpful:

Some towering figures of the 1930's and 1920's are not represented in this book, even though several of them were still publishing economic articles and books of high merit subsequent to 1945. We refer particularly to John D. Black, Joseph S. Davis, and Edwin G. Nourse. After 1945, Black was still writing primarily in agricultural economics; Davis and Nourse were writing primarily in other fields. Each of these three men served as president of the American Farm Economic Association (in 1932, 1936, and 1924) and also of the American Economic Association (in 1955, 1944, and 1942 respectively).

A considerable number of John D. Black's contributions are contained in his *Economics for Agriculture* (1959), edited by James P. Cavin. This book also contains appraisals of John D. Black's contributions to various fields of agricultural economics by recognized authorities in the respective fields.

Black, Davis, and Nourse contributed to a series of books on agricultural programs and policies of the 1930's, a series sponsored by the Brookings Institution. Several volumes of this series are listed in the references at the end of this introduction.

Agricultural marketing is somewhat underrepresented in our readings. Here the reader is referred to Frederick V. Waugh's *Readings on Agricultural Marketing* (1954), which was assembled and published under the sponsorship of the American Farm Economic Association. This book will provide a good introduction to the agricultural marketing literature up to 1953.

A historical perspective on agricultural policy is provided by Murray R. Benedict's *Farm Policies of the United States, 1790-1950* (1953). Benedict supplies a great many references to bills, acts, and policy statements as well as to the relevant economic analyses, and describes the economic and political settings in which the successive major policy issues were debated.

Henry C. Taylor's *The Story of Agricultural Economics* (1952) covers the period from 1840 to 1932. A considerable part of the story is told in terms of the contributions of outstanding individuals in the land-grant university system and the U.S. Department of Agriculture. Taylor was personally involved in the organization of the American Farm Economic Association, the U.S. Bureau of Agricultural Economics, and the Farm Foundation and his book sheds a great deal of light on the origins, intended goals, and achievements of these major organizations and institutions concerned with the agricultural economics profession.

The "state of the arts" in agricultural economics research as of 1931–33 is illuminated by a series of reports on *Scope and Method* (in agricultural economics and rural sociology), sponsored by the Social Science Research Council under the general coordination and editorship of John D. Black. This series shows that a high level of achievement and sophistication had been reached by 1933 in several fields of agricultural economics; the outlines of research yet to be done were ambitious and imaginative in most cases.

However, the acute distress of farmers as a result of the Great Depression and the institution of massive federal programs in 1933 drew a whole generation of agricultural economists into program administration, program analysis, and action-oriented research. Ezekiel and Bean became economic advisers to Secretary of Agriculture Henry A. Wallace. The Agricultural Adjustment Administration during 1933–38 contained an outstanding program development and appraisal staff drawn largely from the Bureau of

Agricultural Economics, including H. R. Tolley, F. F. Elliott and O. V. Wells. A good many Ph.D.'s of the 1920's became high ranking administrators by the end of the 1930's; from 1933 on, new Ph.D.'s and near-Ph.D.'s flowed into the commodity divisions of the Agricultural Adjustment Administration, where some first-rate analyses of demand, supply, tax incidence, and other phenomena were made. World War II siphoned agricultural economists into high administrative and advisory positions in the War Food Administration, the Combined Food Board, the Office of Price Administration, the Board of Economic Warfare, the Office of War Mobilization and Reconversion, and other agencies. At the end of the war, Tolley and Ezekiel helped organize the Economics Division of the Food and Agriculture Organization and continued with FAO; Waugh joined the newly established Council of Economic Advisers under the chairmanship of Edwin G. Nourse; Wells and Elliott became Chief and Associate Chief respectively of the Bureau of Agricultural Economics.

Thus, the high promise shown by the journal literature of the 1920's and the *Scope and Method* series of 1931–33 was not borne out by the journal literature and formal research bulletins of 1933–45. Many good articles and some excellent ones were, of course, published during 1933–41, but the 1920's had seemed to presage something more and better. The times demanded action and, as a rule, anonymity for those agricultural economists who were closest to policy formation. The books on evaluation of the AAA programs by Nourse, Davis, and Black—who retained their respective Brookings Institution, Stanford, and Harvard connections—were perhaps the most outstanding contributions by agricultural economists to the scholarly record of the 1930's.

Further perspective for the period from 1886 through 1954 may be gained by scanning the first four volumes of the American Economic Association's *Index to Economic Journals*. A reader who is fairly well oriented as to leading names in both agricultural economics and other fields in the United States and England can gain some feeling for the changing areas which attracted the interests of leading agricultural economists and also of the effects of the Great Depression and World War II upon fields of research and upon individual careers.

Last but not least, the reader is referred to the *Journal of Farm Economics*, which commenced publication in 1919. (The name has been changed to *American Journal of Agricultural Economics* as of January, 1968.)

Trends and cycles in agricultural economics research since 1945 no doubt reflect the particular institutional characteristics of this field. A large proportion of all agricultural economists in the United States are employed in colleges of agriculture in the land-grant universities or by the U.S. Department of Agriculture. These institutions were designed to aid commercial agriculture and the rural community. In these institutions, agricultural economists form a minority of perhaps 10 or 15 percent as compared with scientists who are primarily concerned with the technology of crop and livestock production and food processing—fields in which research results are of primary interest to commercial agriculture. Much research in agricultural economics is also intended to increase the efficiency of commercial agriculture and the associated processing and marketing industries. The responsibilities of agricultural economists for helping other members of the rural community are less easily defined, particularly in view of the present *de facto* synthesis of rural and urban communities into multicounty functional economic areas or commuting fields.

In their institutional settings, most agricultural economists try to adapt their research programs in the light of changes in (1) problems of U.S. agriculture as directly perceived by themselves; (2) agricultural policy issues as reflected in dialogues between farm leaders, members of Congress, the President, the Secretary of Agriculture, and the various administrators responsible to him; and (3) the availability of research funds from state and federal appropriations, including the earmarking of funds to encourage or discourage research in specific areas. For example, marketing research was given special funding and encouragement in the mid-1920's and again through the Research and Marketing Act of 1946.

It is not our intention to characterize these institutional relationships as either good or bad. However, these special features of the agricultural economics community (or at least a large segment of it) must be recognized as major factors shaping the direction, volume, and quality of agricultural economics research at any given time. In recent years the Ford and Rockefeller Foundations have also encouraged agricultural economists to involve themselves in research and advisory activities in the developing economies of Asia, Africa, and Latin America.

SELECTED REFERENCES

The following references include items specifically mentioned in the preceding pages and others which will facilitate access to bodies of literature described in more general terms, primarily literature published before 1945. The articles in the present volume in most cases contain references to related works published in and after 1945.

A. Works of Broad Scope

1. Taylor, Henry C., and Anne Dewees Taylor. *The Story of Agricultural Economics in the United States, 1840–1932*. Ames: Iowa State University Press, 1952.
2. Benedict, Murray R. *Farm Policies of the United States, 1790–1950*. New York: The Twentieth Century Fund, 1953.
3. Waugh, Frederick V. (ed.). *Readings on Agricultural Marketing*. Ames: Iowa State University Press, 1954.

4. Black, John D. *Economics for Agriculture: Selected Writings of John D. Black*, edited by James Pierce Cavin. Cambridge: Harvard University Press, 1959.
5. Arnold, Carl J., and Raleigh Barlowe. "The Journal of Farm Economics—Its First 35 Years," *Journal of Farm Economics*, Vol. 36 (August 1954), pp. 441–52.
6. Black, John D. (ed.). Social Science Research Council *Scope and Method* series, Bulletin Nos.:
    1. Research in Public Finance in Relation to Agriculture—Scope and Method, 1931.
    3. Research in Agricultural Credit—Scope and Method, 1931.
    2. Research in Agricultural Land Utilization—Scope and Method, 1931.
    7. Research in Marketing of Farm Products—Scope and Method, 1932.
    4. Research in Rural Population—Scope and Method, 1932.
    13. Research Relating to Farm Management—Scope and Method, 1932.
    9. Research in Prices of Farm Products—Scope and Method, 1933.
    20. Research in Agricultural Land Tenure—Scope and Method, 1933.
    16. Research in Farm Labor—Scope and Method, 1933.
    15. Research in Agricultural Cooperation—Scope and Method, 1933.
    12. Research in Rural Organization—Scope and Method, 1933.
    11. Research in Farm Family Living—Scope and Method, 1933.
    6. Research Relating to Agricultural Income—Scope and Method, 1933.
    10. Research in Agricultural Index Numbers—Scope and Method, 1938.
7. American Economic Association. *Index of Economic Journals.* Homewood, Ill.: Richard D. Irwin, Vols. I through VII, 1886–1967; publication dates 1961 through 1968.
8. *Journal of Farm Economics*, Vols. 1–48, 1919–67. Name changed effective 1968 to:
   American Journal of Agricultural Economics, Vol. 49, 1968 and continuing.

B. Empirical Demand and Supply Studies and Closely Related Works on Statistical Techniques and Economic Theory

Demand and Supply Studies:

1. Moore, Henry L. *Economic Cycles: Their Law and Cause.* New York: Macmillan, 1914.
2. Moore, Henry L. *Forecasting the Yield and Price of Cotton.* New York: Macmillan, 1917.
3. Moore, Henry L. "Empirical laws of demand and supply and the flexibility of prices," *Political Science Quarterly*, Vol. 34 (1919), pp. 546–67.
4. Wallace, Henry A. *Agricultural Prices.* Des Moines: Wallace Publishing Co., 1920.
5. Working, Holbrook. Factors determining the price of potatoes in St. Paul and Minneapolis. University of Minnesota Agr. Exp. Sta. Tech. Bul. 10, St. Paul, October 1922.

6. Waugh, Frederick V. Factors influencing the price of New Jersey potatoes on the New York market. N.J. Department of Agriculture, Circular 66, Trenton, July 1923.
7. Schultz, Henry. "The statistical measurement of the elasticity of demand for beef," *Journal of Farm Economics*, Vol. 6 (July 1924), pp. 254–78.
8. Wright, Sewall. Corn and hog correlations. U.S. Dept. Agr. Bul. 1300, 1925.
9. Smith, Bradford B. "Forecasting the acreage of cotton," *Journal of the American Statistical Association*, Vol. 20 (March 1925), pp. 31–47.
10. Killough, Hugh B. What makes the price of oats. U.S. Dept. Agr. Bul. 1351, 1925.
11. Smith, Bradford B. "The adjustment of agricultural production to demand," *Journal of Farm Economics*, Vol. 8 (April 1926), pp. 145–65.
12. Haas, George C., and Mordecai Ezekiel. Factors affecting the price of hogs. U.S. Dept. Agr. Bul. 1440, 1926.
13. Bosland, Chelcie C. "Forecasting the price of wheat," *Journal of the American Statistical Association*, Vol. 21 (June 1926), pp. 149–61.
14. Elliott, Foster F. "The nature and measurement of the elasticity of supply of farm products," *Journal of Farm Economics*, Vol. 9 (July 1927), pp. 299–302.
15. Elliott, Foster F. Adjusting hog production to market demand. University of Illinois Agr. Exp. Sta. Bul. 293, 1927.
16. Bean, Louis H. "The farmers' response to price," *Journal of Farm Economics*, Vol. 11 (1929), pp. 368–85.
17. Smith, Bradford B. Factors affecting the price of cotton. U.S. Dept. Agr. Tech. Bul. 50, Washington, 1928.
18. Warren, George F., and Frank A. Pearson. Interrelations of supply and price. Cornell University Agr. Exp. Sta. Bul. 466, Ithaca, 1928.

Statistical Techniques:

19. Wright, Sewall. "Correlation and causation," *Journal of Agricultural Research*, Vol. 20 (1921), pp. 557–85.
20. Wright, Sewall. "The theory of path coefficients: A reply to Niles' criticism," *Genetics*, Vol. 8 (May 1923), pp. 239–55.
21. Smith, Bradford B. The use of punched card tabulating equipment in multiple correlation problems. U.S. Department of Agriculture, Bureau of Agricultural Economics, 1923 (mimeographed).
22. Tolley, Howard R., and Mordecai Ezekiel. "A method of handling multiple correlation problems," *Journal of the American Statistical Association*, Vol. 18 (December 1923), pp. 994–1003.
23. Ezekiel, Mordecai. "A method of handling curvilinear correlation for any number of variables," *Journal of the American Statistical Association*, Vol. 19 (1924), pp. 431–53.
24. Wallace, Henry A., and George W. Snedecor. Correlation and machine calculation. Iowa State College Bul. 35, Ames, 1925.

25. Bean, Louis H. "A simplified method of graphic curvilinear correlation," *Journal of the American Statistical Association.* Vol. 24 (December 1929), pp. 386–97.
26. Ezekiel, Mordecai. *Methods of Correlation Analysis.* New York: John Wiley, 1930.
27. Frisch, Ragnar, and F. V. Waugh. "Partial time regressions as compared with individual trends," *Econometrica*, Vol. 1 (October 1933), pp. 387–401.
28. Wright, Sewall. "The method of path coefficients," *Annals of Mathematical Statistics*, Vol. 5 (1934), pp. 161–215.
29. Waugh, Frederick V. "A simplified method of determining multiple regression constants," *Journal of the American Statistical Association*, Vol. 30 (1935), pp. 694–700.

Econometric Theory:

30. Working, Holbrook. "The statistical determination of demand curves," *Quarterly Journal of Economics*, Vol. 39 (August 1925), pp. 503–43.
31. Working, Elmer J. "What do statistical 'demand curves' show?" *Quarterly Journal of Economics*, Vol. 41 (February 1927), pp. 212–35.
32. Ezekiel, Mordecai. "Statistical analyses and the 'laws' of price," *Quarterly Journal of Economics*, Vol. 42 (February 1928), pp. 199–227.
33. Schultz, Henry. *Statistical Laws of Demand and Supply.* Chicago: University of Chicago Press, 1928.
34. Ezekiel, Mordecai. "Some considerations on the analysis of the prices of competing or substitute commodities," *Econometrica*, Vol. 1, (April 1933), pp. 172–80.
35. Schultz, Henry. "A comparison of elasticities of demand obtained by different methods," *Econometrica*, Vol. 1 (July 1933), pp. 274–308.
36. Waugh, Frederick V., E. L. Burtis, and A. F. Wolf. "The controlled distribution of a crop among independent markets," *Quarterly Journal of Economics*, Vol. 51 (November 1936), pp. 1–41.
37. Ezekiel, Mordecai. "The cobweb theorem," *Quarterly Journal of Economics*, Vol. 52 (February 1938), pp. 255–80.
38. Schultz, Henry. *The Theory and Measurement of Demand.* Chicago: University of Chicago Press, 1938.

C. Production Economics

1. Taylor, Henry C. *An Introduction to the Study of Agricultural Economics.* New York: Macmillan, 1905.
2. Warren, George F. *Farm Management.* New York: Macmillan, 1913.
3. Taylor, Henry C. *Agricultural Economics.* New York: Macmillan, 1919.
4. Spillman, William J., and Emil Lang. *The Law of Diminishing Returns.* Yonkers-on-Hudson: World Book Company, 1924.
5. Black, John D. *Introduction to Production Economics.* New York: Henry Holt, 1926.

6. Black, John D., and Albert G. Black. *Production Organization.* New York: Henry Holt, 1929.
7. Black, John D., Marion Clawson, Charles R. Sayre, and Walter W. Wilcox. *Farm Management.* Cambridge, Mass.: Harvard University Press, 1947.
8. Heady, Earl O. *Economics of Agricultural Production and Resource Use.* Englewood Cliffs, N.J.: Prentice-Hall, 1952.

D. Agricultural Policy

1. Nourse, Edwin G. "The place of agriculture in modern industrial society," Pts. I–II, *Journal of Political Economy* (June, July 1919), pp. 466–97, pp. 561–77.
2. Wallace, Henry A. "Controlling agricultural output," *Journal of Farm Economics*, Vol. 5 (January 1923), pp. 16–27.
3. Warren, George F., "The agricultural depression," *Quarterly Journal of Economics*, Vol. 38 (February 1924), pp. 183–213.
4. Nourse, Edwin G. *American Agriculture and the European Market.* New York: McGraw-Hill, 1924.
5. Schultz, Henry. "Cost of production, supply and demand, and the tariff," *Journal of Farm Economics*, Vol. 9 (April 1927), pp. 192–209.
6. Davis, Joseph S. "The export debenture plan for aid to agriculture," *Quarterly Journal of Economics*, Vol. 43 (February 1929), pp. 250–77.
7. Black, John D. *Agricultural Reform in the United States.* New York: McGraw-Hill, 1929.
8. Ezekiel, Mordecai, and Louis H. Bean. Economic bases for the Agriculture Adjustment Act. Washington: U.S. Department of Agriculture, 1933.
9. Black, John D. *The Dairy Industry and the AAA.* Washington: Brookings Institution, 1935.
10. Davis, Joseph S. *Wheat and the AAA.* Washington: Brookings Institution, 1935.
11. Nourse, Edwin G., Joseph S. Davis, and John D. Black. *Three Years of the Agricultural Adjustment Administration.* Washington: Brookings Institution, 1937.
12. Davis, Joseph S. *On Agricultural Policy, 1926–38.* Stanford, Calif.: Stanford University Press, 1939.

Part I Some Special Characteristics of Agriculture

1 The Machine Process in Agriculture and Industry*

JOHN M. BREWSTER†‡

It has been said that because of mechanization, "A family farm in agriculture makes as little sense as a family factory in industry." Is this so? Evidently not. Family units of production are unthinkable in car and steel manufacture, but *both* family and larger-than-family units are as common in agriculture after mechanization as before. Why? Does not the reason lie in some profound difference in the nature of machine production in agriculture and in industry? On what physical foundations does this difference rest? Why are family and larger-than-family farms both compatible with either hand or machine technology? What non-technological factors are responsible for the dominance of each system in different regions, both now and in the pre-machine era? What important habits of life and thought does the advent of the machine process tend to conserve in agriculture but replace in industry?

I

In pre-machine times, farming and manufacture were alike in that operations in both cases were normally done sequentially, one after another; usually by the same individual or family. The rise of the machine process has

---

* *Journal of Farm Economics,* Vol. XXXII, No. 1 (February, 1950), pp 69–81.

† Deceased 1965; formerly with the U.S. Department of Agriculture, Washington, D.C.

‡ For helpful criticism and encouragement throughout the preparation of this paper, the author is much indebted to Howard L. Parsons, John C. Ellickson and Bushrod Allin of the Bureau of Agricultural Economics, John A. Baker and Sydney Reagan of the Production and Marketing Administration and Mrs. Barbara Reagan of the Bureau of Home Economics and Human Nutrition.

forced agriculture and industry to become progressively different in respect to the sequence in which men once performed both farm and industrial operations. For in substituting machine for hand power and manipulations in agriculture, individuals in no wise disturb their pre-machine habit of doing their production steps one after another whereas in making the same substitution in industry men thereby force themselves to acquire increasingly the new habit of performing simultaneously the many operations in a production process. As a consequence, the "Industrial Revolution" in agriculture is merely a spectacular change in the implements of production whereas in industry it is a further revolution in the sequence (order) in which men use their implements.[1]

II

In thus affecting differently the pre-machine sequence of operations, the substitution of machine power and manipulations in industry calls for a corresponding revolution in the pre-machine social structure whereas the contrary is true in agriculture.

For in transforming the older sequence of operations into the modern simultaneous pattern, industrial mechanization quickly multiplies the number of concurrent operations, in a production unit far beyond the number of workers in a household. Hence, in adopting machine techniques, men thereby force themselves to replace the older society family production units with enormously larger units, disciplined and guided by a hierarchy of bosses and managers.

---

[1] This fundamental difference between machine industry and agriculture stems from the contrasting nature of materials handled in each case. In farming, land is a basic resource, but normally absent from industrial production, except as a building site. Moreover, farming deals with living things, fixed in the soil; whereas industry deals with lifeless and mobile materials. Since land is not involved in industrial operations, transport and processing functions are usually separated, the job of transport being to carry materials to their (processing) operations. Hence industrial mechanization results in operationally interdependent machines (moment by moment) inasmuch as no transport or processing machine is normally able to operate except through receiving materials from simultaneously operating machines. Their actual functioning in this manner is made possible through the further fact that the mobile and lifeless qualities of industrial materials jointly enable both (1) the increased scale of production and (2) the concentration of operations required for their simultaneous performance. In contrast, transport and processing functions are inseparable aspects of any operation involving land, the job of transport being to carry operations to their materials. Hence, farm mechanization results in independent (moment by moment) machines inasmuch as each machine (doing an operation involving land) must embody both these functions and is therefore able to provide itself with its own materials. Though such machines are structurally capable of operating simultaneously, they are prevented from doing so by the fact that the seasonality of climate, biological cycles of living things, and the "spreadoutness" of the soil prevent (1) expansion of the scale of production and (2) the concentration of operations anywhere near the point required for their simultaneous performance.

In agriculture, however, machine methods remain as compatible as hand techniques with either (1) family or (2) larger-than-family units.[2] Their compatibility with family units lies in the fact that farm operations are as widely separated by time intervals after mechanization as before; hence, the number of things that must be done at the same time on a farm remains as close as ever to the number of workers in an ordinary family. But machines are equally compatible with larger-than-family units as they introduce no new obstacle to expanding a farm substantially beyond the capacity of a family to do the work in any *particular* operation. It is as easy (or difficult) for a large operator to grow more corn than a family can harvest when harvesting is done with a mechanical picker as when it is done with a husking peg. In general, sheer size alone thus distinguishes larger-than-family farms from family units, as there is nothing technologically unique about either.

III

But if neither hand nor machine techniques determine either family or larger-than-family farms, what is responsible for the dominance of the one or the other in various regions, both now and in the pre-machine era of American agriculture?

The answer seems to lie (1) in the degree to which a given farming area is more suitable for (approximately) single or multiple product farming plus (2) customs which free a larger-than-family operator from labor upkeep during periods of farm unemployment.[3]

In areas more suitable for multiple enterprise farms, family operators have the advantage. Increasing the number of enterprises so multiplies the number of on-the-spot supervisory-management decisions per acre that the total acreage which a unit of management can oversee quickly approaches the acreage which an ordinary family can operate. The reverse is true in areas more suitable for single enterprise farming. As a consequence, the family operator has the advantage in the first case while the larger operator has the edge in the second case.

But more important, growing fewer and fewer products on a farm greatly lengthens unemployment periods between operations. Since most labor on family farms is family labor, this means that family operators must pay (in the form of family living expenses) for their labor in both farm employment and unemployment periods. In other words, labor for the most part, is a fixed cost for the family operator but not for the larger operator as he pays labor only for the time it is actually employed on his farm. Were some

---

[2] For definition and analysis of these classes of farms as used in this paper, see "Can Prices Allocate Resources in American Agriculture," John M. Brewster and Howard L. Parsons, November 1946, *Journal of Farm Economics,* pp. 946–47.

[3] For ideas of this section, the author is especially indebted to conversations with Howard L. Parsons.

custom available that would free the family as well as the larger operator from labor upkeep during the long unemployment periods between farm operations, it is highly questionable if the larger operator's managerial advantage would enable him to crowd out the family operator in even single product farming areas. For it is well known that before mechanization of industry, the "handicraft" factory made little headway over family units, an important reason being that the nature of industrial materials made possible a continuity of employment so the so-called efficiency of both functional and task forms of specialization, which such factories made possible, did not enable them to go far in forcing family units to the wall. Large units in industry finally won out only as they could and did become technologically unique through the rise of the machine process.

While much research is needed to measure the degrees of relative advantage of family and larger-than-family farms in various types of agriculture, everyday facts apparently justify the view that both are mainly explained by the principles just set forth. First, areas most suitable to single enterprise farming are in limited parts of the South, West, and the wheat belt; and larger-than-family farms are most common in those areas. Only in these areas is there any available evidence that larger units are growing more rapidly than family units.[4] Still again, in the early-day extensive type of farming in the Corn Belt, larger-than-family units were frequent but they mostly passed out with the shift to more diversified enterprises.[5] Also, as cotton gave way to a greater variety of enterprises in the Piedmont, family units displaced the plantations. Finally the "bonanza" wheat farms of North Dakota increasingly gave way to family units with the advent of mechanization and disappearance of a handy migratory labor supply as a result of a decline in the lumber industry of the Lake States.[6]

IV

The question now arises as to what pre-machine habits of life and thought tend to be perpetuated by the shift to the machine process in agriculture but radically modified or wiped out by it in industry. In developing this point we shall first presuppose, as a base line of comparison, a pre-machine agriculture and industry, both organized into family production units, and then note the contrasts which emerge with the shift to machine methods. (The next section uses a similar procedure with respect to larger-than-family farms.)

---

[4] Ellickson, John C., Brewster, John M., "Technological Advance and the Structure of American Agriculture," *Journal of Farm Economics,* November 1947.

[5] Gates, Paul Wallace, "Large Scale Farming in Illinois, 1850–1870," *Agricultural History,* Vol. 6, January 1932.

[6] "Early Bonanza Farming in the Red River Valley of the North," Biggs, Harold E., *Agricultural History,* Vol. 6, January 1932. "Large Land Holdings in North Dakota," Benton, Alva H., *Journal of Land and Public Utility Economics,* October 1925.

In these terms, technological advance increasingly underlies the growth of at least five prominent cultural differences between the farm and industrial segments of our society. First, such advance accelerates the functional and task forms of specialization in industry but not in agriculture. In working simultaneously, manufacturing machines so multiply the number of concurrent operations as to (1) wipe out the union of the managerial, supervisory, and labor employments in the same individual (or family) and re-establish them as full-time occupations of different classes, and further (2) destroy a similar union of labor operations. But since farm mechanization in no wise increases the number of things which must be done at the same time, it provides no new basis whatever for either the functional or task form of specialization.[7] Not only are different forms of specialization thus required by machine industry and agriculture, but any exchange of these forms would result in enormous inefficiencies. For the absence of the functional and task forms of specialization in industry would cause the worker to waste time in *going* from one operation to another, while any marked degree of task specialization in agriculture would cause the workers to waste time in *waiting* from one operation to another. To keep "modern" in respect to efficiency, farming must remain "old-fashioned" in respect to the "higher forms" of specialization.

Second, in industry and in agriculture, machine methods require quite different relationships of the worker to the product, on the one hand, and to operations on the other hand. The relationship that once prevailed in both was personal identification of the worker with the product, as the sequential pattern of operations in each case enabled him to guide materials through one operation after another until the final product was the embodiment of his planning and effort. This relationship still holds in machine agriculture because the older sequence of operations still remains. But in working simultaneously, industrial machines have long since loosened the worker from the product and tied him to the repetitive performance of a particular operation, as he cannot be in different places at the same time.

Third, the machine has created entirely different types of causal connections between operations in agriculture and in industry, the upshot of which is to leave farmers undisturbed in their old standing as purposive (self-directing) beings in their working activity while strongly tending to reduce industrial workers to the status of machines.

The output rate and quality of any operation is functionally related to the rate and quality of every other, irrespective of whether they are done simultaneously or sequentially, by hand or by machine. But the causal connection within the simultaneous and the sequential patterns of operations is quite

---

[7] This does not mean that specialization is not present in agriculture. Quite the contrary. But it comes in mostly by way of differentiating the functions of farming areas instead of those of the farmer.

different. When done concurrently, the input-output rate and quality of any particular operation is controlled by the moment-by-moment flow of materials between operations. But when done sequentially, the input-output rate of a present operation obviously cannot be governed by the flow of materials from others which do not yet exist. As the control connection thus cannot be mechanical, it must be purposive—one's idea of the amount and quality of output at which he aims in later operations. For these reasons, the shift to machine methods in agriculture leaves the farmer in the same self-directing status which the industrial worker enjoyed in the handicraft era. In industry, however, this shift results in the use of the flow-rate of materials as the immediate control over the performance rate of each particular operation. As a consequence, it is commonly held that machine industry tends to reduce workers to the status of machines.

It should be noted, however, that the input-output rate and quality of operations is the expression of someone's will and purpose as it does not fix itself. Hence the tendency of the factory system to reduce workers to machines hardly reflects an inherent quality of its simultaneous operations but rather a cultural lag. In the older economy of family units, control over the performance of production units was regarded as the sole and rightful prerogative of men in their proprietary (managerial) capacity—not in their labor capacity. The carry-over of this proprietary habit into the factory system reduces men as laborers to the status of machines since it lodges in managers sole control of machine behavior, which in turn automatically controls labor motions. This condition is materially modified, if not completely removed, as this older handicraft conception of management is replaced by effective collective bargaining procedures. Under this custom, the power to fix the performance rate and quality of a producing unit (as well as to distribute its output among contributing producers) ceases to be the sole prerogative of men in the capacity of either labor or management and becomes the joint power (privilege) of equally self-directing men around the bargaining table. In this way the aims and methods of the industry become expressions of the common purpose of all concerned (instead of the dictate of any occupational group).

Evidently, then, the so-called mastery of men by machines in industry is in great measure but a disguised way of saying that proprietary habits of life, indigenous to an economy of family units, may become tyrannical when transferred to an economy of factory units. In a machine agriculture of family units, these habits are now as always the heart and core of a free life but in control of machine industry they may become unbearable. In the shift to machine agriculture, the requirements of a free society do not call for a revolution in our older proprietary (managerial) habits of mind. The like may not be true in industry.

Fourth, not only does machine agriculture conserve men as self-directing workers without requiring any change in their pre-machine proprietary habits, but it also conserves and expands the traditional human satisfactions in work whereas the contrary is true in industry. The old handicraft form of production met rather well the individual's need for finding evidences of personal significance through (1) writing large his creative powers into the products of his hands and (2) being the master of the rate and quality of his labor motions. When work meets these conditions, it is commonly recognized that the "human costs" of production are minimized and its human satisfactions maximized. In these terms, machine farming remains even more in line with traditional work-satisfactions than hand techniques. For in leaving unaltered the product of farming as the expression of the farmer's planning and effort, machine agriculture likewise leaves the farmer in possession of the old artisan's creative satisfactions that arose from guiding materials through their many operations into finished products. Also it leaves the farmer in full possession of the artisan's power to control his labor motions by his idea of the output desired from later operations because it does not tear apart his management and labor activities. Finally, machine agriculture expands these satisfactions of self-directing and creative workmanship through releasing human energies from the brute strain of operations into the larger life of will and imagination on which farming so intimately depends. On the other hand, in shifting from the sequential to the simultaneous pattern of operations, machine industry (1) institutes the hum-drum of a repetitious task and (2) further tends to inflict the pains of status degradation through reducing the worker from a self-directing to a mechanical agent in his labor activity.

Fifth, in industry the machine has been and continues to be a breeder of social unrest; always plunging the underlying population into the teeth of old traditions, while the contrary is true in agriculture.

This is true, first, in terms of the need for creative and self-directing workmanship. The pains of monotony inflicted by task specialization have forced and continue to force the working folks of industry to seek outside their jobs a mosaic of satisfactions to displace the boredom of routine work. This escape-quest has taken such forms as the struggle for recreational diversions both inside and outside the shop, vacations with pay, and a steady shortening of the working day—all a sharp break with traditions indigenous to a society of family production units, and therefore opposed at every step.

But the pains of status degradation that have accompanied the shift to the simultaneous pattern of operations run deeper than any discomforts of monotony, as they signify the struggle of workmen to remain men in their working as well as in their other activities; so much so that they cannot accept the tendency of the factory system to reduce them to machines. For, as Rousseau long ago pointed out, the essence of manhood lies in one's purposive capacity—the power (freedom) to formulate, or at least share in formulating the rules which his limbs must obey; irrespective of whether such rules be for a card game, the affairs of state, or the speed rates of a production line. Hence, in running counter to this self-directing element of human nature, machine industry under a carry-over of proprietary (managerial) habits from an economy of family units, forces the underlying population to grips with one of the most fundamental traditions of the past—the deep conviction that industrial policy-making is the sole and rightful prerogative of the proprietors of industry much as political policy-making was once believed to be the sole and rightful prerogative of the king; i.e., the chief proprietor of the realm.

In contrast, the shift from hand to machine farming accomplishes the amazing feat of increasing the productivity of farmers at a rate[8] comparable to that of industrial workers, and at the same time reenforces views and sentiments of life that were nourished several centuries ago in industry by the handicraft regime. For in addition to visiting upon farmers no additional pains of monotony and not molesting the fusion of managerial and labor employments in the same person, the shift to machine production raises to new heights the traditional dignity of farmers as self-directing agents by removing drudgery from their work. In this respect, at least, the chief cultural effect of agricultural industrialization may well be to invoke in farmers an even deeper contentment than ever, with a frame of mind and values that first took root in the handicraft era.

The same principle is true from the standpoint of security needs. Machine farming daily reenforces the pre-machine gospel of self-help as being the truly respectable basis of security; and quite properly so, for as long as the household and the firm remain fused into one organization, business is not free to hire and fire most of its workers at will but must meet their livelihood needs from the cradle to the grave. But by separating firms from households, machine industry tends to make the businessman a conservative and the worker a disciple of change. It does so through enabling business to free itself from the enormous welfare load of family production units by shifting this load from firms to individual workers while continuing to use the older self-help habits of thought as justification for its new freedom. From this standpoint the great danger to freedom is the urge for security. For the older litanies of self-help gradually lose the ring of sound principle to those who do the work of industry. Saddled with a greater degree of insecurity than was ever loaded onto solitary individuals by any economy, they are driven to seek ways of re-shifting to the state and modern firms the welfare obligations, assumed as a matter of course by the earlier order of family production units. In this livelihood perspective, freedom and security are as inseparable as the fingers and the hand.

Finally, from an overall social point of view, the machine process in industry tends to weaken the enterprise regime while reenforcing it in agriculture. The simultaneous pattern of operations makes possible such an expanded scale of production that the efficient utilization of industry may require only one, or at most a very few firms, each so large as to substantially

---

[8] Though not yet to the same level.

influence the price at which it buys and sells. On the other hand, the guarantee of impersonal competitive forces, that the businessman will actually operate industry in line with the public interest, disappears. The upshot of this paradox is to keep alive the question as to whether public need for greater wealth and comfort does not require more and more state intervention.

But no such question is fostered by the shift to machine agriculture. Only as a defense against monopolistic elements of industrial firms do farmers reluctantly accept "government programs." Shift to machine methods has neither added to nor detracted from the primitive competitive character of American agriculture. In fact, machine farming does not so much as even fully commercialize the production process. While it does call for a greater purchase of fuel and power inputs, it calls for less hired labor; since the more mechanized the farm, the more a family is able to do the work. As much after the industrialization as before, "farming as a business" means about what it has always meant—the opportunity of being a self-directing workman.

V

By the criteria of functional specialization, there is indeed a strong similarity between factories and larger-than-family farms, as labor and management are separated in both cases. Since this separation is a stereotype of progress, larger-than-family farms are able to share vicariously the great prestige that gathers about the factory system. They are easily pictured as the outposts of farm technological advance; even though exactly the same separation of functions was as prevalent in agriculture before the machine as afterwards, and therefore is actually no indicator of such advance. But while the institution of larger-than-family farms signifies no technological uniqueness, the question remains as to whether it (unlike family units) may signify lingering habits of life that even antedate the handicraft era.

The basis of this contingency is the fact that the cause and cultural background of functional specialization are quite different in industry and in agriculture. In industry such specialization arises as a result of technological advance—the need for supervisors and managers to coordinate the great multitude of concurrent tasks which arise in the shifting from the sequential to the simultaneous pattern of operations. While this advance destroyed the economy of family production units, the value sanctions and character traits fostered by that economy were carried over as the cultural foundations of the factory system. For example, controlling the operation of producing firms through "free" contract largely stems from this source; the chief reason being that the union of labor, supervision and management in the great bulk of individuals ingrained the habit of self-direction and personal independence as a matter of bread and butter survival. So much was this the case that when the factory system smashed the older unity of functions, men would tolerate their reestablishment as different occupations only through the legal procedure of managers and workers meeting as equal bargainers, each seeking his own advantage.[9] Again, by making families responsible for their own keep from birth to death, this same unity of functions ingrained into the rank and file the habit of rigorously skimping present consumption so as to produce more tomorrow. Out of the saving habit thus fostered finally came in great measure the capital in the form of factories that destroyed the older economy of family units, though not its frugal habits of life.

Thus as incubators of the *spirit* of capitalism, family production units have always been without an equal, though by specialization criteria which characterize factories and "large scale" farms, they are a back-number.

In contrast, it is quite possible that the institution of larger-than-family farms, for all its greater similarity to the factory system, may still bear traces of a pre-capitalistic culture. In agriculture, functional specialization does not stem from any technological advance but from the power of a few to expand farm holdings substantially beyond the ability of a family to do the work in any particular operation. Historically, the first expression of this power was physical prowess—the right of possession by conquest. The relationship of superior and inferior, involved in some sense in all functional specialization, was thus initially established on the land through physical subordination. The result was a larger culture of servile relations—feudalism and even slavery in all their various shades. This does not mean that free contrast and its spirit of equality and enterprise has not in great measure replaced subordination and its spirit of domination and servility, as a basis for the superior-inferior relationship on larger-than-family farms. Quite the contrary. But it does mean that this cultural advance in agriculture owes little to any disruptive pressure of the shift from hand to machine farming upon older servile habits of life. Instead, it stems chiefly from the smothering effect of the surrounding culture of self-directing individuals—habits of life that first got their toe-hold on modern society mainly through an economy of family production units, chiefly limited to industry in pre-machine Europe but including most of American agriculture, both now and in the pre-machine era.

VI

An important tool of social analysis is the hypothesis that cultural change is largely the function of technological change. This idea usually carries the tacit assumption that the machine process is "all of one piece" as it were, so

---

[9] This does not mean that coercion was not employed in subordinating a society of family operators to a hierarchy of bosses and managers in the factory system. Rather it means that the coercion used was not physical but pecuniary pressure—the power to withhold from others what they need but do not own. One could not club another into a "free" contract, though he might starve him into it. Shift from feudalism to the free society of capitalism was thus not a shift from coercion to an absence of coercion but rather a change in the type of *legitimate* coercion.

that its substitution for hand methods in all major industries will result in similar occupational adjustments, and hence policy attitudes, throughout all important sectors of the economy. Theory thus squeezes agriculture and industry into a common mold, both technologically and culturally.[10]

This view would seem to require some revision as it overlooks the fact that the machine process itself may be the basis of profound cultural lags. At every turn, the shift from the hand to machine industry is found to be mechanically progressive and socially revolutionary in that it is able to increase the productive power of the hand only through grinding away the basic habits of work and life that were indigenous to a handicraft economy. On the other hand, this shift in agriculture is mechanically progressive but socially conservative in that it is ever able to increase the power of the hand without disturbing many strategic beliefs and practices, first fostered by the older economy of family production units, or even the remoter servile habits nourished by a still older economy of feudal relations. It creates no new (occupational) class of people, whose new ways of living and making a living, force them to work out a new view of man and society as means of reshaping older frames of thought in line with their new needs of livelihood and social status. In this limited but important sense, machine agriculture is mechanically progressive but socially conservative. Owing to pervasive technological differences between farming and industry, agriculture is thus one of the last outposts of "rugged individualism" with its creed of the "self-made man"; and for similar reasons, agricultural and business economists—in marked contrast to labor economists—are still the most ardent devotees of laissez-faire.

---

[10] For a recent example of this mode of analysis see Geroid Tanquary Robinson, "The Ideological Combat," *Foreign Affairs,* Vol. 27, pp. 527–28, July 1949.

2 The Three Economies of Agriculture*

HAROLD F. BREIMYER†

American agriculture and its disciplinary companion of agricultural economics have long been troubled by uncertainties of self-definition. That agriculture begins with producing primary products of the soil is perhaps least disputed. Any challenge to this near-consensus is largely confined to the agribusiness school, which would push the baseline back to include the supplying of fuel and fertilizer and similar production items. As to terminal boundary there is less agreement. Nevertheless, evidence points to partiality for a wide compass. Certainly agricultural economists have addressed themselves freely both to the marketing sector and to the characteristics of final consumer demand for goods of farm origin. Market researchers have studied, in the presumed interest of farmers, the best design for food supermarkets and how to promote sale of lamb and apples. Secretary of Agriculture Orville Freeman has laid claim to a considerable direct service to consumers as a proper function of his agency. Broad constructionists seem to be a working majority.

Clearly, a broadly interpreted agriculture departs far from a synonym with farming, and it casts the farm management origin of the discipline of agricultural economics into remote status. Yet there can be no rule of catholic definition. The right of scholarly choice is freely acknowledged. The scholar's obligation devolves into dealing consistently with whatever definition be selected.

The thesis of this paper is that modern agriculture as broadly defined to embrace the distributive destiny of its products is a composite, or sequence, of three separate and distinct economies. These are the production of primary

* *Journal of Farm Economics*, Vol. XLIV, No. 3 (August, 1962), pp. 679–99.
† University of Missouri, Columbia, Missouri.

products from soil, the conversion of feedstuffs into livestock products, and the marketing of products from farm to retail. As classification of itself is sterile, it will be pointed out further that the economic forces governing each of these three economies are distinctive, and that the differences are meaningful to analysis and to formulation of policy.

Of the three economies, the first constitutes what is probably the traditional or classic view of agriculture. The observations drawn from agriculture by Petty, Smith, Ricardo, *et al.* were essentially confined to crop production, with wheat ("corn") the commodity of common reference. Production of the herbaceous products of agriculture remains its peculiarly identified portion. It, and it alone, is an enterprise of producing primary products from that unique resource, the soil.

The second economy of agriculture is the production of livestock. Although commonly associated locationally with crop production, it is a secondary enterprise. It is a process of conversion of bulky raw materials into less bulky finished or semi-finished goods (largely the latter). It is no less a secondary enterprise than is the crushing of soybeans or the smelting of iron ore.

Habits of thought that conveniently have treated crop and livestock economics together arose from the association of the two enterprises on family farms. The association, in turn, is to be ascribed primarily to the economy of reducing bulkiness of feedstuffs close to their source. It is easier to ship cattle than corn, and cream than alfalfa hay. This saving of tonnage in shipment was an especially strong force when transport was slow and costly. Another factor in combining crops and livestock has been the advantage of sharing year-long use of family labor between complementary seasonal needs for the two enterprises. In addition, crop-livestock combination is implicit in the grazing of livestock on range and pasture, a kind of self-harvesting, a simple form of vertical integration. Despite their frequent physical association, crop and livestock production are of two separate economic categories, the former primary, the latter secondary.

The third economy of a broadly-defined agriculture is the long and complicated process of marketing. In it the products of crop and livestock agriculture are assembled, transformed, stored, conveyed and distributed. It is usually regarded as extending to retail sale. Formerly thought of as a nonproductive junction between farm and consumer, a gap to be crossed, it is now recognized as a sector in which large economic values are created as well as the one in which the vital price-making function is carried out. The marketing economy, once partly farm-based, is now virtually entirely removed from the farm. It is the wholly nonfarm economy of agriculture.

Two Economic Models

A reference point for review and interpretation of the three economies of agriculture is found in two basic economic models. Although the concepts are of long standing, they have recently been delineated with perception by Joan Robinson in two articles.[1] The first model is the earliest stage of development, in which land and men are the only existing factors of production and their native qualities are controlling. This is the primitive state, marked by the simplest economic pursuits. The second, and opposite, system is that of a fully developed economy. The latter is essentially capital-using. In its absolute version all factors of production are produced within the economy. Even labor and management are trained according to the needs of the market. As all are subject to change, "there are no persistent differences between factors of production."[2]

In their pure form these definitions describe in the one case an economy governed entirely by fixed, predetermined factors of production, and in the other a totally self-contained and self-sustained economy in which no factors are fixed, but all are variable. Neglecting for convenience both the obvious absence from the real world of either model in absolute state, and the influence of time on the fixity of any resource, the two definitions broadly distinguish between a primitive, fixed-resource economy and the ultimate form of an industrialized economy. They are polar categories for analysis, and therefore useful. For convenience they may be short-titled as primitive and industrial models.

The two models present two entirely different systems of value and income distribution. A primitive economy of immutable resources of heterogeneous endowment is a grim one indeed. All populations are in the iron grip of their particular resources. Demand schedules are practically non-existent, as most of the needs that can be met at all are vital ones. Production capabilities dominate valuation. The incapacity to offset natural deficiences in productive resources (other than by territorial aggression, a not uncommon resort) gives occasion for tremendous unevenness in prices of products. The historical monopoly power of possession of salt is a familiar example. Scholars have often speculated on the elements of valuation in exchange in such a primitive economy, but it is doubtful that any system approaching a free market economy would be permitted. Its impact would be too oppressive. Much credence must be attached to the firm conclusion of Mrs. Robinson that a degree of conventional pricing usually existed historically and was warranted.[3] Where there is natural monopoly of scarce resources and natural dispersion of plentiful ones, the "natural" consequences are product prices that are intolerably high to society in the former case and intolerably low to producers in the latter. Moreover, the inconstancy of crop harvests, due

---

[1] Joan Robinson, "Some Reflections on the Philosophy of Prices," *J. Manchester School of Economic and Social Studies,* May 1958; and "The Basic Theory of Normal Prices," *Quar. J. Econ.,* February 1962.

[2] "The Basic Theory of Normal Prices," *op. cit.,* p. 6.

[3] "The exchange of products . . . is largely governed by traditional and ceremonial rules."—"The Basic Theory of Normal Prices," *op. cit.,* p. 2.

chiefly but not exclusively to variable rainfall, magnifies the problem. Some means to amelioration are probably universal in such an economy. The need for them is inherent.

The contrast between the rigorous primitive model and its opposite, the industrial model, forms a matrix for observing economic development. Economic development, as a process, is basically a progressive release from the shackles imposed by natural factors of production. It comes about through introduction of capital, both as production goods and as provision for training of labor.[4] This is what happened in the Western world during recent centuries and is happening worldwide today.

Unwitting prophet of the unfolding of an industrial economy was that inscrutable pamphleteer, David Ricardo. Nominally, Ricardo was concerned with the price of corn and whether it made landlords exploiters. Yet, in the sort of contradiction in which fate seems to delight, Ricardo anticipated the economic forces of the forthcoming industrial period with more clarity than did Adam Smith, who was vocal refuter to the agriculturally oriented Physiocrats and otherwise usually regarded as precursor to an industrial age.[5] Ricardo's genius was in seeing things in the large—he was an early macro-economist. His principal, or at least most lasting, contribution was to bring an understanding of the economic role of land as a fixed natural resource. It will be remembered that Ricardo inveighed against regarding land as a slowly-consumable factor and thus akin to a capital good. In the passage that is assigned reading for every graduate student in economics, rent is a return ". . . for the original and indestructible powers of the soil."[6] In perceiving how the existence of a fixed stock of land of variable quality bore on rent as a distributive share, Ricardo gave great impetus to developing economic theory. The idea soon was extended into a general interpretation of rent or quasi-rent to any capital good that is scarce and not reproducible within the period under consideration.

Ricardo intuitively saw and dealt with, without explicitly recognizing it, the principle of diminishing marginal returns in production. That principle embraces combining one or more variable factors of production with a fixed factor. As such it related to an economy that is at least one step removed from the primitive stage wherein all factors are fixed, yet that is short of a perfectly industrial economy of only variable factors.

In one notable respect the Ricardian vision was only a limited improvement over a primitive economy. This applies to his view of a mechanical and almost hopeless destiny for human labor, which he saw as usually striving for little

---

[4] In today's parlance the latter is cast as "investment in human resources."

[5] Some Smithian scholars oppose calling him anti-Physiocratic. However, Smith himself declared he was. Cf. *The Wealth of Nations,* Cannan ed., Modern Library, New York, 1937, pp. 627–52.

[6] David Ricardo, *Principles of Political Economy and Taxation,* Gonner ed., G. Bell and Sons, London, 1929, p. 44.

more than minimum sustenance.[7] Therein lies a moral. Theories of value and distribution based on a marginal return to a single factor that must do all the adjusting have a sombre cast. They are doubly gloomy when labor is the variable. It was they which led to the "dismal science" tag for economics. Their import is the dominion of the least common denominator: whatever return the most disadvantaged laborer or producer is willing, or forced, to accept shall set the standard of return for all. Unless the economy as a whole is thriving, that no-recourse marginal return can be low. (Hence the call for sustained economic growth.) Marginal-return valuation is the kind of principle to which many pay homage and few adhere. Organized labor has shown itself more than ready to avoid the income-autocracy of the marginal worker, even at the price of some unemployment. So has much of industry with respect to its marginal output—it has developed a wide repertory of protective devices. Likewise that part of present-day agriculture having the help of support prices. But this is an aside.

Back to Ricardo. Though he did not recognize diminishing returns well enough to call them by name, his successors did. For a generation or more they developed the theory of the diminishing returns that result as successive doses of a variable factor are brought to bear on an unchanging quantity of a fixed factor. Thus did the notion of a fixed land resource build the base for economic thought.

The system was brought to fruition as the counterpart in consumption, marginal utility, was introduced. When Walras, among others, hooked diminishing returns in production with diminishing marginal utility in consumption an ingeniously symmetrical system was completed.

Three conditions are essential to the Walrasian system: a fixed-variable factor relationship in production; a matching marginal schedule in the psychology of consumption; and a close physical connection between the two. The third condition is easily overlooked, yet is indispensable. Unless the consumption and production functions are linked closely together, the nicely poised system breaks down. This condition requires both that the producer-to-consumer span be short and that products retain their essential identity throughout it. Significantly, at the time of Walras these three conditions were met fairly well.

An economic theory derived from agriculture, as was Ricardo's, could be applied well enough to nascent industry. As economic development progressed and industry took on more of its own distinctive character, it no longer suffic-

---

[7] Samuelson has taken issue with some of the Ricardian interpretation, particularly the thesis that establishing values at the (land) margin, where land earns no distributive share, lays groundwork for a labor theory of value. He goes farther, not by a step but by a trans-theory leap: "Having demolished labor as an absolute standard of value, we can turn Ricardo upside down and find in his simplest long-run model a 'land theory of value'."—Paul A. Samuelson, "A Modern Treatment of the Ricardian Economy," *Quar. J. Econ.*, February and May 1959, p. 19.

ed. Emblem of change was the nature of marginal returns. Unlike an agricultural economy, epitomized in diminishing returns, a highly industrial economy is notable for a capacity for constant or increasing returns. Ricardo himself saw this, clairvoyantly.[8] Marshall saw it also, in contemporary observation.[9] He recognized it, however inadequately, in his theories. Joan Robinson has capsuled the transition in thought by naming Walras as still in allegiance to an extractive economy but Marshall, observer of the upsetting influence of economy of scale, as a scholar of a manufacturing economy.[10]

The ultimate, purely refined form of an industrial economy, toward which economic life has tended and which, like rainbow's end, has visible meaning despite its unattainability, is in all respects the opposite of a primitive economy. In a pure version of an industrial economy all means of production are produced to order, including education and training of labor. In such an economy, if perfect divisibility of all factors be also assumed, there can be neither increasing nor decreasing returns to scale. There can be no rent or quasi-rent—no returns to a monopolizing factor.[11] The conclusions reached by Mrs. Robinson are pertinent and sound: "Where all means of production are produced within the economy and there are no economies or diseconomies attaching to the scale of production of particular commodities, the normal prices corresponding to any level of the money-wage rate and rate of profit are determined by the technical conditions of production; they are independent of the composition of output or the tastes of consumers. Demand has no effect whatever on relative prices. In Marshall's language, there is 'constant supply price' for each product . . . , so that their relative prices . . . cannot vary with their rates of output."[12]

It is not that consumers' wishes are ineffectual or unmet. Quite the opposite is true. They are met perfectly, or at least to a universally equal degree of perfection. No shortcoming in a factor of production prevents attainment of that common level of satisfaction or gives rise thereby to a differential return to the factor.

The primitive is an economy of nature, the industrial an economy of man. The limitations as well as opportunities are natural in the former, man-made in the latter. Whether a primitive economy turns out to be good or bad depends on the bounty or niggardliness of nature—including the native

---

[8] ". . . in the production of manufactured commodities, every portion of capital is employed with the same results . . ."—*op. cit.*, p. 235.

[9] ". . . we say broadly that while the part which nature plays in production shows a tendency to diminishing return, the part which man plays shows a tendency to increasing return."—Alfred Marshall, *Principles of Economics*, 8th ed., Macmillan Co., New York, 1925, p. 318.

[10] "Some Reflections on the Philosophy of Prices," *op. cit.*, pp. 116–17.

[11] Except when institutional devices create them—e.g., brand-name protection by patent and copyright.

[12] "Basic Theory of Normal Prices," *op. cit.*, p. 9.

endowments of the aboriginal population. The achievements of an industrial economy are the outcome of the wisdom or baseness of civilized and educated man.

Until man improves his own character, it is interesting to speculate as to whether it be propitious if some forces remain outside his control. If scientists should learn to regulate rainfall, would mortal man be able to exercise that regulation equitably? What are his capabilities in joint self-management? The answer bears on farm policy, as will be noted below.

Two Models in Three Economies of Agriculture

U.S. agriculture has moved progressively along the long trail from primitive to industrial sketched above. It did so first at a walk and then at a jog-trot. In recent years its motion has quickened to a dash. As such it has progressively taken on more of the characteristics of an industrial economy. This is the heart of the economic aspect of the technological revolution in agriculture.

This trend has encompassed each of the three economies of agriculture, changing the make-up of each. In so doing it has resulted in disproportionate growth of the more industrialized among the three. And it has detached each of the three economies of agriculture more sharply from the others. The impact is possibly most telling upon the first, primary-product, economy of agriculture, converting it to a natural resource-industrial composite and removing it farther from the other two economies and the consumer.

Use of Capital. Production on U.S. farms has been shifting at fast pace to an industrial, capital-using, character. Relevant data descriptive of this trend are computed and published by the Farm Production Economics Division of the Economic Research Service of USDA.[13] There are estimates of all inputs entering into farm production each year. Unfortunately, the published data do not distinguish between the crop and livestock portions of farming. However, evidence is that trends are of roughly the same magnitude for each.

Total inputs for crop and livestock production scarcely changed at all between 1940 and 1960 (see chart).[14] Yet the composition of the total has been altered drastically. The proportion of "farm" inputs, land and farm-resident labor, decreased from 66 percent of the total in 1940 to 38 percent in 1960. Nonfarm inputs, which comprise machinery, fuel, fertilizer, pesticides, feed supplements and mixing, and many other goods and services including non-farm hired labor, increased from 34 percent of total inputs in 1940 to 62 percent in 1960. Their relative proportion almost doubled within 20 years.

---

[13] Data are from Ralph A. Loomis and Glen T. Barton, *Productivity of Agriculture, United States, 1870–1958*, U.S. Dept. Agr. Tech. Bul. No. 1238, 1961.

[14] *Ibid.*, p. 61. As the authors point out, the statistical techniques employed influence somewhat the particulars of these comparisons but do not affect the overall picture.

INPUTS OF U.S. AGRICULTURE*

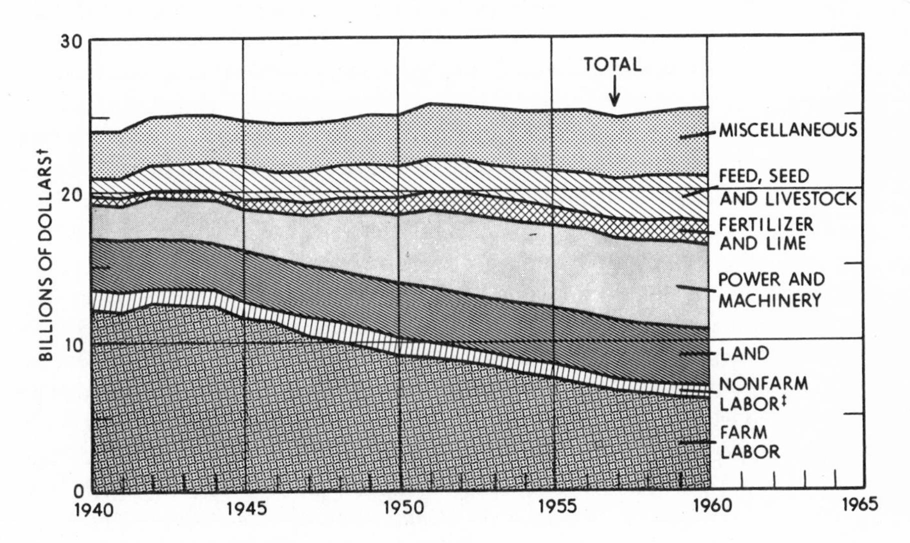

* Annual inputs as computed from quantity-price aggregates.
† Based on 1947–49 price weights.
‡ Nonfarm residents hired for farm work.
Source: U.S. Department of Agriculture; data taken from U.S.D.A. Tech. Bul. 1238. Neg. Ams 269–62(4)
Agricultural Marketing Service

The significant feature of the new, purchased, agents of farm production is that almost all of them are themselves the product of a production process. Their supply and use are subject to expansion and contraction. They are industrial goods and their use in primary agriculture makes it partially industrial. Thus does U.S. farming move away from the fixed-resource primitive model toward a capital-using economy of variable resources. It takes on ever more of the attributes of Mrs. Robinson's second model, wherein the quantity of inputs utilized and volume of output can be regulated according to the needs—or whims—of the market.

Since so much of the increase in use of purchased inputs in farming has taken place since 1940, those 20 years can justifiably be called an age of transformation. After countless centuries of history, production from farms is no longer so closely predestined by the mineral content of soils, the vagaries of rainfall, and the assiduousness of a labor force tied to the land. Now it is subject also to the governing influence of the resources fed into it. This is the fundamental significance of widely heralded "galloping technology": it is not that it necessarily expands farm output, but that it makes output expans*ible.*[15]

And yet the primary, crop producing, economy of agriculture remains land-based. It is a hybrid, an amalgam. It is fish *and* fowl. It has some,

[15] And contractible too, a derivation often lost sight of.

and increasingly more, of the features of a flexible industrial economy. It also retains a solid core of the features of a fixed-resource primitive economy. From its composite character arise many of the conflicts and many of the knottiest problems in economic analysis and policy-making for primary agriculture.

The other two economies of agriculture, those of livestock production and of marketing, are highly capital-using. If livestock production be viewed as a secondary enterprise, its principal input is feedstuffs. Feeds are a capital good in all cases except possibly the grazing of native range. They are particularly to be viewed as a capital good now that an "ever-normal" reserve has made feed grains constantly available at fairly well-stabilized prices. Urea and aureomycin are feed ingredients that never saw a farm. An outcome of the present system of feed supply is that annual livestock production is no longer tied closely to the size of each year's feed harvest. It can be expanded or contracted with comparative ease.[16]

The marketing of farm products has become almost exclusively a non-farm, capital-using undertaking. Any remaining tie to land is negligible.

Greater Growth of Livestock Production and of Marketing. The land-based, crop-production portion of agriculture is concerned with turning out raw materials ready for a long journey through processing, perhaps recombination, and ultimately final distribution for consumption. More value is created in that sequence of conversion and marketing than in the original production. Moreover, the difference in relative values has become steadily wider. Both the livestock production and the marketing economies have been expanding disproportionately to primary crop production. Their rapid growth, like the increased use of capital inputs in primary agriculture, reflects the extension of industrialization to all of agriculture.

For many years production of livestock has expanded more than crop production. A familiar outcome has been the increased portion of consumers' diets made up of livestock foods, in partial replacement of cereals. Evidence of production trends is gross output indexes which show, for crops, an advance from 71 in 1910–14 (1947–49 = 100) to 116 in 1957–61, but for livestock a more rapid rise from 62 in 1910–14 to 126 in 1957–61.[17] Moreover, as a source of cash receipts to farmers, all livestock and livestock products increased from 50 percent of total receipts in 1910–14 to 55 percent in 1956–60. If government payments be excluded as a source of receipts, the proportion of the total coming from livestock in 1956–60 was 56 percent.[18]

---

[16] It has at times been expanded too readily. Witness the broiler and turkey over-expansion debacles of 1961. Hog production has displayed some of the cyclicality formerly reserved to cattle. Cf. Harold F. Breimyer, "Emerging Phenomenon: A Cycle in Hogs," *J. Farm Econ.*, November 1959, pp. 760–68.

[17] *Changes in Farm Production and Efficiency*, U.S. Dept. Agr. Stat. Bul. No. 233, July 1961, p. 11. Indexes are gross for both crops and livestock. Livestock indexes exclude workstock.

[18] *Livestock and Meat Situation*, U.S. Dept. Agr., Econ. Res. Serv., July 1961, p. 25.

Marketing services for foods and other products originating on farms have proliferated in recent years. Standard source of data on relative values in production and marketing is the "food marketing bill" and "market basket" calculations of the Department of Agriculture. These data report the retail value embodied in original products as they leave the farm, and that arising between farm and retail. Over many years there was more cyclical variation than trend in the relationship between the two values. Since the end of World War II, however, the two have diverged persistently. From 1948 to 1960 the total value of all farm food products as they leave the farm increased only 7 percent, which is appreciably less than the growth in population. By contrast, the total food marketing bill increased 71 percent.

In 1948, the value of products at the farm was 51 percent of retail value. Marketing services thus received 49 cents—almost an even split. By 1961, the farmer's share was down to 38 percent, and the farm-to-retail margin up to 62 percent. The latter had become almost one-and-two-thirds times the farmer's share.

The published data on values at the farm include the value of livestock and livestock products marketed. These are secondary products. If data for the value of livestock products be replaced by the value of equivalent quantities of their primary constituent, feedstuffs, the farmer's share of the consumer's food dollar in 1961 is computed to be about 27 cents. Only 27 cents of each retail dollar spent for food in that year was returned to the farmer for his production of food and feed crops. Thus the approximate distribution of values for all food products of farming in 1961 was 27 cents to primary production, 11 cents to conversion of feedstuffs to livestock products, and 62 cents to marketing.

For nonfoods the value to primary production was even less. In 1961, only 14 percent of the consumer's dollar spent for 25 cotton products was returned to the original producer. Of the cigarette dollar for 1960, 15 percent reverted to the tobacco producer.[19]

The values created in primary agriculture are now a rather small fraction of values ultimately realized in sale of final goods at retail.

Mutual Detachment. Separation of the three economies of agriculture is old and now virtually complete for marketing, recent and still partial for livestock production.

Livestock enterprises have been undergoing progressive organizational detachment from feed production. Many cattle are concentrated for feeding in large commercial feedlots, especially in the West. These use little land and give a strong manufacturing flavor to the cattle feeding operation. Broiler production is not only semi-factory style but it seems to gravitate locationally to areas of the nation where costs are lowest or, it is sometimes reported,

---

[19] *Marketing and Transportation Situation,* U.S. Dept. Agr., Econ. Res. Serv., February 1962.

where contractees are most tractable. Egg production may be going the broiler route. Feeder pig production now rings the Corn Belt as a halo. And so it goes.[20]

Among factors that currently are wedging crop and livestock production apart are improved transport, notably barge shipping of corn; increased commercial preparation of mixed feeds; the need for, and premium on, specialized knowledge in livestock production; the mechanical, managerial, and manipulative forces underlying vertical integration in poultry; and the tremendous impact of the Commodity Credit Corporation's storage program for feed grains, which assures at all times a resting place for those feedstuffs between field and livestock and therefore facilitates separation of the two. The price support program makes clear distinctions between crops and livestock. It has been largely an aid to crop prices, as dairy products and wool are the only livestock products to be accorded continuous support. Price trends for livestock and feed have demonstrated more independence recently than in earlier years. Livestock prices, and livestock-feed price ratios, have been highly cyclical but have not trended downward since the late 1940's as have crop prices. Feeding margins for hogs and cattle, far from being narrowed by feed price supports, have if anything been wider during postwar years of feed support than before.[21]

The marketing sector has been detached more and more from crop and livestock production. Only a few lingering ties to the farm remain. This observation needs only brief substantiation. Almost complete is farmers' withdrawal from turning out final products such as home-churned butter. Vestige of direct marketing from farm to consumer is just about confined to sale of fresh fruits and vegetables at roadside stands near large cities. Furthermore, not only is the marketing sector now more completely separated, but the products it turns out depart more drastically from the original farm products. Food products at retail bear less and less resemblance to their basic raw material. For nonfoods the farm-retail contrasts are even more evident. If the test of parenthood be ability to recognize offspring, farmers must feel hard pressed to declare progenitorship for many foods and fabrics on retailers' shelves.

Further Implications

An overriding implication of the presentation thus far is found in mere extrapolation of trends. There is as yet no sign of let-up in those underway. Primary production continues to become more capital-using. Livestock

[20] The separation between livestock and feed crops referred to here is managerial, not necessarily locational. Livestock production is independent to the extent it is managed as a separate entity, even though still located on combination farms. However, managerial independence is likely to lead to some locational change by livestock, and has in fact done so.

[21] Harold F. Breimyer, *op. cit.*, p. 766.

enterprises still threaten to leave their traditional home. Marketing gains ever more size and dominance. How fast and how far these trends will extend is a weighty question involving not only economic analysis but also prognosis as to policy. The economic and institutional character of agriculture has never in the nation's history been independent of influence by conscious act of government. It will not be independent in the future.

Analytically, the description of a tripartite agriculture presented herein can be useful. If the three parts of agriculture are significantly different, they should be dealt with differently. If "agriculture" is to be defined so broadly as to encompass all those parts, it cannot be equally broadly generalized for analysis and policy purposes. A degree of disaggregation is necessary.

Beyond that, as the three economies of agriculture take on ever more of the characteristics of Mrs. Robinson's second, industrial, model, countless other changes can be expected in addition to the broad ones enumerated in the previous section of this paper. A few selected ones will be described. They will be directly principally, but not exclusively, to primary agriculture.

Reduced Role of Land. As primary agriculture rests increasingly on inputs of nonfarm origin, the role of land as such becomes partly eclipsed. To be sure, the relative status of land and of variable nonfarm inputs depends on the conformation of production surfaces, as described by iso-cost and iso-product curves and the other paraphernalia of productivity analysis. Yet almost certainly the governing influence of inherent productivity of land is being compromised relatively if not absolutely. The land under a skyscraper seems astronomically valuable dollarwise, but is probably a smaller fraction of the value of the structure than is the land under an economist's suburban split-level home. Similarly, land values in agriculture are probably destined for gradual subordination relatively even though they may hold up well in dollars per acre.

Manifestations of this realinement are being obscured by various resistances and delaying actions. For instance, open-end price support to farm commodities has had such an effect. When support rates are at incentive level, open-end support encourages liberal use of nonfarm inputs in farming; but unless acreage allotments are very tight it also keeps land in productive use. Thus the Federal Government has subsidized both fertilizer manufacturers and landholders. Future changes in support policies, such as a shift to quantity marketing quotas, could change significantly both the amount and relative proportion of succor to each.

Ricardo saw land as single-purpose. Some farm programs have offered a competitive purpose; this too enters into land valuation. The Soil Bank was such a counter-offer. Land rental under the feed grain programs of 1961 and 1962 was another. The proposed Food and Agriculture Act of 1962 provided for a competitive recreational demand for land.

Changes in the relative status of the various factors of production reweight some of the vested interests in primary agriculture. At first glance, the interest of landholders might seem to fade. Yet bearing on this is the place seen for farm labor as a rival production factor. Is it to be viewed primarily as fixed or variable? To what extent do farmers and farm workers as seekers of employment look to a prosperous primary agriculture versus a vibrant, expanding nonfarm economy as augury for their future? For centuries farm labor was indeed almost fixed, chained to the land. It is held a mark of enlightenment that our industrialized modern society has tended to convert it to a variable—to make easier the departure of farm people from land. Recently a number of program proposals, such as the idea of homesteads-in-reverse, have sought to speed that exodus. Yet the process is not universally seen as unmixed blessing. Many farmers with modest acreages seek not the opportunity to be displaced from them, but to receive adequate income while remaining on them.

Similarly, the principle of management control has undergone some redefinition, and its resting place some change. Formerly, land ownership provided the major instrument of control. Now, control of variable nonfarm inputs, and notably the possession of technical know-how as to their use, are potent forces. They explain some of the transfer of management off the farm —more to date in livestock than in primary crop production but significantly in some fruit and vegetable crops, for instance.

Yet land remains essential to primary production, and the old conflicts between valuation of a fixed and a variable factor, while perhaps dampened, are not ended. Valuation of land as a fixed factor remains highly sensitive to any under- or over-valuation of variable factors. Relevant is Paarlberg's remark that "farmers subconsciously value their own labor and management at a low level," resulting in "well rewarded" land as "residual claimant."[22]

More Controllable Farm Output. A more industrialized primary agriculture, operating on more variable inputs than previously, should also be more capable of a managed variability of output. The new kind of farming ought to have a more responsive supply function. Nonfarm inputs are a spigot that can be turned on and off fairly readily; they provide an output-regulating device that was not so available in the days of simpler organization of agriculture.[23] Of itself, this would seem to offer a welcome prospect for more stability in primary agriculture, and perhaps even for an ending of any need for farm control programs. In another sense, though, the new primary

[22] Don Paarlberg, "Should We Have Supply Management to Improve Prices Paid to Producers?", paper presented at staff seminar, Dept. of Agr. Econ., Univ. of Ill., March 21, 1962 (proc.), p. 3.

[23] Hathaway has treated the subject briefly but persuasively, concluding, ". . . because of the steadily increasing importance of purchased inputs in agriculture, input variations will probably become an increasing cause of output variation in the future."—Dale E. Hathaway, "Agriculture in an Unstable Economy Revisited," *J. Farm Econ.*, August 1959, p. 494.

agriculture merely shifts the point of control. It posits it more on the forces and techniques by which the inflow of capital resources is managed.

More Inelastic Demand for Primary Farm Products. Before the institutions of agricultural management are dealt with further it is necessary to consider the kind of market which primary agriculture faces. Perhaps unhappily, the industrializing of the three economies of agriculture which has made primary agriculture more flexible and adjustable has also made the farm-level demand for its products less flexible and harder to adjust to.

Demand for primary products has become less flexible, more inelastic, first because final demand by consumers has become more inelastic as their incomes have risen. But even more influential has been the widening of the marketing sector, which has pushed primary products into more distant, remote status. Due to that wider marketing gap, the pricing of products of primary agriculture is no longer a local facsimile of retail pricing. It is truly a pricing peculiar to primary commodities.

In a bigger and more complex marketing system, price signals are likely to be transmitted less efficiently. Prices at primary level will therefore lose sensitivity to small ups and downs in the consumer market. Contrariwise, prices at retail will be less influenced by small variations in prices at the farm; and this latter insensitivity will have the important result that the quantity utilized will not be very responsive to small price changes at the farm. Furthermore, the transformation so many goods undergo between farm and consumer can make the idea of price transmission less meaningful. Not only are many products now processed and blended but they often are sold under trade marking, brands, and other means of differentiation that affect their price and demand at retail but have little or no meaning for the original raw product. All these factors make the primary product market more independent and therefore usually more inelastic.

Yet even to the extent price signals are carried faithfully between the two market levels, the increase in size of the farm-to-retail price margin, reported above, results in greater inelasticity of farm-level demand. When farm-to-retail margins widen relatively and farm-level prices decline, as has happened in recent years, demand for primary commodities at the farm becomes more inelastic compared with consumer demand.[24]

For a few commodities, demand for domestic utilization is so inelastic that the quantity so used is almost independent of their prices. This is true of wheat. Domestic food use will approximate a half billion bushels annually even though the price should vary over a sizeable range. An Iowa study, for example, projected domestic use of wheat to be the same quantity at either

[24] The arithmetic is simple. A constant farm-to-retail margin conveys a given cents-per-pound price change at retail to an equal cents-per-pound change at the primary product level. But that price change is a greater percentage of the lower farm-level price than of the retail price; that is, the demand elasticity is less elastic, or more inelastic, at the farm than at retail.

$1.15 or $1.50 per bushel.[25] The Department of Agriculture, in preparing its 1960 report to Senator Proxmire on the projected effect of certain farm programs, similarly held wheat use unchanged at alternative prices. Demand for cotton and soybeans is notably inelastic at the farm level.

A more inelastic demand at the farm puts a high penalty on instability of primary farm production. Or, from the opposite point of view, it establishes a premium on well-regulated production. Viewed according to the geometry of a demand curve, an inelastic demand also promises a dividend to farmers from designed underproduction, for the gross value or revenue curve derived from it peaks out well to the left of current supply levels. It was common practice a few years ago for economists to compute for various farm products the size of supply that would maximize total value. This exercise became less popular as the danger that too high a price would shrink a market was recognized. Moreover, that calculation was appropriate only to an older primary agriculture of more nearly fixed resources, that is to say, of fixed total cost. Where inputs, and costs, are variable, a maximum value calculation has little applicability.

A more inelastic demand and a more manageable supply constitute a change in demand and supply relationships in primary agriculture. In effect, the demand and supply curves have been rotated. A previously moderately inelastic demand curve and highly inelastic supply curve have turned clockwise into a more inelastic demand and less inelastic supply. Increasingly, the burden of achieving an acceptable degree of stability in primary agriculture falls on the supply response.

The Institutional Organization of Farming. To recapitulate briefly, an earlier primary agriculture of more nearly fixed resources was notable for its uncontrolled and unpredictable output. That system forced most of the adjustment to a fluctuating production to be made in consumption. Fortunately for that era, the consumer market was close at hand and relatively elastic. A flexible and readily available consumer market can be a grand shock absorber to an erratic primary agriculture. It can take the blows, without intolerable recoil, of alternate surpluses and deficits in primary production. And analytically, a consumer demand so close at hand can permit consumer demand curves to be superimposed directly on a farm supply curve to describe a meaningful equilibrium, *a la* Walras.

Today's mixed primary agriculture combines the attributes of industrial and primitive economic models. Through use of nonfarm inputs, its production is much more controllable than before. However, it also remains partly subject to the persistent if not perverse influence of that unique fixed factor, land. Demand signals that reach the farm can be partially but not wholly responded

---

[25] Arnold Paulsen *et al.*, "The Amount and Cost of Grain Land Retirement to Balance Production and Reduce Stocks Under Two Levels of Prices in the Mid-1960's," Center for Agr. and Econ. Adjustment, Iowa State Univ., Econ. Inf. 157, 1960 (proc.).

to. And those demand signals now originate from afar off and are more inelastic. Hence, pricing in primary agriculture will mix the rules of price-making under the industrial and primitive models. To the extent production can be adjusted to conform to changes in demand, no lasting differences in relative prices of commodities, other than those induced by technology, will result. To the extent production cannot adjust efficiently, but instead remains unresponsive, unstable and unpredictable, prices of commodities will be similarly quixotic and develop varying interrelationships.

Viewed differently, the larger role of variable inputs, partly unharnessing primary agriculture from the binding limitations of native resources, makes it more subject to the individual and collective controls of man. This conforms to the general characteristics of an industrial economy. It remains to be seen how, and how wisely, man uses his new power. The older agriculture, resistant to man's control, was protection against his errors. Its limited productivity, while not surfeiting consumers and often a harassment to farmers, yet served to prevent serious progressive declines of prices and values in farming. It was not so easy to over-produce then as it is now.

How, then, will the newer form of primary agriculture be employed? And of all farming, including livestock production? What institutional organization will farming take? These questions involve both the future for the traditional family farm organization, and the role of government.

The family farm structure is an anomaly. It is small scale, decentralized organization existing in the midst of a nonfarm economy of large scale organization for mass production. Primary agriculture's historical reliance on a fixed, immovable, extensive resource, land, was a mighty force leading to the small family unit. Furthermore, the built-in limitation on total farm output helped to preserve land values and thereby protected against unsettling influences which would challenge that order.

Now some of the protections are weakening and the order is being challenged. It is being challenged because primary agriculture is loosened from its natural output-limitation bonds and, through use of nonfarm resources, is taking on a more industrial form. The question now faced is whether a system of small independent businesses in agriculture can meet the test of managerial techniques and competence to respond to market forces accurately enough to achieve an acceptable degree of stability. It is a question as to whether it can be adequately self-regulating. The long production interval that prevails in so many farm enterprises is a disadvantage. The increasing complexity of scientific knowledge in agriculture is another. These make the assignment doubly difficult. One school of thought and circle of farm organizations declares American farming can meet that test, as presently organized and without extensive government assistance; another asserts it cannot, and that if survival of the family farm system is desired the protection of government is necessary.

To complicate the matter further, some economies of mass production have begun to appear, as in broilers. In an atomized industry notable for the horizontal demand curve that each firm faces, constant or increasing returns to scale are frightfully disequilibrating. The family farm unit has always depended on its upsweeping marginal cost curve, the consequence of diminishing marginal physical returns, to achieve equilibrium. Without it, stable equilibrium for the individual firm is hard to come by.

Manufacturing industry has developed its own recourse for such a situation: it has arranged for a downsweeping demand curve. This has been done sometimes by means of monopoly or oligopoly, but far more often by that pervasive protective device of modern trade, product differentiation. But differentiation of product is unavailable to an atomistic farm economy. Its advantages could be obtained only by means of some form of horizontal or vertical combination. One of the ways to view vertical integration in poultry is to regard poultry production, lacking product differentiation of its own, as latching on to differentiation provided by nonfarm agents.

Emerging economy of scale relates more to production of livestock than to primary production of crops. As was observed above, livestock production has become more and more detached from production of feed crops; it is more disjoined managerially from land as a fixed resource. Grazing on native range is the only exception. Thus livestock production has much more of the character of the industrial model of an economy than does primary agriculture. It is therefore much more susceptible to taking on the institutional make-up of an industrial economy. Questions of evolving institutional organization of American farming have more immediate significance to the livestock portion of farming than to the crop portion.

The mechanics and powers of government have always been looked to for help in charting the course of U.S. farming. Yet the particular meaning of this analysis to programs of government is not easily discovered. As primary agriculture remains mixed, a certain ambiguity attends it. Stability in farm prices and incomes must increasingly be sought from the supply side of the supply-demand equation. The extent to which it can be attained without government programs is simply not known. Recent experience is of little help in pointing to an answer. The last quarter century of explosive technology in farming—of a rapid transition to a more industrial primary agriculture—has also been, unfortunately for researchers, a quarter century of federal programs. It is a laboratory that yields few generalized and wholly conclusive findings.

Paradoxically, any need for government programs in farming could have two contrasting origins. One would result from the instability that remains in primary production due to use of land as a fixed natural factor of production. Government help in this respect is of the category of the conventional pricing Mrs. Robinson attached to a primitive economic model. Need for it arises not from technology, as so often asserted, but from its remaining partial absence. On the other hand, a second possible origin for government programs lies in uncertain capability of the present institutions of farming to accommodate a more industrialized agriculture. Nonfarm inputs are tools of supply control; can they, without government help, be utilized effectively enough by four million independent production units, under the handicap of the horizontal demand curve each faces, to attain a satisfactory degree of equilibrium?

This analysis neglects the problems of transition as such. It is important to distinguish between the throes of shifting from a primitive to an industrial primary agriculture, and the implications of the latter when achieved. And devices to ease the transition by freezing against the outcome can present some real dangers.

Farm Program Pointers. If national supply control is to be practiced, this analysis offers pointed lessons as to techniques. The importance nonfarm inputs have gained in governing farm output cannot be neglected in control design. If incomes to farmers were to be supported by means of attractively high commodity prices, it would probably be highly ineffectual to try to limit output by means of control of the single factor of land acreage. Incentive prices would induce use of too many nonfarm inputs. Some kind of quantity quota on marketing probably would be essential. If, however, incomes were to be sustained primarily by direct payments, in the form of compensatory payments on marketings or rental on land or reimbursement for practices performed, acreage allotments might well be reasonably effective. The lower prices would not be so great a lure to use of nonfarm inputs.

Differences by Commodities. This paper is necessarily general. Let it be admitted that many distinctions are to be made by commodities. Economic and institutional issues in production of wheat bear little resemblance to those for winter pears. Those for producing beef calves are immensely different from those relating to commercial broilers.[26]

Revision of Concepts; e.g., "Cost of Production," "Surplus." For decades various farm spokesmen have sought to build price support policies on a base of cost of production. Agricultural economists have usually opposed; some have scoffed. To the extent farm output now rests on variable nonfarm capital inputs, cost of production may at last achieve respectable status. At the least it is not as inapplicable as it once was.

Similarly, in the term "surplus" a notion of a predetermined normal volume of farm output is implicit. The excess beyond it is the surplus. As the idea of

---

[26] Beef cattle and potatoes offer a study in contrasts. A large industry still based on natural grass resources, runaway expansion in beef cattle is prevented by limitation on those resources, while a fairly elastic demand cushions the effect of supply fluctuations. Potato production is freely expansible as soil resources are not limiting and heavy fertilization is common, but demand is very inelastic, a combination guaranteed to bring instability. Cf. Will M. Simmons, *An Economic Study of the U.S. Potato Industry,* U.S. Dept. Agr., Econ. Res. Serv., Agr. Econ. Rept. No. 6, March 1962.

Absence of natural limits to their production potential is doubtless a reason a number of fruit and vegetable producer groups have made use of marketing agreements.

controllable variability in production is accepted, the surplus concept will tend to lapse.

Meaning to Marketing. Lastly, implications of the new organization of agriculture are to be found for the marketing economy. That economy has grown in size and dominance. It isolates primary agriculture, and secondary also, more completely from the consumer. Once regarded as a mere transmission agent, innocuous if not inert, it is now recognized as an active area indeed. It still conveys, however imperfectly, countless messages that originate with the consumer, and it adds a great many market influences of its own.

Various private and government services are directed toward improving the operations of the marketing system. Marketing research, expanded under the Research and Marketing Act of 1946, serves this end. Significantly, that research is undergoing redirection. It formerly stressed consumer behavior and physical efficiency. As products undergo more transformation between farm and consumer, consumer performance conveys a more blurred message to farm-level demand. The bread and pastries consumers buy are a long way removed from the farmer's wheat. Likewise salad oil and shortening from soybeans. It is highly doubtful that consumer preferences among various types of breakfast rolls or between white and yellow shortening can be translated with any precision into economic forces bearing on the price of wheat or of soybeans.

Similarly, it is by no means certain that improved physical efficiency in marketing universally, or even generally, redounds to the benefit of the farmer. Question may be raised as to whether the benefits of marketing research are more properly chargeable to society than to farming. Such a hypothesis is not new; it is often contended that all agricultural research should be viewed in such a light.[27] And yet, even though not all improvements in marketing are automatically reflected at the farm level, the marketing system has great meaning to farmers. Both enhancement of its efficiency and understanding of its structure are needed. The system itself is called on to perform more services year by year. For instance, a more discriminating demand by consumers and processors has led to wide use of specification buying, always difficult to apply to the products of the farm. The grading and inspection services of government are intended to facilitate specification trading, particularly in conventional open markets.

Furthermore, some of the trends within marketing have impeded its capacity to function well. An example is the waning of the influence of the open central market. Irrespective of whether that market was the best in all respects,

---

[27] "Food research in the 1960's is chiefly for the consumers of 1970 to 2000. On those grounds it should stand or fall."—John A. Schnittker, "Positive Policies for American Agriculture," paper presented at Conference on Goals and Values in Agricultural Policy, Iowa State Univ., Ames, Iowa, June 27–29, 1960 (proc.), p. 12.

it made prices more observable and reportable, and it thereby aided, as Collins has noted, the communication process in marketing.[28]

For all these reasons more critical attention is now being given to those aspects of the marketing system which extend beyond the physical getting-the-job-done and relate to performance in terms of the accuracy and equity under which prices are made. Received theory has been far from adequate for this purpose, for not only does much of it still hinge on the perfect-competition model but it carries connotations of a Walrasian matching up of a producers' supply schedule and consumers' demand schedule. In reality most prices are made through the agency of traders, whose supply schedule is a market rather than production schedule, and whose demand schedule is complicated by all the merchandising practices and gimmicks of modern retailing. Furthermore, the problem is made more formidable by arrangements such as vertical integration and contracting, themselves viewable as, in some respects, a reaction to, and means of circumventing, an over-extended marketing system.[29] Impressive and promising new market research is being directed to these subjects, usually employing the three concepts of market structure, conduct and performance. In addition, both the United States Department of Agriculture and various State Departments of Agriculture are stepping up market regulatory activities in an effort to protect against monopoly, collusion, and various other malpractices.

Lastly, the marketing system is looked to as the sector in which it may be desirable and possible to aid the management of production and marketing in a more industrialized primary as well as secondary agriculture—including the choosing of the kind of products wanted in the more discriminating markets of today. In so doing, not only the time-honored goal of "stability" might be pursued effectively but the institutional forms society desires for farming could be brought about or preserved. It may be necessary first to address attention to the institutions of marketing itself. Means to these idealistic ends run the gamut from informational services such as market news reporting and economic forecasting through market inspection and regulation to market controls by means of agreements and orders. Legal provisions for cooperative marketing are of the same nature. Typically these are partial devices, midway between laissez-faire on the one hand, and strict regulation through the agency of government on the other. Most already exist in some form but could be modified, expanded, or extended to new commodities or areas. Their potential for the future is certain to come under increasing exploration. The marketing economy, the third and most industrialized of the three economies of agriculture, can be important to the first two economies in its own right, and also as a vehicle for determining the form those two will take as they progressively industrialize further.

---

[28] Norman R. Collins, "Changing Role of Price in Agricultural Marketing," *J. Farm Econ.*, August 1959, pp. 528–34.

[29] Collins, *ibid.*, p. 530.

Part II Econometric Analysis of Demand and Supply

3 Factors Affecting Farm Income, Farm Prices, and Food Consumption*

KARL A. FOX†

SOURCES OF CASH FARM INCOME

One approach to the subject of demand for farm products is to consider the stream of goods marketed from farms and the ultimate destinations of the components of that stream. A stream of cash receipts flows back to farmers from each of the component flows of goods.

The volume of cash received from a particular source is only an approximate measure of its importance in the determination of farm income. The net effect of each flow of goods depends upon the elasticity of demand for farm products in other uses as well. For example, if there had been no price-support program on corn and cotton in 1948, cash income from commercial sales might have been considerably lower.

In table 1, cash receipts are separated into five components: (1) sales to other farmers, (2) sales to domestic consumers, (3) sales to the U.S. armed forces, (4) sales for export, and (5) net proceeds from price-support loans.

The first of these components, sales to other farmers, is frequently overlooked. In 1949, some 1,363 million dollars' worth of livestock (mainly feeder and stocker cattle) were sold by one group of farmers, were shipped across state lines, and were bought by other farmers. This represents an internal flow of commodities and money within agriculture, and is not a net contribution from agriculture to other sectors of the economy. Farmers in 1949 also spent 3,080 million dollars for purchased feed. According to rough calculations, approximately 55 percent of this amount, or 1,700 million dollars, was reflected back into cash receipts for other farmers.

* *Agricultural Economics Research,* Vol. III, No. 3 (July, 1951), pp. 65–82.
† Iowa State University, Ames, Iowa.

TABLE 1

SOURCES OF CASH FARM INCOME, UNITED STATES, 1940, 1944, AND 1949
(in billions of dollars)

Source	Cash Farm Income[1]		
	1940	*1944*	*1949*
1. Sales to other farmers[2]	*0.9*	*2.0*	*3.1*
a) Livestock	0.5*	0.7*	1.4*
b) Feed[3]	0.4	1.3	1.7
2. Sales to domestic consumers	*6.8*	*14.5*	*20.3*
a) Food	6.0*	11.7*	18.0*
b) Fibers[4]	0.5	1.1	1.3
c) Tobacco	0.2	0.6	0.7
d) Others[5]	(0.1)	(1.1)	(0.3)
3. Sales for the U.S. armed forces (food only)[6]	...	*1.9*	*0.3*
4. Sales for export	*0.4*	*1.8*	*2.8*
5. Net proceeds from price support loans[8]	*0.3*	*0.2*	*1.6*
Total, all sources	8.4*	20.4*	28.1*

[1] Each stream of goods valued at farm prices. Most of these figures are unofficial estimates.
[2] Used for further agricultural production.
[3] Fifty-five percent of total farm expenditures for purchased feed in 1944 and 1949; 45 percent in 1940.
[4] Cotton, wool, and mohair.
[5] Net result of (*a*) sales of miscellaneous nonfood crops, (*b*) equivalent farm value of hides and other nonfood livestock byproducts, (*c*) changes in commercial nonfarm stocks, (*d*) farm income from CCC price-support purchases minus CCC sales which appear in domestic consumption, purchased feed, and exports, and (*e*) errors of estimation and rounding.
[6] Excluding purchases for civilian feeding in occupied territories.
[7] Including military shipments for civilians in occupied territories.
[8] Net proceeds to farmers from CCC loans. Does not include returns from CCC purchase and disposal operations, as on potatoes.
* Official estimates (rounded).

The movement of livestock and feed between farmers in 1949 accounted for 3.1 billion dollars, or about 11 percent of total cash receipts from farm marketings. The value of this internal flow is affected by changes in prices of livestock and feeds and by changes in the volume of movement between farms.

The second and by far the largest component of cash receipts is derived from sales to domestic civilian consumers. The total amount of this flow in 1949 was about 20.3 billion dollars. Between 85 and 90 percent of the total (18.0 billion dollars) was from sales of food. Sales of cotton, wool, and mohair, returned 1.3 billion dollars, and sales of tobacco for domestic use 0.7 billion dollars. The other item shown in table 1 under sales to domestic consumers is really a residual from the remaining calculations in the table, and is explained in its footnote 5.

The third component of cash farm income is from sales to the armed forces for the use of our own military personnel. During most of the postwar period, the military has also bought food for relief feeding in occupied territories. As these shipments are included in the value of exports (item 4 of table 1) and as their volume is not directly dependent on the size of the armed forces, they are not included here. Food used by the armed forces represented only about 1½ percent of our total food supplies in 1949. At the height of our war effort in 1944, however, the armed forces required nearly 15 percent of our food supply.

The fourth major component of farm income is from sales to foreign countries, and military shipments for civilian feeding in occupied areas. For several years the volume of exports has been unusually dependent upon programs of the U.S. government. During 1949, more than 60 percent of the total value of agricultural exports was financed by ECA and military relief feeding programs.

The fifth component is net proceeds to farmers from CCC commodity loans. Under the terms of price-support legislation this is a residual source of income after all commercial demands at the prescribed price-support levels have been satisfied. During 1949, loans taken out by farmers on commodities exceeded farmers' redemptions of such loans by some 1.6 billion dollars. Although this item represented a substantial contribution to cash farm income in 1949, it could well be a negative item in other years. The rapid redemption of cotton of the 1949 crop during the summer of 1950 is an excellent illustration of this.

Table 1 shows that the great bulk of cash farm income is determined by domestic factors. More than 70 percent of total cash receipts come from sales to domestic consumers. The 10 or 11 percent of cash receipts representing sales to other farmers moves with the domestic demand for livestock products. The volume of food required for our armed forces depends upon governmental decisions. Even sales for export are considerably influenced by domestic factors. This point is developed further in the following section.

Factors Affecting General Level of Farm Income

A number of basic factors must be considered in appraising the outlook for farm income at any given time.

Disposable Income of Consumers. The disposable income of domestic consumers has proved to be the best overall indicator of the demand for agricultural products consumed by them. Our livestock products, fresh fruits, and vegetables are consumed almost wholly in this country. Cash receipts from these products are closely associated with year-to-year changes in disposable income. Disposable income affects receipts from such export crops as wheat, cotton, and tobacco, but foreign demand conditions are also highly influential.

Obviously, a key problem in forecasting demand for farm products is to anticipate changes in disposable income. To see the factors that influence this variable, we must place it in a still broader context—that is, the total volume of economic activity of individuals, corporations and government. Table 2 shows the major components of this total as estimated by the Department of Commerce.

In most years the strategic factors causing changes in disposable income are (1) gross private domestic investment and (2) expenditures of federal, state, and local governments. Government expenditures are a substantial factor in the peacetime economy, and the dominant element in time of mobilization or war. Gross private domestic investment includes new construction—residential, commercial, and industrial—expenditures for producers' durable equipment, and changes in business inventories.

The Securities and Exchange Commission has had considerable success in estimating changes in business expenditures for new plant and equipment on the basis of information submitted by businessmen. Actual construction of buildings or delivery of heavy equipment lags several months to a year behind the issuance of contracts or orders. Hence, knowledge of new contracts and orders gives us valuable insights into the level of employment and industrial activity to be expected, several months ahead.

Changes in business inventories are an active element in the economy in some years. "Pipe-line" stocks of consumer durable goods were practically zero at the end of World War II, and the pressure to build up working stocks was a significant addition to the final consumer demand. At other times the change in business inventories is a surprise to businessmen themselves. It means that they have been producing or buying at a faster rate than was justified by the existing level of demand. An unplanned increase in business inventories may be followed by a sharp contraction in manufacturers' output, with a consequent reduction in employment and payrolls in the industries that are overstocked. This, in turn, depresses the demand for consumers' goods, including food.

In 1950, government purchases and gross private investment amounted to 33 percent of the gross national product. The other 67 percent consisted of personal-consumption expenditures. These expenditures are divided into three broad categories. In 1950, services, including rent and utilities, amounted to 59.9 billion dollars. Expenditures for nondurable goods amounted to 101.6 billion dollars, of which about 52 billion dollars went for food. The remaining 49 or 50 billion dollars went for clothing, household textiles, fuel, tobacco, alcoholic beverages, and a wide variety of items. Expenditures for such consumers' durable goods as automobiles and household appliances reached 29.2 billion dollars in 1950.

Under peacetime conditions consumer expenditures are generally regarded as a passive element in the economy, following rather than causing changes in employment and income. Expenditures for food, clothing, and other non-

TABLE 2

GROSS NATIONAL PRODUCT, DISPOSABLE INCOME, AND CONSUMER EXPENDITURES, UNITED STATES, 1950
(in billions of dollars)

Item	*Amount*
A. Expenditure Account	
Gross national product	*279.8*
Government purchases of goods and services	*42.1*
Federal	22.7
State and local	19.4
Gross private domestic investment	*49.4*
Nonfarm residential construction	12.5
Other construction	9.3
Producers' durable equipment	23.4
Change in business inventories	4.1
Net foreign investment	*−2.5*
Personal consumption expenditures	*190.8*
Nondurable goods	*101.6*
Food	[1]52.2
Tobacco products	4.4
Clothing and shoes	18.7
Other (including alcoholic beverages)	[1]26.3
Services	*59.9*
Housing	18.3
Other	41.6
Durable goods	*29.2*
Automobiles and parts	12.1
Other	17.1
B. Income Account	
Gross national product	*279.8*
Minus: Business taxes, despreciation allowances, undistributed profits and other items[2]	75.6
Equals: Personal income from current production of goods and services	204.2
Plus: Government transfer payments	19.1
Equals: Total personal income	223.2
Minus: Personal taxes and related payments	20.5
Equals: Disposable personal income	*202.7*
Personal savings	11.9
Personal consumption expenditures	190.8

Source: U.S. Department of Commerce.
[1] Estimated.
[2] Includes capital consumption allowances, indirect business tax and nontax liabilities, subsidies minus current surplus of Government enterprises, corporate profits and inventory revaluation adjustment minus dividends, contributions for social insurance (included in Supplements to wages and salaries) and a statistical discrepancy.
Note: Details will not necessarily add to totals, because of rounding.

durable goods seem to adapt themselves rapidly to changes in disposable income. Outlays for such services as rent and utilities change more slowly.

Expenditures for consumer durable goods normally fluctuate 1.5 to 2.0 times as much from year to year as does disposable income. In years of low employment, consumers sharply reduce their outlays for new durables and get along on what they have. Toward the top of a business cycle deferred purchases are caught up, so that the rate of new purchases in a year like 1929 (or 1950) is higher than could be maintained indefinitely even under conditions of full employment.

Although expenditures for consumer durables generally move with consumer income, the fact that they *can* be either deferred or advanced makes them a potential hot-spot in the economy. The wave of consumer buying that immediately followed "Korea" is a dramatic illustration. Expenditures for durable goods had been unusually large from 1947 through 1949 and many economists had expected them to slacken in 1950. Actually, the 1950 expenditures for consumer durables were up 22 percent from 1949, with the bulk of the rise concentrated in the second half of the year.

In summary, we may say that year-to-year changes in disposable income depend on the decisions of businessmen (including farm operators), the decisions of consumers, and the decisions of federal, state, and local governments. Ordinarily, the strategic decisions are made by business and government. Although decisions of consumers usually follow changes in disposable income, they may become as influential as the decisions of businessmen in initiating changes at critical junctures. The "potential" of consumer initiative has been increased by the abnormally large holdings of liquid assets by individuals. Installment and mortgage credit give additional scope to consumer initiative in an inflationary period unless curbed by government action.

Changes in Marketing Margins. Disposable income is the chief determinant of consumer expenditure for food in retail stores and restaurants. But between consumer expenditures and cash farm income lies a vast, complex marketing system. During 1949, farmers received slightly less than 50 cents of the average dollar spent for food at retail stores. Still higher service charges were involved in food eaten at restaurants. For nonfood products, as cotton, wool, and tobacco, farmers received about 15 percent of the consumer's dollar.

Marketing margins for food crops show great variation. Fresh fruits and vegetables grown locally during the summer and fall may move directly from farmers to consumers. In winter, fresh truck crops are transported long distances from such states as California, Texas, and Florida, and the freight bill takes a substantial share of the consumer's dollar.

Grain products undergo much processing between farms and consumers. A loaf of bread is a far different commodity from the pound or less of wheat which is its main ingredient. During the years between World War I and World War II farmers received, for the wheat included in a loaf of bread, anywhere from 7 to 19 percent of the selling price of the bread itself. Bread includes such other ingredients as sugar and fats and oils, which are also of farm origin, but 70 percent of the retail price of bread in 1949 represented baker's and retailer's charges over and above the cost of primary ingredients.

Meat-animal and poultry products have relatively high values per pound and most of them move through the marketing system in a short time. Farmers receive anywhere from 50 to 75 percent of the retail dollar spent for various food livestock products.

During the period between 1922 and 1941 a change of 1 dollar in retail food expenditures from year to year was usually associated with a change of 60 cents in farm cash receipts. But during World War II, marketing margins were limited by price-control and other measures, so that from 1940 through 1945 farm income from food products increased 78 cents for each dollar increase in their retail-store value. Following the removal of subsidies and special wartime controls in 1946, marketing margins for farm products rapidly "reflated." From 1946 to 1949 the national food marketing bill increased more than twice as much as did farm income from food products. Farmers got only 26 percent of the increase in retail food expenditures.

The mild recession of 1949 seemed to presage a return to the prewar relationship between changes in consumer food expenditures and farm cash receipts. If so, it has probably been disturbed again by the advent of mobilization and price control.

Cotton and wool are elaborately processed and may change hands several times before reaching the final consumer. The manufacturing and distributing sequence takes several months. Tobacco is stored for 1 to 3 years before manufacture. Excise taxes absorb close to 50 cents of the consumer's dollar spent for tobacco products. The marketing processes for these products are so expensive and time-consuming that short-run changes in their retail prices may show little relationship to concurrent price changes at the farm level.

Government Price Supports. Domestic demand for such commodities as wheat, cotton, and tobacco is rather inelastic. Consumption varies little from year to year in response even to drastic changes in their farm prices. Therefore, government loans have become extremely influential in maintaining farm income from these crops in years of large production.

Ordinarily government price-support programs may be regarded as a passive factor in the demand for farm products, once the level of support has been prescribed by legislation or administrative decision. The loan program stands ready to absorb and hold any quantities that cannot be marketed in commercial channels, either domestic or export.[1] Government purchases under Section 32 of the Agricultural Adjustment Act have been of strategic importance in relieving temporary gluts of perishable commodities.

Export Demand. At first glance it might appear that the demand for our agricultural exports is completely independent of decisions made in our own

[1] Subject to restrictions on eligibility for price support, such as compliance with marketing quotas or acreage allotments.

country. But foreign buyers must have means of payment, typically dollars or gold. United States imports of goods and services are usually by far the largest source of such means of payment. Our imports from other countries are closely geared to the disposable income of our consumers and to the level of industrial production. Prices of industrial and agricultural raw materials usually respond sharply to increases in demand. In consequence, the total value of our imports is closely correlated with our gross national product and disposable income. During the 1920's and 1930's nearly 75 percent of the year-to-year variation in the total value of our exports was associated with changes in disposable income in the United States.

In the postwar period, loans and grants by the government have been of tremendous importance in determining our agricultural exports. During 1949 some 60 percent of the total value of our agricultural exports was financed from appropriations for ECA and for civilian feeding in occupied countries.

There are many independent elements in the demand from abroad for our agricultural commodities. Unusually large crops in importing countries in a given year reduce their import requirements. An increase in production in other exporting countries also reduces the demand for our products. The effect of supplies in competing countries has been even more direct in the postwar years of dollar shortages than it was before World War II.

Factors Affecting Prices of Farm Products

During the last few months, the author has developed statistical demand analyses for a considerable number of farm products. Practically all of these analyses are based on year-to-year changes in prices, production, disposable income, and other relevant factors, during the period between 1922 and 1941.

Price ceilings and other controls cut across these relationships during World War II and may well do so again during this mobilization period. But 1922–41 relationships are in most cases still the best bases we have for appraising short-run movements in, or pressures upon, the price structure. In practical forecasting, new elements which arise during the mobilization period must be given weight in addition to the variables included in our prewar analyses.

Method Used

Considerations of space make it necessary to assume that most readers are familiar with the statistical method by which the results of this section were derived. The method used was multiple regression (or correlation) analysis using the traditional least squares, single-equation approach. The recent development of a more elaborate method by the Cowles Commission of the University of Chicago necessitates a few words in explanation of the author's procedure.

In general, demand curves for farm products that are perishable and that have a single major use can be approximated by single-equation methods.[2] Most livestock products and fresh fruits and vegetables (and, pragmatically, feed grains and hay), fall in this category. Such products contribute more than half of total cash receipts from farm marketings. With other farm products—as wheat, cotton, tobacco, and fruits and vegetables for processing—two or more simultaneous relationships are involved in the determination of free-market prices. The multiple-equation approach of the Cowles Commission may be fruitful in dealing with such commodities. Even in the case of wheat or cotton, however, it is possible to approximate certain elements of the total demand structure by means of single equations.

The demand curves shown in this section have been fitted by single-equation methods after considering the conditions under which each commodity was produced and marketed. Commodities with complicated patterns of utilization have been treated partially or not at all.

The functions selected were straight lines fitted to first differences in logarithms of annual data. In most cases, retail price was taken as the dependent variable and per capita production and per capita disposable income undeflated as the major independent variables. To adapt the results to the requirements of a mobilization period in which consumption or retail price, or both, are controlled variables, per capita consumption was substituted for production in some analyses. Further adjustments were made in a few cases for the purpose of comparing net regressions of consumption upon (deflated) income with the results of family-budget studies.

The logarithmic form was chosen on the ground that price-quantity relationships in consumer demand functions were more likely to remain stable in percentage than in absolute terms when there were major changes in the general price level. First differences (year-to-year changes) were used to avoid cycles in the original variables, and for their relevance to the outlook work of the Bureau of Agricultural Economics which focuses on short-run changes.

Before World War II, commodity analysts frequently expressed the farm price of a commodity as a function of its production and some measure of consumer income. But consumers respond to retail prices. It will contribute to clear thinking if we derive one set of estimating equations relating retail prices and consumer income, and another set expressing the relationships between farm and retail prices. At certain periods, sharp readjustments may take place within the marketing system. For this reason, an equation that expresses farm price as a function of consumer income would have missed badly during 1946–49. We should not have known whether its failure was due to changes in

---

[2] For a fuller treatment of this point and for a brief account of the history and present status of agricultural price analysis see the author's paper, "Relations Between Prices, Consumption and Production," *American Statistical Association, Journal,* September 1951.

consumer behavior or to changes in the marketing system, as both were telescoped into a single equation.

Results Obtained

Food Livestock Products. Some consumer-demand curves for livestock products are summarized in table 3. A 1 percent increase in per capita consumption of food livestock products as a group was associated with a decrease of more than 1.6 percent in the average retail price. The relationships in table 3 are based on year-to-year changes for the 1922–41 period.

Two sets of relationships are shown in the case of meat. During the early and middle 1920's we exported as much as 800 million pounds of pork in a year. The export market tended to cushion the drop in prices of meat when there was an increase in hog slaughter. As total meat production was fairly stable to begin with, small absolute changes in exports, imports, and cold-storage holdings, substantially reduced the percentage fluctuations in consumption of meat. During the 1922–41 period as a whole, meat consumption changed only about 70 percent as much from year to year as did meat production.

The first set of price-quantity coefficients for meat indicates that a 1 percent increase in meat production caused a decline of little more than 1 percent in the average retail price of meat. Increases of 1 percent in pork or beef production were associated with declines of less than 1 percent in their retail prices, and the net effect of lamb and mutton production upon the price of lamb was even smaller.

In a mobilization period the total civilian supply of meat is subject to control. The second set of meat analyses is more relevant to our current situation. A 1 percent decrease in per capita consumption of meat was associated with an increase of 1.5 percent in its average retail price.[3] A 1 percent change in the consumption of pork alone was associated with an opposite change of about 1.2 percent in its retail price. An increase in supplies of pork also had a significant depressing effect on the prices of beef and lamb.

A 1 percent increase in the consumption of beef was associated with slightly more than a 1 percent decrease in its retail price, if supplies of other meats remained constant. If the supply of other meats also increased 1 percent, the price of beef tended to decline another 0.5 percent. Supplies of beef and pork seem to have had fully as much influence on the price of lamb as did the supply of lamb itself.

Increases of 1 percent in supplies of chicken and turkey have depressed their retail prices by about the same amount. The price of chicken was significantly affected by supplies of meat, and the price of turkey was significantly

[3] In an inflationary period, commodity prices rise more rapidly than would be indicated by prewar relationships. This does not mean that the price elasticities of demand have changed. The disturbing factors are more likely to affect the relationship between price and consumer income.

TABLE 3

FOOD LIVESTOCK PRODUCTS: FACTORS AFFECTING YEAR-TO-YEAR CHANGES IN RETAIL PRICES, UNITED STATES, 1922–41

Commodity or Group	Coefficient of Multiple Determination[1]	*Effects of 1 Percent Changes in:* Production or Consumption[2]		Disposable Income[2]		Supplies of Competing Commodities[2]	
		Net Effect (Percent)[3]	Standard Error	Net Effect (Percent)[3]	Standard Error	Net Effect (Percent)[3]	Standard Error
All food livestock products[4]	.98	−1.64	(.13)	0.84	(.03)		
All meat (production)	.98	−1.07	(.07)	.86	(.07)		
Pork	.92	− .85	(.09)	.93	(.10)		
Beef	.96	− .83	(.09)	.83	(.05)	[5] −.38	(.05)
Lamb	.91	− .34	(.15)	.78	(.07)	[5] −.40	(.11)
All meat (consumption)	.98	−1.50	(.08)	.87	(.03)		
Pork[4]	.97	−1.16	(.07)	.90	(.06)		
Beef[4]	.95	−1.06	(.12)	.88	(.06)	[6] −.52	(.09)
Lamb[4]	.94	− .50*	(.14)	.78	(.06)	[6] −.65	(.14)
Poultry and eggs:							
Chickens[4]	.86	− .75*	(.18)	.76	(.09)	[7] −.42	(.16)
Turkeys (farm price)	.90	−1.21	(.25)	1.06	(.20)	[8] −.97	(.48)
Eggs (adjusted)	.87	−2.34*	(.44)	1.34	(.13)		
Dairy products:							
Fluid milk	.87			.55	(.05)		
Evaporated milk	.84			.59	(.06)		
Cheese	.84			.77	(.08)		
Butter	.84			1.01	(.11)		

[1] Unadjusted. Represents the percentage of total year-to-year variation in retail price during 1922–41 which was "explained" by the combined effects of the other variables.
[2] Per capita basis.
[3] Coefficients based on first differences of logarithms. Can be used as percentages without serious bias for year-to-year changes of as much as 10 to 15 percent in each variable
[4] Based on *consumption* per capita. Other analyses based on production per capita.
[5] Production per capita, all other meats.
[6] Consumption per capita, all other meats.
[7] Consumption per capita, all meat.
[8] Production per capita, chickens.
* Probably understates true effects of changes in production or consumption upon price.

affected by supplies of chicken. It is evident from these two relationships that supplies of meat were also a factor in the determination of prices for turkey. In a special analysis not shown in table 3, supplies of pork during October–December appeared to have a significant effect upon the farm price of turkeys.

The retail price of eggs responded more sharply to changes in production than did prices of any of the livestock products previously mentioned. The change of −2.3 percent (table 3) probably understates the true effect of a 1 percent change in per capita egg production. For reasons discussed later, no price-production relationships are shown for dairy products.

If we turn briefly to the price-income relationships in table 3 we find that many of the coefficients run between 0.8 and 1.0. If we had an adequate retail-price series for turkeys, the regression of retail price upon disposable income would probably be somewhat less than 1.0. Prices of eggs appeared to respond more sharply to changes in consumer income than did those of other livestock products.

There are many difficulties in price and consumption analysis for dairy products. All of these products stem from the same basic flow of milk. The fluid milksheds are only partially insulated from the effects of supplies and prices of milk in other areas. Surpluses from these milksheds are converted into manufactured products, thereby affecting prices of manufacturing milk and butterfat.

In the major manufacturing milk areas there are at least three alternative outlets for milk. Competition between condenseries, cheese factories, and creameries (including "butter-powder" plants), keeps prices of raw milk in the different uses approximately equal. The retail price of each product reflects the common price of manufacturing milk plus processing margins and mark-ups. Dairy products which have wide dollars-and-cents margins show a small percentage relationship between retail price and consumer income. Butter has a small processing and distributive cost relative to its value and shows a sharper "response" of retail price to disposable income.

Table 4 shows some relationships between year-to-year changes in retail prices and associated changes at the farm level. The coefficients are all in percentage (logarithmic) terms.

It has long been recognized that farm prices fluctuate more violently than retail prices because of the presence of fixed costs or charges in the marketing system. The coefficients in table 4 bear out this observation. Prices of livestock products as a group, during 1922–41, were approximately 1.5 times as variable (in percentages) at the farm level as at retail. The relationships for hogs, beef cattle, and for meat animals as a group ranged from 1.5 to 1.75 percent. The relationship for chickens was about 1.35 percent. The percentage change in the farm price of eggs was only slightly larger than the percentage change at retail.

Farm prices of milk and butterfat fluctuate considerably more than do

TABLE 4

FOOD LIVESTOCK PRODUCTS: RELATIONSHIPS BETWEEN YEAR-TO-YEAR CHANGES IN FARM PRICE AND RETAIL PRICE, UNITED STATES, 1922–41

		Effects of 1 Percent Changes in:			
		Retail Price		*Other Factors*	
Commodity or Group	*Coefficient of Determination*	*Net Effect (Percent)*[1]	*Standard Error*	*Net Effect (Percent)*[1]	*Standard Error*
All food livestock products	.97	1.47	(.07)		
Meat animals—all	.91	1.57	(.12)		
Hogs (1)	.86	1.75	(.17)		
Hogs (2)	.87	1.35	(.44)	[2]0.28	(.29)
Beef cattle	.91	1.74	(.14)		
Lambs	.85	1.06	(.18)	[3] .26	(.05)
Poultry and eggs:					
Chickens	.93	1.35	(.09)		
Eggs	.97	1.08	(.05)		
Dairy products:					
Milk for fluid use	.93	1.64	(.11)		
Condensery milk	.79	2.13	(.27)		
Milk for cheese	.79	1.76	(.22)		
Butterfat	.95	[4]1.35	(.06)		
Creamery milk	.95	[4]1.19	(.08)	[5] .13	(.04)

[1] Coefficients based on first differences of logarithms.

[2] Wholesale price of *lard* at Chicago. Coefficient not significant owing to high intercorrelation ($r^2 = .85$) between retail price of pork and wholesale price of lard.

[3] U.S. average farm price of *wool*.

[4] Coefficient derived by algebraic linkage of two regressions: (1) Farm price upon wholesale price of butter and (2) wholesale price upon retail price. Coefficients of determination have been reduced and the standard error increased to allow for residual errors in both equations.

[5] Wholesale price of dry nonfat milk solids (average of prices for both human and animal use).

retail prices of the finished products. Butter has the smallest marketing margin and the smallest percentage relationship between farm and retail price changes. The farm price of fluid milk changed about 1.6 times as sharply as the retail price and the price of milk used for cheese fluctuated about 1.8 times as much as the retail price of cheese. The price paid for milk by condenseries fluctuated more than twice as sharply as the retail price of evaporated milk, owing to the importance of fixed costs and charges in the marketing system.

At least three of the commodities listed in table 4 have important by-products. Thus, the price of wool is a highly significant factor affecting prices received by farmers for lambs. The price of lard is a recognized factor in market prices for hogs, including price discounts for heavier animals. However, since the wholesale price of lard during 1922–41 was highly correlated with the retail price of pork, the coefficient that relates hog prices to the price of lard is not statistically significant. The price of whole milk delivered to creameries is significantly related to the price of dry nonfat milk solids, as well as to the price of butter.

Other commodities shown in the table have byproducts of some value, including hides and skins. The value of these byproducts is undoubtedly reflected in market prices to some extent and enters into the calculations of processors. But it is not always possible to measure these relationships from time series.

Table 5 summarizes relationships between farm prices, production and disposable income. In most cases the effect of a 1 percent change in production or consumption per capita is associated with more than a 1 percent change in the farm price. There is some indication that the price of hogs during April–September is less sharply affected by changes in pork production than during the heavy marketing season, October–March. Prices of eggs respond more sharply to changes in production than do prices of other livestock products. The price-quantity coefficients for individual dairy products have little significance. The regressions of consumption upon price shown in table 6 are more meaningful and are considered later.

For most livestock products the response of farm price to disposable income is more than 1 to 1. Coefficients seem to center around 1.3. Exceptions to this are prices received by farmers for all dairy products and for wholesale milk, where the coefficients are approximately 1.0.

As in table 3, supplies of competing commodities influence the farm prices of beef cattle, calves, lambs, chickens, and turkeys. The price of dry nonfat solids is again included as a factor affecting the farm price of creamery milk.

Food Crops and Miscellaneous Foods. Table 5 also shows factors affecting farm prices of several fruits and vegetables. Prices of some of the deciduous fruits responded less than proportionately to year-to-year changes in production. The response for apples averaged −.8 percent, and for peaches (excluding California) approximately −.7. Peaches in other states are produced mainly for fresh market, whereas half or more of the California peaches are clingstone, produced for canning. In California, freestone peaches also are used extensively for canning and drying. Because of the complex utilization pattern, no single estimating equation for California peaches is likely to yield meaningful results.

Before 1936, about 90 percent of all cranberries were marketed in fresh form. Marketings were confined to the fall. A bumper crop in 1937 caused a sharp expansion in processing, and this utilization continued to increase. There is some evidence in the data for later years that the demand for cranberries has become somewhat more elastic as a result. That is, the farm price has been somewhat less responsive to changes in production than it was during the 1922–36 period. On the debit side, farm prices have been depressed in some recent years by excessive carry-overs of processed cranberries.

TABLE 5

Factors Affecting Year-to-Year Changes in Farm Prices, United States, 1922–41

Commodity or Group	Coefficient of Multiple Determination	*Effect of 1 Percent Changes in:* Production or Consumption: Net Effect (Percent)[1]	Production or Consumption: Standard Error	Disposable Income: Net Effect (Percent)[1]	Disposable Income: Standard Error	Supplies of Competing Commodities: Net Effect (Percent)[1]	Supplies of Competing Commodities: Standard Error
Food Livestock Products (per capita basis)							
All food livestock products[2]	.95	−2.45	(.31)	1.23	(.07)		
All meat animals (production)	.88	−1.60	(.26)	1.43	(.15)		
Hogs—cal. yr.	.82	−1.54	(.26)	1.63	(.28)		
Hogs—Oct.–Mar.	.81	−1.52	(.26)	2.08	(.28)		
Hogs—Apr.–Sept.	.69	− .99*	(.25)	1.50	(.37)		
Beef cattle	.90	−1.19	(.23)	1.27	(.13)	[3]— .40	(.15)
Veal calves	.93	− .82	(.16)	1.30	(.10)	[3]— .75	(.16)
Lambs	.87	−1.50	(.31)	1.09	(.15)	[3]— .70	(.24)
Poultry and eggs:							
Chickens	.86	− .62*	(.28)	1.06	(.12)	[4]—1.01	(.30)
Turkeys	.90	−1.21	(.25)	1.06	(.20)	[5]— .97	(.48)
Eggs (adjusted)	.82	−2.91*	(.55)	1.43	(.17)		
Dairy products:							
All	.87			.98	(.09)		
Milk, wholesale	.88			1.05	(.10)		
Milk, fluid use[6]	.91	−1.49	(.42)	.79	(.07)		
Condensery milk[6]	.76	[7]− .41	(.47)	1.34	(.19)		
Milk for cheese[6]	.71	[7]−1.01	(.59)	1.47	(.23)		
Butterfat[6]	.85	[7]−1.13	(.55)	1.28	(.15)		
Creamery milk	.79			[8]1.21	(.14)	[9] .13	(.04)
Fruits and Vegetables (per capita basis unless otherwise noted)							
All fruits (total)	.82	− .94	(.12)	1.06	(.21)		
All deciduous fruits (total)	.82	− .68	(.09)	1.08	(.18)		
Apples (total)	.96	− .79	(.04)	1.04	(.12)		
Peaches (total)[10]	.80	− .67	(.09)	.96	(.30)		
Cranberries (1932–36)[11]	.86	−1.49	(.19)	.78	(.31)		
All citrus fruits (total)	.92	−1.32	(.10)	.98	(.20)		
Oranges	.93	−1.61	(.11)	1.34	(.25)		
Grapefruit	.72	−1.77	(.28)	1.29	(.55)		
Lemons, all	.61	−1.69	(.34)	[12] .78	(.59)		
Lemons shipped fresh:						*Temperature*	
Summer[13]	.79	−2.48	(.40)	1.07	(.30)	[14] .98	(.17)
Winter[13]	.88	−1.39	(.16)			[15]—1.69	(.37)
Potatoes	.93	−3.51	(.26)	1.20	(.33)		
Sweet potatoes	.75	− .77	(.16)	.89	(.24)		
Onions:							
All[1]	.89	−2.27	(.20)	1.00	(.29)		
Late summer[16]	.85	−2.90	(.32)	[17] .72	(.60)		
Truck crops for fresh market:[18]							
Calendar year (total)	.85	−1.03*	(.26)	.81	(.12)		
Winter (total)	.67	−1.13	(.35)	.92	(.31)		
Spring (total)	.49	[17]− .95*	(.48)	.63	(.22)		
Summer (total)	.87	−1.72	(.34)	1.23	(.19)		
Fall (total)	.84	−1.67	(.35)	.85	(.20)		

[1] Coefficients based on first differences of logarithms.
[2] Consumption per capita (index).
[3] Production per capita, other meats.
[4] Consumption per capita, all meat.
[5] Production per capita, chickens.
[6] Equations include per capita consumption of end product.
[7] These coefficients do not have "structural" significance, and two of them are statistically nonsignificant also.
[8] Coefficient obtained by algebraic linkage of three equations. Coefficient of determination reduced and standard error increased to allow (approximately) for residual errors in all three equations.
[9] Wholesale price of dry nonfat milk solids (average of price for both human and animal use).
[10] United States, excluding California.
[11] Processing outlet expanded rapidly after 1937. There is evidence that demand is now elastic.
[12] Nonsignificant.
[13] Adapted from analyses originally developed by George M. Kuznets and Lawrence R. Klein in "A Statistical Analysis of the Domestic Demand for Lemons, 1921–1941," Giannini Foundation of Agricultural Economics, Mimeographed Report No. 84, June 1943. Prices are measured at the f.o.b. level. The adaptations consist in (1) converting all variables into logarithmic first differences (year-to-year changes), and (2) substituting disposable personal income for nonagricultural income. The latter adjustment had little effect on the results.
[14] Index of summer temperatures in major U.S. cities (Kuznets and Klein).
[15] Index of winter temperatures in major U.S. cities (Kuznets and Klein).
[16] Analysis developed by Herbert W. Mumford, Jr.
[17] Nonsignificant at 5 percent level.
[18] Equations fitted to 1928–41 data only.
* Probably understates true effect of production on price.

Prices of citrus fruits responded more than proportionately to changes in production. The regression coefficients for oranges, grapefruit, and lemons, individually ranged from −1.6 to −1.8 percent. Adaptations of analyses originally developed by Kuznets and Klein suggest that prices of lemons respond much more sharply to year-to-year changes in fresh-market shipments during the summer than during the winter.

The regressions of farm prices upon disposable income center around 1.0. As in most of the analyses the price-income coefficient is not so accurately established as the price-production coefficient, little significance can be attached to deviations above or below 1.0 in the former.

Kuznets and Klein introduced an interesting feature into their analyses—an index of temperatures in major consuming centers. Temperature appears to be a highly significant factor in both summer and winter. Hot weather in the summer increases the demand for lemons in thirst-quenching drinks. On the other hand, unusually cold weather in the winter appears to increase the demand for lemons; the reputation of lemon juice as a preventive of colds may be influential.

Prices of potatoes and onions respond rather sharply to changes in production. In the prewar period, when there were no price-support programs of consequence for potatoes, a 1 percent change in potato production per capita was associated with a 3.5 percent opposite change in the U.S. farm price. Prices of the late summer crop of onions, from which most of our storage supplies come, showed a price-production response of approximately −2.9. The 12-month average price of onions indicates a less violent response to changes in production, or about −2.3.

The analyses for fresh-market truck crops are based on indexes of prices and production recently developed by Herbert W. Mumford, Jr. These indexes have not yet been thoroughly tested. The correlations between price and production in the summer and fall look reasonable. They indicate a price response to production of about −1.7 percent. The analyses for the winter and spring are not so accurately established. It seems probable that the true response of price to production in these seasons and for the calendar year as a whole is somewhat greater than is implied by table 5.

The regressions of farm prices of vegetables upon disposable income in table 5 center around 1.0. The standard errors of these coefficients are, in general, sufficiently large that the deviations from 1.0 are not significant.

Responses of Consumption to Price. Table 6 summarizes responses of the consumption of various food livestock products to changes in retail price and disposable income. These coefficients are estimates of the elasticity of consumer demand. For food livestock products as a group, elasticity of demand during 1922–41 seems to have been slightly more than −.5.[4] The

---

[4] The words "more" or "less" applied to demand elasticities in this article refer to absolute values. In this case, the estimated elasticity is between −.5 and −.6.

TABLE 6

FOOD LIVESTOCK PRODUCTS: FACTORS AFFECTING YEAR-TO-YEAR CHANGES IN PER CAPITA CONSUMPTION, UNITED STATES, 1922–41

Commodity or Group	Coefficient of Determination	Effects of 1 Percent Changes in: Retail Price		Price of all other Commodities		Disposable Income		Supply of Competing Commodities[1]	
		Net Effect (Percent)[2]	Standard Error	Net Effect (Percent)[2]	Standard Error	Net Effect (Percent)[2]	Standard Error	Net Effect (Percent)[2]	Standard Error
	Multiple								
All food livestock products:									
Actual income	.91	−.56	(.04)			0.47	(.04)		
Deflated income	.95	−.52	(.03)	[3] .70	(.10)	[4] .40	(.03)		
All meat:									
Actual income	.96	−.64	(.03)			.56	(.04)		
Deflated income	.96	−.62	(.04)	[5] .69	(.15)	[4] .51	(.05)		
Pork	.94	−.81	(.05)			.72	(.07)		
Beef	.86	−.79	(.09)			.73	(.08)	[6] −.41	(.09)
Lamb	.59	−.91*	(.26)			.65	(.23)	[6] −.83	(.20)
	Partial								
Poultry and eggs:									
Chicken	.54	−.72*	(.17)						
Turkey (farm price)	.74	[7] −.61*	(.13)						
Eggs	.48	[7] −.26	(.07)						
Dairy products:									
Milk for fluid use (farm price)	.44	−.30	(.08)						
Evaporated milk	.28	−.84	(.32)						
Butter	.21	[8] −.25	(.12)						

[1] Per capita basis.
[2] Coefficients based on first differences of logarithms.
[3] Special index, retail prices other than food livestock products.
[4] Disposable income deflated by retail price index.
[5] Special index, retail prices other than meat.
[6] Consumption per capita, other meats.
[7] Production per capita.
[8] Based on algebraic linkage of three equations. Elasticity of demand for butter has probably increased in recent years.
* Probably understates true effect of price upon consumption.

elasticity of demand for all meat appears to have been slightly more than −.6. Demand elasticities for individual meats, assuming that supplies of other meats remained constant, ranged from −.8 for pork and beef to at least −.9 for lamb. It is possible that the true elasticity of demand for lamb (with supplies of other meats held constant) was somewhat more than −1.0.

For certain technical reasons the elasticities of demand for chicken and turkey at retail are probably higher than the least-squares coefficients in table 6. The coefficient for turkey is based on farm prices and the response of consumption to a 1 percent change in retail price would certainly be somewhat larger. It seems probable that the elasticities of consumer demand for both chicken and turkey were not far from −1.0 during the 1922–41 period.

The elasticity of demand for eggs is estimated at −.26. It is the least elastic of the livestock products included in table 6 with the possible exception of fluid milk and butter.

The demand elasticities for individual dairy products are not so accurately established as are those for meat and poultry products. There is some evidence that the elasticity of demand for fluid milk (based on year-to-year changes) is about −.3. The elasticity of demand for evaporated milk may be as high as −1.0 although the standard error of this coefficient is fairly large. The only statistically significant coefficient obtained for butter consumption indicated a demand elasticity of about −.25 during 1922–41. Even if this result is correct it seems probable that the consumption of butter under present conditions would respond more sharply than this to changes in price. The increasing use of oleomargarine as a bread-spread is the main reason for this belief.

Table 7 summarizes coefficients for fruits and vegetables which, in general, may be taken as approximations to the elasticity of dealer demand. This is strictly true only if production and sales are exactly equal. These coefficients can also be used as a basis for estimating elasticities of demand at retail if (1) supplies actually reaching consumers are nearly equal to production and (2) if we have appropriate equations relating percentage changes in prices at retail and farm levels. If there are any fixed elements in the marketing margin, the elasticity of demand at the consumer level will be greater than at the farm price or dealer level.

The demand for apples and peaches at the farm-price level was moderately elastic, averaging about −1.2. The demand for cranberries before 1936 was moderately inelastic (about −.6). The elasticity of −1.1 for deciduous fruits as a group was a weighted average for an extremely heterogeneous group of commodities, including fruits used for processing. Apples carried a heavier weight than any other deciduous fruit and contributed largely both to the regression coefficient and to the coefficient of partial determination for the deciduous group as a whole.

Demand elasticities for individual citrus fruits at the packinghouse door appear to have ranged from −.6 down to −.3. Demands for oranges and

TABLE 7

FRUITS AND VEGETABLES: NET REGRESSIONS OF PRODUCTION UPON CURRENT FARM PRICE UNITED STATES, 1922–41[1]

Commodity or Group	*Coefficient of Partial Determination*	*Net Regression of Production Upon Farm Price*[2]	
		Coefficient (Percent)[3]	*Standard Error*
All fruits (total)	.77	− .82	(.11)
Deciduous fruits (total)	.76	−1.11	(.15)
Apples (total)	.96	−1.21	(.06)
Peaches[4] (total)	.79	−1.18	(.15)
Cranberries (1922–36)[5]	.85	− .57	(.07)
All citrus fruits	.91	− .69	(.05)
Oranges	.92	− .58	(.04)
Grapefruit	.70	− .40	(.06)
Lemons, all	.59	− .35	(.07)
Lemons shipped fresh:			
Summer[6]	.72	− .29	(.05)
Winter[6]	.85	− .61	(.07)
Potatoes—production	.92	− .26	(.02)
Potatoes—consumption[7]	.81	− .22	(.03)
Sweet potatoes	.57	− .74	(.16)
Onions—all[8]	.88	− .39	(.03)
Onions—late summer[8]	.83	− .28	(.03)
Truck crops for fresh market:[9]			
Calendar year (total)	.61	− .59	(.15)
Winter (total)	.51	− .45	(.14)
Spring (total)	.28	[10]− .30	(.15)
Summer (total)	.72	− .42	(.08)
Fall (total)	.69	− .41	(.09)

[1] If consumption is nearly equal to production, these coefficients may be taken as approximations to the elasticity of *dealer* demand. Demand at the consumer level will typically be more elastic than at the farm or f.o.b. level.

[2] Production per capita unless otherwise noted.

[3] Based on first differences of logarithms.

[4] United States, excluding California.

[5] Processing expanded rapidly after 1936. There is some evidence that demand is now more elastic.

[6] Adapted from data and analyses originally developed by George M. Kuznets and Lawrence R. Klein, Giannini Foundation, 1943. (See table 5, footnote 4).

[7] Response of per capita consumption to retail price.

[8] Analysis developed by Herbert W. Mumford, Jr.

[9] Equations fitted to 1928–41 only.

[10] Unrounded coefficient not significant at 5 percent level.

winter lemons were the most elastic, grapefruit was of intermediate elasticity, and summer lemons had the least elasticity. Processing outlets for citrus fruits have expanded greatly over the last 15 years. Processing has extended the marketing season and increased the variety of product for each of the citrus fruits. On logical grounds, at least, this should have increased the elasticity of demand for them at the farm level. Consequently, the elasticities in table 7 should not be applied to the current situation without careful statistical and qualitative study of recent experience. In particular, the phenomenal expansion of frozen concentrated orange juice since 1948 may have had a substantial effect on the elasticity of demand for oranges.

During 1922–41, the elasticity of demand for potatoes at retail seems to have been little more than −.2. The extremely inelastic demand contributes to price-support difficulties for this crop, for relatively small surpluses have a considerable depressing effect on both retail and farm prices. The elasticity of demand for onions at the farm-price level appears to have been −.3 or less for the late summer crop, and about −.4 for the year as a whole.

The elasticity of demand for sweet potatoes is less meaningful than those for potatoes and onions. Some 50 or 60 percent of all sweet potatoes produced are used on the farms where grown. The elasticity of market demand may be decidedly different from the production-price coefficient in table 7.

Elasticities of demand for fresh-market truck crops seem to center around −.4 at the farm-price level. These coefficients are based on indexes which include a heterogeneous group of commodities. For example, the indexes include onions for which the demand elasticity in late summer and fall was −.3 or less. Implicitly, it appears that demand elasticities for some individual truck crops may be considerably higher than −.4 if supplies of competing truck crops are held constant. The analyses for fresh-market truck crops are little more than exploratory. More detailed analyses for individual commodities will be made as time permits.

An analysis of the demand for all food represents too high a degree of aggregation for most purposes. Livestock products account for more than 60 percent of the retail value of food products sold to domestic consumers and originating on farms in the United States. Consumer purchases of livestock products respond significantly to changes in price. Demand elasticities for several of these products range from −0.5 to −1.0.

The foods mainly of plant origin include some fruits and vegetables for which demand is even more elastic than the demand for meat. They also include potatoes, dry beans, cereals, sugar, and fats and oils, for which both price and income elasticities of consumption are extremely small.

Aggregative analyses of the demand for all food yield regression coefficients which are weighted averages of these diverse elasticities for individual foods. If the price of every food at retail dropped 10 percent (income remaining constant in real terms) total food consumption might increase by something like 3 to 4 percent. However, the consumption response is not independent of the distribution of price changes for individual foods if we relax the assumption of parellel price movement. A drastic decline in prices of potatoes, flour,

TABLE 8

FEED GRAINS AND HAY: FACTORS AFFECTING YEAR-TO-YEAR CHANGES IN FARM PRICES, UNITED STATES, 1922–41

		Effect of Changes of 1 Percent in:			
		Supply Factors		*Demand Factors*	
Commodity	*Coefficient of Multiple Determination*	*Net effect (Percent)*[1]	*Standard Error*	*Net Effect (Percent)*[1]	*Standard Error*
Hay	.89	−1.39	(.15)	[2]0.83	(.16)
Corn	.85	[3]−1.93	(.21)	[4] .89 [5]2.26	(.20) (.71)
Corn	.82	[6]−1.26 [7]− .89	(.28) (.40)	[8]1.06	(.25)
Corn	.85	[6]−1.22 [9]− .82 [10]+1.72	(.27) (.29) (1.19)	[8] .89	(.25)

		Average Percent Change in Price Associated with 1 Percent Change in Price of Corn	
Commodity	*Coefficient of Simple Determination*	*Percent Change*[1]	*Standard Error*
All feed grains: Prices received by farmers	.99	.91	(.02)
Hominy feed (Chicago)	.97	.86	(.03)
Prices paid by farmers for purchased feed	.91	.55	(.04)
Grain sorghums	.88	.97	(.09)
Oats	.82	.73	(.08)
Barley	.77	.68	(.09)
Soybean meal (Chicago)	.67	.59	(.13)
Hay	.51	.40	(.09)
Tankage (Chicago)	.35	.41	(.13)

[1] Coefficients based on first differences of logarithms.
[2] Cash receipts from beef cattle and dairy products, weighted approximately in proportion to total hay consumption by each type of cattle.
[3] Total U.S. supply of corn, oats, barley and grain sorghums.
[4] Index of prices received by farmers for grain-consuming livestock (weighted according to gain requirements).
[5] Number of grain-consuming animal units on farms, January 1.
[6] U.S. supply of corn (adjusted for net changes in CCC stocks).
[7] U.S. supply of other feed grains and byproduct feeds.
[8] Product of numbers and prices of grain-consuming livestock.
[9] U.S. supply of oats, barley and grain sorghums, plus wheat and rye fed.
[10] U.S. supply of byproduct feeds. Regression coefficient is statistically nonsignificant.

sugar, and lard would have a negligible effect on total food consumption if prices of meats, poultry, fruits and vegetables, remained constant. On the other hand, a 10 percent drop in an index of food prices caused by a 30 percent drop in the price of meat might well lead to a 6 percent increase in an index of total food consumption.

Feed Crops. Table 8 summarizes some price-estimating equations for hay and corn. The U.S. average farm price of hay generally dropped about 1.4 percent in response to a 1 percent increase in total supply of hay. The demand factor used in the hay analysis is an index of cash receipts from sales of dairy products and beef cattle, weighted in proportion to total hay consumption by dairy and beef cattle respectively. The price of hay changed somewhat less than proportionately to this demand index.

The first analysis shown for corn expresses corn prices as a function of total supplies of corn, oats, barley, and grain sorghums. These grains are closely substitutable for corn in most feeding uses. A 1 percent increase in total supplies of the four grains generally reduced the price of corn almost 2 percent.

Two demand factors are used in this analysis. The first is an index of prices received by farmers for livestock products, with each product weighted approximately by its grain requirements. The regression coefficient indicates that a 1 percent increase in the average price of grain-consuming livestock is associated with very nearly a 1 percent increase in the price of corn. This is consistent with the function of livestock-feed price ratios as equilibrating mechanisms for the feed-livestock economy. The second demand factor in this equation is the number of grain-consuming animal units on farms as of January 1. This coefficient is significant but is not so accurately established as the other coefficients in the equation. It implies that a 1 percent increase in grain-consuming animal units from one year to the next tends to increase corn prices by perhaps 2 percent.

The other two analyses for corn illustrate points that are sometimes overlooked in price analysis. As other feed grains are substitutable for corn the net effect of a 1 percent increase in corn supplies upon corn prices (supplies of other feeds remaining constant) is less than the effect obtained if supplies of all feed grains increase by 1 percent. The last analysis subdivides the total supply of feed concentrates into three parts. During 1922–41 the net response of corn price to corn supply was not much more than -1.2. The response of corn prices to changes in supplies of other feed grains was approximately $-.8$. The regression of corn prices upon supplies of byproduct feeds was positive but statistically nonsignificant. The positive sign is not wholly implausible since these feeds are used to a large extent as supplements rather than substitutes for corn.

Table 8 also summarizes some simple regression relationships between year-to-year changes in prices of other feeds and the price of corn. The level of correlation obtained is a rough indicator of the closeness of competition between the other feeds and corn on a short-run (year-to-year) basis.

Export Crops. All of the analyses referred to in tables 3 through 8 are based on the traditional single-equation approach. This approach is not conceptually adequate to derive the complete demand structures for export crops such as wheat, cotton, and tobacco. In the absence of price supports, at least two (relatively) independent demand curves are involved in determining their prices—domestic and foreign.

It is possible, however, to get approximate estimates of the response of domestic consumption of wheat and cotton (and possibly tobacco) to changes in their farm prices. An exploratory analysis by the author yielded a demand elasticity (with respect to farm price) of −.07 (± .027) for the domestic food use of wheat. Other investigators have obtained elasticities of about −.2 (with respect to spot market prices) for the domestic mill consumption of cotton. The domestic consumption of tobacco products also appears to respond very little to changes in the farm price of tobacco.

Comparison of Time-Series Results with Family-Budget Studies

The problem of reconciling time-series and family-budget data on demand has interested economists for many years. Among other difficulties, few analysts have found sufficiently good data of both types to work with. These pages are exploratory, but they may stimulate some fruitful discussion and criticism. Space does not permit a full exposition of the methods used in this section, but a brief indication is given in table 9, footnote 1.

Table 6 contains two time-series analyses that were designed to simulate as nearly as possible the conditions prevailing in family-budget studies. One coefficient in each equation measures the relationship between consumption

TABLE 9

Relationships between Consumption and Income as Measured from Time Series and from Family Budget Data, United States, 1922–41 and 1948

Item	*Net Effect of 1 Percent Change in Per Capita Income upon:*		
	Consumption Per Capita (Time Series Data, 1922–41) (Percent)	*Expenditure Per Capita*[1] *(Family Budget Data, Spring 1948) (Percent)*	*Quantity Purchased Per Capita*[1] *(Family Budget Data, Spring 1948) (Percent)*
All food livestock products	0.40 [2] (.03)	0.33	0.23
All meat	.51 [2] (.05)	[3] .36	.23

[1] See table 10, footnote 2. A fuller statement of the methods used to obtain these coefficients will be supplied on request.

[2] Standard error of time series coefficient. Comparable measures for the family budget coefficients are not available, as the coefficients were calculated from grouped data.

[3] Meat, poultry, and fish. Coefficient for meat alone would be slightly higher.

and real disposable income with prices of all commodities held constant by statistical means. These coefficients are compared in table 9 with corresponding family-budget regressions based on data collected by the Bureau of Human Nutrition and Home Economics in the spring of 1948. (See also table 10.)

Consumption in the time-series equation for food livestock products is measured by means of an index number. A pound of steak is weighted more heavily than a pound of hamburger and, of course, much more heavily than a pound of fluid milk. The weights are average retail prices in 1935–39. Hence the time-series regression implies that if all prices are held constant, *expenditures* will increase with income in the proportions indicated.

Conversely, the expenditures shown in family-budget data are analogous to price-weighted indexes. As the price of each type, cut, and grade of product is the same to consumers of all income groups during the week of the survey, expenditures for livestock products at two family-income levels are equal to the different quantities bought, multiplied by the same fixed prices.

Consumption in the time-series analysis for meat is measured in pounds (carcass-weight equivalent) but each "pound" is a composite of all species, grades, and cuts. Expenditures at constant prices will change almost exactly in proportion to these "statistical pounds." But the actual pounds shown in family-budget data reflect more expensive cuts and grades at high- than at low-income levels. In the 1948 study, average prices per pound paid by the highest income group exceeded those paid by the lowest in the following ratios: All beef, 34 percent; all pork, 28 percent; all meat, 35 percent; meat, poultry, and fish combined, 32 percent. On the average, a pound of meat (retail weight) bought by a high-income family represented a greater demand upon agricultural resources than a pound of meat bought by a low-income family.

There are strong arguments for comparing the expenditure-income regressions from family-budget data with the consumption-income regressions from time series. The coefficients are not unduly far apart, considering the possible factors that make for differences. Among other things, 1948 was a year of full employment. As the income elasticity of food consumption decreases at higher family-income levels, and as the family-budget observations have been weighted according to the high-income pattern of 1948, the regression coefficients in table 10 are probably lower than would have been obtained on the average during 1922–41.

Some internal features of the family-budget data for 1948 deserve comment. In the case of livestock products the expenditure coefficients more nearly reflect demands upon agriculture (hence, real income to agriculture) than do the quantity coefficients. The differences between the two sets of coefficients are largely due to differences in type and quality of products consumed, with the significant aspects of quality being reflected back to farmers in the form of higher farm values per retail pound.

The situation with respect to two of the fruit and vegetable categories seems

TABLE 10

FOOD EXPENDITURES AND QUANTITIES PURCHASED: AVERAGE PERCENTAGE RELATIONSHIP TO FAMILY INCOME, URBAN FAMILIES, UNITED STATES, SPRING 1948

Item	Relative Importance[1] (1)	*Effect of 1 Percent Change in Income upon:* Expenditure (Percent)[2] (2)	Quantity Purchased (Percent)[2] (3)	Col. (2) Minus Col. (3) (Percent)[2] (4)
A. Per family:				
All food expenditures		*0.51*		
At home		.40		
Away from home		1.12		
B. Per family member:[3]				
All food expenditures		*.42*		
At home		.29		
Away from home		1.14		
C. Per 21 meals at home:[3]				
All food (excluding accessories)	*100.0*	*.28*	[4]*0.14*	*0.14*
All livestock products	*50.8*	*.33*	[4] *.23*	*.10*
Meat, poultry and fish	29.2	.36	.23	.13
Dairy products (excluding butter)	16.9	.32	.23	.09
Eggs	4.7	.22	.20	.02
Fruits and vegetables	*19.0*	*.42*	[4] *.33*	*.09*
Leafy, green and yellow vegetables	4.9	.37	.21	.16
Citrus fruit and tomatoes	5.2	.41	.42	− .01
Other vegetables and fruits	8.9	.45	.35	.10
Other foods	*30.2*	*.08*	[4]− *.12*	*.20*
Grain products	11.4	.02	− .21	.23
Fats and oils	9.8	.13	− .04	.17
Sugars and sweets	5.2	.20	− .07	.27
Dry beans, peas and nuts	1.5	− .07	− .33	.26
Potatoes and sweet potatoes	2.3	.05	− .05	.10

[1] Percent of total expenditures for food used at home, excluding condiments, coffee, and alcoholic beverages.

[2] Regression coefficients based upon logarithms of food expenditures or quantities purchased per 21 meals at home and logarithms of estimated Spring 1948 disposable incomes per family member, weighted by proportion of total families falling in each family income group. The object was to obtain coefficients reasonably comparable with those derived from time series.

[3] Per capita regression coefficients are lower than per family coefficients in this study whenever the latter are less than 1.0. This happens because average family size was positively correlated with family income among the survey group. A technical demonstration of this point will be supplied on request.

[4] Weighted averages of quantity-income coefficients for subgroups.

Source: Basic data from United States Bureau of Human Nutrition and Home Economics. *1948 Food Consumption Surveys. Preliminary Rept.* No. 5, May 30, 1949; tables 1 and 3.

to be similar to that of livestock products (table 10). The difference between expenditure and quantity coefficients probably reflects increasing use of the more expensive types and qualities within each commodity group. The higher income families may be paying more for marketing services, but they are also paying more per pound to the farmer.

This is only partly true in the "other foods" group. *Grains* at the farm level are fairly homogenous. The difference between expenditure and quantity regressions for grain products must largely reflect differences in marketing services (baked goods versus flour, and so forth). *Sugars* and *sweets* include candy, soft drinks, and preserves, and sugars and sirups. To the extent that candy includes domestically produced nuts, or that preserves include domestic fruits and berries, the positive expenditure coefficient indicates some benefits to farmers. But most of the difference between expenditure and quantity regressions for sweets goes to bottlers, confectioners, and distributors.

The positive expenditure coefficient for *fats* and *oils* is mainly due to the greater use of butter by the higher income groups. Because of this fact, the expenditure coefficient more nearly represents the demand for agricultural resources in the production of fats and oils. In the group comprising dry beans, peas, and nuts, the first two decline rapidly and the third increases rapidly as family income rises, so the expenditure regression is more relevant to farm income than is the quantity coefficient.

For all foods (excluding condiments, alcoholic beverages and coffee) the 1948 survey of BHNHE indicates a tendency for expenditures per 21 meals at home to rise about 28 percent as much as family income per member. The weighted average of the quantity-income regressions is about 14 percent. One fourth, or one third, of the difference probably goes to marketing services. On balance, it appears that, in 1948, a 10 percent difference in income per family member meant a difference of roughly 2.5 percent in the per capita demand for agricultural resources used in food production.

This effect was a weighted average of 3.3 percent for livestock products, 4.2 percent for fruits and vegetables other than potatoes, and *slightly less than zero* for other foods as a group. These coefficients indicate the direction in which consumers tend to adjust their food patterns as their incomes increase. At present, per capita consumption of grain products and potatoes is 15 percent lower than in 1935–39. The demand for spreads for bread has also been caught in this downtrend, so that the per capita consumption of butter and oleomargarine combined in 1950 was 3 pounds, or 15 percent, below the prewar average. Consumption of sugar and total food fats and oils per person was about the same in 1950 as in 1935–39. On the other hand, per capita consumption of livestock products (excluding butter and lard) was up more than 23 percent and consumption of fruits and vegetables (aside from potatoes and sweet potatoes) was up 9 percent.

Two other points might be noted in closing: (1) The regression of *calories* upon income per family member is somewhat less than the average quantity gradient of 14 percent would suggest, as costs per calorie are considerably lower for sugar, fats and oils, and grain products, than for livestock products and fruits and vegetables; (2) the demand for *restaurant meals* seems to increase slightly more than 10 percent in response to a 10 percent increase in income per family member. This implies of course, a similar increase in demand for restaurant services.

4 Estimates of the Elasticities of Supply of Selected Agricultural Commodities*

MARC NERLOVE†‡

This paper deals with the role that farmers' expectations of future relative prices plays in shaping their decisions as to how many acres to devote to each crop. Although the writer and most previous workers in the field of supply response have concentrated on acreage decisions, it should be recognized at the outset that acreage response to price is only one facet of the much more complicated problem of obtaining a comprehensive supply function. Within this limited context I shall try to answer two questions: First, why have such low elasticities of acreage to deflated price been obtained? Second, is it possible to obtain measures of the elasticities that are more in line with what we know from studies made on production functions and on farmers' reactions to the allotment and price support programs? In connection with this second question, I shall present a few tentative and preliminary estimates of the elasticity of acreage to deflated price for cotton, wheat and corn, for the period 1909–32.

---

* *Journal of Farm Economics,* Vol. XXXVIII, No. 2 (May, 1956), pp 496–509. Based on an investigation of the relationship of acreage to deflated price for cotton, wheat and corn, during the period 1909–32. This paper is a preliminary report on research still in progress. Subsequent findings may alter the conclusions reached.

† Yale University, New Haven, Connecticut.

‡ I wish to acknowledge the financial and computational assistance of the Social Science Research Council, the Earhart Foundation, and the Department of Economics at the University of Chicago. I am deeply grateful to Professors C. F. Christ and A. C. Harberger, both of the University of Chicago, for many stimulating comments and criticisms on earlier drafts of this paper and on the research upon which this paper is based. I alone, however, am responsible for any errors that occur.

I

Many fewer studies have been made on the response of supply to price in comparison with the number of studies on demand. What little work that has been done is mainly for agricultural products. The more important of these studies are those of Bradford Smith, Louis Bean, Robert Walsh, and R. L. Kohls and Don Paarlberg.[1] *All these studies suggest that farmers respond very little to price in planning their acreage.* The most intensively investigated commodity has been cotton. Walsh found that the elasticity of acreage with respect to last year's deflated price, while significantly greater than zero, was of the order of only 0.2. Kohls and Paarlberg estimated an elasticity of acreage with respect to price of about 0.07 for corn and 0.2 for wheat. In a number of regressions of acreage on deflated price lagged one year and trend, for the period 1909–32, I have obtained similar results. The results of Smith and Bean cannot conveniently be summarized by a single numerical measure of elasticity.

These numerical estimates seem to be contradicted by experience under the support programs. In 1948, about 36% of the cotton crop, 28% of the wheat crop, and 15% of the corn crop was placed under loan. The estimates of the elasticities of demand for these three crops are quite low: between —.3 and 0 for cotton and wheat, and less than —1 for corn.[2] If the supply elasticities are as low as previous measurement would suggest, then support prices for cotton, wheat, and corn must have been greatly in excess of the equilibrium prices in 1948. On the other hand, somewhat higher elasticities of supply would not imply support prices that were greatly out of line with the equilibrium prices. It is difficult to believe that the supported cotton price was 70% above the equilibrium price, the supported wheat price 50–60%, and the supported corn price more than 15%.[3] It seems far more

[1] Bradford B. Smith, *Factors Affecting the Price of Cotton*, USDA Technical Bulletin 50 (Washington, D.C., 1928); L. H. Bean, "The Farmers' Response to Price," *Journal Farm Economics,* Vol. 11 (1929), pp. 368–85; Robert M. Walsh, "Response to Price in the Production of Cotton and Cottonseed," *Journal Farm Economics*, Vol. 26 (1944), pp. 359–72; R. L. Kohls, and Don Paarlberg, *Short-Time Response of Agricultural Production to Price and Other Factors,* Purdue Univ. Agri. Expt. Sta. Bul. 555 (1950).

[2] See Frank Lowenstein, and Martin S. Simon, "Analyses of Factors That Affect Mill Consumption of Cotton in the United States," *Agricultural Economics Research,* Vol. 6 (1954); Kenneth W. Meinken, *The Demand and Price Structure for Wheat*, USDA Technical Bulletin 1136 (Washington, D.C., 1955), pp. 42–43; and Richard J. Foote, John W. Klein, and Malcolm Clough, *The Demand and Price Structure for Corn and Total Feed Concentrates,* USDA Technical Bulletin 1061 (Washington, D.C., 1952), pp. 39–41.

[3] These figures were crudely derived on the basis of the following considerations:

Let q = the quantity produced;

P_0 = the equilibrium price;

$P + \Delta P$ = the support price;

$\frac{\Delta q}{q}$ = the quantity placed under loan as a percent of the total crop.

The elasticity of demand ϵ is approximately equal to

reasonable that supply elasticities are higher than previous measurement would suggest.

Estimates of farm production functions give additional reason to question previous estimates of the elasticities of supply. Heady has found that, on the individual farm, substitution among crops is relatively easy.[4] This means that on typical farms small changes in the relative prices of crops may make large changes in the cropping practices profitable. Beneke and Howell have investigated Iowa farmers' reactions to corn acreage allotments.[5] They find that farmers not participating in the allotment program increased substantially the acreage they planted to corn, at the expense of soybeans and other crops. Presumably these farmers shifted because they could anticipate that a combination of both the supports for corn and the existence of allotments would make it profitable for them to do so. Individual farmers, then, *can* and *do* shift when conditions make a shift profitable. This fact suggests that there may be substantial response to price in the production of individual crops.[6]

One reason why such low estimates may have been obtained may be that the elasticity of supply has been identified with the elasticity of acreage with respect to price. The elasticity of acreage is probably only a lower limit to the supply elasticity. More important, though, is the fact that price lagged one year has been identified with the price to which farmers react, i.e., the price that they expect will prevail at some future time. Kohls and Paarlberg have pointed out that farmers would not be acting in their own

---

$$\epsilon = -\frac{\Delta q/q}{\dfrac{\Delta P}{P_0}}.$$

Therefore, if the elasticity of supply is close to zero, the excess of the support price over the equilibrium price is

$$\frac{\Delta P}{P_0} = \frac{\Delta q/q}{\epsilon}.$$

If the elasticity of supply is not zero but η, we have

$$\frac{\Delta P}{P_0} = \frac{\Delta q/q}{\epsilon+\eta},$$

where all elasticities are measured from the disequilibrium quantity actually produced.

[4] E. O. Heady, "The Supply of U.S. Farm Products under Conditions of Full Employment," *American Economic Review,* Vol. 45, No. 2 (May 1955), p. 230.

[5] R. R. Beneke and H. B. Howell, "How Do Farmers React to Corn Acreage Allotments?" *Iowa Farm Science,* Vol. 10 (October 1955).

[6] High elasticities of substitution on individual farms do not, however, necessarily entail a high elasticity of supply for the industry as a whole. The extent of change of relative prices may have to be very great before any substantial number of farms will shift. The more diverse are the farms with regard to the suitabilities of their lands and managements for production of various crops, the lower will be the elasticity of supply. With high elasticities of substitution among crops, however, we must assume almost unreasonable diversity among farms in order that the observed elasticities of supply be as low as previous studies have indicated.

interest if they did, in fact, take last year's price as an indication of what this year's price was going to be.[7] I think we would all agree—after all, agricultural prices are among the most volatile in the economy. Farmers would probably find themselves with lower incomes if they extensively revised their production plans in response to the wide swings that take place in the relative prices of various crops. Surely farmers must base their decisions on some reasonable assessment of the supply and demand conditions for the commodities they produce. *Farmers react, not to last year's price, but rather to the price they expect, and this expected price depends only to a limited extent on what last year's price was.*

II

In taking the position that we should not identify expected price with price lagged one year, we are letting ourselves in for trouble. In theory we can always find out what today's expected prices are by asking farmers; but we cannot find out what expected prices were in the 'twenties by asking the farmers of 1955. In practice, therefore, we cannot observe expected prices. If we do not identify expected price with last year's price, with what, then, can we identify it? If you will grant that we can use the elasticity of acreage with respect to expected price as a measure of the elasticity of supply, then this question is really the second question posed at the beginning of this paper: Can we obtain more reasonable estimates of the elasticities of supply?

If more specific information is not available, it seems reasonable to assume that the price expected to prevail at some future date depends in some way on what prices have been in the past. Price expectations are, of course, shaped by a multitude of influences, so that a representation of expected price as a function of past price may merely be a convenient way to summarize the effects of these many and diverse influences. In some situations certain influences may be controlling, and in those situations we should utilize what knowledge we have of the controlling influence to take account of it directly. For example, it is difficult to believe that the operations of the Commodity Credit Corporation can have failed to exert an influence on price expectations far in excess of those factors whose influences may be summarized by past prices. Because of the special difficulties presented by the support programs and the acreage allotments, this discussion will be confined to the period before 1933.

How should we use past prices to represent expected price? Each past price represents only a very short-run market phenomenon, an equilibrium of those forces present in the market at the time. It is for precisely this reason that farmers may not react only to last year's price. This does not

[7] Kohls and Paarlberg, *op. cit.*, p. 7.

mean, however, that the past has no relevance for the future. I think it can be said in general that more recent prices are a partial result of forces expected to continue to operate in the near future; the more recent the past price, the more it expresses the operation of those forces relevant to expectations. Hence, I assume that the influence of more recent prices should be greater than the influence of less recent prices. What could be simpler than to represent expected price as a weighted moving average of past prices in which the weights decline as one goes back in time?

The practice of representing expected price by price lagged one year is clearly a special case of this more general hypothesis. In the special case a weight of one is arbitrarily assigned to last year's price and zero weight to all other prices. In allowing for the possibility that the weights for prices other than last year's price are not zero, we should use farmers' behavior to help us decide on an appropriate weighting system. We clearly do not have enough observations on the acreages devoted to major field crops to permit us to include prices separately back to Adam and Eve in a multiple regression of acreage on past prices. The sensible procedure readily suggests itself: Why not restrict the form of the weighting system but allow the actual values of the weights to be determined by the data? Since, for any declining weight system, prices beyond a certain point in time exert only a negligible influence in total, we can economize the available degrees of freedom, estimate the elasticity of acreage with respect to expected price, and determine the number of past prices influencing expected price; and we can do these things all at the same time.

There are many forms we might give to a weighting system such as I have described. How can we settle on a particular form? We might obtain a sensible form for the weighting system by beginning a bit farther back with some very specific hypothesis about the way in which expectations are formed and then *deriving* the result that expected price may be represented by a weighted moving average of past prices. One such hypothesis that seems plausible to me, but which is by no means the only possibility, is that *each year farmers revise the price they expect to prevail in the coming year in proportion to the error they made in predicting price this period.*[8] Let us denote the price expected this year by P^*_t, the price expected last year by P^*_{t-1}, the actual price last year by P_{t-1}. Let the proportion of the error by which farmers revise their expectations be a constant, β, which lies between zero and one. I shall call β the coefficient of expectation. The hypothesis just stated can be expressed mathematically as follows:

$$P^*_t - P^*_{t-1} = \beta[P_{t-1} - P^*_{t-1}], \qquad 0 < \beta \leqq 1. \tag{1}$$

---

[8] Substantlally the same hypothesis was originally developed by Philiip Cagan in "The Monetary Dynamics of Hyper-Inflations," unpublished Ph.D. dissertation, the University of Chicago (March 1954). Only minor modifications are necessary in order to apply Cagan's formulation to the problems under consideration in this paper.

Let me illustrate the meaning of this hypothesis with a numerical example. Suppose that farmers expected a price of \$2 per bu. of wheat this year but that the realized price was only \$1.90. Shall they now immediately reach the conclusion that their previous prediction had no value whatsoever, that the best they can do is to predict a \$1.90 for next year? If we agreed with the procedure usually followed, namely that of arbitrarily assigning unit weight to last year's price and zero weight to all other prices, we would have to say that farmers placed no faith at all in their previous predictions. Farmers as a group, however, are known for the strength of their convictions. Some farmers might revise their expectation downward from \$2 to \$1.90, but I suspect that most farmers would revise their expectations down only, let us say, to \$1.95. Some farmers might not revise their expectations at all. In this case the average expected price might turn out to be \$1.94, so that the magnitude of the coefficient of expectation would be 60% for the group as a whole.

It can be shown that the hypothesis, stated in equation (1), that farmers revise the price they expect in proportion to the error they have made in prediction, is equivalent to one in which expected price is represented as a weighted moving average of past prices where the weights are functions solely of the coefficient of expectation.[9] Mathematically the result is as follows:

$$P_t^* = \beta P_{t-1} + (1 - \beta)\beta P_{t-2} + (1 - \beta)^2 \beta P_{t-3} + \cdots \tag{2}$$

The variables have the same meaning as before. Since the coefficient of expectation, β, is between zero and one the weights will decline toward zero as we go back in time. Although in theory *all* past prices must be included, the fact that the weights decline means that practically we can safely ignore prices in the very distant past. At just what point in the past we can safely begin to ignore all previous prices depends on the size of the coefficient of expectation: the closer is the coefficient of expectation to zero, that is, the greater the tenacity with which farmers cling to their previous expectations, the greater will be the number of past prices we cannot ignore. When the coefficient of expectation is 50%, we must include about the five past actual prices to come within 5% of the expected price.[10] Taking account of five

[9] This result may easily be derived by recognizing that equation (1) is a first order difference equation in expected price. On the assumption of the appropriate initial conditions, it will be found that the solution to the difference equation is the same as that given in equation (2) below.

[10] The sum of weights for a number N of past prices is

$$1 - (1 - \beta)^{N+1}$$

The number of past prices that should be included in order that the approximate error be less than or equal to some small positive amount e can be found from the following formula:

$$| 1 - (1 - \beta)^{N+1} | \leqq e.$$

past prices is certainly quite different from taking account of only one past price.

We can use the hypothesis that farmers revise their expectations by a portion of the error they make in prediction to obtain estimates both of the elasticity of acreage to expected price and of the coefficient of expectation. Let us restrict ourselves to the simple case in which the acreage devoted to a crop is a linear function of the expected relative price of that crop alone. We might in practice wish to include a trend variable, but for the purpose of this exposition I shall leave it out. Let x_t be acreage this year, P^*_t be the price expected this year, and u_t be a random residual term. Then we can write the acreage response function as follows:

$$x_t = a_0 + a_1 P^*_t + u_t. \tag{3}$$

We cannot observe P^*_t and so we cannot estimate equation (3) quite as we would any other simple equation. We must represent P^*_t in terms of variables we can observe. Equation (3) means that we can write any expected price, P^*_t, as a linear function of acreage x_t. In particular, last year's expected price, P^*_{t-1}, can be represented by last year's acreage, x_{t-1}. But this means that expected price this year is a function of last year's actual price and last year's acreage. Why? Because our expectation model, as expressed in equation (1), says that expected price this year is a function of actual price last year and expected price last year. We can replace last year's expected price in equation (1) by a linear function of last year's acreage. If we now substitute this new expression for expected price into the acreage response function, equation (3), we obtain a new relation between acreage this year and last year's actual price and last year's acreage. It is

$$x_t = \pi_0 + \pi_1 P_{t-1} + \pi_2 x_{t-1} + v_t, \tag{4}$$

where v_t is a random residual different from u_t. π_0 turns out to be equal to $a_0\beta$, π_1 equals $a_1\beta$, and π_2 equals $1 - \beta$.[11] We cannot, in practice, observe

[11] This method of transforming the original acreage response function was suggested by the work of L. M. Koyck on *Distributed Lags and Investment Analysis* (Amsterdam: North Holland Publishing Co., 1954), chap. II. Koyck, however, *postulates* the existence of a distributed lag, whereas equation (1) above *explains* its existence. The advantage of using two relationships, such as (1) and (3), to obtain (4) rather than obtaining (4) from a relationship such as

$$x_t = a_0 + a_1[\beta P_{t-1} + (1 - \beta)\beta P_{t-2} + \cdots] + u_t,$$

is that it is still possible to perform this same kind of transformation on the acreage response function when more than one expected price is included. When the coefficients of expectation for different crops are not restricted to be the same, however, it is necessary to transform the whole set of all related acreage response functions simultaneously. It is then also necessary to estimate *all* such transformed relations in order to estimate the coefficients in any one of the original response functions. A great advantage of this method is, however, the ease with which we can make the change in expected price depend on factors other than the error of prediction (i.e., past prices). For example we might wish to take account of the influence of anticipated changes in livestock numbers on the expected price of corn.

expected price, but we can observe last year's price and last year's acreage. Hence, if acreage really does respond to expected price we should observe a correlation between acreage this year and actual price last year and acreage last year. The relationship between the π's in equation (4) and the a's and the β in equation (3) allows us to work back from equation (4) to the acreage response function expressed by equation (3).[12]

At this point a parenthetical remark about the statistical properties of the estimates we obtain from an equation relating this year's acreage to last year's actual price and last year's acreage should be inserted. Most economic time series are known to exhibit a great deal of serial correlation. Normally, in estimating an equation like (3), we would assume that the residuals u_t were not serially correlated. Suppose for the moment that we could observe P_t^* and we went ahead and estimated equation (3). If the residuals u_t were positively serially correlated our estimates of the coefficients in equation (3) would be biased and statistically inconsistent. The residuals v_t of equation (4) will be serially uncorrelated only if the residuals u_t are positively serially correlated.[13] Hence, estimates of a_0 and a_1 derived from

---

[12] A major difficulty exists in interpreting the results of a regression of acreage on lagged price and lagged acreage: In the discussion in the text, a relationship between acreage and expected price, (3), and a relationship between expected prices and past prices, (1) and (2), are assumed; on the assumption that *observed* acreage represents *desired* acreage, equation (4) is derived. Alternatively, we might assume that expected price was equal to last year's price, but that *desired* acreage was not the same as observed acreage. In order to make these hypotheses operational we would have to assume some relation between desired and actual acreages. For example,

$$x_t - x_{t-1} = \gamma[x_t - x_{t-1}], \tag{1'}$$

where x_t^* = desired acreage, x_t = actual acreage, and γ = a constant. (1′) states that the change in actual acreage is proportional to the difference between desired and actual acreage. If we assume the particular relation stated in (1′), we find that acreage is again a linear function of lagged price and lagged acreage, only γ now enters where β did before. Hence, estimation of equation (4) cannot distinguish between two cases: (1) actual acreage is equal to desired acreage, but expected price is not equal to last year's price, and (2) desired acreage is not equal to actual acreage, but expected price is equal to last year's price. The difficulty inherent in the interpretation of equation (4) of the text is common to all empirical work in economics. Theory does not always provide us with relationships between variables which can be observed. Further relations between the nonobserved variables and other variables that can be observed must be postulated. Only then can we test hypotheses concerning the theoretical relationship. Additional empirical evidence must be brought to bear on the problems of how strongly farmers react to actual prices in altering their expectations and how rapidly they react to expected prices in the adjustment of actual acreage to desired acreage.

[13] In order that the residuals v_t be serially uncorrelated, the residuals u_t must follow an auto-regressive scheme of the following sort:

$$u_t = (1 - \beta)\, u_{t-1} + \epsilon_t,$$

where ϵ_t is randomly and independently distributed and β is the coefficient of expectation. To assume that this is so, is no worse an assumption than to assume no serial correlation among the u_t.

equation (4) may be better estimates than those we would obtain if we could observe P_t^* independently.[14]

In Table 1, page 74, some of the main empirical results are summarized and compared. The results obtained from the regressions of acreage on lagged deflated price and trend are summarized in column (2). These regressions were carried out for three crops, cotton, wheat and corn, for the period 1909–32. The estimates of the elasticities, coefficients of trend and the multiple correlation coefficients are comparable with such estimates that have been obtained by other workers in the field of supply response. I have called the procedure, which yields the estimates summarized in column (2), the "special" method, because it rests on the arbitrary assumption that the coefficient of expectation is one. Column (3) summarizes the results obtained from the regressions of acreage on lagged deflated price, trend, *and* lagged acreage. I have called the procedure, which yields these estimates, the "general" method, because it allows the data to determine the coefficients of expectation.

---

[14] If the residuals u_t are actually uncorrelated serially, the residuals v_t should be negatively serially correlated. Tests I have made, however, on the calculated residuals v_t do not indicate significant negative serial correlation. (See the table below.)

Another method for estimating the coefficients in equation (3) and the coefficient of expectation is available. This method rests on the assumption that the residuals u_t are *not* serially correlated. An alternative way of looking at expected price is that it is a weighted moving average of past prices where the weights are determined by the coefficient of expectation. If we knew the coefficient of expectation we could calculate all the expected prices using past actual prices. If we tried a number of different values for the coefficient of expectation we could find a value that would yield the greatest correlation between acreage and expected price. In this way we could obtain estimates of both the coefficient of expectation and the elasticity of acreage response. By stepwise maximization of the likelihood function we can show that this iterative procedure yields maximum likelihood estimates, provided the residuals u_t are not serially correlated. Confidence intervals for the estimates would be very difficult to obtain, but any point hypothesis can be tested by means of the likelihood ratio.

This procedure has been used to obtain estimates of the elasticities of acreage with respect to expected price. The estimated elasticities, the multiple correlation coefficients and the estimates of β are presented in the table below.

Crop	*Elasticity of Acreage with Respect to Expected Price*	*Coefficient of Expectation* β	R^2	*Durbin-Watson Statistic*	
				For Regression Discussed in This Footnote	*For Regression Discussed in the Text*
(1)	(2)	(3)	(4)	(5)	(6)
Cotton	4.53	0.04	0.80	1.71[a]	2.34[a]
Wheat	1.18	0.37	0.77	1.25[b]	2.19[a]
Corn	0.35	0.25	0.43	1.54[b]	2.04[a]

[a] Insignificant serial correlation at the .05 level.
[b] Durbin-Watson test inconclusive at the .05 level.

The values of the Durbin-Watson statistic, used for testing for the presence or absence

The main things we want to compare between the special and general methods are: (1) the magnitudes of the elasticities of acreage to expected price; and (2) the percentage of the variance of acreage explained, i.e., the R^2's. The squares of the multiple correlation coefficients are substantially higher using the general method than they are using the special method. Dropping the arbitrary assumption that the coefficient of expectation is 1 leads to an increase in the R^2 of .15 for cotton, .13 for wheat and .13 for corn.[15] The general method also yields estimates of the elasticities of acreage to expected price that are two to three times as large as those yielded by the special method.[16] See Table I. Earlier in the paper I indicated why I thought a higher estimate of the elasticity was preferable to a lower estimate. Qualitatively, at least, the estimates obtained by the general method are more reasonable than those obtained when the coefficient of expectation is arbitrarily assumed to be one.[17]

It is also especially interesting to note the decrease in the significance of the trend variable in explaining acreage when we allow the coefficient of expectation to be determined by the data. The necessity of including a

---

of serial correlation, are given in column (5) for the results obtained by the iterative procedure under discussion. These values are given in column (6) for the results obtained by the procedure discussed in the text. The Durbin-Watson Test does not appear powerful enough to distinguish between the iterative and noniterative procedures: the statistic indicates insignificant *negative* serial correlation among the residuals v_t obtained by the noniterative procedure, but it also indicates that the hypothesis of no *positive* serial correlation among the residuals u_t cannot be rejected. It should be noted, however, that the estimates of the coefficients of expectation obtained by the iterative procedure are unreasonably low and also quite different from one another. The rather strange results obtained by the iterative procedure may be due in part: (1) to the presence of positive serial correlation among the u_t; and/or (2) to the presence of a lag in the adjustment of actual to desired acreage in addition to the lag in the adjustment of expected to actual price; and/or (3) to the presence of additional variables that should have been, but were not, taken into account in the acreage response function. The estimates of the elasticities obtained by the iterative procedure are higher than those obtained by the noniterative (see the table in the text). These higher estimates correspond to the lower estimates of the coefficients of expectation.

[15] These increases are all significant at the .05 level or better.

[16] It should be noted that the results obtained by the general method are consistent with those obtained by the special method. When we use the special method what we really estimate is the elasticity of acreage times the coefficient of expectation; hence, the estimates of the elasticities obtained by the general method should be about twice as large as those obtained by the special method, if the coefficient of expectation is about 50%.

[17] The estimates of β (none significantly different from 0.50) indicate that five or more past prices should be used to approximate expected price. A somewhat more restrictive approach would be to assume that expected price was a weighted moving average of the last two past prices where the weights are determined by including prices lagged one and two years in a regression with acreage. This restriction might be justified by the following model of expectation formation:

$$P_t^* - P_{t-1}^* = \alpha[P_{t-1} - P_{t-2}], \qquad |\alpha| \leqq 1.$$

As might be expected this model does less well in explaining acreage than the more general model.

TABLE 1
A COMPARISON OF TWO METHODS (SPECIAL AND GENERAL) FOR ESTIMATING THE ELASTICITY OF SUPPLY AS MEASURED BY THE RESPONSE OF ACREAGE TO EXPECTED PRICE FOR COTTON, WHEAT AND CORN (1909–32)

Crop and Magnitude Compared	*Special Method* [*Restricted* β: ($\beta = 1$)]	*General Method* [*Unrestricted* β]
(1)	(2)	(3)
Cotton:		
Elasticity	0.20	0.67
Coefficient of expectation (β)	1.0	0.51
		(±.17)
R^2	0.59	0.74
Trend	0.48	0.18
	(±.10)	(±.12)
Wheat:		
Elasticity	0.47	0.93
Coefficient of expectation (β)	1.0	0.52
		(±.14)
R_2	0.64	0.77
Trend	1.03	0.53
	(±.17)	(±.17)
Corn:		
Elasticity	0.09	0.18
Coefficient of expectation (β)	1.0	0.54
		(±.24)
R^2	0.22	0.35
Trend	0.21	0.16
	(±.10)	(±.11)

(The figures in parentheses below the estimates are the standard errors of the estimates.)

trend, that is to say the finding of a significant trend, is tantamount to an admission of ignorance, ignorance of either the relevant trend-causing factors or of the whereabouts of data by which to measure the force of these factors. To the extent to which the use of the general method leads to a reduction in the ratios of the trend coefficients to their standard errors, we have reduced our ignorance.[18]

III

The explanation of changes in corn acreage is substantially poorer than the explanations of changes in the acreages devoted to cotton and wheat. It is sometimes said that the price of livestock products is more influential in determining corn acreage than corn prices are. Such a statement is, I

[18] The ratio of the trend coefficient to its standard error falls, in passing from column (2) to column (3), from 4.8 to 1.5 for cotton, from 6.0 to 3.1 for wheat, and from 2.1 to 1.5 for corn.

believe, incorrect. The price of livestock products is a factor determining the demand for corn and not its supply. The expected level of future livestock prices would reflect itself in the expected price of corn. A large differential between the price at which a farmer can sell corn and the price at which he can buy corn to feed his livestock would tend to reduce the elasticity of supply of corn, but such a differential will not introduce a factor that is really in the demand function into the supply function as well. The difficulty with corn is probably due in large part to the fact that corn is harvested after or during the period when winter wheat is planted. Corn and winter wheat compete for acreage throughout the Corn Belt. When deciding how much acreage to plant to winter wheat, the farmer must also decide how much he will later plant to corn. In addition, he is restricted in his decision by the fact that it is difficult for him to plant acres on which corn is still standing. Corn price lagged one year appears to be less relevant to the determination of expected corn price than does the price lagged two years.[19]

Another factor that may influence price expectations is the existence of the Commodity Credit Corporation, which has introduced an entirely new element into the problem of how farmers form their expectations of future prices. The loan rates on various crops are generally known by farmers before they make their final decisions on what to plant. Actual prices at harvest may, of course, be higher than the support level and they may even fall below it when sufficient storage facilities are not available in the immediate vicinity of farmers. In spite of this fact, it seems to me that the level of support will be the best available indication at planting of what prices will be at harvest. The Commodity Credit Corporation has probably been instrumental in raising the levels of expected prices for corn, cotton and wheat relative to price levels of other agricultural products not included in the support programs, or whose prices are supported at a lower percentage of parity.

In addition to raising the level of expected price, the Commodity Credit Corporation has probably reduced the price uncertainty that farmers face. Such a reduction in uncertainty would probably lead to decreased capital rationing and a better allocation of resources between agriculture and the rest of the economy, as Professor D. Gale Johnson has shown.[20] Both the higher level of prices and reduced capital rationing would have the effect of speeding up the adoption of new and better techniques of agricultural

---

[19] When corn acreage is regressed on corn price lagged two years, corn acreage lagged one year, and trend, an R^2 of 0.43 is obtained. Corn price is highly significant and its coefficient indicates an elasticity of acreage with respect to expected corn price of 0.23. These considerations indicate that it is highly important to take careful account of harvesting and planting times. The competition between corn and winter wheat will be more thoroughly investigated in future research.

[20] D. Gale Johnson, *Forward Prices for Agriculture* (Chicago: University of Chicago Press, 1947).

production.[21] Many economists have observed (1) a great increase in yields, when acreage has been restricted; and (2) an increase in acreage, when acreage has not been restricted. Those that believe that the elasticities of supply are low have argued that both these increases in yields and increases in acreage have been a result solely of shifts in the supply schedules caused by forces set in motion by the policies of the Commodity Credit Corporation. The evidence presented in this paper suggests that the elasticities of supply are considerably higher than previous measurements indicate. If the elasticities of supply are higher, a large part of the alleged shifts in the supply schedules may be explained simply on the basis of the fact that the Commodity Credit Corporation has raised the levels of expected price and, thus, farmers have more or less moved along the original schedule that relates supply to expected price. Since shifts in the supply schedule due to decreased capital rationing and adoption of new techniques of production are likely to be largely irreversible, it seems worthwhile to find out how much of the alleged shift in the supply schedules is in reality due only to increases in the levels of expected prices. This means that analyses carried out for the period before 1933 should be applied to the period after 1933. Thus, in order to assess the effects of the Commodity Credit Corporation on capital rationing and technological change, we will first have to assess its effects on price expectation formation.

IV

At the beginning of this paper two questions were posed: First, why have such low elasticities of acreage with respect to price been obtained? And second, how is it possible to obtain elasticities of supply more in line with our experience with price supports and more compatible with the results of the studies on production functions and farmers' reactions to the allotment programs? The answer given to the first question was that previous estimates of the elasticity of acreage response to price have been based on the arbitrary and possibly incorrect assumption that the expected price is last year's price. The answer to the second question was that by making a more general assumption about price expectations it is possible to obtain higher elasticities of *acreage* response to price; and, insofar as the elasticity of acreage with respect to price represents a lower limit to the elasticity of supply, higher and more reasonable estimates of the elasticity of supply are implied.

Obviously the method presented in this paper is not a panacea for all problems connected with the estimation of supply functions for agricultural products. Good estimates of the elasticity of supply response to price can

[21] See W. W. Cochrane, *An Analysis of Farm Price Behavior*, Pennsylvania State College Agri. Expt. Sta. Progress Report No. 50 (May 1951), pp. 33–37.

be obtained only from comprehensive supply functions. This means that at least the expected prices of alternative outputs and the expected prices of variable inputs must be taken into account. In addition, the responsiveness of yields to various prices must be investigated, and the role of technological change must be examined. The way in which farmers form their expectations of future prices is only one facet of the complex and interesting problem of measuring supply response, but I believe it is an exceedingly important facet. The method that has been presented for obtaining expected price in an operational manner is only one of possibly many such methods. I do not want to assert that it is the best one. What I do assert is that consideration of the role that expectations of future price plays in shaping farmers' decisions is not a trivial nor an unimportant occupation. More sophistication in the matter of price expectations will help us greatly in estimating supply functions and will reduce the amount of sophistication necessary to the solution of the other problems involved in the development of comprehensive supply functions for agricultural commodities.

5 Farm Supply Response in India-Pakistan: A Case Study of the Punjab Region*[1]

RAJ KRISHNA†

INTRODUCTION

In this paper I present some estimates of the "short-run" and "long-run" elasticities of supply (acreage) of agricultural commodities derived from time series data for the Punjab,[2] which has always been an important agricultural region of the Indo-Pakistan sub-continent.

The study was intended to put to a test the widely prevalent notion that peasants in poor countries do not respond, or respond very little, or negatively, to price movements.[3]

---

* *Economic Journal,* Vol. LXXIII, No. 291 (September 1963), pp. 477–87.

† Rajasthan University, Jaipur, India.

[1] The work reported in this paper started in the Ph.D. dissertation "Farm Supply Response in the Punjab: A Case Study of Cotton" submitted by the author to the University of Chicago in September 1961 as a fellow of the Council of Economic and Cultural Affairs. It was continued and completed at the Institute of Economic Growth, Delhi (India), with a grant from the Rockefeller Foundation.

The author is grateful to the Economics Faculty of the University of Chicago, and especially to Professors T. W. Schultz, D. G. Johnson, Zvi Griliches and A. C. Harberger for continuous help in developing the dissertation.

[2] "Punjab" means undivided Punjab throughout this paper.

[3] See, for example, R. N. Poduval and P. Sen, "Prices, Trade and Marketing of Agricultural Commodities in India," in J. P. Bhattacharjee (ed.), *Studies in Indian Agricultural Economics* (Bombay: The Indian Society of Agricultural Economics, 1958), pp. 88–89. N. S. Joshi and B. R. Dhenkey, *Irrigation and Agriculture in the First Five-Year Plan: An Appraisal* (Poona: Deccan Book Stall, 1954), pp. 164–65. Mahesh Chand, "Agricultural Terms of Trade and Economic Growth," *Indian Journal of Agricultural Economics,* 1958, pp. 191–92. B. Misra and S. P. Sinha, "Agriculture and Its Terms of Trade with Special Reference to India," *Indian Journal of Agricultural Economics,* 1958, pp. 196–97. B. K. Madan, "Presidential Address," *Proceedings of the Eighteenth Conference of the Indian Society of Agricultural Economics,* 1958, pp. 13–14. Walter C. Neale, "Economic Accounting

The choice of the region has been dictated by the availability of relatively reliable long-period data. Moreover, since agriculture is a location-bound industry, the real alternatives faced by farmers can be formulated and the relevant variables (such as relative price indices) defined more appropriately for a region than for an aggregate of heterogeneous regions.

THE MODEL

The basic model used is the Nerlovian "adjustment" model:[4]

$$X_t^* = a + bP_{t-1} + cY_{t-1} + gZ_{t-1} + hW_t + u_t \quad (1)$$

$$X_t - X_{t-1} = B(X_t^* - X_{t-1}) \quad (2)$$

X_t^* is the standard irrigated acreage that farmers would plant in the year t if there were no difficulties of adjustment.[5] X_t is the standard irrigated acreage *actually* planted to the crop in the harvest year t. The "standard irrigated" acreage of the crop is the irrigated acreage plus the unirrigated acreage multiplied by a standardisation factor.

P is the relative price of the crop, *i.e.*, the post-harvest price of the crop deflated by an index of the post-harvest prices of the alternative crops.

Y is the relative yield of the crop, *i.e.*, the yield of the crop deflated by an index of the yields of alternative crops.

Z is the total irrigated area in all crops of the season.

W is rainfall.

u is the error term.

B is the Nerlovian coefficient of "adjustment." The farmers, it is postulated, are able to increase the acreage of a crop in any year only to the extent of a fraction B of the difference between the acreage they would like to plant and the acreage actually planted in the preceding year.

Equations (1) and (2) yield the estimating equation:

$$X_t = a_0 + b_2P_{t-1} + b_3Y_{t-1} + b_4Z_{t-1} + b_5W_t + b_6X_{t-1} + v_t \quad (3)$$

where $a_0 = aB$, $b_2 = bB$, $b_3 = cB$, $b_4 = gB$, $b_5 = hB$, $b_6 = (1 - B)$ and $v_t = Bu_t$.

Out of the "shifter" variables Y, Z and W, shifting the acreage-price

---

and Family Farming in India," *Economic Development and Cultural Change*, Part I (April 1959), pp. 297–98. R. O. Olson, "Discussion: Impact and Implications of Foreign Surplus Disposal on Underdeveloped Economies," *Journal of Farm Economics*, December 1960, pp. 1043–44.

The last three references contain very pointed opinions in favour of negligible or negative supply response.

[4] Marc Nerlove, *Dynamics of Supply* (Baltimore: Johns Hopkins Press, 1958); and *Distributed Lags and Demand Analysis for Agricultural and Other Commodities* (Agriculture Handbook No. 141 [Washington, D.C.: U.S. Department of Agriculture, 1958]). This paper owes a great deal to the pioneer work of Marc Nerlove.

[5] The year is the harvest year, which runs in the Punjab from July to June.

relation, only those are included in the estimating equation of a given crop which were found, on preliminary analysis, to be important factors determining the acreage of that particular crop. Thus, yield has been included in the equations for cotton and rice, because the yield of these crops registered a significant upward trend during the period 1913–14 to 1945–46, to which the data relates, and strongly influenced the acreage of these crops. The trend was due to varietal improvements and the expansion of irrigation brought about by the government.

Rainfall has been included in the equations for bajra (millet), jowar (sorghum), wheat (unirrigated), gram and barley.[6] It is an important factor determining the acreage planted to these crops, for a large part of the total acreage (40% in the case of wheat and 70–80% in the case of other crops) was unirrigated.

In the case of cotton (A)[7] and wheat (irrigated), whose acreage recorded a long-term upward trend over the period due to the allocation of a substantial part of the newly irrigated land to them, lagged irrigated acreage in all crops is used as one of the determining variables.

The dependent variable is acreage planted and not output. But the elasticity of planned output with respect to price can be supposed to be at least equal to the elasticity of acreage planted if it is reasonable to assume that inputs other than land are varied at least in proportion to acreage and returns to scale are not diminishing.[8] This is a reasonable assumption with regard to poor regions, where the rural man-power finds gainful employment for only a part of the year, and, therefore, the labour input can be increased with the land input without much additional cost, and, at the prevailing level of technique, the cost of capital service per unit of land is also small. Hence in the following discussion it will be supposed that the response of the demand for the input of land is a good (minimum) approximation to the response of planned supply.

Changes in input prices have been neglected for want of adequate data.

---

[6] The acreage of these crops in a given harvest year is influenced by the rainfall of the same year. Two-thirds of the annual rain in the Punjab falls in the monsoon season—June to September. The summer crops, bajra and jowar, are sown soon after the onset of the monsoon during June and July. The farmers make their best guesses about the state of the season from the weather indications in the early monsoon weeks and adjust their crop acreages accordingly. There are also late sowings of some summer crops in August and September. The winter crops, wheat, barley and gram, are planted from the middle of October onwards, and their acreage is influenced in part by the moisture left in the fields by the monsoon. (See H. K. Trevaskis, *Punjab of Today, An Economic Survey of the Punjab in Recent Years, 1890–1925,* Vol II [Lahore: Civil and Military Gazette, 1932]), p. 161. E. M. Puder, "Agricultural Adjustments to the Natural Environment in the Punjab," unpublished MS. dissertation, University of Chicago, 1925. M. S. Randhawa, *Agriculture and Animal Husbandry in India* (New Delhi: Indian Council of Agricultural Research, 1958), pp. 340–41.

[7] Cotton (A) stands for the so-called "American" varieties and cotton (D) for the local varieties grown in the Punjab.

[8] Marc Nerlove, *Dynamics of Supply, op. cit.,* pp. 67–68.

But the little evidence that is available about a few farms in the thirties suggests that up to the onset of World War II the deflated cost of cultivation did not vary significantly.

No demand relation has been specified on the assumption that the demand curves for individual crops facing Punjab producers were highly elastic. This is not an unreasonable assumption considering that the output of each crop in the Punjab before World War II was only a small fraction of the total Indian output.

An "adjustment" model was chosen in preference to an expectational model for several reasons. It may be useful to discuss these reasons briefly.

The choice between different lag models depends, in the first place, on whether the different lags postulated in them are plausible formalisations of the institutional, technological and expectational facts of the sector concerned. Secondly, it depends on the difficulties of estimation presented by them.

The distinction between expectation lags and adjustment lags is important in theory; for the former are supposed to reflect the manner in which past experience determines the expected values of the variables such as prices and yields, which in turn determine the levels of output and inputs intended by producers, while the latter reflect technological and/or institutional constraints which permit only a fraction of the intended levels to be realized during a given short period. Assuming that both types of lag are important, and neither can be supposed a priori to be non-existent, which means that none of the lag coefficients is unity, ideally a model should specify a separate lag coefficient for each expectational variable and a different adjustment lag coefficient. But such a model presents serious estimation problems.[9]

We have to choose, therefore, between a model which provides for an adjustment lag only and a model which neglects the adjustment lag in favour of expectation lags.

In a pure expectation lags model a simplification may be made by assuming that the expectation lag coefficients of different expectational variables are identical. Thus, if all our variables were expectational we could write:

$$X_t = a + bP_t^* + cY_t^* + gZ_t^* + hW_t^* + u_t \tag{4}$$

$$P_t^* - P_{t-1}^* = B(P_{t-1} - P_{t-1}^*) \tag{5}$$

$$Y_t^* - Y_{t-1}^* = B(Y_{t-1} - Y_{t-1}^*) \tag{6}$$

$$Z_t^* - Z_{t-1}^* = B(Z_{t-1} - Z_{t-1}^*) \tag{7}$$

$$W_t^* - W_{t-1}^* = B(W_{t-1} - W_{t-1}^*) \tag{8}$$

[9] Models of this type and the difficulties involved are discussed in Marc Nerlove, *Distributed Lags and Demand Analysis* (Washington, D.C., 1958), pp. 68–69, and *Dynamics of Supply* (Baltimore, 1958), pp. 236–40. A model specifying separate price expectation and yield expectation equations and a separate acreage adjustment equation was also tried in connection with the present analysis. But the results only confirmed the difficulty, mentioned by Mr. Nerlove, of estimating unique and distinct values of the expectation lags and the adjustment lag, apart from the general serial correlation problems common to distributed lag models, which are briefly discussed below.

This model yields the estimating equation:

$$X_t = a_0 + b_2 P_{t-1} + b_3 Y_{t-1} + b_4 Z_{t-1} + b_5 W_{t-1} + b_6 X_{t-1} + w_t \qquad (9)$$

where $a_0 = aB$, $b_2 = bB$, $b_3 = cB$, $b_4 = gB$, $b_5 = hB$, $b_6 = (1 - B)$ and $w_t = u_t - (1 - B)u_{t-1}$.

The estimating equation (9) derived from the pure expectation model is the same as equation (3) derived from a pure adjustment model except for the lag in W and the error term, which has serial correlation in equation (9) but not in equation (3).

The difficulties due to serial correlation peculiar to distributed-lag models have been discussed by Koyck, Klein, Nerlove and Griliches.[10] The essential difficulty is illustrated by our second model. If the u_t in this model is supposed to be serially uncorrelated, then the w_t in the estimating equation (9) is automatically serially correlated, since $w_t = u_t - (1 - B)u_{t-1}$. If, on the other hand, w_t is taken to be serially independent, u_t is serially correlated.[11]

Various ways have been suggested to meet this problem. Koyck and Klein have suggested a method for estimating coefficients on the assumption that $u_t = ru_{t-1} - e_t$, where e_t is serially independent.

But neither this method nor the model yielding equation (9) has been used in this paper, for, in the first place, the assumption made in this model of identical expectation lags for different expectational variables may be questionable. Secondly, if different coefficients of expectation are specified for the two or more expectational variables the number of variables in the resulting estimating equation becomes very large. Even for a model with only two expectational variables the estimating equation has six determining variables;[12] and with only twenty to thirty observations available many degrees of freedom are lost. Moreover, the estimates are not unique.[13] When many expectational variables are involved, and equations for many commodities have to be estimated, iterative procedures too become very cumbersome.

It was therefore decided to use only the adjustment model yielding equation (3). The advantage of this model is that if the estimated residuals v_t of equation (3) are found to be serially uncorrelated, then, since $v_t = Bu_t$, the u_t are also serially uncorrelated. And, therefore, the estimated coefficients are not likely to be affected by serial correlation. It is true that the adjustment

---

[10] L. M. Koyck, *Distributed Lags and Investment Analysis* (Amsterdam: North Holland Publishing Com., 1954); L. R. Klein, "The Estimation of Distributed Lags," *Econometrica*, 1958, pp. 553–65; Nerlove, *Distributed Lags and Demand Analysis* (Washington, D.C., 1958) and *Dynamics of Supply* (Baltimore, 1958); and Zvi Griliches, "A Note on Serial Correlation Bias in Distributed Lag Functions for Fertilizer," *Journal of Farm Economics*, February 1959.

[11] Klein, *op. cit.*, p. 560; Nerlove, *Distributed Lags, op. cit.*, p. 76.

[12] Nerlove, *Distributed Lags, op. cit.*, p. 60.

[13] Nerlove, *Distributed Lags, op. cit.*, p. 62.

model oversimplifies expectation behaviour. But in view of the difficulties involved, it was regarded as the best feasible choice.

ESTIMATES

Multiple regression coefficients of equation (3) with suitable shifter variables for each crop computed with 1914–15 to 1945–46 data for 11 crops are shown in Table I. The facts relevant to the interpretation of the results and the inferences suggested by them are discussed below.

RESULTS FOR INDIVIDUAL CROPS

Cotton (A). The acreage of cotton (A) registered a steep increase from about 400,000 acres in 1922 to more than 1,800,000 acres in 1944. A part of this increase came from the substitution of American varieties for the local varieties—the former yielding about 8% more fibre than the latter, and a price premium of 31% on an average during the period. The yield of cotton (A) itself was almost doubled between the early twenties and the early forties. The main explanation of the increase in acreage lies, however, in the increase in the total canal-irrigated area of the province from 4.5 million acres in 1901 to 12.5 million acres in 1943. In the ten major cotton (A) districts 975,000 acres were added to cotton (A) out of 1,535,000 acres of additional irrigated land made available for all summer crops during 1922–41. Thus nearly two-thirds of the additional irrigated kharif area was devoted to cotton (A).

The estimated elasticities show that the acreage of cotton (A) has been highly responsive to both its relative price and the expansion of total irrigation capacity. These variables, along with lagged acreage, explain as much as 92% of the variance of acreage.

Cotton (D). Relative yield is an important explanatory variable besides relative price in the equation for cotton (D). The acreage of cotton (D) also increased due to the expansion of irrigation and the upward trend in yield in the middle of the period under study, but declined steeply during the early forties. The price elasticity of the acreage of cotton (D) is also significantly high.

Maize. No shifter variable turned out to be important in the case of maize. Therefore, price elasticity has been calculated from a regression of acreage on relative price and lagged acreage only.

Sugar-cane. Sugar-cane occupies the field for ten to twelve months. Since planting begins in March, the acreage planted in the crop year t is influenced more by the post-harvest price of the year $t - 2$ than the post-harvest price of the year $t - 1$, for the preparations for plantings of the year t begin even before the sugar season (December–March) of the immediately preceding harvest is over. Hence the larger and more significant effect of P_{t-2} than of P_{t-1} in the estimated equation.

TABLE I (*A*)

ACREAGE RESPONSE FUNCTIONS FOR SOME PUNJAB CROPS

Equation Symbol	*Crop, Period*	*Regression Coefficients*					*R*
		P_{t-1}¶	Y_{t-1}††	Z_{t-1}**	W_t	X_{t-1}‖	
CA................	Cotton (A)* 1922–23 to 1941–42	6.23 (1.08)	—	0.34 (0.09)	—	0.56 (0.13)	0.96
CD................	Cotton (D)* 1922–23 to 1943–44	6.83 (1.36)	3.24 (1.14)	—	—	0.45 (0.13)	0.85
M....................	Maize* 1914–15 to 1943–44	2.12 (0.51)	—	—	—	0.60 (0.13)	0.79
S......................	Sugar-cane* 1915–16 to 1943–44	P_{t-2} 1.45 (0.38)	P_{t-1} 0.72 (0.49)	—	—	0.44 (0.20)	0.66
R	Rice* 1914–15 to 1945–46	3.07 (0.99)	8.01 (3.16)	—	—	0.48 (0.15)	0.79
BJ....................	Bajra† 1914–15 to 1945–46	0.03 (0.01)	—	0.17 (0.06)	−0.12 (0.05)	0.76 (0.09)	0.92
J	Jowar‡ 1914–15 to 1943–44	−4.70 (2.75)	—	−0.30 (0.12)	8.80 (3.85)	—	0.59
WW..............	Wheat§ 1941–15 to 1943–44	4.74 (2.08)	—	2.61 (1.18)	—	0.41 (0.24)	0.92
WD	Wheat‡ 1914–15 to 1945–46	8.44 (4.96)	5.36 (4.19)	—	59.16 (13.20)	—	0.71
G	Gram‡ 1914–15 to 1945–46	−11.48 (7.96)	—	—	111.11 (26.77)	—	0.66
B	Barley‡ 1914–15 to 1945–46	3.02 (3.59)	—	—	20.50 (6.46)	0.23 (0.17)	0.54

* The dependent variable is standard irrigated acreage.

† The dependent variable is the ratio (%) of the unirrigated area under bajra to the unirrigated area in all kharif (summer) crops.

‡ The dependent variable is unirrigated area.

§ The dependent variable is irrigated area.

¶ In the case of jowar the relative price variable is an index of the own price of jowar deflated by an index of the price of bajra only. In the case of wheat (unirrigated) the own price index of wheat is deflated by the price index of gram only; and in the case of wheat (irrigated) the deflator is an index of ten alternative crops. In the barley and gram equations the deflator is an index of the price of wheat only. In the case of all other crops the deflator is an index of the prices of six alternative kharif crops.

The appropriate deflators for the price of each crop were selected on the basis of an analysis of acreage shifts.

†† The yield of wheat (unirrigated) is relative to the yield of gram; and that of cotton (D) and rice to an index of the yields of six alternative summer crops.

** In the wheat (irrigated) equation Z is the irrigated area in all rabi (winter) crops; in the case of jowar and cotton (A) it is the irrigated area in all kharif (summer) crops; and in the case of bajra it is the ratio (%) of the irrigated area in kharif crops to the total kharif area.

‖ In the equations for gram, jowar and wheat (unirrigated) the lagged acreage variable has been omitted after preliminary experiments showed its coefficient to be small and non-significant.

TABLE I (*B*)
ACREAGE RESPONSE FUNCTIONS FOR SOME PUNJAB CROPS

Equation Symbol	*Crop, Period*	*Adjustment Coefficients and Elasticities*						*Serial Correlation according to Durbin–Watson Test*
		B	E_{XP}		E_{XO}			
			SR[3]	*LR*[3]		*SR*[3]	*LR*[3]	
CA	Cotton (A) 1922–23 to 1941–42	0.44	0.72	1.62	(*Z*)	1.28	2.87	No S.C.
CD	Cotton (D) 1922–23 to 1943–44	0.55	0.59	1.08	(*Y*)	0.39	0.72	No S.C.
M	Maize 1914–15 to 1943–44	0.40	0.23	0.56		—	—	Test inconclusive
S	Sugar cane 1915–16 to 1943–44	0.56	P_{t-2} 0.34 P_{t-1} 0.17	 0.60 0.30		—	—	No S.C.
R	Rice 1914–15 to 1945–46	0.52	0.31	0.59	(*Y*)	0.90	1.72	No S.C.
BJ	Bajra 1914–15 to 1945–46	0.24	0.09	0.36	(*Z*) (*W*)	0.20 −0.08	0.83 −0.34	No S.C.
J	Jowar 1914–15 to 1943–44	—	—	−0.58	(*W*) (*Z*)	— —	0.30 −0.60	No S.C.
WW	Wheat 1914–15 to 1943–44	0.59	0.08	0.14	(*Z*)	0.45	0.77	No S.C.
WD	Wheat 1914–15 to 1945–46	—	—	0.22	(*Y*) (*W*)	— —	0.15 0.36	No S.C.
G	Gram 1914–15 to 1945–46	—	—	−0.33	(*W*)	—	0.87	No S.C.
B	Barley 1914–15 to 1945–46	0.77	0.39	0.50	(*W*)	0.91	1.19	No S.C.

[1] E_{XP} is elasticity of acreage with respect to relative price.
[2] E_{XO} is elasticity of acreage with respect to other variables.
[3] *SR* is short-run; *LR* is long-run.
See also footnotes to Table I (*A*).

Rice. As in the case of cotton, yield was specified as one of the explanatory variables in the rice equation. And the response of the rice acreage with respect to yield is quite significantly high: 0.9 in the short-run and 1.7 in the long-run.

Bajra. In the bajra equation the dependent variable is not the absolute bajra acreage, but the ratio of the unirrigated acreage in bajra to the unirrigated acreage in all kharif (summer) crops. Bajra is a dry crop with nearly 80% of the acreage unirrigated. It is, in fact, one of the best dry-area crops.[14] That is why, interestingly, the coefficient of rainfall is significantly negative: the lower the rainfall, the larger the proportion of the kharif area allocated to bajra. Although bajra is one of the inferior food grains, the acreage of bajra recorded a sharp upward trend during the inter-war period. The hypothesis which seems to explain this phenomenon is that as the proportion of the irrigated area in all kharif crops to the total area in all kharif crops, Z, rose (from about a third to about a half) the proportion of the unirrigated kharif area devoted to bajra increased *pari passu*. In other words, as more irrigated area became available for the kharif crops which did well only under irrigation the peasants devoted an increasing proportion to the unirrigated area to the best dry kharif crop, viz., bajra. Hence the significant coefficient of Z in the bajra equation.

Jowar. The R^2 of the equation for jowar, another inferior grain crop, is very low indeed. But the coefficient of rainfall is significant. And the coefficient of relative price is negative and significant at the 10% level. Jowar thus turns out to be the only important Punjab kharif crop whose acreage is not responsive, or possibly negatively responsive, to relative price movements.

Wheat. Of the total area in wheat about half used to be irrigated and half unirrigated. Separate regressions have been run for the irrigated and the unirrigated area, for the patterns of crop substitution and other factors determining wheat acreage in the irrigated and unirrigated tracts are different. The unirrigated area is largely determined by rainfall, the price coefficient being only marginally significant. The irrigated area had a marked trend due to the expansion of irrigation and was significantly responsive to relative price movements.

Barley and Gram. In the rabi crop complex gram and barley like wheat (unirrigated) turn out to be crops whose acreage is more or less insensitive to relative price movements, but depends significantly on rainfall.

GENERAL CONCLUSIONS

The estimated coefficients of adjustment and elasticities of acreage with respect to price, are presented in Table II, along with elasticities of acreage estimated by other workers for other regions for comparison.

The estimated elasticities presented will, it is hoped, be a useful addition to the existing repertory of the elasticities of supply (acreage) of different agricultural commodities in different parts of the world.

The estimates can be used in a number of ways. They are useful for cross-checking the acreage forecasts for individual crops. At present the forecasts in India are based almost entirely on an assessment of climatic factors. But the

---

[14] See M. S. Randhawa, *Agriculture and Animal Husbandry in India* (New Delhi: Indian Council of Agricultural Research, 1958), p. 119.

TABLE II

ESTIMATED COEFFICIENTS OF ADJUSTMENT (B) AND PRICE ELASTICITIES OF ACREAGE

Commodity and Period		*B*	*Elasticity*	
			Short Run	*Long Run*
	Punjab (Our Estimates)			
Cotton (A)	(1922–41)	0.44	0.72	1.62
Cotton (D)	(1922–43)	0.55	0.59	1.08
Maize	(1914–43)	0.40	0.23	0.56
Sugar-cane	(1915–43)	0.56	0.34	0.60
Rice	(1914–45)	0.52	0.31	0.59
Bajra	(1914–45)	0.24	0.09	0.36
Jowar	(1914–43)	—	—	−0.58*
Wheat (irrigated)	(1914–43)	0.59	0.08	0.14
Wheat (unirrigated)	(1914–45)	—	—	0.22*
Barley	(1914–45)	0.77	0.39†	0.50†
Gram	(1914–45)	—	—	−0.33†
	India (Mr. Venkataraman's Estimate)‡			
Jute	(1911–38)	0.64	0.46	0.73
	U.S.A. (Mr. Nerlove's Estimates)§			
Cotton	(1909–32)	0.51	0.34	0.67
Wheat	(1909–32)	0.52	0.48	0.93
Corn	(1909–32)	0.54	0.10	0.18

* Coefficient significant only at the 10% level.

† Coefficient not significant.

‡ L. S. Venkataraman, "A Statistical Study of Indian Jute Production and Marketing with Special Reference to Foreign Demand," Unpublished Ph.D. Dissertation (Department of Economics, University of Chicago, June 1958).

§ Marc Nerlove, "Estimates of the Elasticities of Supply of Selected Agricultural Commodities," *Journal of Farm Economics*, 1956, pp. 496–509.

acreage predicted by a model of the type used in this paper is a resultant of the effect of climatic as well as economic factors.

The estimates can also be used to gauge the effects of given policies—taxes, subsidies, price supports, etc.—on the relative acreages of different crops and facilitate the choice of maximum net-benefit policies.

The following conclusions may be drawn from our analysis and results.

It will be seen that of the major Punjab crops, jowar seems to be the only crop which might possibly have a negative response to relative price movements. Barley and gram seem to be rainfall crops. All other crops have positive short-run price elasticities varying from as low a figure as 0.1 in the case of wheat and bajra to the medium magnitudes 0.2–0.4 in the case of maize, sugar-cane and rice up to 0.6 and 0.7 in the case of cotton. The corresponding long-run elasticities range from 0.15 to 1.6. It is significant that the long-run elasticity of cotton acreage exceeds unity.

The models of farm supply behaviour which have been found to work with the data for Western countries not only do not break down when applied to Indian data but yield plausible, interesting and internationally comparable results.

If we compare[15] our estimates for the Punjab with Mr. Nerlove's estimates for the United States we find that while the elasticity of the acreage of wheat in the Punjab was much lower than that in the United States, the elasticities of cotton and maize acreage in the Punjab were significantly higher. This is a remarkable result for a poor agricultural economy like that of the Punjab in the inter-war period. The elasticity of cotton in the Punjab was also higher than that for jute—another fibre crop—for India as a whole.

Our analysis shows that the more correctly we are able to specify the relevant non-price variables, the more significant are the net regression coefficient and elasticities of the price variable that we get. The arguments between the protagonists of the price variable and the non-price variables thus appear to be barren and superfluous. In the context of econometric work on supply response the net effect of price variables can be properly measured only if the non-price variables determining supply are well-specified, and vice versa.

The price-factor versus non-price-factors debate also turns from an either–or debate into a how-much-this-and-how-much-that debate. Our results show, for example, that in the determination of acreage, price alone was the important factor identified in the case of maize and sugar-cane; price was a more important factor than yield (in terms of elasticities) in the case of cotton (D); irrigation capacity was more important than price in the case of cotton (A), bajra and wheat (irrigated); yield was more important than price in the case of rice; and rainfall was almost all-important in the case of unirrigated wheat, barley and gram.

Our analysis also reveals that a priori beliefs about the responsiveness of the output of individual crops to price movements and other factors cannot be accepted at their face value. No general presumption in favour of the irresponsiveness of crop output to prices in poor economies can be upheld. The responsiveness, however, varies as between different crops and regions. When more studies of the responsiveness of crop output in other poor regions are carried out, inter-regional comparisons of responsiveness can be made.

The coefficient of adjustment (B) estimated from our equations indicate that the rapidity of adjustment of the acreages of crops by the peasants in response to changing circumstances are not very different from those estimated for the United States. The Punjab peasants were evidently not unusually tardy in adjusting fairly "rationally" to changes in their economic environment.

RAJ KRISHNA

Institute of Economic Growth,
Delhi, India.

[15] Mr. Nerlove and Mr. Venkataraman used only relative price and lagged acreage as determining variables, while we have used other relevant variables as well. But the elasticities may still be compared, as they are computed from "net" regression coefficients—net of the effects of other relevant variables. The "relative price" is relative to an index of the relevant "substitute" crop or other prices in each case.

6 Cobweb Models*

FREDERICK V. WAUGH†‡

In recent years, economists have become much interested in recursive models. This interest stems from a growing need for long-term economic projections and for forecasting the probable effects of economic programs and policies. In a dynamic world, past and present conditions help shape future conditions. Perhaps the simplest recursive model is the two-dimensional "cobweb diagram," discussed by Ezekiel in 1938. The present paper attempts to generalize the simple cobweb model somewhat. It considers some effects of price supports. It discusses multidimensional cobwebs to describe simultaneous adjustments in prices and outputs of a number of commodities. And it allows for time trends in the variables.

Ezekiel's excellent article, "The Cobweb Theorem," published in 1938, still stands as a landmark in the theory of prices and production. His theory was realistic and operational. It was based upon the flood of statistical findings in the 1920's, following the pioneering work of Moore. Economists are again becoming interested in simple cobweb models and in more elaborate, but related, recursive models. It seems appropriate to review cobweb models in view of developments of the past 25 years in economics, statistics, and data processing, and in view of current needs for program analysis and economic projections.

HISTORY

The classic paper on the cobweb theorem was published by Ezekiel[1] in 1938. In that paper, Ezekiel pointed out that the basic idea of a cobweb model was implied in much of the excellent econometric research of the 1920's, and that it had been discussed by several writers.

---

* *Journal of Farm Economics*, Vol. XLVI, No. 4 (November 1964), pp. 732–50.

† University of Maryland, College Park, Maryland.

‡ I gratefully acknowledge suggestions from four pioneers in this field: Mordecai Ezekiel, Wassily Leontief, Jan Tinbergen, and Herman Wold; as well as from my present colleagues in the Economic Research Service, Shlomo Reutlinger, W. Neill Schaller, and Forrest Walters, and from the two helpful reviewers of the draft.

[1] Mordecai Ezekiel, "The Cobweb Theorem," *Quarterly Journal of Economics*, Vol. 53 (February 1938).

As early as 1917, Moore[2] had demonstrated that the current price of cotton was determined by the size of the current crop; while the current crop was influenced by the previous year's price. Other studies of Moore showed that this same pattern applied to potatoes and to other farm products. Economists in the former Bureau of Agricultural Economics (including Ezekiel) and in the colleges found similar patterns for a wide variety of farm products. And, in 1928, Hanau[3] found that current hog prices in Germany reflected current hog production; while current hog production was influenced by previous hog prices.

A most curious coincidence happened in 1930. In that year, three economists independently of one another published cobweb diagrams like the one discussed by Ezekiel. All three papers were published in the German language. None was written by a German. Ricci,[4] an Italian, and Tinbergen,[5] a Dutchman, wrote the first two articles in the same issue of the same journal. Schultz,[6] an American, wrote in the same year in another journal. These three articles treated the cobweb theorem rather briefly, but did discuss its main features.

Leontief[7] also wrote in German in 1934. Kaldor,[8] writing in 1934, apparently was the first to use the word "cobweb" to describe the typical diagram. Leontief's 1934 paper used the equivalent German word "Spinnwebenbild," and also the descriptive word "Zickzack," or in English zigzag. But Ezekiel's 1938 paper was the first to discuss the cobweb model in detail.

The diagrams of Ricci, Tinbergen, Schultz, Leontief, and Ezekiel were needed to explain the statistical findings of the 1920's. The static theories of Cournot[9] and Marshall[10] were doubtless all right for some purposes, but they did not explain the common facts of the marketplace. To do this, we needed a new kind of diagram, like Figure 1.

The curve labeled "price" shows how current prices are related to current

---

[2] Henry L. Moore, *Forecasting the Yield and Price of Cotton* (New York: Macmillan Co., 1917).

[3] Arthur Hanau, *Die Prognose der Schweinpreise*, Sonderheft 7 and 18 (Berlin: Vierteljahrshefte zur Konjunkturforschung, 1928 and 1930).

[4] Umberto Ricci, "Die Synthetische Ökonomie von Henry Ludwell Moore," *Zeitschrift für Nationalökonomie,* Vol. 1 (Wien, 1930).

[5] Jan Tinbergen, "Bestimmung und Deutung von Angebotskurven: ein Beispiel," *Zeitschrift für Nationalökonomie*, Vol. 1 (1930).

[6] Henry Schultz, "Der Sinn der Statistischen Nachfragen," *Veröffentlichen der Frankfurter Gesellschaft für Konjunkturforschung,* Vol. 10 (Bonn 1930).

[7] Wassily Leontief, "Verzögerte Angebotsanpassung und Partielles Gleichgewicht," *Zeitschrift für Nationalökonomie,* Vol. 5 (1934).

[8] Nicholas Kaldor, "A Classificatory Note on the Determinateness of Equilibrium," *Review Economic Studies,* Vol. 1 (February 1934).

[9] A. Augustin Cournot, *Recherches sur les Principes Mathématiques de la Théorie des Richesses* (Hachette: Paris, 1838) (American ed.: New York: Macmillan Co., 1927).

[10] Alfred Marshall, *Principles of Economics* (8th ed.: London: Macmillan & Co., Ltd., 1946).

FIGURE 1
SIMPLE COBWEB MODEL

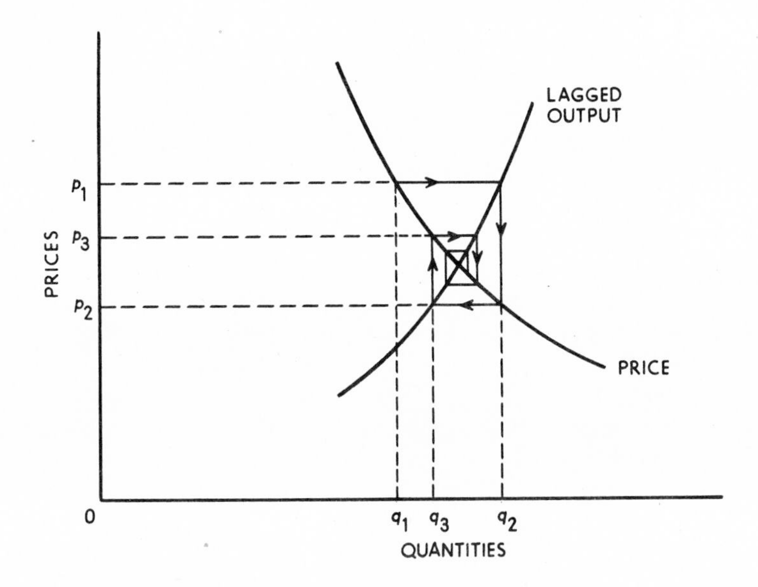

production. Both price and production may be measured as deviations from their respective time trends.

The curve labeled "lagged output" shows how current output is related to *past* prices. Specifically, output here is lagged one period after price. It is not Marshall's instantaneous supply function. If output in the first period is q_1, price is p_1. This leads to an output of q_2 and a price of p_2 in the second period, and so on. Thus, a high price in period 1 would set in motion a series of future changes in output and prices. In the absence of new counter forces, these changes would persist for an indefinite time in the future.

Ezekiel, and several previous authors, considered not only the case in which the cobweb converges toward an equilibrium—but also the case in which it diverges ("explodes"), and the case in which there is a tendency for continuous oscillation of the same magnitude. I shall discuss these cases later in this paper.

For some time after 1938, economists gave little attention to cobweb models. Some textbooks used Ezekiel's diagram. But in recent years, the work of Wold[11] and his associates has demonstrated the importance of stochastic cobweb models. In agriculture, at least, such models seem to be appropriate—both as a basis for practical forecasting and as tools of realistic

[11] Herman Wold and Lars Juréen, *Demand Analysis* (New York: John Wiley & Sons, Inc., 1953).

economic theory. Fortunately, economists are again becoming interested in cobweb models, and in other recursive systems.

A recent study by Harlow[12] developed a useful recursive model for hogs. Much more work of this kind is needed—especially on the effect of prices on future supplies. Some promising work on recursive models is under way in the Farm Production Economics Division, ERS, following the general lines worked out by Day,[13] Schaller,[14] and their associates. They are using linear programming techniques to discover the expected adjustments of production on various types of farms under given price and other conditions, including restraints to the degree of change in any year. They realize that any such adjustment may affect future prices and cause a readjustment in optimum output. Thus, their approach leads to recursive programming. Any model is recursive if it shows how certain initial conditions will affect conditions in a coming period, say, $t + 1$; then how conditions in period $t + 1$ will affect conditions in period $t + 2$; and so on. The cobweb model is the simplest recursive model in economics, but it is not the only recursive model. I believe the Day-Schaller model has great possibilities.

CONVERGENCE AND DIVERGENCE

The cobweb shown in Figure 1 converges; that is, the fluctuations of price and production get smaller and smaller as time goes on. If there were no disturbing force, the cobweb would run down. But it is easy to draw cobwebs that diverge; that is, cobwebs illustrating situations in which the fluctuations would get larger and larger as time went on. Unless some new force prevented it, these cobwebs would "explode." Also, it is easy to draw a cobweb which would result in continuous oscillations of the same magnitude.

Most discussions of cobweb models say that a model will converge if the lagged-output curve is steeper than the price curve; that it will oscillate continuously if the slopes of the two curves are equal; and that they will diverge if the price curve is steeper than the lagged-output curve. These statements are correct in the special case in which both functions are linear—either in p and q, or in log p and log q. This is perhaps obvious from graphic considerations in Figure 2.

Note that in part A of Figure 2 the cobweb converges because the lagged-output function is steeper than the price function. The slope of the price

---

[12] Arthur A. Harlow, "Factors Affecting the Price and Supply of Hogs," USDA, Technical Bulletin 1274, 1962.

[13] Richard H. Day, *Recursive Programming and Production Response* (Amsterdam: North-Holland Publishing Co., 1963).

[14] W. Neill Schaller, "Improving the Predictive Reliability of Regional Analysis Through the Use of Recursive Programming," *Western Farm Economics Association Proceedings*, 1963.

FIGURE 2
THREE LINEAR CASES

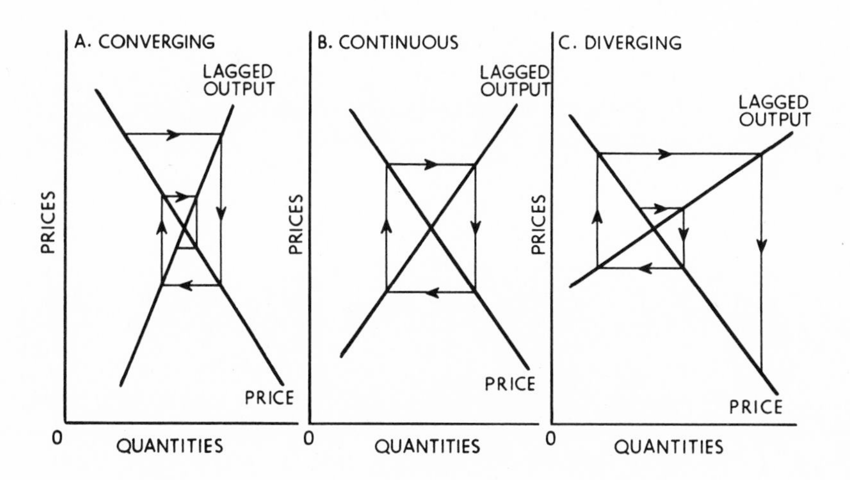

line is $-$ a. The slope of the lagged-output line is 1/b. If the two slopes are equal, $-ab = -1$. Note that part B illustrates the case of continuous oscillation because the slopes of the functions are equal. And the cobweb in part C explodes because the price line is steeper than the lagged-output line. So the common statements are confirmed for linear cases. They can also be demonstrated easily by algebra.

In the linear case, the two basic functions are

$$\begin{aligned} &\text{price:} & p_t &= -aq_t, \quad \text{and} \\ &\text{lagged output:} & q_{t+1} &= bp_t = -baq_t, \end{aligned} \tag{1}$$

where the subscripts refer to time periods. The prices and quantities in (1) are measured as deviations from their respective "normal," or "equilibrium," values in period t. Throughout this paper, I consider the cobweb as a picture of movements around the moving equilibrium. For example, each variable may be measured as a deviation from its respective time trend. The trends are not necessarily linear. The values of the moving equilibrium are those obtained when there are no deviations from trend. Moore and other pioneers in demand analysis often expressed each variable as a deviation from its trend.

From the second equation in (1) we get, recursively,

$$\begin{aligned} q_{t+2} &= -abq_{t+1} = (ab)^2 q_t \\ q_{t+4} &= (ab)^2 q_{t+2} = (ab)^4 q_t \\ &\cdots\cdots\cdots \\ q_{t+2k} &= (ab)^{2k} q_t. \end{aligned} \tag{2}$$

So, if $(ab)^2 < 1$, the system converges; if $(ab)^2 > 1$, the system diverges; if $(ab)^2 = 1$, the system oscillates continuously.

Wold calls equations (1) and (2) "deterministic," or "residual-free." In actual statistical practice, they are not exact, errorless equations. Rather, they are estimates of the *expected* values of p_t, q_{t+1}, p_{t+1}, q_{t+2}, and so on. In practical statistical work, there are always errors of estimate (residuals). Thus, (1) could be written

$$\begin{aligned} &\text{price:} && p_t = -aq_t + u_t \\ &\text{lagged output:} && q_{t+1} = bp_t + v_{t+1} = -baq_t + bu_t + v_{t+1}, \end{aligned} \qquad (1a)$$

where u is the error of estimating p_t and v_{t+1} is the error of estimating q_{t+1}. The errors, u_t and v_{t+1}, like p_t and q_{t+1}, are measured as deviations from their respective trends. Thus, the expected values of u_t and v_{t+1} are each zero, and (1) gives the expected values of p_t and q_{t+1}.

Stochastic equations similar to (2) would be

$$q_{t+2} = (-ba)^2 q_t - babu_t - bav_{t+1} + v_{t+2}, \qquad (2a)$$

and so on. Again, since the expected values of u_t, v_{t+1}, and v_{t+2} are each zero, the expected value of q_{t+2}, q_{t+4}, and so on, are given by equations (2).

In commenting upon the two paragraphs immediately above, Wold said:

> The passage from (1a) to (2a) and the ensuing interpretation of the relations in terms of expected values is a simple example of the mathematical problems that arise in the transition from deterministic to stochastic formulation of econometric models. The mathematical operations that are legitimate when dealing with deterministic relations may or may not be valid when dealing with mathematical expectations. For example, addition is, but reversion is not legitimate, and substitution is legitimate under certain general conditions.

Wold's ideas on this subject have been developed in several recent papers, including those given at the Berkeley Symposium in 1960, and the Brown Symposium in 1962.

In this paper, I deal only with expected prices and expected quantities. In general, there will be errors of forecasting. These errors are likely to be compounded when forecasts are made recursively over a period of many years. Yet, if equations (1) or (1a) are our best linear estimates of the price and lagged output functions, equations (2) are our best linear estimates of expected quantities over an indefinite period in the future. Similar recursive estimates could be made of expected future prices.

Equations (1) and (1a) are linear. Linear functions may be reasonably satisfactory to describe data within the narrow ranges often covered by available time series. But there are good theoretical reasons, and considerable statistical evidence, that the actual functions are not linear. For example,

Hotelling[15] reasoned that output would be elastic for small changes, but increasingly inelastic for larger and larger changes because of the nature of the frequency distribution of costs. Ezekiel gave additional reasons in his original paper on cobwebs. Bean[16] found statistical evidence of such supply functions for several farm commodities.

Leontief's paper (*op. cit.*) developed mathematical conditions for convergence and divergence in the general case, where the slopes of the two functions need not be constant. Samuelson[17] discusses these conditions. But few economists seem to have considered them important. For example, Ezekiel (*op. cit.*) wrote:

> Leontief, loc. cit., has shown that in cases where the supply curve and the demand curve are of erratic shape, with marked changes in elasticity along one or both curves, the cobweb reaction may be convergent at some points of the curves, and divergent at others.

I see nothing erratic about curves that change in slope or in elasticity. I even think that such curves are normal and that linear functions are very special cases. This is especially true of the lagged-production function. Ezekiel's excellent paper gave good reasons for thinking that this curve would be quite elastic for small changes and increasingly inelastic for larger changes.

I shall not give the Leontief-Samuelson conditions in detail. But I shall analyze a particular example and then discuss the general principle. For this example, assume that

$$p_t = -2q_t, \text{ and} \\ q_{t+1} = 2p_t^{1/3}, \tag{3}$$

where p and q are measured as deviations from the intersection of the two curves.

Two cobwebs are shown in Figure 3. One starts with $q_1 = -2$. This cobweb diverges until it reaches the heavy rectangle; then oscillates between ($q = -4$, $p = 8$) and ($q = 4$, $p = -8$). The other starts with $q_1 = 6$. It converges until it reaches the same heavy rectangle; then it, too, oscillates regularly.

Whatever the initial q and p, any cobweb drawn with the two curves in Figure 3 will move toward continuous oscillation, except for the trivial case when the initial q and p are both zero; that is, where the initial point is exactly at the intersection of the two curves. Starting with small q and p, the fluctuations will grow larger until constant oscillation is reached.

---

[15] Harold Hotelling, "Edgeworth's Taxation Paradox and the Nature of Demand and Supply Functions," *Journal of Political Economy*, Vol. 40 (October 1932).

[16] L. H. Bean, "The Farmers' Response to Price," *Journal of Farm Economics*, Vol. 11 (July 1929).

[17] Paul A. Samuelson, *Foundations of Economic Analysis* (Cambridge, Mass.: Harvard University Press, 1948), pp. 390–91.

Starting with large q and p, the fluctuations will be damped until constant oscillation is reached.

I think Figure 3 illustrates an important case—perhaps the normal case. Of course, the particular equations (3) are not important. But, allowing the general shape of the lagged-production curve in Figure 3, continuous oscillation may be the normal case. I shall discuss this in more detail later in this paper.

FIGURE 3
CASE LEADING TO CONTINUOUS OSCILLATION

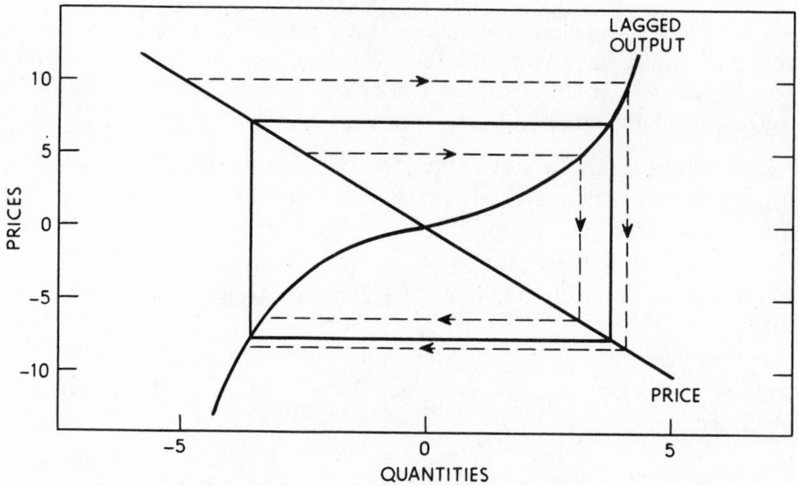

Continuous oscillation is possible with any pair of curves that go through the points of a rectangle, such as abcd in Figure 4.

The slopes at b and c need not be equal—nor need the slopes at a and d be equal. Whatever the slopes, if you start at a, you will move to b, then to c, then to d, then back to a. The necessary geometric condition for continuous oscillation is that a rectangle abcd can be drawn so that the curves pass through the corners. But such a solution might be either stable or unstable. It is stable if small deviations from the rectangle would set up cobwebs that converged back to the rectangle. This was the case that was illustrated by Figure 3 and by equations (3). It could be tested graphically by drawing several cobwebs in any diagram, such as that in Figure 4.

Suppose we have a situation such as illustrated in Figure 4, where the curves go through the corners of a rectangle. We then ask what would happen if, instead of starting at q_1, we started at any nearby point. The change in q_3 associated with a very small change in q_1 would be

$$\frac{dq_3}{dq_1} = \frac{dp_1}{dq_1}\frac{dq_2}{dp_1}\frac{dp_2}{dq_2}\frac{dq_3}{dp_2} \tag{4}$$

where dp_1/dq_1 and dp_2/dq_2 are the slopes of the curves at points b and d, and where dq_2/dp_1 and dq_3/dp_2 are the slopes at a and c.

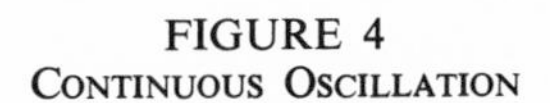

FIGURE 4
CONTINUOUS OSCILLATION

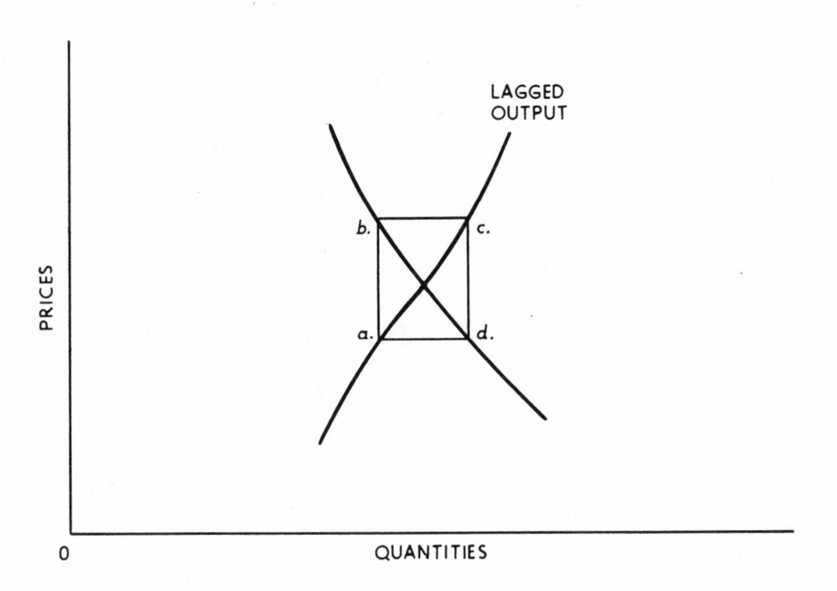

The Leontief condition is that the oscillation is stable if $dq_3/dq_1 < 1$. In this case, a small departure from the rectangle leads to still smaller departures at each round of the spiral. But if $dq_3/dq_1 > 1$ any departures become larger and the situation is unstable.

In the case of equations (3), $dp_1/dq_1 = dp_2/dq_2 = -2$, and $dq_2/dp_1 = dq_3/dp_2 = 2/3p^{-2/3}$. When q oscillates between -4 and 4, and when p oscillates between 8 and -8, equation (5) gives

$$\frac{dq_3}{dq_1} = (-2)\left(\frac{2}{3.4}\right)(-2)\left(\frac{2}{3.4}\right) = \frac{1}{9} \qquad (5)$$

Since this is less than 1, the oscillation is stable. We already knew this from graphic analysis, but it is well to have a precise mathematical test.

PRICE SUPPORT MODELS

Ezekiel (*op. cit.*) wrote:

> The cobweb theory can apply only to commodities which fulfill three conditions: (1) where production is completely determined by the producer's response to price, under conditions of pure competitition . . . ; (2) where the time needed for

production requires at least one full period . . . ; and (3) where the price is set by the supply available. Obviously, commodities where either price or production is set by administrative decisions, (i.e., where monopolistic competition prevails), or where production can respond almost immediately to changed demands, cannot be expected to show the cobweb reaction.

Until the 1930's agricultural markets in the United States were governed largely by competition. Current price was set mainly by current supply; and current price was an important factor in determining output in the following period. I would not say that agricultural production was ever "completely determined by the producer's response to price," nor that the market price was ever set solely "by the supply available." Such other factors as weather and technology also affected output. And such factors as changes in population and consumer incomes and programs, such as import duties, affected demand. But we can modify the cobweb model (as discussed earlier in this paper) to consider deviations from trend, or from "normal." That is, we can correct the output function and the price function for other factors. Then the deviations in agricultural production may be due mainly to farmers' responses to past prices, and the deviations in prices may be due mainly to concurrent deviations in output.

But Ezekiel's restriction to conditions of pure competition, and his exclusion of cases in which either price or production is set by administrative decision, raise questions as to the applicability of cobweb models in the modern world. Today, most governments have active programs to maintain farmers' incomes by supporting prices, by limiting production or marketing, or by purchasing surpluses and diverting them to noncompetitive markets. Thus, even agriculture today operates under conditions that depart significantly from those of pure competition.

Yet, the Congress and the Department of Agriculture have found that they cannot safely ignore the effects of output upon price, nor the effects of current prices upon future output. The government programs may have partially suppressed the cobweb behavior, but they have not replaced it. Some people used to say in the 1920's "You can't repeal the law of supply and demand." But we have modified the workings of the law of supply and demand, and also of the cobweb theorem, by acreage allotments, by marketing quotas, and especially by price supports. The following diagrams illustrate two cases involving price supports.

Essentially, an effective price support puts a kink in the price curve. When output is very low, prices are on the old curve. But as output increases, the price drops until it reaches the support level. As output increases still further, the price remains at the support level, assuming that the support is fully effective.

If the support level is below the equilibrium price, as in part a of Figure 5, there will be a tendency for alternate periods of overproduction and underproduction, with prices alternating from the support level to somewhat above and back again. When price rests upon the support, the government will have to buy the "surplus"; that is, the difference between production and consumption. The support price modifies the cobweb. It reduces the fluctuations in quantity and in price. As the diagram is drawn, it quickly establishes a two-period cycle. On alternate years, when output was high, q_1 would be produced, while q_1' would be sold. The government would have to take over the surplus (that is, $q_1 - q_1'$). If it sold this surplus the following year, the price-and-quantity fluctuations would be still further reduced.

FIGURE 5
PRICE SUPPORT MODELS

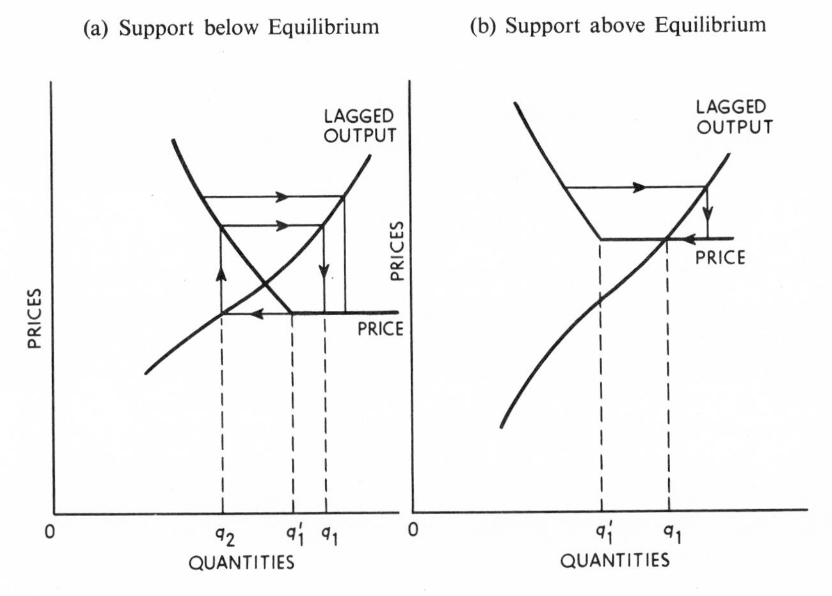

Part a illustrates the kind of "stop-loss" supports that have been advocated by some economists. But the main interest has been in supporting prices at above normal levels. Such a support price is illustrated in part b of Figure 5.

This kind of support really interrupts the cobweb. If poor weather should result in a high price in any period, output would expand in the next period, price would drop to the support level, and farmers would immediately adjust to an output of q_1. Market sales would be q_1'. The government would have to take over the surplus, $q_1 - q_1'$. In this case, storing up the surplus would not help, because there would be no alternate periods of short supply. The surplus would have to be diverted to noncompetitive markets and doubtless sold at a substantial loss to the taxpayer.

Figure 5 assumes that the price support would be fully effective. For example, it assumes that if the wheat support were set at $1.50 a bushel, wheat farmers would get the full $1.50 regardless of their production. In actual practice, the supports usually are not fully effective when the crop is exceptionally large. Thus, the price curve may slope slightly downward to the right of the kink. This would complicate the diagrams somewhat.

Also, the lagged-output curve may shift somewhat to the right as a result of price supports. Thus, if the farmer is assured of at least $1.50 a bushel for wheat, he may produce more than he would if last year's price were $1.50 and this year's price were uncertain. The shifting of the output curves to the right tends to aggravate surpluses and to raise costs to the taxpayer.

A MULTIDIMENSIONAL COBWEB MODEL

The models discussed in previous parts of this paper were two-dimensional. They exhibited the relationships between current output and current price, and between current price and lagged output, for a single commodity.

But, in terms of matrices and vectors, the same general principles apply to cases in which there are many commodities. For example, they apply to livestock and feed, or to all of agriculture. The output of feed next year may depend partly upon the current price of feed and partly upon the current price of livestock. In a general way, at least, the output of any farm product may be influenced somewhat by past prices of a wide variety of other farm products that compete for the farmer's land, labor, and capital.

If we limit ourselves to linear functions, equations (1) become

$$\begin{aligned} p_t &= Aq_t \quad \text{and} \\ q_{t+1} &= Bp_t = BAq_t. \end{aligned} \tag{6}$$

Moreover,

$$p_{t+1} = Aq_{t+1} = ABp_t.$$

In equations (6), p_t, q_t, and q_{t+1} are $n \times 1$ vectors, indicating prices and quantities of the n commodities. Again the p's and q's are deviations from basic "normal" values, adjusted for such "shifters" as population, consumer income, and technology. A and B in (6) are $n \times n$ matrices of coefficients.

Recursively,

$$\left.\begin{aligned} q_{t+2} &= BAq_{t+1} = (BA)^2 q_t \\ &\cdots\cdots\cdots \\ q_{t+k} &= (BA)^k q_t \end{aligned}\right\} \text{ and } \left\{\begin{aligned} p_{t+2} &= (AB)^2 p_t \\ &\cdots\cdots \\ p_{t+k} &= (AB)^k p_t \end{aligned}\right. \tag{7}$$

The system converges to zero (that is, to the basic "moving equilibrium" values) if the maximum absolute root of BA, or of AB, is less than 1.0. The roots of AB and of BA are identical. Since the maximum absolute root can be no greater than the norm, the system will converge if the norm of BA is less than 1.0. Bowker's[18] norm is a good one to use, since its computation is easy and quick. If the maximum absolute root is 1.0, the system oscillates continuously. If the maximum root is greater than 1.0, the system explodes.

To use equations (6) and (7) we need statistical estimates of matrices A and B. The A matrix of interrelationships between p_i and q_j would be somewhat similar to Brandow's [19] demand matrix. His matrix was developed by a combination of statistical estimates and logical principles about such things as symmetry and sums of rows and columns. So far, we have nothing approaching matrix B, showing how the price of commodity i affects future output of commodity j. We should develop one.

The logical conditions about symmetry and about sums of rows and columns of such an output matrix have been spelled out by Hicks.[20] These conditions are somewhat simpler than the logical conditions for the demand matrix. The difficulty is not with the logical conditions. Rather, it is with the paucity of statistical measurements.

But, while we are far from having a complete B matrix for all segments of agriculture, we could doubtless make at least rough estimates of some small matrices that aggregated farm commodities into a few groups.

As a numerical illustration, suppose the price equations for livestock and feed were

$$\begin{aligned} p_{1(t)} &= -4q_{1(t)} - 2q_{2(t)}, \text{ and} \\ p_{2(t)} &= -1q_{1(t)} - 3q_{2(t)}, \end{aligned} \tag{8}$$

where $p_{1(t)}$ and $p_{2(t)}$ are deviations of the logarithms of livestock prices and of feed prices from their "normals" in year t, and where $q_{1(t)}$ and $q_{2(t)}$ are the deviations of the logarithms of livestock output and of feed output from their trends. The coefficients (price flexibilities) in (8) are roughly in line with the findings of my colleagues, Rex Daly and Alvin Egbert.

In matrix and vector notation (8) can be written as

$$p_t = Aq_t, \quad \text{where} \quad A = \begin{bmatrix} -4 & -2 \\ -1 & -3 \end{bmatrix}. \tag{9}$$

We do not have statistical equations similar to (8) for lagged output. But to illustrate a principle, let us first assume that

$$\begin{aligned} q_{1(t+1)} &= 0.3p_{1(t)} - 0.2p_{2(t)}, \quad \text{and} \\ q_{2(t+1)} &= -0.1p_{1(t)} + 0.4p_{2(t)}. \end{aligned} \tag{10}$$

---

[18] Albert H. Bowker, "On the Norm of a Matrix," *Annals of Mathematical Statistics*, Vol. 18 (July 1947).

[19] George E. Brandow, *Interrelationships Among Demands for Farm Products and Duplications for Control of Market Supply*, Pennsylvania State University, Bulletin 680, August 1961.

[20] J. R. Hicks, *Value and Capital* (2d ed.; Oxford: Clarendon Press, 1946).

This can be written in the form,

$$q_{t+1} = Bp_t \quad \text{where} \quad B = \begin{bmatrix} 0.3 & -0.2 \\ -0.1 & 0.4 \end{bmatrix}. \tag{11}$$

In this case, $B = -A^{-1}$, so $AB = BA = -I$. The system will oscillate continuously around the moving equilibrium of price and production as shown by (7). Thus, if the original deviations of production in period t were $q_{1(t)} = -0.2$ and $q_{2(t)} = -0.5$, future production would oscillate like this:

t =	1	2	3	...
$q_{1(t)}$	−0.2	+0.2	−0.2	...
$q_{2(t)}$	−0.5	+0.5	−0.5	... .

(12)

In this special case, prices would oscillate in a similar fashion. But now let us assume that the matrix of lagged production is

$$B = \begin{bmatrix} 0.2 & -0.1 \\ -0.1 & 0.2 \end{bmatrix}. \tag{13}$$

Now

$$AB = \begin{bmatrix} -0.6 & 0.0 \\ +0.1 & -0.5 \end{bmatrix} \quad \text{and} \quad BA = \begin{bmatrix} -0.7 & -0.1 \\ +0.2 & +0.4 \end{bmatrix}. \tag{14}$$

The roots of AB, and of BA, are −0.6 and −0.5. Since the maximum absolute root is less than 1, the system will converge toward the moving equilibrium. Thus, if $q_{1(t)} = -0.2$ and $q_{2(t)} = 0.5$, future production would follow this pattern,

t =	1	2	3	
$q_{1(t)}$	−0.2	+0.09	−0.029	...
$q_{2(t)}$	+0.5	−0.24	+0.114	... .

(15)

These values are from (4). Prices would follow the pattern,

t =	1	2	3	
$p_{1(t)}$	+1.8	−1.08	+0.648	...
$p_{2(t)}$	+1.7	−0.067	+0.227	... .

(16)

According to (15) and (16), production and prices seem to be converging toward zero; that is, to their normal values. It may be interesting to look many years ahead, as we must do in many economic projections. Suppose we ask how much is left of our cobweb after eight years? We find that

$$(AB)^8 = \begin{bmatrix} 0.0168 & 0.0000 \\ -0.0129 & 0.0039 \end{bmatrix}. \quad (17)$$

So, using (7) again, we find that if $p_{1(t)} = +1.8$ and $p_{2(t)} = +1.7$, the prices eight periods later would be $p_{1(t+8)} = +0.030$ and $p_{2(t+8)} = 0.017$. Thus, even in eight years, the cobweb has not completely disappeared. Actually, of course, it would never disappear completely, but after several years its effects might be so small that they would be covered up by other influences, such as new developments that shifted the output-price curve or the price-lagged output curve.

DISTRIBUTED LAGS

So far, we have discussed cobweb models in terms of a single lag of one period. This is fairly adequate in the case of some annual crops. Thus, if the price of onions is high in the fall of 1964, the farmer may plant more onions in May 1965, harvest them in September 1965, and sell them in November 1965. The lag is longer for beef cattle, and still longer for apples, because it takes several years to change the output of those commodities significantly. All such one-lag models imply that the farmer is influenced only by last year's price when he adjusts this year's production.

But the work of Fisher[21] and especially the work of Nerlove[22] indicate that the output of most commodities is likely to be affected by prices over several years in the past.

In the general case, the appropriate model might be

$$\begin{aligned} p_t &= Aq_t, \quad \text{and} \\ q_t &= Bp_{t-1} + Cp_{t-2} + \cdots + Dp_{t-r}, \end{aligned} \quad (18)$$

where we assume that prices more than r years ago have no significant effects upon current production.

Then

$$\begin{aligned} q_t &= BAq_{t-1} + CAq_{t-2} + \cdots DAq_{t-r}, \quad \text{and} \\ p_t &= ABp_{t-1} + ACp_{t-2} + \cdots +ADp_{t-r}. \end{aligned} \quad (19)$$

Equations (19) are difference equations. If the q's and p's are known for the past r years, the future cobweb can be projected recursively.

A special case of some possible interest is the following model:

$$\begin{aligned} p_t &= Aq_t \\ q_{t+1} &= Bp_t + B^2p_{t-1} + B^3p_{t-2} + \cdots. \end{aligned} \quad (20)$$

---

[21] Irving Fisher, "Our Unstable Dollar and the So-Called Business Cycle," *Journal of the American Statistical Association*, Vol. 20 (1925).

[22] Marc Nerlove, *The Dynamics of Supply: Estimation of Farmers Response to Price* (Baltimore: Johns Hopkins Press, 1958).

This is similar to Nerlove's distributed-lag model for a single commodity. In (20) we can assume that the maximum absolute root of B is less than 1.0. This is because we can assume that prices in the distant past affect current output less than do prices in the recent past.

From the second equation in (20) we have

$$\begin{aligned} q_{t+1} &= Bp_t + B^2p_{t-1} + B^3p_{t-2} + \cdots \\ q_t &= \phantom{Bp_t + {}} Bp_{t-1} + B^2p_{t-2} + \cdots . \end{aligned} \tag{21}$$

Premultiply the second equation in (21) by B and subtract from the first equation, getting

$$q_{t+1} - Bq_t = Bp_t. \tag{22}$$

Then, substituting the value of p_t from (20), and transposing

$$q_{t+1} = Bq_t + BAq_t = B(I + A)q_t. \tag{23}$$

Then, recursively,

$$\begin{aligned} q_{t+2} &= [B(I + A)]^2q_t, \quad \text{and} \\ q_{t+k} &= [B(I + A)]^kq_t. \end{aligned} \tag{24}$$

If the maximum absolute root of B (I + A) is less than 1.0, the system converges.

I doubt if the special form of distributed lag indicated by (20) applies to all agricultural commodities. But it might be fairly realistic for annual crops. And perhaps such a matrix could be estimated from the analysis of several annual crops.

In the general case, we would need estimates of matrices B, C, · · · , D in (18). This would be difficult from time series alone. The economist would need to use judgment—even intuition. He might, for example, assume that certain submatrices were composed of zeroes. Or, instead of using time series, he might use some kind of programming techniques like those of Day and Schaller. But, theoretically, the economist who makes projections of prices and quantities cannot avoid making some explicit or implicit assumptions about such matrices.

CONCEPTS

The Ezekiel-Ricci-Tinbergen-Schultz-Leontief concept of a cobweb describes the lagged relationship between two curves. I have called one of them the price curve; the other the lagged-output curve. These are not the Cournot-Marshall demand curve and supply curve. Nor are they simultaneous. They are different concepts, and must be considered on their own merits. Ezekiel was careful to point out that the price curve showed how current total production affected current price—not what amounts some group of consumers would buy if the price were set at various levels. He emphasized especially that his lagged-output curve differed greatly from a supply curve indicating how much of a commodity sellers would be willing to offer currently at various current prices.

Ezekiel, and other economists in the 1920's, made great progress in studying and forecasting prices. In this process, they developed new concepts and the germ of a dynamic economic theory. Of course, the dynamic cobweb concept did not replace the Cournot-Marshall concept of simultaneous demand and supply curves. They doubtless always do exist for any commodity. But they are not what the statistician observes when he draws a dot diagram showing time series of prices and production. The plain fact is that the price curve and the lagged-output curve are not simultaneous, even though they are generally drawn on the same diagram. As Ezekiel put it, "the cobweb theory reveals a series of reactions . . . since the two curves . . . exist in different time dimensions." This, I think, is the key distinction between the cobweb model and Marshall's model.

Essentially, Ezekiel was discussing what Wold later called a "causal chain." The diagram of the simplest cobweb type of causal chain is

$$\begin{array}{ccccccc} q_1 & & q_2 & & q_3 & & \cdots \\ \downarrow & \nearrow & \downarrow & \nearrow & \downarrow & \nearrow & \\ p_1 & & p_2 & & p_3 & & \cdots \end{array}$$

indicating that q_1 determines p_1, which in turn determines $q_2 \cdots$, and so on. This is essentially different from the simultaneous determination of supply, demand, and price pictured by the Marshallian diagram.

Ezekiel noted that many cobwebs in agriculture would soon run down unless they were kept in motion by new forces—such as exceptionally good or bad weather, or by big changes in demand. The continuation of cycles in farm production and prices could be due to such new forces. Fisher (*op. cit.*) discussed this in an interesting way:

> In order to be kept going, the cycle must from time to time be activated by some outside or *external* forces . . . Perhaps a more exact analogy is that of the swinging of a tree-top. If let alone, the tree-top would sway regularly with a certain periodicity, but the swaying would gradually taper off and stop. The wind keeps it swaying, but makes the oscillations irregular. The swaying of a tree-top varies moment by moment, in direction, in amplitude, and rhythm because of the changing impulses of the wind which varies continuously in force and direction. This irregularity, however, does not do away with the underlying *tendency* toward a regular sway.

New forces may be one reason for continuing cycles in hogs, beef cattle, potatoes, apples, and many other farm products. Another possible reason is that the lagged-output functions are shaped like those in Figure 3. The cobweb in Figure 3 would neither run down nor explode, even if there were no new forces. I believe that the lagged-output curves for most commodities are shaped somewhat like the one shown in Figure 3. If this is so, agricultural cycles would tend to persist, even without any new forces. The actual cycles in agriculture probably are due partly to the shape of the lagged-output functions and partly to new forces.

The usual cobweb model assumes that the price curve and the lagged-production curve are each fixed through time. It assumes that actual price and production fluctuate around the intersection of these stationary curves. If the cobweb converges, price and production gravitate toward this intersection, or "equilibrium point." The models I have presented allow for trends in prices and output. In projecting prices and output for future years, the economist will often first project trends in p and q, corresponding to assumed trends in such shift variables as population and productivity. The cobweb analysis indicates how the present patterns of prices and outputs are likely to affect future movements around their projected trends.

Most discussions of cobweb models are limited to a single commodity. But the cobweb model can be extended to cover cases of several commodities. Using the notation of vectors and matrices, the algebra of such a multidimensional model presents no problems, at least in linear cases. It is exactly parallel to the scalar linear algebra for a single commodity.

There is room for many concepts in economics, as in other sciences. The simultaneous supply-and-demand model of Marshall is a useful concept of theory. But as Bishop[23] recently remarked, "As soon as we recognize that there are comparatively few markets in which 'demand and supply' operate in the essentially symmetrical way that is the essence of that famous law, many things become analytically clear for the first time."

Bishop's remarks concerned the theory of monopolistic competition, but they are pertinent to the cobweb theory, too.

Any kind of economic planning requires some sort of recursive analysis. How will this year's plans, policies, programs, affect next year's output, prices, consumption? This is especially important in agriculture, where programs and policies are being constantly debated and changed. And because of this, agricultural economists are being asked for long-term economic "projections," indicating what agricultural output, prices, consumption, foreign trade, government costs, and so on, would be under various programs. For this purpose, we certainly need good cobweb models and more elaborate recursive systems. With the wonderful advances in automatic data processing, and with better statistics, we have the means to quantify and to analyze such models. The cobweb principle may well become one of the most important tools not only for practical forecasting, but also for realistic economic theory.

---

[23] Robert L. Bishop, "The Impact on General Theory," *American Economic Review*, Vol. 54, (May 1964).

7 Recursive Programming and Supply Prediction*

RICHARD H. DAY†

For analysis and prediction of aggregative production, it seems evident from past theoretical and empirical research that at least the following interrelated categories must be considered:

1. The interdependence of outputs using common inputs;
2. Technological change;
3. Planned or programmed policy actions;
4. Changes in both acreage and yield components in field crop production;
5. Uncertainty;
6. Demand, supply, and price interactions;
7. Adjustment over time;
8. The aggregate supply of production inputs;
9. Rates of investment in factors fixed in the short run; and
10. Regional specialization and competition.

Econometricians, in their use of multiple regression and simultaneous equation techniques have made considerable progress in accommodating

* Earl O. Heady, C. B. Baker, Howard G. Diesslin, Earl Kehrberg, and Sydney Staniforth (eds.), *Agricultural Supply Functions: Estimating Techniques and Interpretations,* (Ames: Iowa State University Press, 1961), chap. v. pp. 108–25. The research on which this paper is based was begun while the author was research assistant at the Harvard Economic Research Project. It was continued while he was Teaching Fellow in the Economics Department at Harvard University and later while a member of the staff of the Farm Economics Research Division, ARS. At the time this was written, the author is on military leave from the latter organization. The specific contents of this paper have profited particularly from the comments of Professors James M. Henderson, Louis Lefeber, and Wassily W. Leontief, all of Harvard University; Hendrick S. Houthakker, Stanford University; and Dr. Glen T. Barton, Farm Economics Research Division, ARS.

† University of Wisconsin, Madison, Wisconsin.

variables and relations which reflect interdependencies among these phenomena. Yet there are certain fundamental difficulties in these techniques which send one in search of different, more suitable methods. This paper is an account of such a quest.

SUPPLY EQUATIONS

Perhaps the simplest of all field-crop supply models is an equation which relates the acreage of a crop in a given year to its own price lagged one year. The simplest form in which this equation can be expressed is

$$X(t) = \alpha\, p(t-1)\,. \tag{1}$$

Suppose an acreage allotment is imposed on the crop. This specifies a constraint on the acreage of the crop which can be expressed

$$X(t) \leq a(t)\,, \tag{2}$$

in which a(t) is the acreage allotment in the year t. If $\alpha\, P(t-1) > a(t)$, i.e., if the acreage predicted by relation 1 is greater than the allotment, the two relations are inconsistent. This inconsistency can be removed if relation 1 is made into an inequality like that of relation 2. However, the system is now underdetermined.

The manipulation of instrumental or policy variables is not the only cause for the intrusion of inequalities in supply systems. A more fundamental cause consists of constraints on output arising from factors of production fixed in the short or long run. An example of the latter is an over-all land constraint in a developed region or country.

Suppose only two field crops are grown in a developed region whose acreages are $X_1(t)$ and $X_2(t)$, respectively. Assuming a lagged price supply relation as before, but including the competing crop's price as well as its own, a typical supply system might be written

$$\begin{aligned} X_1(t) &= \alpha_1\, p_1(t-1) + \alpha_2\, p_2(t-1) \\ X_2(t) &= \beta_1\, p_1(t-1) + \beta_2\, p_2(t-1)\,. \end{aligned} \tag{3}$$

On the basis of economic theory, it would be expected that $\alpha_1 > 0$, $\alpha_2 < 0$, $\beta_1 < 0$, $\beta_2 > 0$, i.e., that acreage increases with an increase in *own* price while it decreases with increases in a competitor's price.

The overall land constraint assumed for this example is

$$X_1(t) + X_2(t) \leq \bar{x}\,. \tag{4}$$

But now a situation analogous to the first example arises. Only if equation 4 holds as a strict inequality—i.e., only if part of the land is idle—can both equations of relation 3 hold. Again, the over-determinancy of the supply system could be avoided by making inequalities of the acreage lagged price relations.

If this is done, however, the model is underdetermined as before. Some kind of mechanism must be added if one is to decide in a meaningful way which of the two supply equations holds whenever the overall land constraint holds. The mechanism which will resolve problems of this kind is the optimizing principle of economics. Rather than trying to force it on supply relations like those of the examples listed, it would seem to be more appropriate to follow the theory of production and to use it to derive supply relations from the underlying technical structure of production.

The suggestion that this principle be applied to predictive problems of supply is a little foreign to usual practice. Ordinarily, one attempts to estimate aggregative supply relations themselves without explicit reference to production structures and their choice mechanism. Even when this is done the optimizing principle plays a role in the evaluation of the results. Thus, it is by means of this principle that one arrives at the conclusion that the response to "own price" will be positive while that to a competing commodity will be negative (7). Consequently, the explicit application of optimization is not as radical an innovation for supply response as it may at first appear.

The important problem is not whether it should be used but rather how it can be used without grossly misrepresenting the simple decision processes governing farm behavior. The attempt to solve this problem leads to a synthesis of time-series analysis and linear programming versions of production theory. It is to such a synthesis that the rest of this paper is devoted. We shall call it *recursive programming.*

A SIMPLE RECURSIVE PROGRAMMING MODEL: FLEXIBILITY IN CHANGING OUTPUT PATTERNS

An important application of linear programming to the problem of aggregative *supply prediction* is due to Professor James M. Henderson (3). The ingenuous innovation on which it rests is the specification of what we shall call *flexibility constraints.* These constraints specify that in any one year only a limited change from the preceding year's production can be expected. This hypothesis is based on the conglomerate of forces which lead to caution by farmers in altering established production patterns. Primary among them are uncertainty of price and yield expectations and restriction on the aggregative supply of production inputs. In short, they are the same factors which underpin Nerlove's adjustment equations (8). During this discussion, we shall split off the factors whose capacities are fixed in the short run for separate treatment. At this point, it will be supposed that the flexibility coefficients contain them as components.

The flexibility constraints can be expressed in dynamic notation as follows:

$$
\begin{aligned}
X_1(t) \qquad\qquad &\leq \quad (1 + \bar{\beta}_1)\, X_1(t-1) \\
X_2(t) &\leq \quad (1 + \bar{\beta}_2)\, X_2(t-1) \\
-X_1(t) \qquad\qquad &\leq -(1 - \beta_1)\, X_1(t-1) \\
-X_2(t) &\leq -(1 - \beta_2)\, X_2(t-1)
\end{aligned}
\qquad (5)
$$

in which $X_1(t)$ and $X_2(t)$ have the same meaning as before and in which we shall call the β's *flexibility coefficients.*

The first equation of relation 5 asserts that the acreage of the first crop will not exceed the previous year's acreage plus some proportion of it determined by the upper flexibility coefficients $\bar{\beta}_1$. Equation 3 of relation 5 asserts that the acreage of the first crop must not be less than an amount determined by the lower flexibility coefficient, β , and the preceding year's acreage. Equations 2 and 4 of relation 5 have the same meanings, respectively, for the second crop. (This example follows the preceding one, assuming that two crops only are grown in the region or country in question.)

The over-all land constraint (relation 4) should also apply here, further limiting the possibilities for change. Together with the inequations of relation 5 this gives a total of five constraints on change in output patterns. These five constraints form a *system of linear nonhomogeneous difference inequations.*

Now let $\pi_1'(t)$ and $\pi_2'(t)$ be the expected per acre net returns to the first and second crops, respectively. The system consisting of relations 4 and 5 can be resolved by an appropriate application of the optimizing principle, thus

$$\text{maximize } \{\pi_1'(t)\, X_1(t) + \pi_2'(t)\, X_2(t)\} \qquad (6)$$

subject to relations 4 and 5. That is, choose $X_1(t)$ and $X_2(t)$ so that total net returns are as great as caution and fixed factors will allow. The flexibility constraints are now seen to enclose the profit motive in a web of dynamic adjustment.

A fundamental theorem asserts that the solution to a linear programming problem is such that the number of constraints which hold as equalities is just equal to the number of nonzero variables. Translated into recursive programming language, this means that a supply system is governed by exactly as many dynamic equations as there are positive variables selected by the optimizing principle.

In our example, at least two variables must be positive because of the lower bounds, relations 2 and 4 of equation 5. As there are only two variables in the system for time t, we know that two equations will govern the behavior of the system over time. Which two there will be for any time period will depend upon which is greater, $\pi_1'(t)$ or $\pi_2'(t)$, and upon the relative magnitudes of the five constraints.

To actually obtain the solution, we must begin at a base period $t=o$. The initial conditions are then $X(o)$. Then as the $\pi_1'(t)$ and $\pi_2'(t)$ are formed (exogeneously so far), a linear programming problem becomes available for each period that can be solved by the usual techniques.

A change in the equations which "govern" the system is called a *phase change* and the period of time during which the same equations hold a *phase.* The operation of this system over time will tend, in general, to exhibit multiple phases (6). During a given phase, simple first-order difference equations will determine the time paths of acreage.
The solution to such an equation is

$$y(t) = \lambda^{(t-t_j)}\, y^{(t_j)} \tag{7}$$

in which $y^{(t_j)}$ is the value of y(t) holding in the time period just prior to a phase change.

To visualize how time paths of acreage might appear, suppose that with each new year, the first crop is expected to be the more profitable ($\pi_1'(t) > \pi_2'(t)$, and that net returns from both crops are positive. Suppose also that the acreage of the first crop is much smaller than that of the second, and that there is some idle land.

The following phases are a possible outcome.[1]

$$\begin{array}{ll}
\text{Phase I} & \\
\quad X_1(t) = (1+\bar{\beta}_1)^t X_1(o) & (t=1,\ldots,t_1) \\
\quad X_2(t) = (1+\bar{\beta}_2)^t X_2(o) & \\
\text{Phase II} & \\
\quad X_1(t) = (1+\bar{\beta}_1)^t X_1(t_1) & (t=t_1+1,\ldots,t_2) \\
\quad X_2(t) = \bar{X} - X_1(t) & \\
\text{Phase III} & \\
\quad X_1(t) = \bar{X} - X_2(t_2) & (t=t_2+1,\ldots) \\
\quad X_2(t) = (1-\beta_2)^t X_2(t_2) &
\end{array} \tag{8}$$

A graphic representation of these phases is shown in Figure 1.

In phase I, the acreage of idle land is sufficient to allow both crops to increase at the maximum rate allowed by caution and growth in the aggregate supply of factors. In phase II, the overall land constraints render inconsistent the maximal growth of both crops, and the less profitable crop merely takes up the slack. Finally, in phase III, the maximal rate of growth demands that more land be released from crop 2 than farmers are willing to release, so that the maximal abandonment rate for the relatively unprofitable alternative dominates supply response.

A linear program has a *dual solution,* as well as the *primal solution* discussed above. The *dual variables* express (in this example) the marginal net revenue productivities of unit changes in the constraints. Call ρ_i (t), $i = \bar{X}, \bar{\beta}_1, \bar{\beta}_2, \beta_1, \beta_2,$

[1] In general, the phases will depend upon net returns, the initial conditions, and the flexibility coefficients.

FIGURE 1

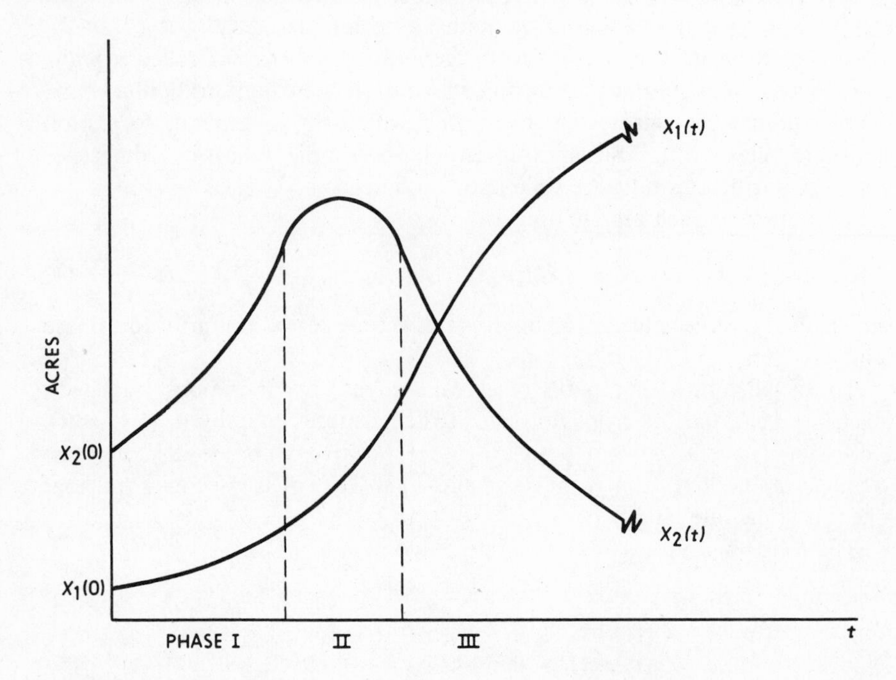

Acreages of both crops expand geometrically until land supplies are exhausted. After this, willingness of farmers to specialize is governed by the upper bound on the first crop (in Phase II) and the lower bound on the second crop (in Phase III).

the dual variables for land, the upper flexibility and lower flexibility constraints, respectively. The dual results are

$$\begin{array}{lcccc}
\text{Phase} & & \text{I} & \text{II} & \text{III} \\
\rho_{\bar{x}}(t) & = & o & \pi_2'(t) & \pi_1'(t) \\
\rho\,\bar{\beta}_1(t) & = & \pi_1'(t) & \pi_1(t) - \pi_2'(t) & o \\
\rho\,\bar{\beta}_2(t) & = & \pi_2'(t) & 0 & o \\
\rho\,\beta_1(t) & = & o & o & o \\
\rho\,\beta_2(t) & = & o & o & \pi_1(t) - \pi_2'(t)
\end{array} \quad (9)$$

Notice that in phase III the marginal return to the lower flexibility constraint for the second crop is positive. This illustrates how lower bounds can be made to reflect the unwillingness of farmers to abandon too rapidly relatively unprofitable alternatives in the face of uncertainty.

The optimizing principle in this application does not imply that long-run or even short-run optima are obtained. Rather, it expresses the empirical fact when farmers change, they cautiously improve their economic positions according to their current uncertain expectations.

The example above may be said to be an "open" model—open with respect to output and input prices. No mechanism was allowed for determining net-return expectations. In aggregative models, this openness is a drastic limitation, for neither net returns, nor their expectations, can be assumed to be independent of past prices and, therefore, of past output. It is to this interdependence we shall now turn.

NET RETURN EXPECTATIONS AND INTERACTION WITH AGGREGATE DEMAND

Net returns are a function of prices and of outputs, inputs, and the technical structure of production. Thus, net returns can be expressed as

$$\pi_i(t) = p_i(t)\, y_i(t) - C_i(t) \tag{10}$$

in which $p_i(t)$, $y_i(t)$ and $C_i(t)$ are the actual price, the yield, and the cost (which is a function of input prices and technical coefficients) for the ith crop in the year t. We could submit net returns to some kind of expectation model, for example, Nerlove's price-expectation model (7). As it seems unlikely that farmers have much notion of what their "long-run equilibrium price" is (even conceding that such a price exists), it may be advisable to use a simple function of past net returns. This can be done while still preserving the properties of the analysis presented so far. What is more important, output plans are independent of current demand, a result that would not be true if no lag were presumed. In the latter case, we would have a model which would represent a region as a monopolist who had complete knowledge of his demand curves and not an agglomerate of atomistic sellers.

Of course, the simplest expectation function is obtained when net-return expectations are equal to the preceding year's actual net returns $[\pi'(t) = \pi(t-1)]$. As this is sufficient to illustrate the generality of recursive programming, we shall hypothesize the validity of this model.

Suppose that the demand structure for our two commodity regions is

$$\begin{aligned} Y_1(t) &= a_1 p_1(t) + a_2 p_2(t); \\ Y_2(t) &= b_1 p_1(t) + b_2 p_2(t)\,, \end{aligned} \tag{11}$$

in which $Y_1(t)$ and $Y_2(t)$ are the demands for production and in which, according to the theory of consumption, we would expect a_1 and b_2 to be negative and a_2 and b_1 to be positive. As with expectations, this model is chosen because it is just sufficient for our present purpose. Suppose further (for simplicity) that yield is constant for each crop: $y_1(t) = y_1$ and $y_2(t) = y_2$ all t. Then, if the market is free to clear itself,

$$\begin{aligned} Y_1(t) &= y_1\, X_1(t); \\ Y_2(t) &= y_2\, X_2(t)\,. \end{aligned} \tag{12}$$

Substituting relation 12 into relation 11 and solving for $p_1(t)$ and $p_2(t)$, the following expressions could be obtained:

$$\begin{aligned} p_1(t) &= a_1'X_1(t) + a_2'X_2(t); \\ p_2(t) &= b_1'X_1(t) + b_2'X_2(t), \end{aligned} \tag{13}$$

in which the coefficients of the X(t)'s are determined by the coefficients of relation 9 and the yields. This closes the model with respect to output price, though not with respect to costs. The latter could be treated similarly, but to avoid further complexities let it be supposed that $C_1(t)$ and $C_2(t)$ are constant over time. This gives the closure needed to develop explicit dynamic solutions for acreage, price, and marginal returns over time.

Returning to phase II, there is a corresponding phase for prices. The reader can verify that it is

Phase II

$$\begin{aligned} p_1(t) &= (a_1'-a_2')\,(1+\bar{\beta}_1)^{t-t_1}\,X_1(t_1) + a_2'\bar{x} \\ p_2(t) &= (b_1'-b_2')\,(1+\bar{\beta}_1)^{t-t_1}\,X_1(t_1) + b_2'\bar{x} \end{aligned} \tag{14}$$

Similarly, price movements can be found for any phase.

By means of relation 10, these price movements can be converted to expected returns. Thus, though they have not exact knowledge of it, farmer expectations follow an inexorable law which is based on the aggregative demand functions for their products.[2] At some place in the course of phase III, for example, net returns will reverse their relation; crop 2 will become less desirable to produce, and farmers will begin a response to the changed price expectations by transferring land from crop 2 to crop 1, thus reversing the former trend. The effect of this process on prices is shown in Figure 2. The price lines cross before the end of a phase because of the lag in expectations and the role of costs and yields. The dual variables can also be expressed as functions of time. For example, in phase II equation 14 can be substituted into equation 10; for $i = 1$ and $i = 2$.

The following results seem most important. First, prices and acreages, *ergo*, net returns, marginal revenues, and outputs undergo multiple phases in which rates of change over time change in each phase. Second, the phases begin to repeat themselves. This is called *phase periodicity*[3] and the results tend to resemble dampened sine and cosine curves! Third, phases occur in which output of a commodity may increase while its price is falling!

The implication of the first result is that the elasticity of supply is not a very stable parameter for predicting response over time. The second result is the attainment of a multivariate cobweb cycle, which is likely to be highly stable (for crops) because of the quick change in phase when relative returns change.

---

[2] Needless to say, this law is inexorable in a statistical sense. In stochastic processes, dynamic laws determine not variable values but rather their probability distributions over time. The rather complicated stochastic processes underlying recursive programming have not been explored very fully as yet. The term "dynamic law" is still used in its stochastic sense.

[3] Again, these may be stochastic laws.

FIGURE 2

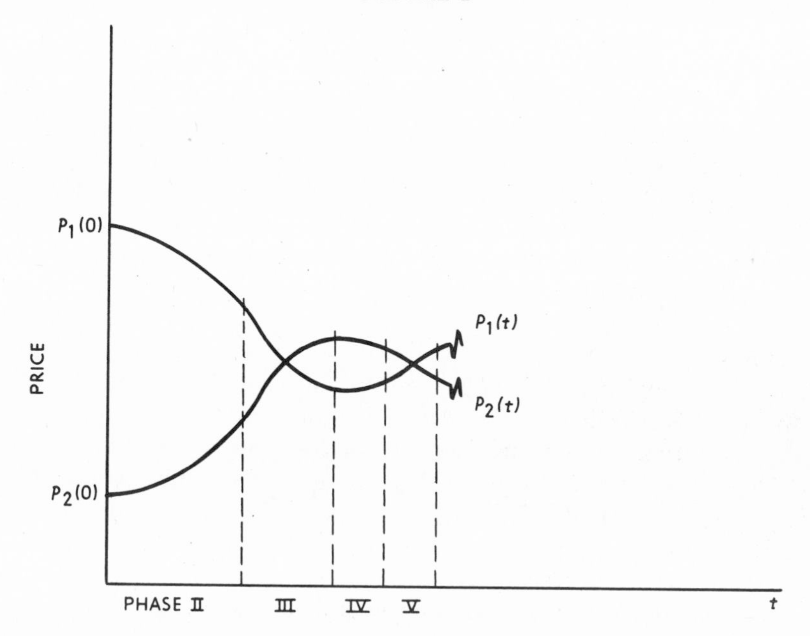

The time paths of output prices in this hypothetical example resemble dampened sine and cosine curves whose periods become shorter with the passage of time.

The third explains the enigma of the downward sloping supply curves sometimes obtained with time-series data! This result stems from the lag in expectations linked through the reaction of output on demand to a production structure with a finite number of alternatives.

This explanation of the inverse supply relation over time is consistent with the Marshallian, positively sloped, short-run supply curve. Such curves are obtained by holding constant everything except the price of a given commodity. The latter is varied continuously over a wide range to obtain the relation between output plans and price for a given time period. This same type of relation can be obtained with this model, which, for a given time period, is a straightforward linear programming problem. "Price mapping" or "parametric programming" is the technique which gives the desired supply functions. These functions will, of course, be step functions which increase discretely. However, the analysis (and synthesis) of this section reveal that the only conditions under which such curves have any real meaning is when the supply system is relieved of the influence of demand on price. Hence, Marshall's purely theoretical construct is useful operationally only for predicting the effect of artificial prices, such as those created by law. In the market, prices and production must be determined by dynamic laws derived from technical and demand structures (1).

INVESTMENT, CAPACITY, AND TECHNOLOGICAL CHANGE

To treat the relation of aggregative investment to output, the constraints on production expansion can be split into two components, one expressed by the flexibility constraint and the second by capacity constraints. The former expresses the reluctance of farmers to specialize too rapidly in a given product. The latter expresses farmers' unwillingness and inability to invest in any particular method of production at a rate greater than some maximum. This inability may come from limitations which are imposed by the rate of expansion of farm machinery and related industries or from external credit rationing. The former might be expressed as internal credit rationing.

Suppose, for example, that the first commodity can be produced by either of two methods. The first of these has been introduced in the recent past and as yet accounts for only a small portion of current practice. Let $X_1^1(t-1)$ and $X_1^2(t-1)$ be the actual capacities in number of acres utilized during the year $(t-1)$. Let $I^*(t)$ and $I_2^*(t)$ be maximal investment patterns *potentially* observable during the year (t). Now let α_1 and α_2 be the *investment coefficients* in the two capacities, respectively. Now suppose that maximal potential investment can be related to the immediate past levels of capacity utilization by

$$\begin{aligned} I_1^*(t) &= X_1^1(t) - X_1^1(t-1) \leq \alpha_1 X_1^1(t-1); \\ I_2^*(t) &= X_1^2(t) - X_1^2(t-1) \leq \alpha_2 X_1^2(t-1). \end{aligned} \tag{15}$$

Expressed as inequalities, these relations determine the maximal potential rate of investment. Predicted capacity in either process is thus constrained by the relation

$$X_1^i(t) \leq (1 + \alpha_i)\, X_1^i(t-1), \quad (i=1,2). \tag{16}$$

The new dynamic production model including both kinds of constraints can be written as:

$$\max \{\pi_1^1(t-1)\, X_1^1(t) + \pi_1^2(t-1)\, X_1^2(t) + \pi_2(t-1)\, X_2(t)\} \tag{17}$$

subject to:

$$\begin{aligned} X_1^1(t) + X_1^2(t) + X_2(t) &\leq \bar{X} \\ X_1^1(t) + X_1^2(t) &\leq (1 + \bar{\beta}_1)\, [X_1^2(t-1) + X_1^2(t-1)] \\ X_1^1(t) &\leq (1 + \alpha_1)\, X_1^1(t-1) \\ X_1^2(t) &\leq (1 + \alpha_2)\, X_1^2(t-1) \\ -X_1^1(t) - X_1^2(t) &\leq -(1 - \beta_1)\, [X_1^1(t-1) + X_1^2(t-1)] \\ X_2(t) &\leq (1 + \bar{\beta}_2)\, X_2(t-1) \\ -X_2(t) &\leq -(1 - \beta_2)\, X_2(t-1) \end{aligned}$$

Actual investment patterns are then predicted by the model. Omitting demand functions to simplify the argument and returning to phase III conditions, the change in capacity might follow the time paths shown in Figure 3. It is presumed that for the period considered, expectations are such that $\pi_1^2(t) > \pi_1^1(t) > \pi_2(t)$, that is, that the second (newest) way of producing crop 1 is most profitable, while the older method is more profitable than production of the second crop.

FIGURE 3

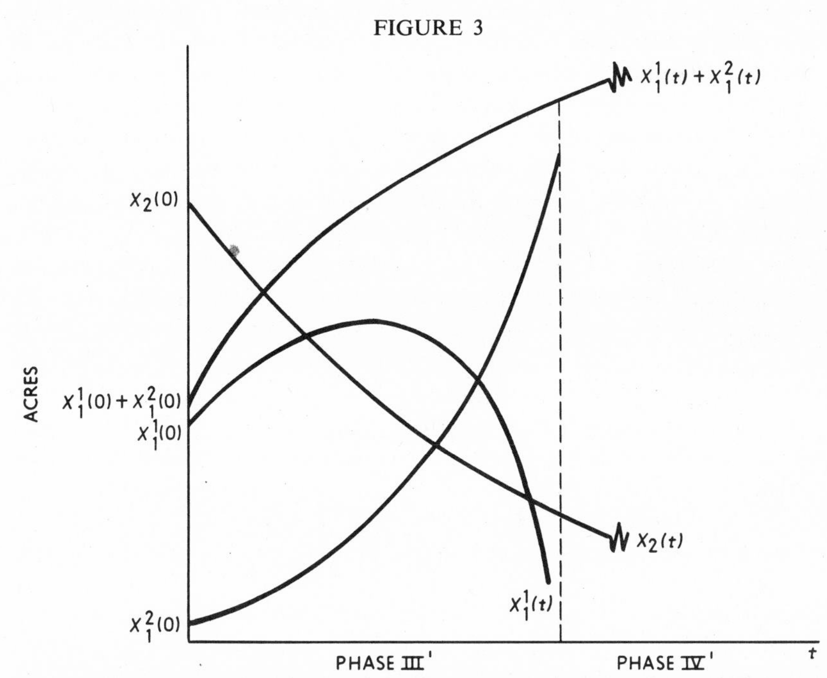

The acreage of crop 1 handled by the older method increases but eventually decreases until the method is entirely abandoned by Phase IV′. Acreage of crop 1 grown under the new method rapidly replaces acreage devoted to the old method until Phase IV′ when uncertainty and other forces constrain aggregate production of the crop.

Here are the main results. First, actual capacity expansion (investment) and abandonment are predicted simultaneously with production patterns. Aggregate production is constrained by the forces acting on the rate of change in output patterns and by the forces which determine maximal potential growth. Second, it is likely that when the capacity of a superior production process is small, investment may occur in a relatively inferior process until sufficient growth has taken place in the former (phase III). Finally, after investment has proceeded long enough in the superior process, not only may capacity of the inferior process be abandoned at an increasing rate, but the unwillingness to alter output patterns beyond a certain rate will prevent investment in a superior process from achieving its maximal potential rate (phase IV). Thus variables may move on paths devious to their "long-run equilibrium" positions as calculated by relative profits alone.

Technological change can be split into three components—invention, innovation, and diffusion. While invention and innovation appear still to belong to historical analysis, technological change, insofar as it is a diffusion process, is solidly within the boundary of economics itself (1). Suppose that in the year $t = o$, the second process for producing crop 1 was innovated. The capacity $X_1^2(o)$ was an historical fact which could not have been predicted, but the diffusion process is expressed now by the same theory under which general investment patterns were predicted. *Diffusion is an investment process.* The growth of knowledge is simply an added component acting on internal and external credit rationing. Its effect may not differ vastly from "normal" investment processes, which probably always contain a knowledge component. If this is true (as we suspect), we need not search too far outside economics for exotic theories of technological change. Further, its effects on output response are traced by considering production decisions as determining investment and capacity abandonment simultaneously with changing output patterns.

PLANNING OVER TIME, REGIONAL COMPETITION, AND OTHER GENERALIZATIONS

While the optimizing principle is the criterion of micro-economic action, it is applied to the regional unit. This is done in a way which does not truly optimize economic action for a region but rather reflects the time distribution of aggregative response to current average expectations. The model has nothing to say about which production units will change in a given year, but only that specific proportions of the region's resources will be reallocated by a corresponding proportion of the region's producers with the passage of time. Such proportions could be interpreted as probabilities of change for the allocation of individual resource units. The peculiarities of individual decision criteria are subsumed in statistical averages.

The model presents a similar attitude toward planning over time. If a given process continues to be relatively attractive as an investment opportunity for some extended period of time, the model predicts a growing rate of investment in it. Again, the individual peculiarities of planning are subsumed. Whatever the varied time horizons among producers may be, the model projects investment for the region, indicating that particular budget limitations and time horizons will lead over time to growing aggregative investment.

For certain applications, however, it is likely that planning over time should be accounted for more explicitly. In doing this, we should not like to sacrifice the rather realistic picture of sequential decision making developed so far. Dynamic programming, as it is currently applied, derives the time distribution of production and investment as the result of a single optimizing decision. Aggregative economic processes, however, do not terminate after some finite period of time in achieved terminal objectives. The ubiquitous presence of uncertainty, the accumulation of knowledge, and the play of more or less fortuitous events prevent such grandiose scheming.

The model can be generalized to include planning over time, but in a way that would preserve the yearly reevaluation of production and investment plans. For this purpose, consider a time horizon of two periods. Relations 4 and 5 are still adequate to express possibilities in the region for the first (imminent) time period. For the second (future) production period for which production and investment plans are projected, a second set of relations is required. It consists of the relations of 4 and 5 advanced one time period. The resulting 10 restrictions on production and capacity change form the following recursive programming system:

$$\begin{aligned} \max \{ & \pi_1'(t+1)X_1(t+1) + \pi_2'(t+1)X_2(t+1) \\ & + \pi_1'(t)X_1(t) + \pi_2'(t)X_2(t) \} \end{aligned} \tag{18}$$

subject to

$$\begin{array}{lllll}
X_1(t) & +\ X_2(t) & & & \leq \bar{x} \\
X_1(t) & & & & \leq (1+\bar{\beta}_1)X_1(t-1) \\
 & X_2(t) & & & \leq (1+\bar{\beta}_2)X_2(t-1) \\
-X_1(t) & & & & \leq -(1-\beta_1)X_1(t-1) \\
 & -X_2(t) & & & \leq -(1-\beta_2)X_2(t-1) \\
 & & X_1(t+1)\ + & X_2(t+1) & \leq X \\
-(1+\bar{\beta}_1)X_1(t) & & X_1(t+1) & & \leq 0 \\
 & -(1+\bar{\beta}_2)X_2(t) & & X_2(t+1) & \leq 0 \\
(1-\beta_{-1})\,X_1(t) & & -X_1(t+1) & & \leq 0 \\
 & (1-\beta_{-2})\,X_2(t) & & -X_2(t+1) & \leq 0
\end{array}$$

in which $\pi_1'(t+1)$ and $\pi_2'(t+1)$ are expected net returns for the future period. The latter might be linked through an expectation model to a demand structure to obtain a closed system. While production and investment in time t is conducted with an eye for the future, the plans made for $t+1$ may be changed as a new plan is generated. For a given year t, the plan is a dynamic linear programming problem of the usual kind, but it is dynamic not only in the Hicks sense, but also in the Frisch-Samuelson sense (4). This methodology can be summarized in Leontief's words (5):

"... [An] economic [process] is ... a continuing, unending process the path of which is determined by a never-ending sequence of choices. Particularly important for this point of view is the fact that the explicit time-horizon of each one of these successive choices is much shorter, in principle infinitely shorter, than the span of time covered by the dynamic process as a whole. Thus while each step ... satisfies certain maximizing conditions, the sequence as a whole does not.

A dynamic process of regional competition can be formulated too. For illustration, suppose there are two regions. Disregarding time-horizon and demand aspects of the model, two sets of relations, 4 and 5, one for each region, might be specified, with the variables labeled with superscripts I or II for the first or second region. Apart from demand, the regions might be interrelated through the growth in the regional capacities of short-run fixed factors and labor. Thus the farm labor force and investment in machines would flow in the direction of highest marginal returns as reflected in the dual variables. Augmented in this way, the model is

$$\max \{\pi_1^{I}(t)X_1^{I}(t) + \pi_2^{I}(t)X_2^{I}(t) + \pi_1^{II}(t)X_1^{II}(t) + \pi_2^{II}(t)X_2^{II}(t)\} \tag{19}$$

subject to

$$\begin{array}{rrrrll}
X_1^{I}(t) + & X_2^{I}(t) & & & \leq & \bar{X}^{I} \\
X_1^{I}(t) & & & & \leq & (1 + \bar{\beta}_1^{I})X_1^{I}(t-1) \\
 & X_2^{I}(t) & & & \leq & (1 + \bar{\beta}_2^{I})X_2^{I}(t-1) \\
-X_1^{I}(t) & & & & \leq & -(1 - \beta_1^{I})X_1^{I}(t-1) \\
 & -X_2^{I}(t) & & & \leq & -(1 - \beta_2^{I})X_2^{I}(t-1) \\
 & & X_1^{II}(t) + & X_2^{II}(t) & \leq & \bar{X}^{II} \\
 & & X_1^{II}(t) & & \leq & (1 + \bar{\beta}_1^{II})X_1^{II}(t-1) \\
 & & & X_2^{II}(t) & \leq & (1 + \bar{\beta}_2^{II})X_2^{II}(t-1) \\
 & & -X_1^{II}(t) & & \leq & -(1 - \beta_1^{II})X_1^{II}(t-1) \\
 & & & -X_2^{II}(t) & \leq & -(1 - \beta_2^{II})X_2^{II}(t-1) \\
X_1^{I}(t) & & + \quad X_1^{II}(t) & & \leq & (1 + \alpha_1)[X_1^{I}(t) + X_1^{II}(t-1)] \\
 & X_2^{II}(t) & + & X_2^{II}(t) & \leq & (1 + \alpha_2)[X_2^{I}(t-1) + X_2^{II}(t-)].
\end{array}$$

This points a way to analysis of the well-known relation between regional competition and technological change.

The applied linear programmer is familiar with the rich variety of production relations which can be accommodated in the linear programming framework. An important generalization for this aggregative model of production response would be to include distinct processes representing several levels of fertilizer application for each basic technological process or "type." If a relation which would determine aggregative fertilizer stocks (purchases for a given year, for example) could be established, the yield component could be subjected to the same analysis as the acreage component of production.

Like other empirical techniques, the generality of recursive programming is determined in practice by a judicious compromise among logical structuring, data availability, and the research budget.

ESTIMATION PROCEDURES

Although simple examples have yielded interesting, theoretical results, it remains to be seen whether an operational tool exists. Given that they are both meaningful and relatively stable, can parameters of a recursive programming model be estimated? The dynamic nature of the model can be invoked to answer the question in the affirmative. The approach to be suggested is closely related to familiar time-series analysis, but it involves some unfamiliar techniques and problems.

Consider the simple model of section 3. During phase I the regional acreages of the two crops follow two simple equations. Therefore, time-series estimates of aggregate acreages can be used to estimate the coefficients $\bar{\beta}_1$ and $\bar{\beta}_2$. Notice, however, that the coefficients β_1 and β_2 cannot be estimated with data from this period. In phase II, time-series data for the first crop can be used to increase the efficiency of the $\bar{\beta}_1$ estimate, but no additional information can be added to the estimate of $\bar{\beta}_2$. In phase III, time-series data for the second crop can be used to estimate β_2.

In summary, the progress of regional production has revealed sufficient information to permit estimation of the upper flexibility coefficients of the two crops and of the lower flexibility coefficient of one of them. Remaining *unidentified* is the coefficient β_1 which determines the lower flexibility constraint for the first crop. Thus, the model introduces a new kind of *identification problem.*

Having information with which to estimate some of the coefficients is quite different from knowing how to use it. We cannot know exactly which phases actually hold over time. Consequently, two distinct sets of hypotheses are involved. Given the set of structural inequalities defining the dynamics of the model (which are, of course, hypotheses too) one must first *guess* which equations actually determined the system for particular periods of time. Second, using the usual time series techniques (least squares, perhaps) one must estimate the parameter (or parameters) of each equation so "identified." A "good" guess can be made by a study of relative net returns and of the data on acreage and production in the region, and with the help of an intimate knowledge of the region's economic conditions.

Having obtained estimates of some of the parameters in this way, one returns to some initial date and begins the model running as described above. If the optimizing principle selects the same phases as those guessed, and if the model estimates explain a fairly large percentage of the total variation in the several variables of interest, then the model's hypotheses appear to be useful approximations of reality. On the basis of this test, future projections could be made and revised with the passage of time to accommodate the latest information and newly revealed structural relations.

Recursive programming does not replace existing statistical methods but rather performs a synthesis between them and explicit choice criteria and modifies the sphere within which their application is valid.

PROOF OF THE PUDDING

It is too early to pass judgment on the empirical usefulness of recursive programming for the study of production response. At this stage only its promise can be described. It is an operational tool constructed to reflect production structures and to simulate explicitly the aggregative implications of decision processes at the firm level. While there is (as yet largely undeveloped) a theory of statistics by which estimates and hypotheses can be evaluated formally, the most attractive feature of recursive programming is its direct relation to the theory of production. Its foundation is not an esoteric theory of statistical decisions, but rather a highly plausible theory of economic action.

In addition to the lack of extensive empirical testing and a well-developed statistical theory, a thorough exploration of the bias of applying a micro-decision criterion at an aggregative level is lacking. Any study of aggregation must begin with a theory of the firm. Recursive programming seems to be well-suited to the job. The fact that certain other statistical methods are not derived from some explicit production structure does not exempt them from aggregation problems. Rather it implies that even the highest correlations do little to illuminate their essentially obscure micro-structural foundations.

REFERENCES

1. Carter, Anne P. *Technological Change.* Report on Research for 1953. Harvard Economic Research Project, 1953, Part 2.
2. Georgescu-Roegen, Nicholas. "Relaxation Phenomena in Linear Dynamic Models," *in Activity Analysis of Production and Allocation* (T. C. Koopman). New York: John Wiley & Sons, Inc., 1951.
3. Henderson, James M. "The Utilization of Agricultural Land," *Review Economics and Statistics,* Vol. 41 (1959), pp. 242–59.
4. Hicks, J. R., *Value and Capital,* 2d ed. Chap. 9. New York: Oxford University Press, 1946.
5. Leontief, Wassily W. *Dynamic Analysis in Studies in the Structure of the American Economy,* chap. iii. New York: Oxford University Press, 1953.
6. ____ . "Time-Preference and Economic Growth": reply, *American Economic Review,* Vol. 49 (1959), pp. 1041–43.
7. Nerlove, Marc. *The Dynamics of Supply: Estimation of Farmers' Response to Price,* Baltimore: Johns Hopkins Press, 1958.
8. ____ , "Distributed Lags and Demand Analysis." *Agriculture Handbook,* No. 141 Washington, D.C.: U.S. Government Printing Office, 1958.

Part III Methodology in the Marketing and Farm Supply Sectors

8 The Minimum-Cost Dairy Feed

(An Application of "Linear Programming")*

FREDERICK V. WAUGH† ‡

The main purpose of this paper is to test a method of determining the least expensive combination of feeds which meets, or surpasses, each of several stated requirements. The "linear programming" techniques recently developed by Koopmans,[1] Dantzig,[2] and others, are used to provide a definitive solution of this problem.

I want to make clear at the start that I do not pretend to be an expert on animal feeding. It is quite possible that the rations indicated by this analysis may be found unacceptable by practical feeders. If so, it is because the requirements used to illustrate this method do not adequately cover feed essentials. I would welcome any suggestions for improving the stated requirements. But the method of analysis used here is, in my opinion, exact. If the prices and nutritive values of all available feeds are known, that method will unfailingly indicate the least expensive combination of feeds meeting whatever requirements may be determined to be acceptable.

---

* *Journal of Farm Economics,* Vol. XXIII, No. 3 (August 1951), pp. 299–310.

† University of Maryland, College Park, Maryland.

‡ Malcolm Clough, of the Bureau of Agricultural Economics, supplied all data used in this study, and also made many practical suggestions concerning analysis and interpretation. Richard J. Foote, of BAE, read an earlier draft of the paper and made several suggestions. Karl Fox, also of the Bureau of Agricultural Economics, supplied a number of excellent footnotes and several other suggestions for clarifying the technical presentation. The author, however, takes personal responsibility for both the analysis and the conclusions.

[1] T. C. Koopmans, "A Mathematical Model of Production," *Econometrica,* Vol. 17 (January 1949), p. 74.

[2] G. B. Dantzig, "Maximization of a Linear Form Whose Variables are Subject to a System of Linear Inequalities," ditto, USAF Comptroller, November 1949.

THE PROBLEM

Dairy cows require a certain minimum combination of nutrients for maintenance and for milk production. Part of these requirements ordinarily are met by pasture and hay. The rest must be supplied by concentrated feeds, including such whole grains as corn and oats, and such mill feeds as bran and cottonseed meal. Dairymen usually produce on their own farms the pasture and hay needed. They usually buy part, or all, of their requirements of concentrated feeds. The cost of purchased feed may represent as much as 35 percent of the total cost of producing milk in an area like New York and New England.

The dairyman naturally searches for any possible way to reduce this feed bill without lowering milk production. The feed manufacturer likewise searches for the lowest-cost feed which he can guarantee will meet nutritive standards. A reduction of even a few cents in the cost of each bag of feed manufactured may well change a loss to a profit.

The economic problem confronting the dairyman, or the feed manufacturer, is essentially one of "linear programming," to use a technical phrase. The amounts of nutrients in the feed mixture are linear functions of the quantities of corn, oats, bran, and other feeds. The dairyman, or the feed manufacturer, wants to adjust his purchases of each feed material in such a way that the mixture will provide at least a minimum amount of each important nutrient. In general, he cannot purchase a negative amount of any feed. He attempts to work out an economic "program", in other words, to determine how much of each feed to buy in order to supply all needed nutrients at the least possible cost. Technically, he is trying to minimize a linear function subject to several linear inequalities. Probably he does not realize this, just as Jourdain did not realize that he had written prose.

The dairyman or feed manufacturer who tries to find this sort of minimum is attempting a difficult piece of mathematical analysis. Perhaps this paper may help him.

THE DATA

The data in Table I were supplied by Malcolm Clough, of the Bureau of Agricultural Economics.

The first column of Table I shows the average quoted prices of 10 feeds in Kansas City for the period from October 1949 through September 1950. For the purpose of this analysis, I assume that a dairyman or feed manufacturer must select some combination of feeds from among these 10, and that he must pay exactly the average quoted price.

The remaining four columns in Part A of the table show the nutritive content of each of the 10 quoted feeds, as given by Morrison.[3]

---

[3] F. B. Morrison, *Feeds and Feeding*, 21st ed., pp. 1172–73.

TABLE I

WHOLESALE PRICES AND NUTRITIVE CONTENT OF FEEDS

Feed	Grade or Type	*Wholesale Price, Kansas City, 1949–50*[a]	*Nutritive Content of Feeds*[b]			
			Total Digestible Nutrients	*Digestible Protein*	*Calcium*	*Phosphorus*
Corn	#3 yellow	2.40	78.6	6.5	0.02	0.27
Oats	#3 white	2.52	70.1	9.4	0.09	0.34
Milo maize	#2	2.18	80.1	8.8	0.03	0.30
Bran	standard	2.14	67.2	13.7	0.14	1.29
Flour middlings	standard	2.44	78.9	16.1	0.09	0.71
Linseed meal	36%	3.82	77.0	30.4	0.41	0.86
Cottonseed meal	41%	3.55	70.6	32.8	0.20	1.22
Soybean meal	41%	3.70	78.5	37.1	0.26	0.59
Gluten feed	23%	2.60	76.3	21.3	0.48	0.82
Hominy feed	white	2.54	84.5	8.0	0.22	0.71
B. Requirements:						
for 18% total protein			74.2	14.7	0.14	0.55
for 24% total protein			74.2	19.9	0.21	0.67

[a] Arithmetic averages of quotations from October through September, dollars per 100 pounds.
[b] Pounds of each element in 100 pounds of feed.

Part B of the table indicates two sets of nutritive requirements used for the purpose of the present study. These requirements are also obtained from Morrison. The figures in the first line of Part B show the average content of six typical dairy rations, published on page 1172 by Morrison, each containing approximately 18 percent total protein. The figures in the second line of Part B show the average contents of six rations, published on page 1173, each containing approximately 24 percent protein.

I assume for the purpose of this study that any combination of feeds meets all nutritive requirements for an 18 percent protein ration if it contains at least 74.2 pounds of total digestible nutrients, at least 14.7 pounds of digestible protein, at least 0.14 pound of calcium, and at least 0.55 pound of phosphorus. Likewise, I assume that any combination of feeds meets all nutritive requirements for a 24 percent protein ration if it contains at least 74.2 pounds of total digestible nutrients, at least 19.9 pounds of digestible protein, at least 0.21 pound of calcium, and at least 0.67 pound of phosphorus. This ignores the possibility that overconsumption of some nutrient might be harmful—an aspect of the problem which doubtless should be studied.

In addition to the nutritive requirements, I shall assume that a feed manufacturer may require a combination of feeds which weighs at least 100 pounds, since he sells feed by weight. I therefore consider four possible sets of requirements—two indicated by the two rows of Part B, Table I, and two more with the additional requirement that the combination of feeds weigh at least

100 pounds. Each of these four sets of requirements is to be met by some combination of feeds selected from the 10 feeds listed in Table I, and we must find the least expensive combination.

LEAST EXPENSIVE SOURCE OF A SINGLE REQUIREMENT

The first step in our analysis is to compute from the data in Table I the proportion of each requirement which can be supplied by one dollar's worth of each feed. For example, 100 pounds of corn supplies 78.6 pounds of total digestible nutrients, at a cost of $2.40, and either ration requires 74.2 pounds of digestible nutrient. So one dollar's worth of corn supplies

$$\frac{78.6}{(2.40)\,(74.2)} = 0.441$$

times the required amount. In general, let X_{ij} represent the pounds of the jth nutrient in the ith feed, let p_i represent the price of the ith feed, and let r_j represent the required amount of the jth nutrient. Then we compute

$$Y_{ij} = X_{ij}/p_i{}^2{}_j.$$

The values of Y_{ij} are shown in Table II.

As a first step in the analysis we consider the least expensive source of each individual requirement. This is found by locating the maximum value in each column of Table II. Thus, the least expensive source of total digestible nutrients is milo maize, of digestible protein it is soybean meal, of calcium it is gluten, of phosphorus it is bran, and of weight it is bran.

Note that a single feed always provides a single requirement at less expense than any combination of two or more feeds. If the buyer were concerned only with total digestible nutrients, he should buy milo maize only.

It is also important to note that a single feed may provide the least expensive source of two or more requirements. One hundred pounds of bran not only is the least expensive source of total weight; it also provides more phosphorus than needed in either ration, and as much calcium as required in the 18 percent protein ration. Thus, in the case of the 18 percent ration, bran alone is the least expensive source of calcium, phosphorus, and weight together;—but it is deficient in total digestible nutrients and in digestible protein. In a different price situation it is quite possible that a single feed might provide all requirements at less expense than any combination of two or more feeds. Thus, in April 1951 the quoted price of gluten was lower than for any other feed—or gluten was the least expensive source of weight. In this case, it is easy to see from Table I that 100 pounds of gluten would supply all five requirements for either the 18 percent protein ration or the 24 percent protein ration. Therefore, in April 1951 the least expensive feed meeting all the specified requirements was gluten alone, unmixed with any other of the listed feeds.

TABLE II

Y_{ij} PROPORTION OF REQUIREMENTS SUPPLIED BY $1 WORTH OF EACH FEED

Feed	Proportion of Required Amount of				
	TDN[a]	DP[b]	Ca[c]	Ph[d]	Weight[e]
	A. *Values for 18 percent Protein Feed*				
Corn	0.441	0.184	0.060	0.205	0.417
Oats	0.375	0.254	0.255	0.245	0.397
Milo maize	0.495	0.275	0.098	0.250	0.459
Bran	0.423	0.436	0.467	1.096	0.467
Flour middlings	0.436	0.449	0.264	0.529	0.410
Linseed meal	0.272	0.541	0.767	0.409	0.262
Cottonseed meal	0.268	0.628	0.403	0.625	0.281
Soybean meal	0.286	0.682	0.502	0.290	0.270
Gluten	0.395	0.557	1.319	0.573	0.385
Hominy feed	0.448	0.218	0.619	0.508	0.394
	B. *Values for 24 percent Protein Feed*				
Corn	0.441	0.136	0.040	0.168	0.417
Oats	0.375	0.187	0.170	0.201	0.397
Milo maize	0.495	0.203	0.066	0.206	0.459
Bran	0.423	0.321	0.312	0.900	0.467
Flour middlings	0.436	0.332	0.176	0.434	0.410
Linseed meal	0.272	0.400	0.511	0.336	0.262
Cottonseed meal	0.268	0.464	0.268	0.513	0.281
Soybean meal	0.286	0.504	0.335	0.238	0.270
Gluten	0.395	0.412	0.879	0.471	0.385
Hominy feed	0.448	0.158	0.412	0.417	0.394

[a] Total digestible nutrients
[b] Digestible protein
[c] Calcium
[d] Phosphorus
[e] 100 pounds
The last column shows the fraction of 100 pounds of each feed which can be bought for one dollar. This may, or may not, be considered a requirement.

But with the average prices of 1949–50 the buyer would have needed at least two feeds to meet all requirements at the least possible cost.

LEAST EXPENSIVE SOURCE OF A PAIR OF REQUIREMENTS

The next step in the analysis is to discover the least expensive combination of feeds which meets two requirements. This combination will not include more than two feeds.[4] And if the least-cost combination of two feeds which

[4] If the two requirements are provided most economically by a single feed, one of the requirements will be met exactly and the other will generally be exceeded. If the most economical source is a combination of two feeds, both requirements will be met exactly. Geometrically, this means that the least-cost combination of two feeds meeting two requirements will lie exactly on the 45 degree line of Figure 1. Once the least-cost combination of two feeds has been located (in this case, gluten and middlings), it can be shown from Figure 1 that any mixture of these two with one or more additional feeds will prove to be a more expensive source of the two requirements.

meets some two requirements, happens also to meet all other requirements, it is obviously the least-cost combination meeting all requirements.[5]

We shall now present a graphic method of finding the least-cost combination of two feeds meeting two requirements. For illustration we shall consider combinations which meet the requirements of total digestible nutrients and digestible protein in the 24 percent protein ration, as shown in Table IIB. The Y_{ij} values for each of the 10 listed feeds are plotted in Figure 1. For example, the appropriate values for corn are TDN = 0.441 and DP = 0.136. So we locate corn by measuring 0.441 unit to the right of the origin and 0.136 unit upward.

The diagram demonstrates that a combination of a substantial amount

FIGURE 1
LOWEST-COST MIXTURE MEETING TWO REQUIREMENTS

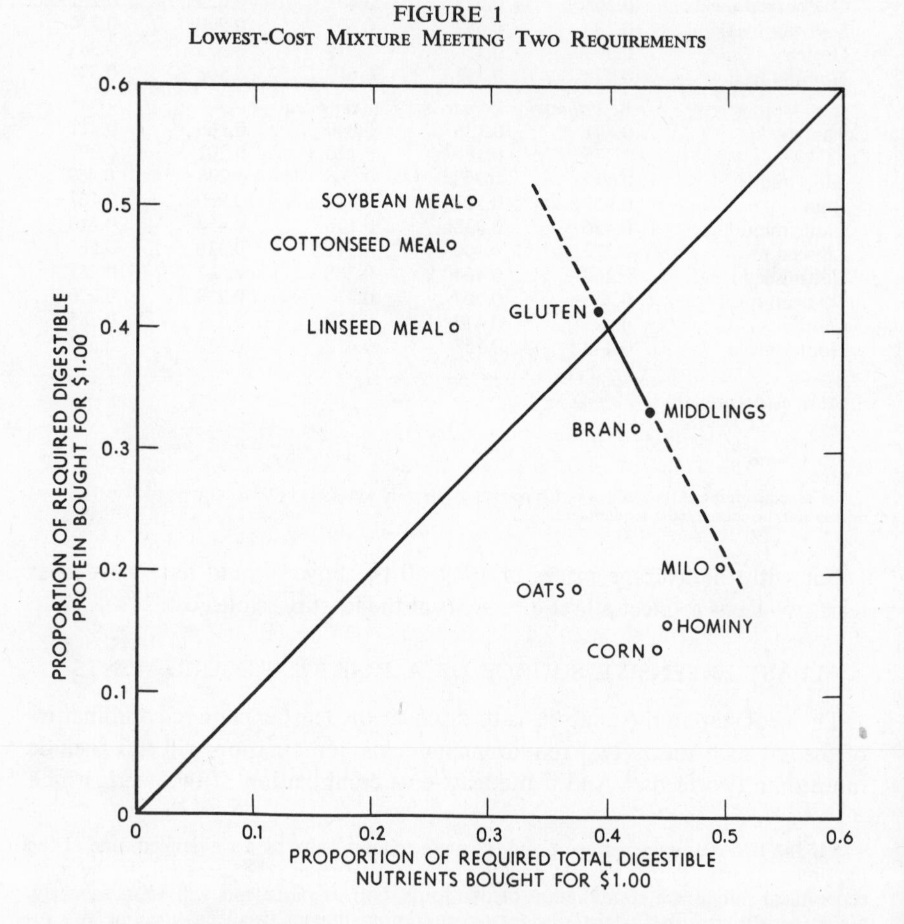

[5] This follows from the preceding footnote, since no possible combination of three or more feeds will meet the initial two requirements as cheaply as the least-cost combination of two feeds.

of gluten and a smaller amount of middlings meets the following tests:

a. It is *feasible,* since it does not require negative purchases of either feed. Geometrically, the test of feasibility is that a line joining the dots representing gluten and middlings cross the 45 degree line shown in the diagram.[6]
b. It is *necessary,* since the two requirements cannot be met at less expense by dropping either feed. Geometrically, the test of necessity is that the line joining the two dots slope downward to the right. If it sloped upward to the right, we would buy only the one feed which was higher on both scales (i.e., the cheaper source of both digestible protein and total digestible nutrients).
c. It is the *least-cost* combination of feeds supplying these two requirements. The geometric test of this is that no dot lie above the line (extended if necessary) joining the two feeds. If a dot did lie above the line it would indicate that the requirements could be met with less expense by substituting some other feed, either for gluten or for middlings.[7]

The above three principles are the key to linear programming.

Finally, it can be shown that this combination of gluten and middlings meets all four nutritive requirements. Thus, it is also *complete* if we do not require it to weigh 100 pounds. This test cannot be shown conveniently on the diagram, but it will be discussed in the following mathematical treatment.

Now let us cover mathematically the same ground we have covered graphically.

If we spend e_1 for middlings and e_2 for gluten, we require that

$$\begin{aligned} 0.436e_1 + 0.395e_2 &= 1, \text{ and} \\ 0.332e_1 + 0.412e_2 &= 1. \end{aligned} \qquad (1)$$

The first equation states that the quantities purchased must exactly meet the TDN requirement, and the second that these quantities must exactly meet the DP (digestible protein) requirement.

The solution may be found by inverting the matrix,[8]

[6] If the point of intersection were midway between the two dots, the least-cost combination would require equal expenditures for each feed. If the point of intersection were one fourth of the way from gluten toward middlings, the least-cost combination would require expenditures for gluten three times as large as those for middlings. A combination of cottonseed meal and linseed meal would not be feasible, although from an algebraic standpoint a combination meeting both requirements can be found by extending the line joining the two feeds to its intersection with the 45 degree line. But this "combination" would require large *n egative* purchases of cottonseed meal!

[7] A combination of gluten and milo exactly meeting both requirements would be feasible but slightly higher in cost than that of gluten and middlings. Any mixture of the two *combinations* would meet both nutritive requirements exactly. But while such a mixture would be less expensive than the gluten-milo combination, it would be more expensive than that of gluten and middlings. This demonstrates the proposition of footnote 3 that the least-cost combination meeting two requirements will not include more than two feeds.

[8] These equations could, of course, be solved by elementary algebra. The matrix method is chosen here because certain criteria relating to row-sums and column-sums can be conveniently generalized to sets of three or more requirements. Equation (1) becomes $eY = i$, and its solution is $e = iY^{-1}$. Equation (4) becomes $Ya' = i'$, and its solution is $a' = Y^{-1}i'$.

$$Y = \begin{matrix} \\ \text{middlings} \\ \text{gluten} \end{matrix} \begin{matrix} \text{TDN} & \text{DP} \\ \begin{bmatrix} 0.436 & 0.332 \\ 0.395 & 0.412 \end{bmatrix} \end{matrix} \tag{2}$$

which gives

$$\begin{matrix} & & & \text{sums of rows} \\ Y^{-1} = & \begin{bmatrix} 8.49625 & -6.84649 \\ -8.14567 & 8.99117 \end{bmatrix} & & \begin{matrix} 1.64976 \\ 0.84550 \end{matrix} \\ \text{sums of columns} & \begin{matrix} 0.35058 & 2.14468 \end{matrix} & & \text{Total cost } \$2.49526 \end{matrix} \tag{3}$$

The sums of columns of Y^{-1} show that the expenditure for middlings is \$0.35058, and for gluten \$2.14468;—a total cost of \$2.49526. The combination is *feasible,* since the sums of columns of Y^{-1} are both positive (i.e., the combination does not involve negative expenditures for either feed).

The equation of the line joining the two appropriate points in the diagram may be found by solving

$$\begin{aligned} 0.436a_1 + 0.332a_2 &= 1 \\ 0.395a_1 + 0.412a_2 &= 1. \end{aligned} \tag{4}$$

The values of a_1 and a_2 are the sums of the first and second rows of Y^{-1}. The combination is *necessary* because both row-sums are positive. If one were negative, the line would slope upward to the right and one feed would be the cheaper source of both requirements.

This is the least-cost combination meeting requirements for TDN and DP because

$$1.64976Y_{i1} + 0.84550Y_{i2} < 1, \tag{5}$$

when the Y values of any other feed than middlings or gluten are used. (Geometrically, this means that no dot in Figure 1 lies above the line joining gluten and middlings.) For example, we can test whether corn is a substitute by computing

$$(1.64976)(0.441) + (0.84550)(0.136) = 0.84253.$$

Since this value is less than 1, the substitution of corn for middlings, or for gluten, would increase the cost of meeting the first two requirements. In a similar way we test each other feed, each time obtaining values less than 1, and therefore rejecting them.

The ration is *complete* except for weight, since \$0.35058 worth of middlings and \$2.14468 worth of gluten supply 1.94688 times the required amount of calcium and 1.16230 times the amount of phosphorus, as may be verified easily from data in Table IIB. However, it weighs only 96.944 pounds. If a manufacturer is concerned with total weight, this combination is incomplete.

If the buyer were concerned only with meeting the four nutritive requirements, the least-cost, complete, necessary, and feasible ration which could have been bought would be $0.35058 worth of middlings and $2.14468 worth of gluten, at a total cost of $2.49526.

But now suppose the manufacturer says, "I sell feeds in 100 pound sacks. What is the cheapest combination of feeds weighing 100 pounds and meeting the nutritional requirements?" Many of my friends answer this in either of two incorrect ways. Some say, "Multiply each expenditure by 1/0.96944 = 1.03152, obtaining 100 pounds at a cost of $2.57391. Others say, "Add to the ration 3.056 pounds of bran, the cheapest feed, at 2.14 cents a pound. This increases the cost by 6.539 cents, making the total cost $2.56065." The second answer is obviously better than the first, but both are wrong, and both miss the main point of the analysis.

A diagram similar to Figure 1 would indicate that a mixture of bran and gluten is the least expensive combination of feeds weighing 100 pounds and supplying enough digestible protein. Without drawing such a diagram, we may proceed mathematically with

$$
\begin{array}{ccc}
 & \text{DP} & \text{Weight} \\
Y = \begin{array}{c} \text{bran} \\ \text{gluten} \end{array} & \left[\begin{array}{c} 0.321 \\ 0.412 \end{array}\right. & \left.\begin{array}{c} 0.467 \\ 0.385 \end{array}\right]
\end{array}
$$

$$
\begin{array}{lcc}
Y^{-1} = \left[\begin{array}{rr} -5.59439 & 6.78592 \\ 5.98672 & -4.66441 \end{array}\right] & \begin{array}{c} 1.19153 \\ 1.32331 \end{array} & \\
\hline
\quad\;\; 0.39233 \qquad 2.12151 & & \text{Cost } \$2.51384
\end{array}
$$

A combination of $0.39233 worth of bran and $2.12151 worth of gluten not only weighs 100 pounds and supplies the required amount of digestible proteins; it also supplies more than the required amounts of the other three nutrients. It is, therefore, complete. It is feasible, since the column-sums are both positive. It is necessary, since the row-sums are both positive. It is the least-cost combination because

$$1.19153\,Y_{i1} + 1.32231\,Y_{i4} < 1$$

for each feed other than bran and gluten.

Summarizing thus far, the least expensive feed at the average Kansas City prices of 1949–50 which meets the four nutritional requirements of the 24 percent protein ration was $0.35058 worth of middlings and $2.14468 worth of gluten—a total cost of $2.49526. The least expensive combination meeting the nutritional requirements and weighing 100 pounds was $0.39233 worth of bran and $2.12151 worth of gluten—a total cost of $2.51384. The second combination weighs 3.059 pounds more than the first, and costs 1.858 cents more.

THE LEAST EXPENSIVE 18 PERCENT PROTEIN RATION

In the case of the 24 percent protein ration, we have seen that the least-cost combination of feeds meeting two requirements happens to meet all others and thus is the least expensive mixture meeting all requirements. Such an easy solution is not always possible. With different prices, or with different requirements, we would generally need to proceed to analyze combinations meeting three, four, or five requirements. This cannot be done conveniently by graphic methods. But the mathematical tests used above apply to the general case of several requirements. This will not be proved here, but if the reader followed the proof of the two-dimensional case, he may be able to see intuitively that the same mathematical conditions apply in cases of three or more dimensions.

I shall proceed to apply the principle to discover the least cost combination meeting the requirements of an 18 percent protein ration. I shall start with the matrix, obtained from Table IIA,[9]

---

[9] These four feeds were chosen on the following, partly intuitive, bases: From Figure 1 and Table IIA it was evident that a combination of milo maize and middlings would be a feasible, necessary, and probably least-cost combination for meeting the TDN and digestible protein requirements of the 18 percent protein ration. The least-cost property could have been confirmed either by plotting the Y_{ij} values of these and other relatively promising ingredients on a chart such as Figure 1, or by applying the criterion, based on matrix Y_2^{-1}, that

$$1.69996 Y_{i1} + 0.57643 Y_{i2} < 1 \qquad (6)$$

for all feeds other than milo and middlings.

The combination of milo maize and middlings also exceeded the minimum requirements for phosphorus. A combination of gluten and milo would have been only slightly more expensive than middlings and milo as a source of TDN's and digestible protein. Equation (6) applied to gluten gave a value of 0.99256. Gluten was a cheaper source of phosphorus than either milo or middlings and was also the cheapest source of calcium. Subsequent tests, using a criterion analogous to Equation (6), demonstrated that milo, middlings, and glutten provided the least-cost combination exactly meeting requirements for TDN's, digestible protein, and calcium. The criterion, based on matrix Y_3^{-1}, was that

$$1.70215 Y_{i1} + 0.56970 Y_{i2} + 0.00783 Y_{i3} < 1 \qquad (7)$$

for all feeds other than the three chosen. The chosen combination was complete except for weight.

Bran was the cheapest source of weight (and phosphorus); it provided more calcium per dollar than did the milo-middling-gluten combination; and it would have been only a slightly more expensive substitute for middlings as a source of TDN's and digestible protein. Equation (6) applied to bran gave a value of 0.97041. Subsequent tests justified the choice of bran to complete the least-cost combination meeting all requirements. The criterion, based on matrix Y_4^{-1}, was that

$$1.32322 Y_{i1} + 0.92175 Y_{i2} + 0.00371 Y_{i3} + 0.41634 Y_{i4} < 1 \qquad (8)$$

for all feeds other than the four included in this matrix.

The sets of equations included in matrix Y could all have been solved by elementary means such as the well-known Doolittle method. However, the calculations would have been much more laborious and the criteria based on row-sums and column-sums could not have been introduced.

$$Y = \begin{array}{l} \text{milo} \\ \text{middlings} \\ \text{gluten} \\ \text{bran} \end{array} \overset{\begin{array}{cccc} \text{TDN} & \text{DP} & \text{Ca} & \text{Weight} \end{array}}{\begin{bmatrix} 0.495 & 0.275 & 0.098 & 0.459 \\ 0.436 & 0.449 & 0.264 & 0.410 \\ 0.395 & 0.557 & 1.319 & 0.385 \\ 0.423 & 0.436 & 0.467 & 0.467 \end{bmatrix}}$$

I proceed to invert Y by a method of "enlargement" based upon methods developed by Fraser, Duncan, and Collar.[10] Let Y_2 represent the submatrix formed by the first two rows and columns of Y, Y_3 the submatrix formed by the first three rows and columns, and Y_4 the whole matrix. We proceed to invert each successively, obtaining

$$Y_2^{-1} = \begin{bmatrix} 4.38669 & -2.68673 \\ -4.25968 & 4.83611 \end{bmatrix} \begin{array}{c} 1.69996 \\ 0.57643 \end{array}$$
$$\begin{array}{ccc} 0.12701 & 2.14936 & \text{Cost } \$2.27637 \end{array}$$

Incomplete (deficient in calcium and in weight), but feasible, necessary, and minimum cost.

$$Y_3^{-1} = \begin{bmatrix} 4.57474 & -3.16647 & 0.29388 \\ -4.83802 & 6.31152 & -0.90380 \\ 0.67305 & -1.71703 & 1.05181 \end{bmatrix} \begin{array}{c} 1.70215 \\ 0.56970 \\ 0.00783 \end{array}$$
$$\begin{array}{cccc} 0.40977 & 1.42802 & 0.44189 & \text{Cost } \$2.27968 \end{array}$$

Complete except for weight, feasible, necessary, and minimum cost.

$$Y_4^{-1} = \begin{bmatrix} 6.48494 & 5.15235 & 3.31116 & -13.62513 \\ -4.79815 & 6.48531 & -0.84076 & -0.28465 \\ 0.69368 & -1.62708 & 1.08443 & -0.14732 \\ -2.08615 & -9.09459 & -3.29866 & 14.89574 \end{bmatrix} \begin{array}{c} 1.32322 \\ 0.92175 \\ 0.00371 \\ 0.41634 \end{array}$$
$$\begin{array}{cccc} 0.29432 & 0.91599 & 0.25617 & 0.83864 \end{array}$$

Cost \$2.30512

Complete, feasible, necessary, and minimum cost.

Thus, buying at the Kansas City prices of 1949–50, and selecting from only the 10 quoted feeds, the least expensive combination meeting the four nutritive requirements of an 18 percent protein ration was \$0.40977 worth of milo maize, \$1.42802 worth of middlings, and \$0.44189 worth of gluten. And the least-cost combination supplying the nutritive requirements and weighing 100 pounds was \$0.29432 worth of milo maize, \$0.91599 worth of middlings, \$0.25617 worth of gluten, and \$0.83864 worth of bran.

---

[10] R. A. Fraser, W. S. Duncan, and A. R. Collar, *Elementary Matrices* (New York: Macmillan Co., 1947), pp. 112–18.

CONCLUDING REMARKS

Some of my friends in the Department of Agriculture are inclined to doubt the acceptability of the rations presented above. They point out that none of the four rations include any oilseeds, and that neither of the 24 percent protein rations includes any whole grain. As a matter of fact, I have computed the minimum-cost 18 percent protein ration, also, using prices of Kansas City and of Minneapolis for 1937–41, for 1946–49, for January 1951, and for April 1951. In no case do these rations include any oilseeds, and only two of the eight rations include any whole grain. It may well be that these rations are unacceptable. If so, the stated requirements are not adequate, and should be improved.

But if the stated requirements are approximately right, it would appear that the mill feeds are relatively underpriced, that the whole grains are somewhat overpriced, and that the oilseeds are greatly overpriced relative to the prices of other feeds.

Since this paper was written I have read the excellent paper by Christensen and Mighell[11] which discusses the minimum-cost combination of corn and soybean meal used as hog feed. Their analysis represents a very restricted form of linear programming. With the techniques explained in the present paper, it should be possible to extend their analysis to a number of feeds.[12]

---

[11] R. P. Christensen and R. L. Mighell, "Food Production Strategy and the Protein-Feed Balance," *Journal of Farm Economics*, Vol. 33 (May 1951), pp. 183–91.

[12] The method of linear programming can in principle be applied to a good many other problems in agricultural economics. An example of such a problem would be to determine the least-cost combination of feeds (and perhaps other resources) which would enable us to meet or exceed specified production goals for each major livestock product. This would require technical coefficients relating output of each class of livestock to inputs of each type of feed, and information on the market prices (and perhaps resource costs) of each feed. The practical value of such an analysis would depend on the accuracy of our estimates of input-output relationships on the national level. For any given set of such estimates, however, the method of linear programming should lead to a unique least-cost solution.

9 Economic Aspects of Broiler Production Density*†

WILLIAM R. HENRY AND JAMES A. SEAGRAVES‡

This paper explores a long-range planning problem of the broiler industry. Broiler processing costs decrease as plant size is increased, but costs of producing and delivering live birds go up as larger numbers are required at a central location. If a supply area is enlarged, longer hauls between broiler farms and the central location are necessary; if production density is increased in an existing supply area, labor costs for broiler growing may increase. What combination of central processing volume and surrounding production density will yield lowest total unit costs for processed broilers and thus put a supply area as a whole in the best possible competitive position?

The following procedure is used: First, relationships of selected transportation cost items to average one-way lengths of haul between farms and off-farm facilities are estimated; the items considered are chick delivery, feed delivery, visits by fieldmen, live-haul loading, live-haul trucking, and losses of marketable weight during the live haul. Second, the above transportation

---

* Journal of Farm Economics, Vol. XLII, No. 1 (February 1960), pp. 1–17.

† Contribution from the Department of Agricultural Economics, North Carolina Agricultural Experiment Station, Raleigh, North Carolina. Published with the approval of the Director of Research as Paper No. 1055 of the Journal Series. The paper is partially based upon research contributing to Southern Regional Cooperative Project SM-15 (Revised).

The authors are grateful for assistance received during preparation of this paper. Suggestions by J. C. Williamson, Jr., George Tolley, Norris T. Pritchard, A. P. Stemberger, and members of the SM-15 Technical Committee were especially helpful. J. C. Williamson, Jr., developed some theoretical aspects of supply area equilibria in a seminar paper, "Locational Differences in Size of Meat Packing Plants," at North Carolina State College, November 1957, . . . and is elaborating upon this topic in a paper in preparation. (Subsequently published as "The Equilibrium Size of Marketing Plants in a Spatial Market," *Journal of Farm Economics,* Vol. XLIV (November 1962), pp. 853–967.

‡ Both of the North Carolina State University, Raleigh, N.C.

costs are added to processing costs for various combinations of production density and processing volume, and least-cost combinations are derived. Third, substitution between additional outlays for transportation and higher payments for broiler-growing labor are examined, and trade practices that encourage development of optimum volume-density combinations are outlined. Finally, implications of scale-density relationships for the competitive positions of regions are pointed out, and a potential limitation upon maximum geographic production density is noted.

RELATIONSHIPS OF TRANSPORTATION COSTS TO AVERAGE LENGTHS OF HAUL—MANY TRANSPORTATION COSTS ARE LINEAR FUNCTIONS OF AVERAGE LENGTHS OF HAULS

Most of the transportation costs affected by production density are associated with trips from off-farm facilities to farms and back. Loads are carried one way and inter-farm travel is negligible. In such hauling, the unit cost of providing a particular service is composed of handling (loading and unloading), over-the-road travel (fuel and other regular servicing, wear depreciation and repair, and wages of traveling employees), and overhead (taxes, insurance, interest, storage, licenses, etc.).

If commercial volumes are involved, unit handling cost is a constant. Unit over-the-road cost varies directly with the average distance each unit must be hauled. Unit overhead cost depends upon the size of truck fleet required to handle a given volume; as average length of haul is increased, discrete additions must be made to the fleet.[1] If a constant over-the-road speed is maintained, additions to the fleet come at regular intervals as average length of haul is increased.

From the above considerations, the unit cost of providing a particular hauling service is approximately a linear function, with a positive constant term, of the average length of haul. The service of providing visits by fieldmen does not quite fit the pattern described above, but cost of this service is approximately a linear function of average length of haul to broiler farms.

AN ASSUMED CIRCULAR SUPPLY AREA IS CONVENIENT FOR BUDGETING TO ESTIMATE TRANSPORTATION COST FUNCTIONS

Unit transportation costs as functions of average lengths of haul are valid regardless of shapes of supply areas, distribution of production or specific locations of off-farm facilities. Also, where commercial volumes are involved,

---

[1] Variations from constant rates of production may also increase the size of truck fleet required to handle a given annual volume.

economies of size in the transportation services of interest may be disregarded. These two considerations allow an important simplification in estimating the cost functions. Any commercial level of output can be assumed for any hypothetical supply area, and the cost functions can then be estimated by budgeting associated activities as average length of haul is varied by changing production density.

The hypothetical supply area used by the authors is isolated and circular; it has all off-farm facilities of interest located at the center, and farm production of broilers is evenly distributed throughout the circle. The authors also assume a steady output rate within each of two seasons and near perfect coordination of all production and marketing activities.

Budgeting to minimize affected costs requires time and space factors for travel within the area. These factors can be easily determined because of the following geometric properties of the assumed supply area:

(1) The relationship among average length of haul, annual volume, and geographic production density is

$$A = \frac{2}{3}\sqrt{\frac{V}{\pi D}}$$

where A is the average length of haul in air miles, V is the annual volume in number of birds, and D is geographic density in birds per square mile per year.[2]

(2) The air distance between adjacent farms is the square root of the land area per broiler farm. This property is helpful in estimating costs of providing visits by fieldmen.

Estimates of production and marketing costs affected by changes in average length of haul are listed in Table 1. Cost levels are budgeted at 10-mile intervals for average lengths of haul varying from 10 to 70 miles. When costs of the separate items are summed across to get total cost for a particular average length of haul, there is an implicit assumption that hatchery, feed supply, live-hauling, and processing firms share a common central location. The costs presented in Table 1 are based on 1959 North Carolina data which are detailed in the notes to the table.

[2] Air distance of average length of haul is related to radius of the hypothetical supply area, R, such that $A = 2/3\ R$. Volume of business in the supply area is related to production density and area, such that

$$V = D\pi R^2 \text{ and } R = \sqrt{\frac{V}{\pi D}}$$

In empirical studies, air distance should be converted to road distance. In the vicinity of Robbins, North Carolina, the average road distance is $1.703 + 1.16A$, where A is air distance in miles. The above equation is a regression estimate based upon a 10 percent sample of all broiler farms in this supply area in June 1957.

TABLE 1
COSTS OF FEED DELIVERY, LIVE HAUL, WEIGHT LOSSES, CHICK DELIVERY, AND FIELDMEN AS FUNCTIONS OF AVERAGE LENGTH OF HAUL TO BROILER FARMS

	1	2	3	4	5	6	7	8
Average Length of Haul	*Feed Delivery*	*Live Haul: Truck*	*Live Haul: Labor*	*Live Haul: Weight Losses*	*Chick Delivery*	*Field-men*	*Total of Six Items*	*Cost of Added 10 Miles*
Miles	*Dollars per Hundredweight Live Broilers*							
10	.1064	.0713	.1749	.0176	.0121	.1134	.4957	—
20	.1485	.0897	.1927	.0352	.0157	.1170	.5988	.1031
30	.1984	.1169	.2105	.0528	.0193	.1205	.7184	.1196
40	.2507	.1353	.2283	.0704	.0229	.1241	.8317	.1133
50	.3005	.1625	.2461	.0880	.0265	.1496	.9732	.1415
60	.3528	.1897	.2639	.1056	.0340	.1531	1.0991	.1259
70	.4026	.2081	.2817	.1232	.0376	.1567	1.2099	.1108

NOTES ON BASIS OF ESTIMATES AND SOURCES OF DATA

The assumed operations are designed to supply live birds to a single-shift processing plant operated during early morning hours for 250 days annually, 8 hours per day. In 77 summer days the plant processes 4,290 birds per hour. During the remaining 173 work days the plant processes 4,526 birds per hour. During the year the firm handles 8,533,000 birds. A 48-hour week is assumed in chick and feed delivery. Truck overhead costs are based on minimum integral numbers required to do the work within the available time; cost estimates are conventional except that depreciation of transportation equipment is considered to be a function of mileage rather than time. Feed efficiency of 2.5 pounds to 1 pound of live weight and average live weight of 3.25 pounds are assumed.

Costs are based upon steady operation at designed capacity of the processing plant and near-perfect coordination of all activities of the integrated firm. Absolute levels of costs do not represent costs prevailing in the Southeast because the constant term is underestimated. However, the estimated increases in transportation costs with increases in average lengths of hauls should be in line with actual experiences of firms in the Southeast.

The following assumptions underlie the specific cost estimates:

Col. 1. Costs are based on 7-ton auger-unloading bulk feed trucks. Number of trucks required for the assumed firm ranges from 4 at the 10-mile average length of haul to 12 at the 70-mile average length of haul. (J. A. Seagraves, *Bulk Feed Handling Reduces Labor Costs,* A. E. Info. Ser. 68, Dept. of Agr. Econ., N. C. State Coll., November 1958).

Col. 2. Overhead costs are $2,410 per truck per year and variable costs are $0.1165 per mile (not including wages of driver). Overhead costs are based on minimum integral number of trucks required for summer hauling. Trucks are used for two loads per shift when this is possible. The number of trucks required for the assumed firm ranges from 6 at the 10-mile average length of haul to 9 at the 70-mile average length of haul. Ten truckloads of 264 coops each are hauled on each of 77 days in summer, and 8 truckloads of 304 coops each are hauled on each of 173 days for the remainder of the year. Average speed of live-haul trucks is 30 miles per hour. Costs do not include office overhead, communication costs, or salary income to the manager of the trucking firm.

Col. 3. Fourteen birds are hauled in each coop except for 77 summer days when 13 are put in each coop. Birds can be caught and loaded at the rate of 20 coops per man-hour with on-truck cooping and bulk weighing. (W. R. Henry, *On-Truck Crating Reduces Broiler Hauling Costs,* A. E. Info. Ser. 63, Dept. of Agr. Econ., N. C. State Coll., 1958.) Truck drivers are assumed to help with loading. Wage rates of $1.00 per hour for loading crew and $1.25 per hour for driver are assumed, and a crew foreman is paid $350 per month. The crew is paid while traveling to and from broiler farms. Crew travel is in 8-passenger station wagons owned by crew members who are paid 8 cents per mile. Average travel rate for crew is 30 miles per hour.

Col. 4. The cost of decreases in chilled eviscerated weight is approximately equal to the value of the pounds of live weight lost at the market price per pound for live birds. Costs are based on live price of 16 cents per pound and live weight losses at the rate of 0.34 percent per hour. Only "over-the-road" costs of weight losses are included. These costs are additions to the lowest weight-loss cost attainable with length of haul near zero. (W. R. Henry and Robert Raunikar, *Weight Losses of Broilers During the Live Haul,* A. E. Info. Ser. 69, Dept. of Agr. Econ., N. C. State Coll., December 1958).

Col. 5. Overhead costs are $1.062 per hatchery truck per year and variable costs are $0.1153 per mile (including wages of driver at 1.$50 per hour). Overhead costs are based on 2 trucks for 60- and 70-mile average hauls and 1 truck for shorter hauls. Truck capacity is 25,000 chicks; average load is 20,000 chicks. Loading and unloading are assumed to take 2 hours per load.

Col. 6. Fieldman costs are based on 196 farms evenly distributed in the supply area, weekly visits and record maintenance requiring 1 hour per farm, and average travel speed of 40 miles per hour. Automobiles are provided by fieldmen and they receive 5 cents per mile for travel. Costs are based on 5 fieldmen for 10- to 40-mile average hauls and 6 fieldmen for 50- to 70-mile hauls. Fieldmen are paid salaries of $500 per month.

COMBINATIONS OF TRANSPORTATION AND PROCESSING COSTS

The transportation costs of Table 1 could be combined with processing costs under many different assumptions about the locations of other off-farm facilities relative to the processing plant. In this paper, costs are combined under the assumption that all off-farm facilities doing business with a particular processing plant are located at or near this plant. Combined costs apply to the output of a single plant and are not affected if the other off-farm facilities of interest also service other plants.

"EFFECTIVE" PRODUCTION DENSITY MEASURES DENSITY FROM THE POINT OF VIEW OF A PARTICULAR FIRM

This paper deals with production density in terms of its effect upon unit costs for the outputs of particular firms. Any particular firm may have to share business in the surrounding trade area with competitors offering the same services. Thus, the "effective" production density from the point of view of a particular firm may be much smaller than the geographic production density of its supply area.

The authors propose to define effective production density by reference to the assumed supply area used in estimating transportation cost functions. Suppose the average length of haul and the volume of business are known for a particular firm. There is some hypothetical production density for the reference area that would result in the same average length of haul for the same volume of business. This hypothetical density is the effective density in the trade area of the firm in question. Specifically,

$$D' = \frac{4V}{9\pi A^2}$$

where D' is effective density in birds per square mile per year, A is the average length of haul in air miles, and V is the annual volume of business in number of birds.

Effective production density, as defined above, has three desirable characteristics. First, the two dimensions of average length of haul and volume of business are readily measurable. Second, average length of haul is also an axis for the transportation cost functions of interest. Finally, effective production density can be used for inter-firm and inter-area comparisons without specifying shapes of supply areas, specific locations of off-farm facilities, distributions of production, or trade-sharing in supply areas.[3]

[3] Average length of haul is often used by businessmen in the broiler industry for inter-firm and inter-area comparisons of production density. Effective density is a better index for such comparisons than average length of haul used alone.

OPTIMUM SIZES OF PROCESSING PLANTS ARE RELATED TO EFFECTIVE PRODUCTION DENSITIES OF THEIR SUPPLY AREAS

Several studies have shown that unit processing costs fall as plant size is increased if plants of various sizes are steadily operated at their designed rates of output.[4] For this paper, cost of processing in model plants of various sizes in New England, as estimated by Rogers and Bardwell, are adjusted to correspond with Southern conditions.[5] A curve is drawn through the adjusted costs to smooth a discontinuity at the 1,200-bird-per-hour capacity and to allow interpolation of estimated costs. The resulting relationship of adjusted costs to plant size is shown in Table 2.

TABLE 2
ESTIMATED COSTS OF PROCESSING BROILERS IN PLANTS OF VARIOUS SIZES, BASED ON 1959 SOUTHERN CONDITIONS

Plant Size, Birds per Hour	600	1,200	1,800	2,400	3,600	4,800	7,200	9,600
Processing costs, dollars per 100 live pounds	3.69	3.41	3.21	3.10	2.90	2.79	2.67	2.62

Since transportation costs are combined here under the assumption that other off-farm facilities are located at or near the processing plant, the transportation costs are taken from the "total" column of Table 1 and are approximated as a linear function passing through the costs at the 10-mile and 70-mile length of haul. This function is

$$C = \$0.3769 + \$0.0119\, M$$

where C is cost per 100 pounds of live weight, and M is the average length of haul in miles of road distance.

Processing costs per unit for plants of various sizes are depicted by the middle curve of Figure 1. Transportation costs per unit for an area with an effective density of 500 birds per square mile are shown by the lower curve, and the corresponding average lengths of haul are posted at intervals along

[4] E. L. Baum, J. E. Faris, and H. G. Walkup, *Economies of Scale in the Operation of Fryer Processing Plants,* Tech. Bull. No. 7, Wash. Agr. Expt. Sta., August 1952; J. R. Donald and C. E. Bishop, *Broiler Processing Costs,* A. E. Info. Ser. 59, Dept. of Agr. Econ., N. C. State College, June 1957; G. B. Rogers and E. T. Bardwell, *Economies of Scale in Chicken Processing,* Bull. 459, N. H. Agr. Expt. Sta., April 1959.

[5] Plant wages were reduced to correspond to an hourly rate of $1.10 instead of $1.30, management costs were reduced by 20 percent, and total costs were adjusted upward to allow processing of 3.25-pound birds instead of the 3.5-pound average assumed for the New England study. Processing technology, plant organization for various capacities, and prices of nonhuman factors are essentially identical throughout the nation. The adjustments described above account for practically all of the differences in processing costs between the two regions.

this curve. The processing cost curve and the transportation cost curve are simply added together to obtain the upper "total" curve. Total cost per unit reaches its lowest point at a plant capacity of 4,800 birds per hour.

FIGURE 1
SELECTED TRANSPORT COSTS, PROCESSING COSTS AND COMBINED COSTS, FOR EFFECTIVE PRODUCTION DENSITY OF 500 BIRDS PER SQUARE MILE PER YEAR, AVERAGE LENGTHS OF HAUL, IN MILES, POSTED ALONG TRANSPORT COST CURVE

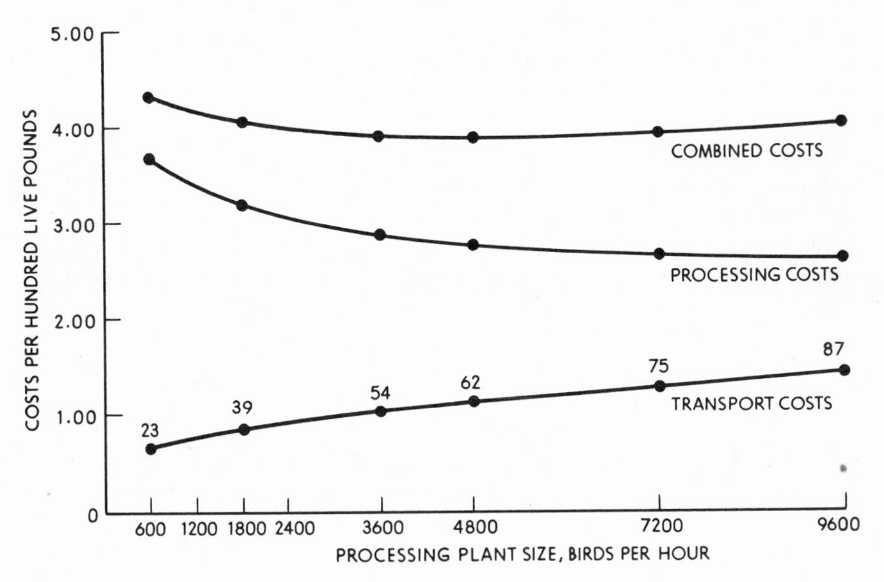

Total processing and transportation costs for six levels of effective density are shown in Figure 2. In computing each curve, effective production density is held constant at a selected level and average length of haul is increased as plant size is increased. The air distance to road distance relationship of the Piedmont broiler area of North Carolina is used in computing transportation costs.[6]

Relatively shallow planning curves of Figure 2 mean that, with constant effective density, there is little difference in total unit costs for a wide range of processing plant sizes. For example, with effective density at 250 birds per square mile lowest total unit costs are $4.18 for a 3,600-bird-per-hour plant, while the range from 1,800 to 4,800 birds per hour does not have total unit costs in excess of $4.23. Selected coordinates of planning curves for supply areas having various production densities are listed in Table 3. Boldface type identifies costs for plants of optimum size. In each case, plant sizes can be increased or decreased from optimum with little effect upon total unit costs.

[6] The methods used to construct the planning curves of Figure 2 could be used with other sets of factor costs for other regions, with alternative assumptions about operating practices, and with economies of scale of integrated hatchery and feed mill incorporated.

TABLE 3

TOTALS OF PROCESSING AND TRANSPORTATION COSTS FOR COMMONLY LOCATED BROILER PRODUCTION AND MARKETING FACILITIES IN SUPPLY AREAS HAVING VARIOUS PRODUCTION DENSITIES

Effective Production Density in Birds per Square Mile per Year	*Design Capacity, Birds per Hour, 2,000 Hours Annually*							
	600	1,200	1,800	2,400	3,600	4,800	7,200	9,600
			Dollars per Hundred Live Pounds					
250	4.45	4.32	4.23	4.22	4.18	4.21	4.32	4.46
500	4.35	4.17	4.05	4.01	3.92	3.91	3.95	4.04
1,000	4.27	4.06	3.92	3.86	3.74	3.70	3.69	3.74
2,000	4.21	3.99	3.83	3.75	3.61	3.55	3.51	3.53
4,000	4.18	3.93	3.76	3.68	3.50	3.44	3.38	3.38
8,000	4.15	3.90	3.72	3.62	3.45	3.37	3.29	3.27
16,000	4.13	3.87	3.69	3.59	3.41	3.31	3.22	3.20
32,000	4.12	3.85	3.66	3.56	3.38	3.28	3.18	3.14

FIGURE 2

RELATIONSHIP OF PROCESSING PLANT SIZE TO COMBINED COSTS OF TRANSPORTATION AND PROCESSING FOR DIFFERENT EFFECTIVE PRODUCTION DENSITIES

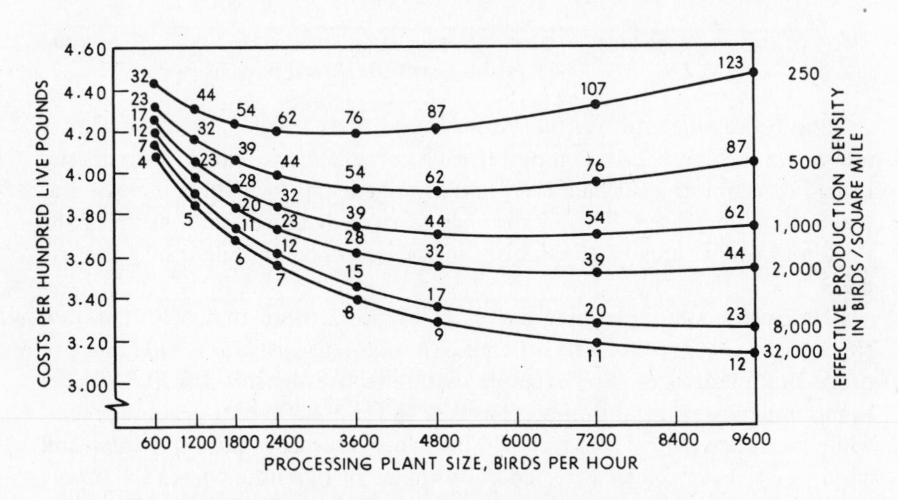

SUBSTITUTION BETWEEN ADDED OUTLAYS FOR TRANSPORTATION AND HIGHER PAYMENTS FOR BROILER GROWING

If production density is increased, internal economies of larger processing plants can be combined with external economies of greater production density to yield substantial reductions in total processing and transportation costs.

Figure 3 shows interrelationships of optimum plant size, effective production density, and total costs. Coordinates of the curve in Figure 3 are the least-cost combinations from Table 3. Minimum total unit costs decrease from $4.18 at an effective density of 250 birds per square mile per year to $3.20 at an effective density of 16,000 birds per square mile per year. This 98-cent saving per hundred live pounds is due to economies of size in processing (28 cents) and reduced transportation costs (70 cents).

FIGURE 3

COMBINED ECONOMIES OF SCALE AND PRODUCTION DENSITY. PROCESSING PLANT CAPACITIES, IN BIRDS PER HOUR, POSTED ALONG CURVE

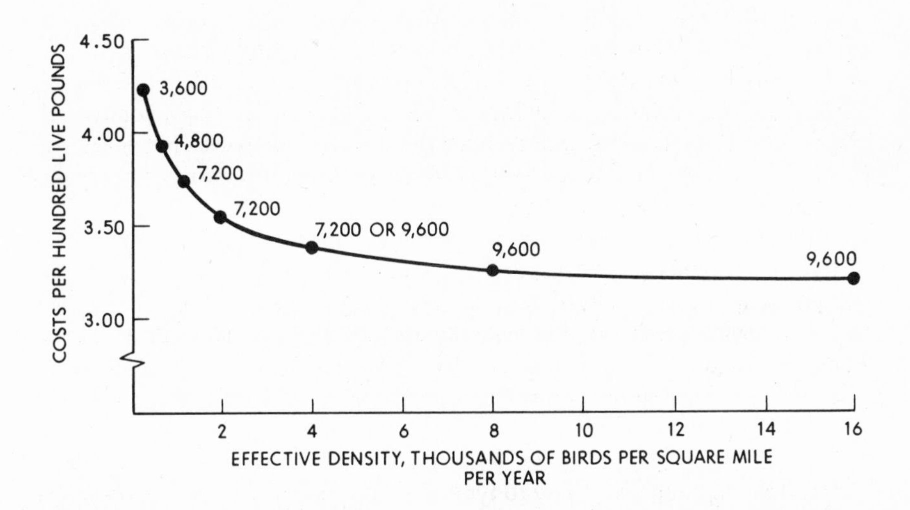

The curve in Figure 3 is based on an assumption that production density can be increased without raising production cost. While this assumption may be realistic in the long run for some supply areas, higher payments for broiler growing would be necessary in many others to get increased density.

OPTIMUM PRODUCTION DENSITY DEPENDS UPON THE SUPPLY CURVE FOR BROILER GROWING LABOR

Costs of obtaining increased production density are mainly increases in labor returns to broiler growers to bid labor away from alternative employments. Payments to growers who own their housing and equipment must, over the long run, cover the costs of these inputs, but these costs are not dependent upon location of these facilities (except for increases in site values near urban centers, which are not important in the context of this paper). Other inputs used in broiler growing (chicks, feed, brooding fuel, health aids, etc.) are provided from off-farm sources. Their supply prices at the center of operations do not depend upon locations of growers. Therefore, if there is a rise in unit production cost as production density is increased, it is derived from the supply curve for labor for broiler growing.[7]

If a given volume is to be produced in a particular supply area, the optimum production density of this area depends upon its least-cost combination of transportation costs that decrease and labor costs that increase as production density is increased. Optimum combinations of this type cannot be determined without precise information about supply curves for broiler-growing labor. However, information that may be useful in making adjustments toward optimum density can be developed.

Suppose annual volume of production is to be increased by a processing plant and the firms supplying live birds to it. Which is the better strategy—an expansion of the supply area with density constant or an increase in production density with average length of haul constant? The increase in production density will be preferred if savings in transportation cost, by avoiding increased length of haul, is greater than the increase in grower labor returns that will produce the necessary increase in production density. Otherwise, enlarging the supply area will be preferred.

Assume a circular supply area, centrally located facilities, and evenly distributed production. Transportation costs increase $0.0119 per hundred live pounds for every mile added to average length of haul. Labor inputs for broiler growing are about one half minute per 3.25 pound bird, or 0.2566 hours per hundred live pounds. A saving of one mile in the average length of haul would cover the cost of a wage increase of $0.0119/0.2566, or $0.0464 per hour.

Now, note two characteristics that apply exactly to the assumed broiler supply area and approximately to typical operating conditions: (a) if average length of haul is held constant, any percentage increase in volume must be accompanied by an equal percentage increase in production density; (b) any increase in average length of haul resulting from holding density constant as volume increases is determined by the percentage increase in volume and the average length of haul before the increase.[8]

---

[7] Three other factors that might set limits to production density were considered: (1) In the short run, capital for construction of new broiler housing may be limiting, but broiler businessmen who are interested in maximizing profits over the long run can overcome this limitation; (2) Increased likelihood of disease spreading from house to house in broiler areas could discourage increases in production density, but contagion-reducing practices that should be used even when production is widely scattered would eliminate this limitation; (3) A possible reduction in value of broiler litter for crop fertilization as broiler growing becomes more centralized was discussed in the original version of this paper.

[8] Starting with

$$D' = \frac{4V}{9\pi A^2}$$

as defined above, to increase V to bV while D' remains constant, A^2 must be increased to bA^2; i.e., A must be increased to $A\sqrt{b}$, or by an amount $\triangle A = A(\sqrt{b} - 1)$. If road mileage, R, were proportional to air mileage, A, then R would increase by the corresponding

Based upon the conditions of the two paragraphs above, Figure 4 shows equally costly increases in hourly grower labor returns and increases in average lengths of haul when annual volume is to be increased by various percentages with various initial values for average lengths of haul.

FIGURE 4

COMPARISONS OF INCREASES IN HOURLY GROWER WAGES WITH EQUALLY COSTLY ALTERNATIVE INCREASES IN AVERAGE LENGTH OF HAUL WHEN BROILER SERVICING AND PROCESSING VOLUME IS TO BE INCREASED BY VARIOUS PERCENTAGES

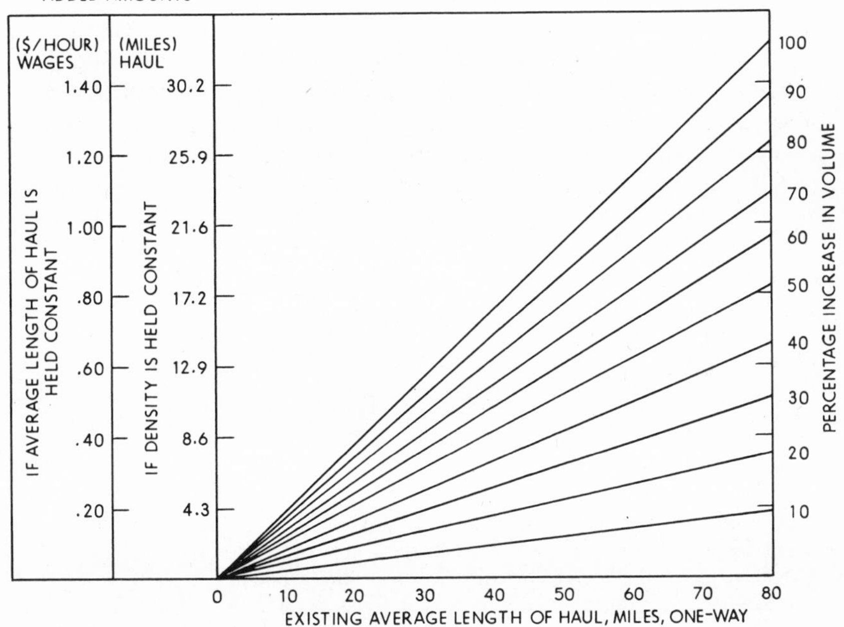

In order to use Figure 4, choose one of the slanting lines corresponding to the percentage increase in volume—for example, a 100 percent increase. Next, draw a vertical line from the present average length of haul to an intersection with the slanting line—for example, from the 50-mile length of haul. Project a horizontal line from the intersection to the scales on the left margin and read the two values found there—in the example, 20.7 and $0.96. Hourly

amount $\triangle R = R(\sqrt{b} - 1)$. Where R is a linear function of A containing a constant term, however, this relationship is only approximate. In our case, $R = 1.703 + 1.16A$; i.e. $(R - 1.703) = 1.16A$. The corrected increase in road mileage is therefore

$$\triangle R = (R - 1.703)(\sqrt{b} - 1)$$

Therefore the increase in road mileage, $\triangle R$, is a linear function of the original mileage, R, with a small negative constant term.

grower labor returns could be increased by as much as \$0.96 without exceeding the alternative increase in unit transportation cost as average length of haul is increased by 20.7 miles. If the required 100 percent increase in production density can be achieved with a smaller increase in hourly grower labor return, it is the better choice of the two alternatives. In many cases, increases in density would be more profitable than increases in sizes of supply areas.

Even if no increase in volume is anticipated, a broiler production and marketing organization may be able to reduce total costs by increasing production density near the operating center. Average length of haul is reduced approximately in proportion to the square root of the increase in geographic density of production coming to the plant. If production density is doubled, average length of haul is reduced to approximately $\sqrt{\frac{1}{2}}$, or 0.707, times its former length. With density quadrupled, average length of haul is approximately $\sqrt{\frac{1}{4}}$, or 0.5, times its former length.

TRADE PRACTICES MAY NEED CHANGING IF BROILER AREAS ARE TO TAKE ADVANTAGE OF ECONOMIES OF DENSITY

An integrated production and marketing organization stands to capture all savings resulting from decreased average length of haul. If such an organization grows broilers in its own housing with hired labor, it can locate broiler housing and equipment close to the operating center. No institutional factors restrict exploitation of economies of density.

However, an obstacle may exist where an integrated broiler producing and processing firm offers typical contracts for broiler growing in grower-owned housing. An ordinary "incentive" contract provides no greater incentive to nearby than to distant growers. Such a firm might find it highly profitable to establish contracts with mileage differentials that would partially reflect out-haul and in-haul costs associated with mileage. The average level of payment for broiler growing might be kept unchanged. Over time, the mileage differentials might be adjusted to give nearby growers the full amounts of savings in transportation costs. Gradual adjustment of the mileage differential would provide time for nearby growers to increase their capacities and for remote growers to depreciate buildings and equipment. As the effective density of the supply area increased, the integrated firm would benefit because the average cost per pound to obtain the desired volume would be gradually lowered. Such a mileage differential should be built into contracts in such a way that other variable payment provisions, such as incentives for efficient feed conversion, would not be affected.[9]

---

[9] Differentials based on zoning might be more practical than differentials based on mileage. They would lead to similar ultimate results: Increased production density, shorter hauls, and lower total production costs.

Obstacles are more difficult to overcome where hatchery, feed supply, broiler growing, live-haul, and processing firms are related by contracts, informal agreements, or open market trading. Each firm stands to gain to some extent if production density is increased, but none can capture all the gains. In any event, these gains come about only if nearby growers are given incentives to increase production. In this type of producing and marketing organization, consideration should be given to the following arrangements: (1) use by the hatchery of mileage charges in pricing baby chicks; (2) use by haulers of mileage charges in rates for live hauling; (3) use by feed dealers of mileage differential contracts with growers; (4) payments by processors for live birds on a delivered and plant-weight basis. Such arrangements would accumulate savings from nearby growing in returns to feed dealers. The feed dealers could then reflect these savings in contracts with growers. Over time, the supply areas would become more compact, hourly grower-labor returns would increase, and total costs per pound of processed broilers would decrease.

COMPARISON OF REGIONAL OPPORTUNITIES TO REDUCE COSTS BY INCREASING EFFECTIVE DENSITIES

Geographic production densities vary widely when specialized broiler-producing regions are compared. Areas with greatest geographic densities are generally believed to have resulting competitive advantages. However, it is effective production densities affecting unit costs building up at particular processing plants, not geographic production densities of regions, that should be compared.

EFFECTIVE PRODUCTION DENSITIES ARE NOT CLOSELY CORRELATED WITH GEOGRAPHIC DENSITIES

The authors queried selected broiler processors by mail during April 1959. Each processor was asked to provide his weekly rate of processing, in number of broilers, and the average length of live hauls in the week prior to receipt of the questionnaire. From this information the effective production density in the supply area of each plant was estimated. Results of the survey are shown in Table 4.

The long hauls of the North Carolina Piedmont stand in sharp contrast to those of the other four regions. Average total cost of live hauling (truck, labor, and weight losses) is estimated to be about one eighth cent per pound higher in Central North Carolina than in the other regions. For this comparison, labor wages, truck costs, and broiler prices are standardized at North Carolina levels.

In the four regions having greater production densities than North Carolina, effective densities range from 3,000 to 4,500 birds per square mile per year.

TABLE 4
ESTIMATES OF EFFECTIVE BROILER PRODUCTION DENSITIES IN THE SUPPLY AREAS OF PROCESSING PLANTS, APRIL 1959, AND A COMPARISON WITH GEOGRAPHIC DENSITIES FOR ESTIMATED 1958 PRODUCTION

Region	Number of Plants Providing Data	Average Length of Live Haul, Mean for Region (Miles)	Effective Density Birds/Sq. Mile/Yr.		Geographic Density Birds/Sq. Mile/Yr.[b]
			Range	Mean[a]	
Maine	4	27.5	2,143–5,270	3,695	3,971
Delmarva	5	23.5	2,380–6,120	4,515	51,874
Central North Carolina	12	47.2	151–8,143	1,382	11,994
North Georgia	4	28.8	1,719–4,619	2,984	38,565
N. W. Arkansas	5	28.0	491–8,360	4,141	22,568

[a] The weighted average for those plants providing data.
[b] Based on estimated 1958 production and the following counties and square miles for each region:
Maine: Kennebec, Knox, Penobscot, Somerset, Waldo, 9,317 sq. miles.
Delmarva: Kent and Sussex in Deleware, Caroline, Talbot, Wicomico, Somerset and Worcester in Maryland, 3,335 sq. miles.
Central North Carolina: Chatham, Moore, Montgomery, Randolph, 2,668 sq. miles.
North Georgia: Banks, Barrow, Cherokee, Cobb, Dawson, Forsyth, Fulton, Gilmer, Habersham, Hart, Hall, Jackson, Lumpkin, Stephens, White, Aiken (S.C.), 4,823 sq. miles.
N. W. Arkansas: Benton, Carroll, Madison, Washington, McDonald (Mo.), 3,855 sq. miles.

Compared among themselves, none of the four regions appears to have a significant competitive advantage in effective density. It may be noted that there are wide variations in effective densities within these regions, and that all could have substantial reductions in transportation costs if effective density were increased to levels approaching 16,000 birds per square mile per year. Efforts to increase effective densities are expected to be accelerated in all regions as the potential gains are appraised by individual firms.

Geographic densities, birds per square mile per year, are listed in the final column of Table 4. Effective density refers to the density for each processing firm while geographic density is based on the combined production of all firms in the area. Geographic densities also would be larger than effective densities if the road pattern and the broiler growing did not cover the entire geographic area. One of the main conclusions of this paper is that the effective production density for each firm is a more useful concept than geographic density in applied studies of this type. Effective density is also very simple to calculate and it requires only knowledge of the volume and average length of haul for each firm.

If the use of the broiler litter by-product is limited to fertilization of nearby cropland then the amount of cropland eventually could become a limiting factor on production density. This possibility was considered in the original version of this paper. Potential density was calculated using the assumption that the litter from 1,000 broilers would profitably be used on no more than one acre of nearby cropland each year. Potential densities were compared with geographic densities for 11 broiler producing regions. Geographic density in 1954 was less than half of this potential density in North Georgia, less than one fourth for Delmarva, but, generally speaking, the results indicated that broiler litter was being used on only about one eighth of the available cropland.

CONCLUSIONS

Economic aspects of broiler production density were investigated by generating costs for assumed operations of varying size and areas of varying production density. Input-output coefficients and factor prices are fairly typical of conditions in the southeastern United States. The conclusions of this investigation are as follows:

1. Costs of transporting feed, chicks, and production supervisors to broiler farms and hauling live birds to processing plants are estimated to increase at a rate of 1.19 cents per 100 pounds of live broilers for each mile added to average length of haul. Substantial reductions in total costs may be possible if production density is increased and the average length of haul for a given scale of operations is reduced.
2. The optimum sizes for processing plants are related to production densities of supply areas. However, combined transportation and processing costs are not much changed when plant sizes are varied from the optimum (Table 3).
3. Although labor costs for broiler growing may increase with production density, the advantages of greater concentration of broiler growing are sufficiently large that progressive firms can be expected to encourage greater concentration in the future. Present pricing schemes are a hindrance to this concentration under most arrangements involving contract growing.
4. Effective production density, based on the volume of production for each firm and its average length of haul, is a useful conceptual device when one wants to include transportation costs in either budgeting or survey studies of economics of size.

Further investigations are needed to evaluate potential economies of centralized broiler growing in factory-type operations. Possibilities for improved techniques of feed and bird transport and for uses of broiler litter other than in crop fertilization might be given special attention. In addition, careful studies of economies of scale in chick hatching and feed milling are needed.

10 Some Considerations in Estimating Assembly Cost Functions for Agricultural Processing Operations*[1]

BEN C. FRENCH†[2]

Supplies of raw products required to increase the output of agricultural processing plants normally must be secured over widening supply areas or by raising prices to nearby farmers to obtain additional production.[3] In either case, procurement costs increase with plant volume and must be considered along with internal plant costs, and sometimes distribution costs, in evaluating the efficiency of alternative plant size, product volume, location, and industry organization. Raw products are commonly assembled with a variety of transportation and handling methods, from scattered locations and from diverse owners. Each assembly job is unique to a particular situation, and each situation or location involves a different relation between plant volume and assembly cost. This greatly complicates the derivation of useful relationships that may form the basis for practical generalizations or comparisons.

Various aspects of these complexities have been recognized for many years and have been incorporated in a number of empirical studies. Examples of pioneering work in this area may be found in the early Connecticut

---

* *Journal of Farm Economics,* Vol. XLII, No. 4 (November, 1960), pp. 767–78.

† University of California, Davis, California.

[1] Giannini Foundation Paper 196.

[2] I am indebted to R. G. Bressler, G. A. King, L. L. Sammet and J. F. Stollsteimer for helpful comments on the paper.

[3] While both methods of increasing supply may ultimately require consideration, the present discussion is confined to the broadening of supply areas. For an interesting study of increasing production density versus expanding the supply area see William R. Henry and James A. Seagraves, "Economic Aspects of Broiler Production Density," *Journal of Farm Economics,* February, 1960.

efficiency studies under the leadership of R. G. Bressler.[4] More recently, papers by Olsen, Henry and Seagraves, and a report by the author have provided further development and analysis of relations among average length of haul, plant volume, production density and marginal and average assembly cost.[5]

The purpose of this paper is to enlarge on the theoretical framework evolved in these studies. Consideration is given to the general relation between assembly cost and plant volume, to a special case involving a square grid system of roads as is typical of much of the central United States, to multiple products, and to the problem of selecting efficient assembly technique and estimating long-run assembly cost functions.

THE SUPPLY PLANE

Visualize a processing plant located at the origin of a set of coordinates, as indicated in Figure 1. The area around the plant is the supply plane and each point in the plane may be identified by the value of its rectangular coordinates (x, y) or its polar coordinates (r, θ). Actual road distance to any point will bear some approximate relation to r.

The plane itself might be visualized as being dotted with islands rising to different heights. The heights measure density of production and the volume of each island represents the supply of product available within the area covered by the island. Density may vary with distance, with time (seasonally, annually, secularly) and with product prices. Effective density (supply actually available to the processing plant) will also depend on the activities of competing firms. Distance to the processing plant is measured from some central point or points within each island.

If the distribution and volume of each island of production is known it is a simple task to compute the total supply encompassed within any radius of the plant and the total travel distance involved.[6] Except in the

---

[4] See especially, R. G. Bressler, Jr. and D. O. Hammerberg, *Efficiency of Milk Marketing in Connecticut, 3. Economics of the Assembly of Milk*, Storrs Agr. Expt. Sta. Bul. 239, 1942. Other studies in this group pertaining to assembly costs include: D. O. Hammerberg and W. G. Sullivan, *Efficiency of Milk Marketing in Connecticut, 2. The Transportation of Milk*, Storrs Agr. Expt. Sta. Bul. 238, 1942 and W. J. Hansen and R. G. Bressler, Jr., *Efficiency of the Transportation of Eggs to Connecticut Cooperative Associations*, Storrs Agr. Expt. Sta. Bul. 241, 1942.

[5] Fred L. Olsen, "Location Theory as Applied to Milk Processing Plants," *Journal of Farm Economics*, December 1959, pp. 1546–55. William R. Henry and James A. Seagraves, *op. cit.* B. C. French and D. G. Gillette, *Cost of Assembling and Packing Apples as Related to Scale of Operation*, Mich. Agr. Expt. Sta. Tech. Bul. 272, 1959.

[6] If density varies throughout the area and if a series of stops is required to complete a load a plant may find it most economical to expand transport distance more in the dense areas than in the sparse areas of the supply plane. This then involves iso-cost zones which ordinarily would not be perfect circles. However, circular zones are appropriate for assembly operations involving a single stop to pick up a load (or a series of stops within small, roughly uniform areas such as orchards). In some cases involving several stops per load, the plant may have only limited practical control over the direction of route expansion and the use of circular areas may simplify the approach.

FIGURE 1
CONCEPTUAL VIEW OF A CIRCULAR PLANT SUPPLY PLANE

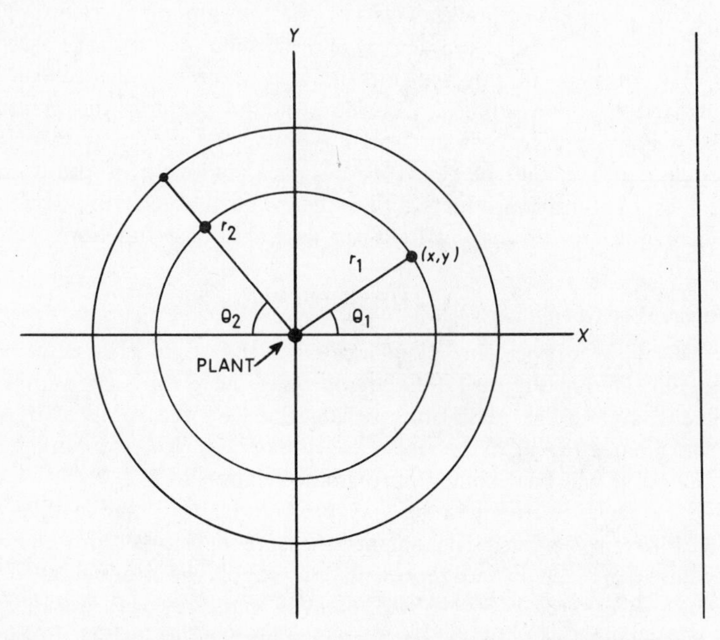

unrealistic case where the islands of production run together to form a continuous production surface, the relation between supply and radius will be discontinuous. If the gaps between islands are not too large, however, a continuous approximation may provide a good indication of the underlying form of the relationship and also serve as a useful and convenient basis for further generalization.

Let $P = g(r, \theta)$ be a function giving the density of production at any point in the supply plane. Total supply (S) within any radius of the plant is found by summing the supplies for all points within the circular area defined. That is,

$$S = \int_0^{2\pi} \int_0^r g\,(r, \theta)\; r dr d\theta. \tag{1}$$

With uniform density $g(r, \theta) = P_0$ and

$$S = P_0 \pi r^2. \tag{2}$$

In this case total supply is simply the area of the supply plane multiplied by the density. Because of difficulties in finding the specific nature of the functions describing distributions of density, use of average density is commonly the only practical approach. Replacing P_0 by $\bar{P}$, the average density of all islands of production in the supply plane, gives a continuous approximation to the actual relation between supply and radius.

RELATION OF ASSEMBLY COST TO PLANT VOLUME

The total cost of transporting the required supplies of a single product from any supply point to a processing or packing plant depends on the equipment used, the labor used with each piece of transport equipment, the work methods employed by the labor, the distance from the supply point (or route distance) to the plant, the speed of travel, the prices of inputs, the total volume of product handled per trip and per season, waiting time at the plant or in the field, and minor environmental factors that may vary from time to time.[7]

Since changes in speed and volume per trip involve intensification on fixed factors there is no reason to expect the relationship among these variables to be linear. With most pieces of equipment, however, a linear function may be an acceptable simplification. The load capacity is often rather strictly limited by the construction of the equipment, and this limit may become effective before costs are increasing at an increasing rate. Moreover, volume per trip typically remains constant at or near some capacity level. Vehicle speeds are commonly restricted by road conditions and legal requirements, and the increasing-cost aspects associated with speed may reasonably and conveniently be averaged.

With these simplifications and with given hauling methods and input prices the *variable cost per unit of commodity* can be represented by (1) a constant part, b_0, associated with loading, unloading, and average waiting time and (2) a constant cost per unit of volume per unit of distance traveled, b_1, which includes costs of labor, gasoline, maintenance, etc.[8] For a single supply source the *total* variable cost of hauling any given volume, S, is

$$C = S(b_0 + b_1 D) = S(b_0 + b_1 wr) \tag{3}$$

where D is road distance, and w is a factor approximately converting air

[7] There is no essential difference between transportation from a single point and a series of points such as an egg pick-up route, providing the same stops are made each trip. Most of the discussion that follows will be in terms of a single pick-up of a load or a series of stops within a small area such as an orchard, but extension to routes is not difficult, given the route organization. The interesting problem of how to arrange pick-up points into efficient routes is beyond the scope of this paper.

[8] For examples of such assembly cost functions see: George G. Judge and Ralph L. Baker, "Time and Cost Functions for Egg Routes," *Poultry Science*, July 1952, pp. 738–44. L. L. Sammet, *Efficiency in Fruit Marketing—Orchard to Plant Transportation*, Calif. Agr. Expt. Sta. Giannini Found. Agr. Econ. Mimeo. Rept. 131, 1952. E. L. Baum and D. E. Pauls, *A Comparative Analysis of Costs of Farm Collection of Milk by Can and Tank in Western Washington, 1952*, Wash. Agr. Expt. Sta. Tech. Bul. No. 10, 1953; Earl W. Carlsen, Lloyd Hunter, Raoul S. Duerden and G. F. Sainsbury, *Methods and Costs of Loading Apples in the Pacific Northwest*, U.S. Dept. Agr., Mktg. Res. Rept. No. 55, 1954; Paul L. Kelley, *Cost Functions of Bulk Milk Assembly in the Wichita Market*, Kan. Agr. Expt. Sta. Tech. Bul. 96, 1958; Robert H. Reed, *Economic Efficiency in Assembly and Processing Lima Beans for Freezing*, Calif. Agr. Expt. Sta. Giannini Found. Agr. Econ. Mimeo. Rept. No. 219, 1959; B. C. French and D. G. Gillette, *op. cit.*

distance to road distance. If the entire supply available at the supply source is hauled to the plant, total supply is, of course, identical with density of that point.

With several discrete supply sources the total variable cost per season is a sum of the cost from each distance, weighted by the volume transported from that distance. That is,

$$C = \sum_{i=1}^{n} (b_0 S_i + b_1 S_i D_i) = b_0 S + b_1 \sum_{i=1}^{n} P_i w r_i. \tag{4}$$

where *S, D, P, w* and *r* are defined as above and *i* refers to a particular source within the supply plane. The relation between assembly cost and plant volume is determined by cumulating supply and cost for the most distant source or sources in relation to increasing radius of the circular supply area.

If supply sources are continuously distributed, or can be so regarded for purposes of approximation, the summation of costs at the margin is replaced by the integral of such costs. With constant density the total variable cost of assembly is

$$C = b_0 S + \int_0^{2\pi} \int_0^{r} b_1 P_0 w r^2 dr d\theta \tag{5}$$

$$= b_0 S + \frac{2}{3} b_1 P_0 \pi w r^3.$$

Since, from equation (2),

$$r = \frac{S^{1/2}}{\pi^{1/2} P_0{}^{1/2}}$$

assembly cost may be expressed directly as a function of plant volume. Substituting in (5) gives

$$C = S\left(b_0 + \frac{2}{3} b_1 w \frac{S^{1/2}}{P_0{}^{1/2} \pi^{1/2}}\right). \tag{6}$$

The terms within the parentheses give the variable cost per unit of product, which increases with volume, but at a decreasing rate.

Total variable cost can also be expressed as

$$C = S(b_0 + b_1 \bar{D}) \tag{7}$$

where $\bar{D}$ is the average length of haul. It follows from equation (6) that

$$\bar{D} = \frac{2}{3} w \frac{S^{1/2}}{P_0{}^{1/2} \pi^{1/2}} = \frac{2}{3} wr. \tag{8}$$

Again, P_0 may be replaced by $\bar{P}$, the average density, to obtain a continuous approximation to the actual relation between assembly cost and plant volume.

In much of the central part of the United States country roads follow along section lines, presenting a square grid system of roads. In this case, the least costly area to haul from is not a circle but a square tilted 45° to the road net, as illustrated in Figure 2.

FIGURE 2
BEST SUPPLY AREA FOR A SQUARE GRID SYSTEM OF ROADS

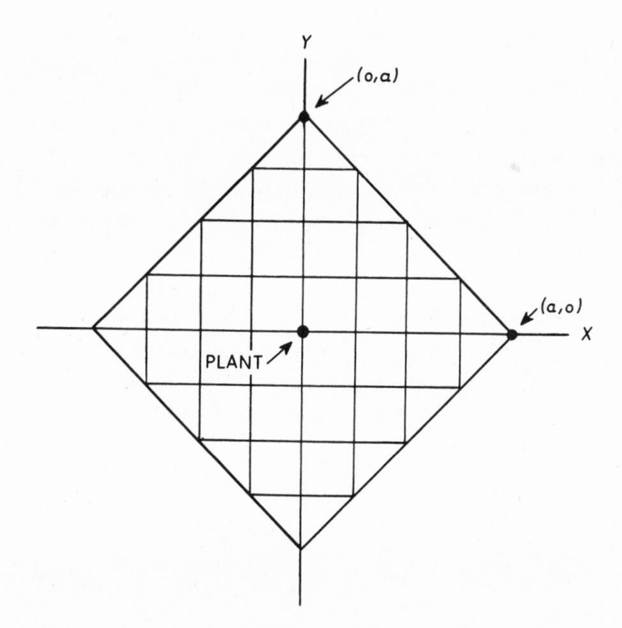

With this system the road distance to any supply point is simply $x + y$, where x and y are the rectangular coordinates of the point. If density is uniform throughout the supply plane the average travel distance for a square area with a diagonal distance of $2a$ is

$$\bar{D} = \frac{4}{\text{area}} \int_0^a \int_0^{a-x} (x + y)dydx \tag{9}$$

$$= \frac{4}{2a^2} \left(\frac{a^3}{3}\right) = \frac{2}{3}a.$$

Total supply in relation to a is

$$S = 2P_0 a^2 \tag{10}$$

and

$$\bar{D} = \frac{2}{3}\,\frac{S^{1/2}}{2^{1/2}P_0{}^{1/2}} = .4714\frac{S^{1/2}}{P_0{}^{1/2}}. \tag{11}$$

Equation (11) may be substituted in equation (7) to obtain an approximation to the relation between assembly cost and plant volume without reference to the relation between air distance and road distance.

If a circular supply area is used with the square road grid the average travel distance with uniform density is

$$\bar{D} = \frac{4}{\pi r^2}\int_0^r\int_0^{\sqrt{r^2-x^2}} (x + y)dydx \tag{12}$$

$$= \frac{8r}{3\pi} = \frac{8S^{1/2}}{3\pi^{3/2}P_0{}^{1/2}} = .4789\frac{S^{1/2}}{P_0{}^{1/2}}.$$

Comparing equations (11) and (12) indicates that the average length of haul necessary to obtain a given supply is slightly higher for the circular supply area, but the difference is quite small.

Over the long run, an allowance must be added for the fixed cost per season associated with ownership or rental of the transport equipment. This cost may be defined as FN, where F is the fixed cost associated with a single equipment unit (or group of combined equipment units) and N is the total number of such transport equipment units employed.

The number of transport equipment units required is determined by total assembly time requirements relative to the available working hours. That is, N is the smallest whole number such that

$$N \geqq \frac{T}{H} = \frac{S(g_0 + g_1\bar{D})}{H} \tag{13}$$

where H is the working hours effectively available, T is the total assembly time required, and $g_0 + g_1\bar{D}$ gives the assembly time per unit of product. The term g_0 includes some allowance for average time loss due to the impossibility of perfectly coordinating plant and assembly operations and H pertains to hours available for delivery plus additional hours that might be used for travel or loading, even though the plant was not receiving. Considerable variation in these magnitudes might be expected depending on location and the specific nature of the processing operation. Instances of delays due to "plant waiting for truck" or "truck waiting for plant" commonly are reduced through temporary storage of the incoming product and having receiving hours extend beyond plant hours. In many plants such storage costs are small relative to waiting costs. However, all of this leads into a queing problem which is beyond the scope of this paper.

The discrete variations in equipment inputs lead to discontinuous total and average total unit cost functions and complicate the calculation of meaningful marginal cost functions.[9] Empirical studies have usually expressed equipment costs as constant per unit of product or constant per unit of product per mile; in other words, equipment inputs have been treated as continuously divisible, rather than discrete.[10]

This certainly simplifies the problem and is probably a reasonable approximation in many instances. But note that some transport costs do remain essentially constant over extended ranges of volume and distance. Expressed on a per unit basis, these "fixed" costs decrease up to a point where each piece of equipment is utilized to its effective capacity, but increase overall as supply is increased since the volume of product that can be handled by each piece of equipment decreases as total travel distance increases.

Frequently assembly equipment is put to multiple use. It may be used for other products delivered to the same plant, to other plants, or for different kinds of operations altogether. If the different uses are at different times, the variable costs associated with each use or commodity may be determined independently. For a given assembly method the variable costs functions might appear as in equation (6), though with different density conditions in each use and possibly with different values for b_0 and b_1. The number of equipment units, and therefore the total fixed cost, will be determined by the commodity or use with the larger volume-distance requirements. Any allocation of fixed costs is purely arbitrary, although as a practical matter, some such allocation may be necessary in specific cases.

SELECTION OF EFFICIENT TECHNIQUE AND LEVEL OF INTENSITY

Typically, the type of equipment unit and hauling method is not given but is selected from the least costly of several alternatives. The alternatives may be defined in terms of assembly *technique* (a particular type of equipment combined with efficiently organized labor) and the *level of labor intensity* (the quantity of labor used in relation to the quantity of equipment). Different techniques and levels of labor intensity are associated with different values of the coefficients for cost (b_0, b_1) and time (g_0, g_1).

Suppose there is a given volume of product, S_0, to be transported from a single source to a processing plant within some time period, H. With S fixed at S_0, total assembly cost can be expressed as a linear function of distance—see equation (3). Assembly cost per unit of product is also a linear

[9] Marginal assembly cost functions do not appear to be essential, as such, for analyzing problems of plant size and location. Olson, *op. cit.*, computed such functions for use in deriving total variable costs of assembly but did not use them for other analytical purposes. Olson also assumed that costs associated with truck loading do not vary with plant volume. Such costs may remain constant on a per unit of product basis but seem likely to vary directly with plant volume. Marginal cost of this component would be constant, but not zero as was apparently assumed.

[10] For example, see Judge and Baker, Henry and Seagraves, and Olson, *op. cit.*

function of distance. Discontinuities will occur at distances where additional equipment units must be employed. The expected breaking points may be found by manipulating equation (13) to obtain the expression,

$$D = \frac{1}{g_1}\left(\frac{NH}{S_0} - g_0\right).$$

Figure 3 illustrates the nature of the cost functions for alternative techniques and labor intensity and the selection of least cost methods for supply sources at various distances from the processing plant. For distances up to D_1 technique I gives the least cost. From D_1 to D_2 technique II is least costly, and beyond D_2, technique III. Additional curves, not shown, would be required to represent variations in labor intensity for each technique. Typically there may be some methods that do not give least cost for any distance.

FIGURE 3
RELATION OF COST TO DISTANCE FROM SUPPLY SOURCE TO PLANT FOR THREE HYPOTHETICAL ASSEMBLY TECHNIQUES AND GIVEN VOLUME OF PRODUCT

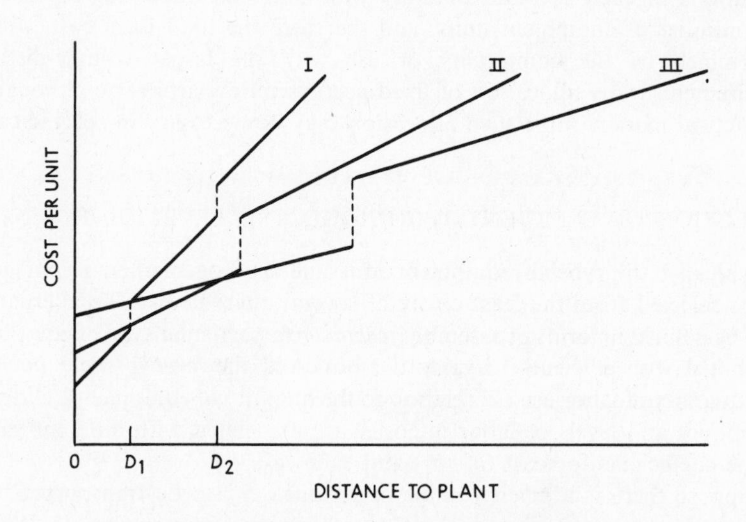

If the volume to be transported, S_0, changes, the level of the cost curves and the locations of the discontinuities change. Altering the length of the assembly period, H, also shifts the discontinuities. Allowing S and H to take on all possible values defines the volume-distance-hours areas for which particular techniques and labor intensities give least cost and, correspondingly, defines the long-run transportation cost surface for efficient operation under these conditions.

The selection process becomes more complicated when a firm transports a single commodity to a processing plant from *several* fixed sources, not necessarily simultaneously, but within some period, H. Selecting a *particular* technique and intensity is not the only possibility; a combination of techniques and/or intensities might be selected. For example, a firm with supply sources located both near and far from the processing plant might use, say, a tractor-trailer for the source near the plant and a large truck for the more distant supplies. If the truck had excess capacity at the distant range it might be used partially at both distances.

One approach to finding the least cost combination of techniques and labor intensity is to define additional assembly techniques, each of which is a particular combination of the basic techniques available. For example, various combinations might consist of a large truck and a small truck, two small trucks and a large truck, a tractor-trailer and a small truck, two small trucks only, and so on. Other combinations might involve variations in labor intensity.

By classifying assembly sources into a finite number of points in the supply plane the matter can be stated as a standard linear programming problem. Let i refer to a particular source ($i = 1, \ldots n$) and j refers to a particular technique and level of labor intensity ($j = 1, \ldots k$). The assembly cost function is

$$C = \sum_{i=1}^{n} \sum_{j=1}^{k} S_{ij}(b_{0j} + b_{1j}D_i) + \sum_{j=1}^{k} F_j N_j. \tag{14}$$

Equation (14) states that for a given set of sources and distances the total assembly cost is the sum of the volume (S_{ij}) transported by each single technique and intensity from each distance times the variable cost per unit for each single technique and intensity and distance, plus the total fixed cost for all items of equipment. For any combination of techniques and labor intensity and given S_i, D_i, there are many values of S_{ij} that will satisfy (14). The problem is to find the values of S_{ij} that will make cost as small as possible subject to the restrictions

$$\sum_{j=1}^{k} S_{ij} = S_i, \tag{15}$$

$$\sum_{i=1}^{n} \frac{S_{ij}}{M_{ij}} \leqq 1, \quad \text{where } M_{ij} = \frac{HN_j}{g_{0j} + g_{1j}D_i} \text{ and,} \tag{16}$$

$$\text{all } S_{ij} \geqq 0. \tag{17}$$

The S_i's are the given quantities to be transported from each source, the M_{ij}'s are the season capacities of single techniques and intensities if used entirely for a particular source, and N_j is the number of multiples of equipment of technique j. Equation (16) gives the capacity restrictions for each single technique and intensity in transporting from various sources or combinations of sources.

Solutions to these equations, giving least cost combinations of techniques, may be obtained for all possible sets of supply-distance requirements.[11] The long-run relation between assembly cost and plant volume may be derived by cumulating total supply and total (least) cost in relation to increasing air distance from the plant. The specific nature of the resulting assembly cost function will be influenced by the institutional arrangements as to who provides the hauling service. If the assembly service is provided by the plant only one set of conditions or restrictions is involved. Where producers transport their own products and receive delivered prices, the selection of methods and corresponding costs depend on the separate conditions facing each producer and many restrictions and computations are involved.[12]

The sheer magnitude of the computations in these procedures plus the extensive and detailed information required leads us to seek approximate methods that give reasonably good estimates of assembly cost-supply relations. One approach is to compute the cost function for each technique for an average or typical volume of product transported from each supply source or concentration point or by each producer. The efficient range for each technique and the corresponding cost can then be determined as indicated in Figure 3 (assuming that a particular equipment unit serves only one source). A single smooth curve may be fitted to the points or segments of the cost curves that indicate least transport cost for supply sources of any distance to the plant. The assembly cost-supply function can then be represented by

$$C = \int_0^{2\pi} \int_0^r h(r) P_0 w r\, dr\, d\theta = P_0 w L(r) = P_0 w G(S) \qquad (18)$$

where $h(r)$ approximates the relation between assembly cost per unit of product and distance, employing the optimum technique at each distance, for given time restrictions and given volume requirements for each supply source.[13]

Where assembly equipment is put to multiple use a reasonable approximation may be obtained by modifying the procedures suggested by equation (18). This will not be elaborated on other than to note that with different commodities handled at different times, (a) variable costs are independent,

---

[11] Feasible solutions will be possible, of course, only for combinations of techniques and intensities that have the capacities to meet the volume requirements. Some modifications would be required to consider the effects of operating a particular equipment unit at several levels of labor intensity.

[12] Assembly costs incurred by producers influence processing plant scale and location decisions through the effect on prices that must be paid to obtain desired supplies.

[13] For an empirical example, see B. C. French and D. G. Gillette, *op. cit.* This procedure has the advantage of permitting fixed equipment cost per unit of product to increase with distance from the plant. The magnitude of possible error or bias should, of course, be investigated in each application.

(b) equipment requirements, and therefore equipment "fixed" costs, typically are determined by a single commodity use that has the larger volume-distance requirements, and (c) the distance range for which a particular technique and level of labor intensity gives least cost is determined in relation to a linear combination of total commodity supplies and the volume of the particular commodity that determines the equipment requirements.

COMBINING PLANT AND ASSEMBLY COSTS

The combining of plant and assembly cost is largely a matter of simple addition. Using these combined functions in determining efficient size, location, and number of processing operations, however, is a most complex and interrelated problem. As indicated at the outset, specific solutions must be keyed to local situations, often with almost limitless possible combinations of locations and routes, and variations in other factors.

The practical approach therefore is to develop plant cost functions, to develop assembly cost functions under simplified situations as suggested above, and to add these to obtain indications of approximate over-all relations between volume and cost with efficient operation. This may involve not one addition but a series, each reflecting alternative density situations and, perhaps both long- and short-run costs. These combined functions may then be used as guides to evaluate the cost advantages of different potential locations and scales of operation, to consider the impact of varying supply density and, ultimately, along with other factors, to develop models of efficient industry or area organization.

11 Cooperative Enterprise as a Structural Dimension of Farm Markets*

PETER G. HELMBERGER†‡

This article reports on a theoretical analysis of cooperative marketing under alternative sets of assumptions regarding market structure. For some major results, consider a market where raw material is sold by a perfectly competitive industry to a processing industry. If the processing industry has an atomistic structure and no barriers to entry, cooperative marketing—where some processors are cooperatively organized by raw material producers—may cause departures from perfectly competitive equilibrium in the short run, but not in the long run. Where there is but one processor and blockaded entry, cooperative organization of that firm leads to smaller departures from competitive equilibrium than that associated with pure monopsony under many circumstances. Restricted membership cooperation, however, can give rise to market results that are undesirable from the viewpoint of all except the member producers. If the finished product is sold in perfect competition and scale diseconomies do not exist, cooperative marketing tends to lead to competitive equilibrium regardless of other structural conditions that would support monopsony elements.

There can be little question that price theory is centered almost exclusively on the profit seeking type of business enterprise. In farm markets both here and abroad, cooperatives often outnumber profit seeking firms; and to the extent price theory plays a useful role in research and government policy in agricultural marketing, the failure of existing theories to deal with the economic impacts of the cooperative form of business organization represents a serious deficiency.

A recent paper has laid the foundation for extending price theory to include cooperative enterprise as a special case by showing how positions of cooperative equilibrium can be derived through postulating maximizing

---

* *Journal of Farm Economics,* Vol. XLVI, No. 3 (August, 1964), pp. 603–17.
† University of California, Berkley, California.
‡ The author wishes to thank Herman Southworth, Lee Bawden, and Paul Nelson for their helpful suggestions.

behavior on the part of the cooperative firm.[1] The present paper extends the analysis further by deducing the economic impacts of cooperative marketing in various environmental settings and by treating explicitly the interaction of business enterprises of the cooperative and noncooperative types in the determination of market performance.[2] In order to narrow the scope of the paper, attention will be focused on farmer marketing cooperatives with the expectation that the reader with a special interest can extend the analysis to include the purchasing cooperative.

COST CURVES AND REVENUE PRODUCT CURVES

It is helpful to begin by reviewing some basic tools of analysis. The profit function for a profit seeking firm and the cooperative surplus function for a marketing cooperative may be written as equations (1) and (2) respectively:

$$\pi = \bar{P}_y Y - \sum_i \bar{P}_i X_i - \bar{P}_m M - F \tag{1}$$

$$P_m M = \bar{P}_y Y - \sum_i \bar{P}_i X_i - F \tag{2}$$

where Y represents the level of output; X_i, the level of the *i*th productive service; F, the level of fixed cost; and M, the level of some raw material. For simplicity, we may suppose that the productive services are purchased and the final output is sold in perfectly competitive markets so that the price of the *i*th productive service, P_i, and the price of the output, P_y, may be viewed as constants, $\bar{P}_i$ and $\bar{P}_y$, respectively. As equation (2) suggests, the cooperative is owned by and operates for the benefit of members who are producers of M. The profit seeking firm here views the price of M, P_m, as a constant, $\bar{P}_m$, whereas P_m is a variable whose value must be determined in the case of the cooperative. We may assume that the noncooperative firm seeks to maximize profit whereas the cooperative seeks as an "intermediate" objective to maximize cooperative surplus for any given level of M. The nature of more ultimate cooperative goals will be clarified as we proceed.

Average revenue product (ARP) and net average revenue product (NARP) for either type of firm are here defined by equations (3) and (4), respectively:

$$ARP = \frac{\bar{P}_y Y - \sum_i \bar{P}_i X_i}{M} \tag{3}$$

---

[1] Peter Helmberger and Sidney Hoos, "Cooperative Enterprise and Organization Theory," *Journal of Farm Economics*, Vol. 44 (May 1962) pp. 275–90.

[2] It will be seen presently that our conclusions generally differ from those of Eugene Clark, "Farmer Cooperatives and Economic Welfare," *Journal of Farm Economics*, Vol. 34 (February 1952), pp. 35–51. Where agreement does exist, it is for different reasons. For a critique of Clark's paper, see Arnolds P. Aizselnieks, "Farmer Cooperatives and Economic Welfare—A Reply," *Journal of Farm Economics*, Vol. 34 (August 1952), pp. 404–7.

$$\text{NARP} = \frac{\bar{P}_y Y - \sum_i \bar{P}_i X_i - F}{M}. \tag{4}$$

The assumption of maximizing behavior allows the construction of ARP and NARP functions that show for any given level of M the associated maximized values for ARP and NARP. The average revenue product curves may be derived by assuming that M is fixed at various alternative levels, and then finding for each the resulting levels of output and productive services that maximize profit (cooperative surplus). Once particular levels of raw material, output, and productive services are known, equations (3) and (4) allow computation of a point on the ARP curve and NARP curve, respectively. The value of marginal product (VMP) function can be found by multiplying both sides of the ARP function by M and finding the first derivative with respect to M of the right-hand side of the equation.[3] These functions might be depicted as in Figure 1. Significantly, *if both the cooperative and non-cooperative firms have the same production functions, they will also have the same revenue product curves.* The distinctive economic nature of the co-operative firm, in comparison with the profit seeking firm, is yet to be shown.

FIGURE 1
Equilibrium Output and Price for a Cooperative Firm

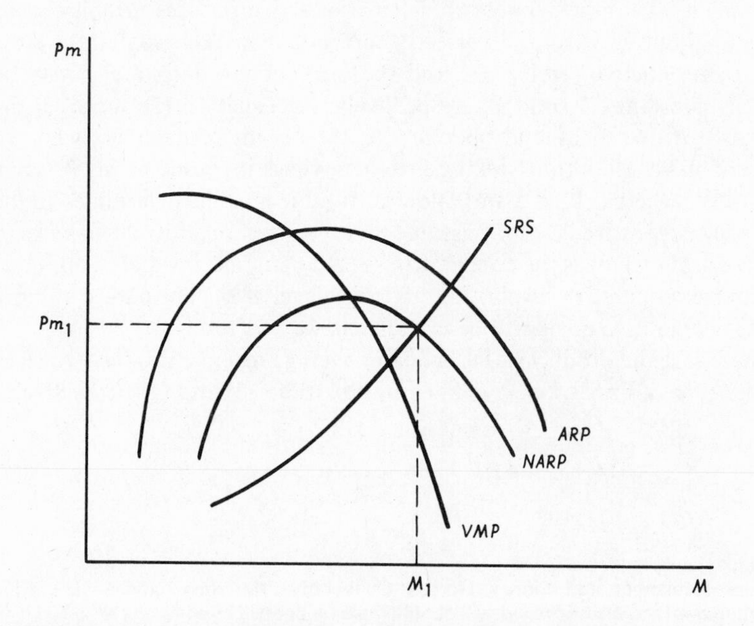

[3] This definition of the VMP function for an input departs from that usually conceived in that prices but *not* the quantities of other productive services are assumed fixed. For more detail on the derivation of the NARP function, see Helmberger and Hoos, *op. cit.;* pp. 282–84.

With the price of Y given and fixed, the portion of the VMP curve that lies below the ARP curve is the profit seeking firm's short-run demand curve for M. In general, no such interpretation can be given to the cooperative's VMP curve. Rather, the NARP curve plays a role in the theory of cooperation that is akin to the role of the VMP curve in traditional theory. Let us assume that the number of members is fixed and that each member determines his output independently. Then the NARP curve, subject to some restrictions to be noted subsequently, shows the maximum P_m that a nonprofit cooperative can return to its members for the various levels of M they might choose to produce. For this reason, it has been called a net returns function.[4] If, for example, the members' supply curve is given by SRS in Figure 1, equilibrium output and price are given by M_1 and P_{m1}, respectively.

Both equations (1) and (2) contain a fixed cost component; short-run models are implied. Long-run revenue product curves for cooperative and noncooperative firms can be derived in a manner analogous to that sketched above except that no distinction between NARP and ARP need be made. Whether long or short run, the assumption that P_y is viewed by the seller as a constant could be relaxed in favor of a weaker assumption that P_y is merely some function of Y, $P_y = P_y(Y)$. If the seller of Y is a monopolist, then clearly the ARP and marginal revenue product (MRP) curves will be downward sloping over some range of output.

COOPERATIVE ENTERPRISE IN VARIOUS STRUCTURAL SETTINGS

Recognition of cooperative enterprise as a dimension of market structure gives rise to a myriad of possible structural cases that are potentially worthy of analysis; only a few of them will be considered here in that our attention will be restricted to marketing cooperatives. Regarding the cooperative enterprise, we will suppose throughout that (1) there are many relatively small member firms, (2) the cooperative objective is the maximization of net returns to members, and (3) no attempt is made to control the production of members.[5] In deciding how much to produce, each member engaged in production equates price received (or average net returns per unit) to the marginal cost of production where price received might equal a provisional price (perhaps equal to a "going market price") plus the average patronage

[4] Helmberger and Hoos, *op. cit.*, p. 284.

[5] The assumption that the cooperative does not directly control production of members, through the issuance of output quotas, for example, is consistent with actual cooperative operations and avoids, in any event, the question of the legality of such a cooperative policy. See Robert L. Clodius, "Lessons for Farm Economists from Recent Antitrust Decisions—An Economist's View," *Journal of Farm Economics*, Vol. 44, (December 1962), pp. 1608–9. This assumption could not be abandoned in favor of others without necessitating important changes in the analysis.

dividend per unit.[6] We will also suppose that where there are no barriers to entry, farmers will organize new cooperatives whenever they can be assured of securing higher net returns as a result.

Cooperative Enterprise in Atomistic Markets

Initially, an environment will be considered with a structure that may be described thus: There are many relatively small firms selling a finished product, Y, in a perfectly competitive market and utilizing, a raw material, M, that is in turn produced by an atomistic industry. M and Y are homogeneous goods. There are no barriers to entry in either the "primary industry," the firms producing M, or the "processing industry," the firms producing Y.

Short-Run Analysis. Assume a fixed number of firms, each with a fixed plant, in the primary and processing industries and suppose only one processor is cooperatively organized. By the market price of M, we mean the price determined by the short-run demand and supply functions for M. (Atomistic structure implies that the demand and supply functions are not noticeably affected by the cooperative's activities.) The NARP, ARP, and VMP curves associated with the cooperative firm are depicted in Figure 2.

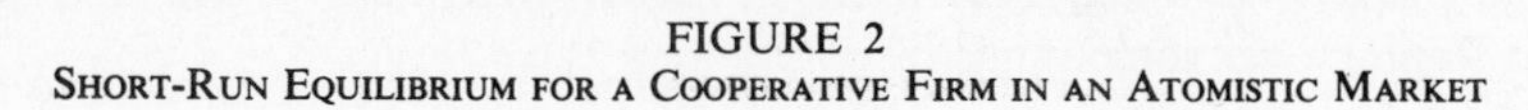

FIGURE 2
Short-Run Equilibrium for a Cooperative Firm in an Atomistic Market

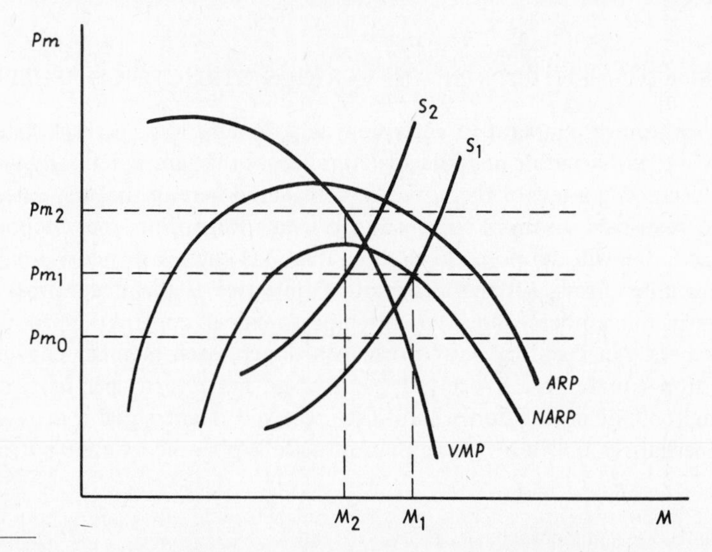

[6] Alternatively, one might assume that producers make their production plans on the basis of the provisional price and view the patronage dividend as some type of unexpected bonus. The larger the patronage dividend and the more consistent is the cooperative in paying such dividends, as say in an equilibrium position, the less attractive is this alternative. For an analysis of a consumer cooperative that utilizes an assumption of this sort, see Stephen Enke, "Consumer Cooperatives and Economic Efficiency," *American Economic Review,* Vol. 35 (March 1945), pp. 148–55.

Let the market price equal P_{m0} and the supply curve for cooperative members be S_1. In this case, the number of cooperative members is such that the net price returned to them by the cooperative, P_{m1}, exceeds the market price. If the cooperative is an open membership type cooperative, membership will grow until net returns are reduced to P_{m0}.[7] A restricted membership type cooperative would not allow entry of new members and as a consequence, net returns to members would exceed market price in short-run equilibrium. If initial membership were such that the net returns from the cooperative fell below the market price, there would be an incentive for some members to leave. The remaining members would surely not object, and we may conclude that exit would continue until net returns increased to P_{m0} regardless of whether the cooperative pursues a policy of open or restricted membership.[8]

In order to bring out an important problem in cooperative theory, suppose that market price equals P_{m2} and the members' supply curve is given by S_2. If, on the one hand, the cooperative returns less than P_{m2}, members will have an incentive to leave the cooperative. (Long-term contracts, if in effect, may forestall exit, but not forever.) As some members leave, the net returns to those remaining will fall so long as the cooperative insists on covering all costs, i.e., moving along the NARP curve. The cooperative's operating policy would appear to be untenable. If, on the other hand, a price equal to P_{m2} (or larger) is returned to members, the cooperative would not be able to meet fixed costs.

In this situation, it appears that the cooperative will simply pay the market price and equate VMP to P_{m2}. In this manner the cooperative, like the profit seeking firm, *can make the greatest possible contribution toward its fixed costs.* This, in turn, is consistent with the goal of survival which may be an even more basic cooperative goal than maximization of net returns to members.[9] It may also be to the advantage of members to minimize their losses rather than simply scrapping the whole operation with no attempt to recoup at least part of the sunk cost. The cooperative principle of service-at-cost apparently goes by the board in this type short-run situation.

---

[7] By an open membership cooperative, we mean an association that always accepts new members. This type of policy may be the result of organizational goals and/or organizational structure as in the case of a federated cooperative with no control over the memberships of local associations. By a restricted membership cooperative, we mean one that will accept new members as long as this does not result in a lowering of net returns. In long-run analysis, we will suppose that this latter type association can decrease the number of members by failing to replace those who retire. The type of association that can dismiss and does dismiss members at will is a sufficiently rare species to justify our ignoring it completely. It is recognized that a cooperative's policy toward membership can be expected to reflect future plans for growth as well as current cost and revenue considerations.

[8] Where the revolving fund method of financing is used, the price returned to cooperative members may include an interest payment for invested capital. Our analysis may be tailored to fit this situation by interpreting price returned by the cooperative as net of any interest payment.

[9] This might be particularly true if the cooperative manager wields effective control over the organization.

Our patience with the assumption of only one cooperative firm can now be shown to pay handsome dividends. In the present model, the short-run net returns (SRNR) function showing the price that will be returned to members for various levels of M exhibits a kink. The function coincides with that part of the NARP curve that lies above VMP and with that part of the VMP curve that lies below ARP and above NARP. Our results may now be extended to markets where numerous cooperatives may be present with the additional assumption that revenue product curves of all firms are identical.

If the policy of open membership is universal among cooperatives, the SRNR functions of cooperatives and the demand functions of noncooperatives can be aggregated. Equating the resulting aggregate relation to the total supply function for M determines equilibrium price and output of M. Once price is known, the equilibrium distribution of M among the firms may be computed from the micro-relations. Clearly this analytical procedure does not depend on having a certain number of cooperatives present in the market. The two polar cases where firms are either all cooperatives or all noncooperatives are merely special cases.

FIGURE 3
COMPARISON OF SHORT-RUN OPTIMUM OUTPUT LEVELS FOR COOPERATIVE AND NONCOOPERATIVE FIRMS

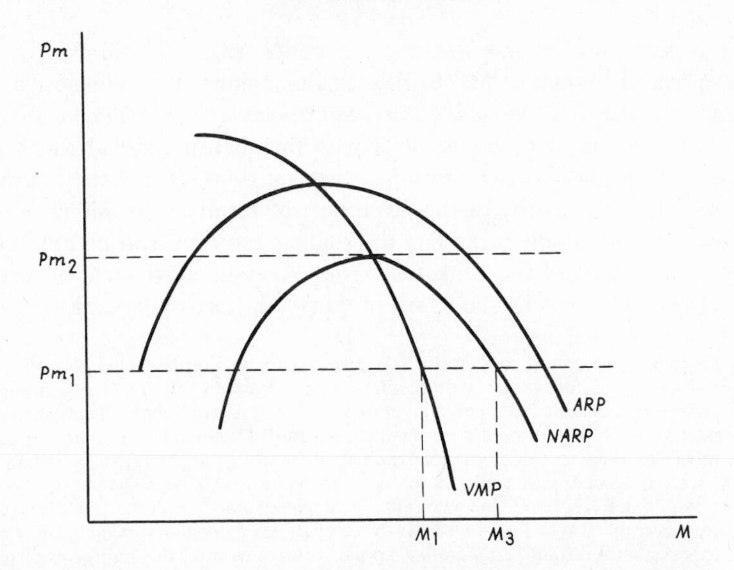

The implications of open membership cooperation for market performance can easily be seen by considering Figure 3 which shows the revenue product curves for any one firm. If equilibrium price equaled P_{m1}, a co-operative would process M_3 and a noncooperative firm M_1. The higher the price of M, the less would be the difference between the input level of the cooperative and that of the noncooperative, until finally, at a price equal to P_{m2} or higher, there would be no difference at all. In a situation where excess profit is observed (or would be if at least one noncooperative firm existed) cooperative enterprise will tend to (1) reduce excess profits received by profit seeking processors, (2) increase the price received by producers of M, and (3) increase the production of M. These tendencies merely indicate the direction of change; the greater the extent of cooperative enterprise, the larger will be the magnitude of change. If the situation is such that excess profit is not observed (and could not be observed even though profit seeking firms existed), the cooperative will behave in a manner no different from that of the noncooperative; and cooperative marketing will make no difference in terms of the resulting market performance. Moreover, this latter "if-then" proposition is logically valid for both the open and restricted membership type cooperative. The likelihood that cooperatives would generally be accepting nonmember patronage might also be noted.

The implications of restricted membership type cooperation for performance in a market where short-run excess profit is observed (or at least would be observed if only profit seeking firms existed) are rather more difficult to analyze. Much depends on the initial distribution of members among cooperatives. With no profit seeking firms in the market, output of each cooperative in short-run equilibrium will be such as to equate the supply function of its members with the NARP function. A single price might prevail but this is neither a necessary condition nor a likely one. If on the other hand, a substantial number of profit seeking buyers exists, it is not entirely clear whether the price to nonmembers would be higher or lower as a result of cooperative enterprise. The initial distribution of cooperative members could very easily be such, however, as to allow prices to some members that exceed the price paid to nonmembers. In any event, market performance will depart from that associated with perfect competition—the nature and magnitude of the departure depending on a variety of circumstances.

Long-Run Analysis. In long-run analysis we assume that firms in the primary and processing industries have neither fixed costs nor fixed plants. Moreover, the number of firms is variable in both industries; entry (exit) occurs whenever profits (losses) are to be had (avoided). As a starter, we again imagine that at most one cooperative exists in the long run. The ARP and VMP curves in Figure 4 summarize the cooperative's cost and revenue data.

A restricted membership cooperative will strive to set its membership so that the aggregate long-run supply curve of its members intersects the ARP curve at its maximum (see Figure 4). At most, P_{mr} could be returned. If the cooperative can exactly duplicate the efficiency of the noncooperative processors, the long-run perfectly competitive price will equal P_{mr}. In this case, open membership cooperation would lead to the same result.

The long-run model where none, some, or all of the firms are cooperatively organized may be treated with dispatch. If all established and potential firms can achieve equally efficient operations, regardless of organizational differences among them, long-run perfectly competitive equilibrium will be the result. If there is a systematic difference in efficiency among firms according to type of organization, the inefficient type will pass out of existence. If noncooperatives can uniformly achieve efficiences that cooperatives cannot duplicate, for example, cooperative marketing will tend to disappear. Significantly, where cooperatives and noncooperatives exist in a market with structural dimensions of the sort assumed here, there will be a long-run tendency for each type of firm to perform in the same manner with the same consequences for total market performance.

FIGURE 4
LONG-RUN OUTPUT AND PRICE EQUILIBRIUM FOR A COOPERATIVE UNDER COMPETITIVE CONDITIONS

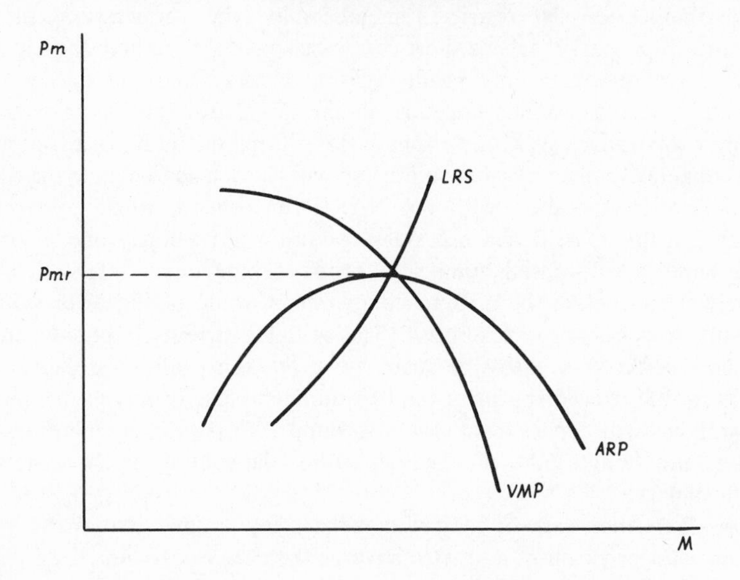

MONOPSONY COMPARED WITH COOPERATIVE ENTERPRISE

Having surveyed the implications of cooperative enterprise in an environmental situation conducive to lively competition, we turn abruptly to the opposite extreme where (1) entry into the processing industry is blockaded, and (2) there is but one processor. We may suppose further that in general $P_y = P_y(Y)$ which comprehends the special case where P_y is viewed by the processor as a constant $\bar{P}_y$.

Proceeding directly to a long-run model, let the ARP and MRP curves in Figure 5 summarize the relevant cost and revenue data. The curve labeled

LRS depicts the long-run supply function for producers of M and the MS curve shows the marginal cost, in contrast to average cost, associated with various input levels of M.

FIGURE 5
COMPARISON OF OPTIMUM LONG-RUN OUTPUT LEVELS FOR A COOPERATIVE AND A MONOPSONIST

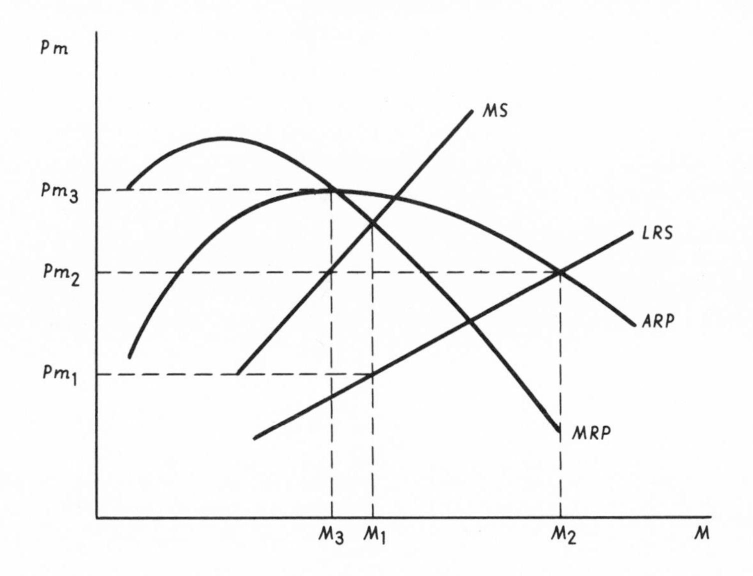

If the processor is a profit maximizing entity, the solution is well-known. The monopsonist will equate MS with MRP; equilibrium price and quantity equal P_{m1} and M_1 respectively.

Market performance changes dramatically, however, if we alter market structure by postulating that the processing enterprise is a producer-owned cooperative. A restricted membership cooperative would determine the number of members so that their resulting long-run aggregate supply curve intersects the ARP curve at its maximum. Equilibrium price and output of M would equal P_{m3} and M_3, respectively. Notice that output restriction in this case exceeds that associated with pure monopsony. Moreover, the high price paid to members would be small consolation to those producers who were entirely excluded from the market. Restricted membership cooperation can apparently lead to a "socially undesirable" market performance.

If the cooperative stands willing to accept all producers who wish to join, equilibrium price and quantity of M would equal P_{m2} and M_2 respectively. At this price, no potential producers would care to enter the industry and join the cooperative venture. Output of M exceeds that associated with pure monopsony as does price received by producers.

As it turns out, however, our conclusions depend in a crucial way not only upon the shapes of the relevant functional relationships but also on how, in Figure 5, the curves are positioned with respect to one another. Taking up the latter qualifications first, if the long-run supply curve cuts through the ARP curve at a point where its slope is nonnegative, cooperation will lead to a larger output of M and a higher price than would be associated with pure monopsony.[10] With cooperative marketing, market performance would tend to be closer to that associated with perfect competition (except where the LRS curve is tangent to the ARP curve).

The particular shape assigned to the ARP curve in Figure 5 could be justified in numerous ways. Only the downward sloping part of the curve and its explanation need occupy our attention at this juncture. If the processor is a monopolistic seller of the finished product, there is no problem. The downward sloping portion of the ARP curve can be attributed to a declining price in the product market. Otherwise, one might fall back on the notion of diseconomies of scale. This latter possibility is not a particularly attractive one since it lacks a strong theoretical foundation and, more importantly, is not entirely consistent with sizes of existing firms in relation to the markets they serve. In other words, if the firm does *not* sell in an imperfectly competitive market, there is not much reason to suppose that the ARP curve should slope downward in the relevant region.

The likelihood that these market conditions might frequently exist arises out of the fact that many industries obtain their raw materials from agriculture where companies buy in local markets and sell in much larger regional and even national markets.[11] It may, therefore, not be amiss to consider a model where our single processor-buyer sells in a perfectly competitive market. Supposing that economies of scale are eventually exhausted, and in the absence of diseconomies, the ARP and VMP curves would be as indicated in Figure 6. The economic implications of the market conduct of a cooperative enterprise, in contrast to a profit seeking pure monopsonist, become quickly apparent. If the long-run supply curve for M passes through ARP to the right of (or at) M_1, cooperation leads to long-run perfectly competitive equilibrium. If the point of intersection is to the left of M_1, the VMP of M will not be equated to the marginal cost of producing M in any case, but cooperation will push market performance closer to this "ideal" than would monopsony. Interestingly, if the long-run supply curve for M passes through ARP in the vicinity of M_1, there will be a substantial barrier to entry arising out of economies of scale. Under these circumstances, cooperative marketing would appear quite definitely to be the superior form of market organization.

---

[10] It matters not whether the cooperative pursues a policy of open or restricted membership since new members will always be accepted if such does not result in lower net returns.

[11] See, e.g., R. G. Bressler, "Pricing Raw Products in Complex Milk Markets," *Agricultural Economics Research,* Vol. 10 (October 1958), pp. 118–19.

FIGURE 6
EQUILIBRIUM IN AN OLIGOPSONISTIC MARKET WITH A COOPERATIVE ENTERPRISE PARTICIPATING

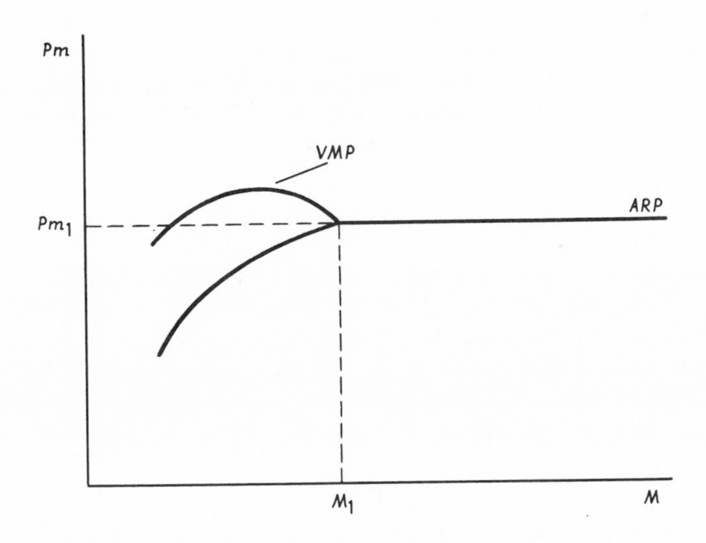

The usefulness of the above model is pegged in part on the insights provided for the study of oligopsony which might be a more realistic case than those considered thus far. While it may indeed be true that oligopsonistic structure is realistic, the attendant theoretical difficulties in deriving associations between market structure and performance must also be recognized.

COOPERATIVE ENTERPRISE IN MARKETS WITH CIRCULAR STRUCTURES

The present discussion of cooperative enterprise in markets with oligopsonistic characteristics will be brief; a comprehensive treatment is not intended. Attention will first be given over to a few models that shed some light on the manner in which the existence of cooperative enterprise affects market performance, given the number of buyers.

Two Models with Concentration in Procurement. Consider a market in which a few processors purchase the entire output of a perfectly competitive selling industry. Suppose that all processors, one of which is cooperatively organized, are equally favored in the marketplace as to efficiency, financial condition, product acceptance, and so forth. Two subcases may be distinguished according to whether the firms are perfectly or imperfectly competitive sellers of the finished product.

If the buyers of the raw material are perfectly competitive sellers in their product market, each may be supposed to have ARP and VMP curves similar to those given in Figure 6. In this situation, there is a maximum likelihood that the existence of a cooperative will push market performance toward the perfectly competitive extreme. The cooperative will be seeking new members so long as net returns are less than the maximum amount obtainable, P_{m1}. If the profit seeking firms fail to match the cooperative's price, their suppliers will seek, presumably with success, cooperative membership. If the long-run supply curve does not fall so far to the left that a price equal to P_{m1} is impossible in any event, long-run equilibrium with a stable market structure will likely satisfy the conditions of perfectly competitive equilibrium.[12] Finally, it needs merely to be pointed out that this conclusion does not depend in a crucial way on the existence of profit seeking firms; all of the firms could be cooperatives.

If the buyers of the raw material are assumed to be imperfectly competitive sellers of the finished product, in contrast to the above case, the implications of cooperative marketing become far more difficult to analyze. In order to circumvent the problems caused by oligopolistic interdependency, one might assume that the sellers have entered some highly collusive agreement in the product market, market sharing for example. This assumption, or one of a similar type, is necessary for the derivation of ARP and MRP curves for each firm. The revenue product curves for any one firm including the cooperative may be supposed to have inverted U-shapes similar to those in Figure 5. The cooperative can be expected to actively seek new members so long as its total input of M is less than that associated with the maximum of the ARP curve. An open membership cooperative would continue admitting new members, in contrast to a restricted membership cooperative, once the maximum of the ARP curve has been reached.

Circularity among processors as sellers and as buyers means that the range of feasible market outcomes is very large. The most one could expect from a priori theorizing are some reasonable conjectures as to the probable market results. For these reasons we will merely note some fairly evident conclusions and pass on to another matter.

First, whereas a cooperative might have an incentive to collude in the product market, much as might a profit seeking firm, there exists no cooperative incentive to exploit member producers through collusive conduct.[13] Second, if the imperfectly competitive sellers are all open membership cooperatives, any gains acquired through the use of monopoly power will be passed back to producers. This means that total output of the cooperatives will exceed that associated with an oligopoly-oligopsony solution that implies excess profits are retained by profit seeking firms. We may expect that open

[12] We say "likely" because perfectly competitive equilibrium is not an inevitable result. Economic warfare is always possible with structural change observed as a consequence.

[13] This should not be taken to mean that the cooperative would never collude with other firms in the procurement of raw material. Even a cooperative might have an incentive to avoid periodic price wars in which prices paid to producers gyrate wildly with seemingly no correspondence to supply and demand factors.

membership cooperation in markets of the type here considered generally tends to increase both production of the raw material and prices paid to producers. Third, if the imperfectly competitive sellers are all restricted membership type cooperatives, members will likely receive a price in excess of that which would prevail given a group of profit seeking firms—albeit some potential producers might be unable to find markets for the outputs they would willingly produce at the cooperative price. Fourth, restricted in contrast to open membership cooperation may result in a price structure where members receive a price in excess of that received by non-members. Finally, if cooperation is of the open membership variety, a single price will likely prevail, with cooperative membership adjusting so as to assure this result.

Barriers to Entry and Cooperative Enterprise. From previous discussion it appears that in many situations the distinction between open and restricted membership cooperation is meaningful in terms of differing implications for market performance. On balance, it appears that in such situations, the welfare implications of restricted membership cooperation leave something to be desired. Where entry is not blockaded, however, the unwillingness of a cooperative to accept patronage if such results in decreased returns to members may be a blessing in disguise. Simply put, the cooperative performance will point up and emphasize any oligopsonistic exploitation of producers that might be present. The greater the exploitation, the larger will be the differential between price returned to members and that received by nonmembers. Cooperative marketing would appear to act as a barometer, measuring the downward pressure of oligopsonistic market conduct on prices received by the primary producers.

If the differential is substantial, one can expect that nonmember producers would go to great lengths to redress their poor market position. Their efforts might be directed toward duplication of known cooperative ventures, securing government intervention to further producer interests, or the organization of cooperative bargaining associations. Remedial measures may exist even where entry is blockaded—antitrust litigation, for example. And the very probability that flagrant oligopsonistic exploitation would engender discontent among producers, perhaps encouraging entry of additional cooperatives, might lead profit seeking firms to temper their use of power with prudence.

POLICY AND RESEARCH IMPLICATIONS

Overall, one can only conclude on the basis of theory that the welfare implications of cooperative marketing are favorable under some sets of market conditions but not under others. The issues raised, however, are most certainly relevant to policy. The special treatment accorded cooperatives in such areas as antitrust, taxation, and various forms of public assistance must surely require some rationalization in terms of the manner in which cooperative marketing affects the allocation of resources, marketing margins, and returns to farmers. That rationalization cannot be pegged on theory alone. Rather, theory will have served its purpose well if it prompts researchers to ask the right questions and provides the frame work for the empirical investigations required to answer them.

A number of important research areas are suggested by the above analysis. There is a need to establish empirically the nature of those structural and environmental characteristics of farm markets which, according to theory, determine and condition the likely consequences of cooperative marketing. Of particular interest would be a study of the extent of restricted (or open) membership cooperation and the commodities and areas where such policies are pursued. Are there, for example, any systematic associations between cooperative policies toward membership and patronage on the one hand, and the market power positions of cooperatives in final product markets on the other? How are such associations affected by whether the cooperatives in question are federated or centralized? A very difficult research assignment would be the empirical testing of the a priori associations between market structure, where cooperative enterprise is viewed an element of structure, and market conduct and performance. Empirical investigation of the crucial assumptions underlying the above analysis—particularly the assumption that the cooperative enterprise can secure a market position (efficiency, progressiveness, price premiums because of brand names, etc.) fully comparable to the position of profit seeking firms—would be most welcome in the study of the industrial organization of farm markets.

Part IV Methodology in Production Economics

12 Elementary Models in Farm Production Economics Research*†

EARL O. HEADY‡

Research in the economics of farm production has a longer history than has any other specialization in agricultural economics. Accordingly, the objectives, the analytical tools and the research methodology should be more highly developed and the findings should provide a greater basis for action in this than in many other sectors of applied economics. These points have been discussed in various degrees of detail over the past three decades. This paper is pointed in the same direction. In terms of economic and statistical analysis it is extremely but purposively elementary. It reviews the analytical setting of farm production economics research, outlines the role of this investigation in the overall structure of economic research, and attempts to reconcile some apparent divergences in objectives. Finally it sets forth some fundamental problems relating to the economics of farm production and questions, on the basis of elementary criteria which are commonly accepted, the extent to which some traditional research techniques provide the basis for action in bettering the administration of farm resources within these specific problem areas.

This paper is prompted by the uneasiness which evidently fills the minds of many as to what research in the economics of farm production can, does, or should accomplish. The thesis behind it is that advancement in a scientific field grows not out of unqualified acceptance of the status quo but by frequent appraisal of the road ahead. Scholars who are interested in furthering the

---

* *Journal of Farm Economics,* Vol. XXX, No. 2 (May 1948), pp. 201–25.

† Journal Paper No. *J-1555* of the Iowa Agricultural Experiment Station, Ames, Iowa, Project No. 976. Suggestions of numerous associates, especially those of Virgil Hurlburt and Ross Baumann, have been helpful in formulating this paper.

‡ Iowa State University, Ames, Iowa.

accomplishments of farm production economics research welcome studies which delve into the theory or analytical tools, methods of empirical analysis, and applied problems. All are needed in a maturing science.

ANALYTICAL SETTING

As an applied field of investigation farm management parallels that sector of economic theory dealing with the economics of the firm or the principles of production. This delineation of the field has been explicitly expressed at various times in the past decades. Early definitions such as those of G. F. Warren[1] and Boss[2] although couched in terms of the application of business principles to and the maximization of farm returns over time spelled out a similar analytical setting. The rational use of resources and the maximization of returns is, of course, the very core of the economics of production or the theory of the firm. It sets forth the necessary conditions for the most efficient use of resources or the maximization of profits. Some few reject the idea that any relationship exists between farm management and the principles or theory of production. It is difficult to understand why this should be so. There are few if any agricultural economists who question that supply and demand determine prices in a competitive market or that this concept is of value as an analytical tool. Yet the conditions which are given as necessary for profit maximization are as commonly and widely accepted in economics as is the law of supply and demand. Furthermore, these necessary conditions are as exact in the sense of mathematical proof as the law of supply and demand, and empirical verification is perhaps even more readily possible.

The principles of production provide both simple and complex models in farm management economics which serve as the fundamental hypotheses of research and furnish the schematic framework for establishing the appropriate empirical analysis (the nature of the data needed in answering problems, the sample or experimental design, and the appropriate statistical analysis) in solving specific problems. It is true that not all economic models have been developed to a point where they are relevant or can be readily integrated with empirical investigations. However, a number of those relating to the economics of production are both simple, obvious, and time-established. It is because even these extremely elementary tools sometimes go unrecognized in the design and analyses of research studies that the findings have little value in the sense that they provide figures and data which can be put into direct use in the management of farm resources.

The objectives of research relating to the economics of farm production have also been given somewhat different connotations down through time.

[1] G. F. Warren, *Farm Management,* Preface.
[2] Andrew Boss, *Farm Management.*

Early workers emphasized entirely the individual farm aspect of research. However, farm management research has generally been given a broader base over the past two decades. Johnson,[3] Wilcox,[4] the American Farm Economics Association Committee,[5] the Social Science Research Council Committee[6] and others have suggested multiple objectives along these lines; (1) to provide guidance to individual farmers in the efficient combination of their resources, (2) to analyze the impact of public and private programs and policies on the use of farm resources and (3) to design programs of adjustment for farming areas. Similarly, S. Warren[7] has suggested the dual objectives of guiding the individual entrepreneur and of acquiring a broader understanding of the agricultural industry.

The individual farm and broader industry or social objectives are sometimes looked upon as incongruous. They are not however. Both channel to the same end in respect to resource efficiency. And in neither case does it make sense to divorce completely the one consideration from the other. Agriculture as a competitive industry provides an environment in which the best use of resources by the individual firm can result in the most efficient use of resources from the standpoint of society with the exceptions noted.[8] Elementary equilibrium analysis suggests that under competitive conditions a maximum social product can be forthcoming (with a given pattern of personal income) only if consumers maximize their satisfactions, business firms maximize profits, and owners of resources maximize their incomes. Theoretically, a perfect use of resources within firms (scale of operations and combination of resources and products) would automatically bring about an optimum use between firms and industries. Likewise an attack on the resource efficiency front which brought about perfect allocations between industries would largely necessitate the optimum within-firm positions. The conditions necessary for maximization of profits by the individual business in a competitive environment are also those necessary for an optimum use of society's

[3] Sherman E. Johnson, "Recent Trends in Farm Management," mimeographed. March 1941.

[4] W. W. Wilcox, "Research in Economics of Farm Production," *Journal of Farm Economics* (August 1947).

[5] Report of Committee on Farm Management Terminology, *Journal of Farm Economics,* February 1941.

[6] W. W. Wilcox, S. W. Warren, and S. E. Johnson, Social Science Research Council Bulletin 52, *Farm Management Research, 1940–41.*

[7] S. W. Warren, "Statistical Analysis in Farm Management Research," *Journal of Farm Economics,* February 1936.

[8] The ends of the individual farmer and of society in respect to use of resources conflict mainly because of divergences in costs and returns. These divergences grow largely out of 1. uncertainty and other imperfections of the market, and 2. leasing arrangements and other institutional factors. Too, there are some segments of agriculture which are not competitive in the sense that an equilibrium of the firm coincides with the most efficient use of society's resources. Other exceptions are pointed out elsewhere. However, within the limits of these conditional forces, more efficient combinations of resources on individual farms augment the social net product.

resources.[9] The pricing and profits system becomes a common vehicle through which these two entities can arrive at mutually consistent solutions.

Some still insist that the sole objective of research is to help the individual farmer "make more profit." However, the ultimate objectives of their research are obviously more deeply rooted. This single avowed objective is untenable on the basis of research in the past. Inherent in past investigations has been the objective of "helping farmers maximize profits in a manner consistent with the most efficient use of resources from the standpoint of society." Had the sole objective been that of helping farmers make more profits (consideration of social welfare excluded) additional alternatives might have been exploited. Farmers might have been shown how and when to form monopolies while curtailing production in cases of inelastic demands; to employ price discrimination between different groups of consumers and to obtain higher protective tariffs and similar devices in instances where individual producer groups might benefit. These are all means which may be employed if the goal were solely that of helping the individual firm maximize returns. And some are obviously more remunerative than the extension of certain simple farm practices. Yet farm management workers have directed efforts in the opposite direction. This is sufficient evidence that even those who have given the farm definition have been, perhaps unwittingly, concerned with at least one welfare objective. Hence, the objectives of farm management research might well be restated in the following manner which reconciles the historic direction of research, all previously stated objectives, and present-day needs. *Farm Management research relates to the study of the economic efficiency and productivity of farm resources. Its specific objectives are (1) to guide individual farmers in the best use of their resources and in a manner compatible with the welfare of society and (2) to provide fundamental analyses of the efficiency of farm resource combinations which can serve as a basis for bettering the public administration of resources where agricultural policy or institutions which condition production efficiency are concerned.*

So defined, the economics of farm production has an important role to play in the overall analysis of agriculture. Equilibrium in respect to resource efficiency requires that an optimum allocation of resources (equation of marginal value productivities) exist within firms, between firms and between industries. Farm management research can accomplish much (but obviously not all) in facilitating these necessary conditions. As long as any vestige of a pricing system is retained as an allocator of resources on the part of the consuming economy, research which relays the relative productivity of resources

[9] There are, of course, numerous qualifications which must be made for this statement. It is recognized that there are certain segments of agriculture which cannot be categorized purely and simply as competitive; that the pricing mechanism is not perfect as an allocator of resources and that institutional and other forces have a heavy impact on the efficiency with which farm resources are allocated. These provide a challenge in economic research, however, to fashion means by which the interests of the individual can be made compatible with the interests of society in the use of resources.

to farm operators and increases the mobility of resources is indeed important. Further, the field of investigation occupies an important pivotal position in the economics of agriculture. Policies, customs, and institutions which condition production efficiency all thread through the individual firm at some point. Accordingly, most have a production economics aspect. The goal of helping farmers make more money is an important and primary objective. But there is also a large need or market for other types of analysis which farm management research is well adapted to perform. It is a basic source for data required in the efficient management of resources either by the individual or by the public.[10]

Thus far we have attempted to reconcile some of the apparent conflicts in objectives. The gap is nowhere nearly as wide as is sometimes imagined. Regardless of the front from which resource efficiency is attacked, all concerned are working toward a common goal. More important than the specific area of concentration is the recognition of interrelationships between the various problem levels and that real accomplishment is attained in each.

PROBLEM CONCEPTS

Objectives of farm production economics research are inherently and inseparably two-fold. However, because of the limited scope of a single paper

[10] Differentiation is sometimes made between farm management and the economics of farm production: The former is taken as embracing the individual firm and the latter as embracing the industry aspects of farm production as well as certain policy implications. Aside from the very real limitation of individual capacities there is little academic justification in drawing this fine line between the study of the tree and the forest. The two are entirely complementary. There are many examples for which a study based on a sample of farms will lead to erroneous conclusions if the population outcome is disregarded. It may be true, for example, that if a fraction of the total number of farms adopt an output-increasing technique their incomes will be increased. But should the majority of the population adopt the technique, and if, as the market specialists indicate, the demand for the product in question is inelastic, farm incomes will eventually be lowered. One may isolate a few farms and study the returns from their adoption of complete soil conservation plans. The returns may appear positive on the basis of the sample study. Yet it may be true that were all farms in the area to produce additional roughage, bid for more cattle as roughage consuming livestock or produce more dairy products the structure of market prices might be altered to change incomes in the opposite direction. Frequently, individual operators cannot adopt recommendations growing out of research unless changes are brought about in the structure of the industry or agricultural region. With a given supply of resources such as land (and land products) individuals can expand their operations (a common recommendation of farm management studies) only if others contract the scale of operations or abandon farming and move into other occupations. Conversely, applied phases of certain broad problems can best be studied through the individual farm. Certainly there is need for linking the firm and aggregate aspects of production efficiency to a greater extent than has held in the past. The research worker is not without public responsibility. Unlike the commercial farm manager or corporation executive, he is not hired from the accounts of the individual resource owner. Instead, as a member of that socially financed institution, the agricultural experiment station, he is charged with extending the welfare of society in general and individual farmers specifically as a means to this end.

we now turn to examination of some traditional research procedures which have first impact in solving the production problems of individual farmers. An important portion of the resources devoted to farm management research have focused on the producing unit. What are the fundamental problems facing this unit? What are the analytical tools and models which furnish the hypotheses about the type of information, design of sample and statistical analysis necessary if concrete data *which farmers can use* is to be provided? How well has farm management research been able to "solve" these problems? These are listed after some elementary but useful concepts and steps in research are outlined. Unless problems, hypotheses and solutions are formulated in some orderly fashion, the research worker is likely to become lost in the throes of collecting figures.

Scientific research should be a problem-solving activity. It is not mere complication of figures. Some fundamental steps in problem solving are these: (1) Formulation of models and criteria which establish the ideal or practical optimum—the conditions which must hold if the given end is to be fully attained. It is this model which provides the theoretical solution and serves as the a priori hypothesis for establishing quantitative relationships with data which can be identified and measured. (2) Determining the extent and the reasons why the existing state deviates from the ideal or practical optimum. (This includes evaluation of the existing state on the basis of the criteria appropriate for the given objective.) (3) Establishing the appropriate means and providing the concrete quantitative data which serve as the basis of action in getting from the "existing" to the "optimum." In other words, scientific research must explain "how far to go" and "how to get there." And at some point it must "provide the figures" which make quantitative solution possible.

Research in the economics of farm production relates to the end of efficiency in the use of farm resources.[11] Accordingly, a "problem" exists in any case where the resources of individual farms (and consequently those of society) are being used inefficiently—whenever a gap occurs between the existing use of resources and the optimum (which may be established quantitatively, theoretically or otherwise). This is the fundamental problem area of production economics research. However, in the next section, the production problems of individual farmers have been presented in a somewhat different vein for obvious reasons.

---

[11] Resource efficiency is only one problem relating to economic welfare. Others include equity in the distribution of income, stability, and security in the economic system, individual choice and economic progress. Several of these are closely allied or are mutually interdependent. It is possible that resource efficiency or its aspect of other welfare goals (as economic progress) might be submerged within limits in favor of still other goals. Even then it is necessary to know the loss in efficiency before social evaluation can be made of extending other objectives or in selecting between alternative means to other ends.

PROBLEMS TO BE SOLVED IN PRODUCTION

Since farm management has been aimed at solving the "problems" of individual farms as business units, we have classified the specific problems of production below. We are interested in the extent to which some traditional procedures "solve" these specific "problems" for farmers. This categorization of the "problems" is perhaps unorthodox. The "problems" and the "problem solving tools" might be presented more concisely in the vein of modern economic terminology.[12] However, in keeping with the nature of this paper they are presented in the sense of the very simplest production system. The following classification has also been employed partly since the problems emerge and must be solved in somewhat this very context in the ebb and flow of everyday life but mainly because certain traditional research procedures partially follow this classification. In the long run numerous of these merge and are identical. However, in the short run they are often separable, and direct solution requires their segregation. Obviously, all are encompassed by the last. In each case the economic concepts which provide the theoretical answer or the hypothesis about the nature and kind of data and the design of the sample appropriate if the problem is to be answered are included (in parentheses).

(1) The level of output to be attained from (or the rate of input applied to) fixed or specialized resources. (Diminishing returns and equation of marginal additional, cost and revenue.)

(2) The combination of resources to produce a given output of product. (Marginal rates of factor substitution, product contours and equation of productivities and costs of resources.)

(3) The combination of enterprises within a given time period. (Marginal rates of transformation, equation of marginal returns in various alternatives or proportionality of prices and marginal rates of product substitution.)

(4) The timing of production (sales) given certainty (near) as to price variation—the problem of seasonal price variations. (A special case of

---

[12] The "problems of production" might have been presented in alternative statements such as—the combination of resources, including scale of operations and enterprise selection, under static and non-static conditions; problems of physical transformations, including product into product and factor into product, and formulation of price expectations; or in a broader sense, the allocation of resources within firms, between firms, and between industries. The mode of presentation employed serves better here. The problem of terminology is important, however, and partially serves as an obstacle to applied-pure scientific progress in economics. Although the problem is mutual and the solution is in common, the "language" of the applied economist is not "fashionable" to the pure economist and vice versa. Accordingly, one does not fully realize the accomplishments of the other and a fertile interflow of ideas is prohibited or each misunderstands and underestimates the accomplishments of the other. In this paper an attempt has been made to link the two "languages" wherever possible by qualifying the one in terms of the other. The stage for progress will indeed be established when the applied economist understands what the pure economist "is about" and equally when the latter understands the activities of the other.

problem 3 with output of a given commodity in two different time periods taking on the same relationships as output of two commodities at a given point in time.)

(5) The level of resource conservation. (A special consideration of problem 1 with a different time span consideration and including considerations of time preference and interest rates.)

(6) The optimum scale of operations. (Returns to scale and short-run and long-run curves; equation of marginal costs and returns, capital rationing, return discounting, and risk aversion.)

(7) The method of obtaining control of the resources to be used in production and the consequent combination of resources. (Equity ratios and principles of increasing risk, resource productivities and market prices for factors, price and production uncertainties and discounting of future returns.)

(8) Adjusting to change and uncertainty of the market and production process including growth of the business over time. (Probability distributions, discounting returns, flexibility and adaptability of the enterprise, timing of production and dispersion and convergence of expected prices.)

These are the specific categories of economic "problems" to be solved in farm production.[13] Our model is over-simplified. Were it true that farmers had unlimited capital, then each specific "problem" could be considered somewhat apart from the others. In actual life the system is more complicated. Farmers generally have limited capital and returns can then be maximized not by attaining the optimum position for any one category, but capital must be allocated to equate the value of its marginal product throughout the business. Then too, the problem of adjusting the risk and uncertainty is much

[13] In order to indicate that though the facet differs even these applied problems of production are common to the individual and society, examples of each are included here. Obviously, farm management research should be able to provide answers in either case. The number refers to the corresponding problem cited in the text. 1. To the individual—the level of yield per acre, milk production per cow of given capacity. To society—the numbers and marketing weight of hogs if world food commitments are met, the intensity of cultivating present before the reclamation of new lands. 2. To the individual—whether to use a chopper or loader for 30 acres of hay, whether to grow 20 litters on concrete or clean ground. To society—the acreage of soybeans and corn to be grown to allow a maximum output of meat and export of cereal grains, the optimum combination of labor and capital in agriculture. 3. Individual—the selection of crop or/and livestock enterprises. Society—the pattern of production most desirable in the current emergency, the extent to which production adequately adjusts to prices expressed by consumers how to facilitate needed adjustments in problem areas. 4. Individual—whether to maintain a "summer" or "winter" dairy. Society (milk marketing administration)—prices and policies to obtain desired seasonal quantities of milk. 5. Individual—level of feeding breeding stock in feed emergencies, level of land conservation. Society—extent of conservation practices vital to society but uneconomic to the individual and how to attain their achievement. 6 & 7. Individual—to buy a small farm or rent a large one, to abstain from borrowing and curtail operations. Society—kinds and amounts of credit not adequately provided through market mechanisms, changes in tenure institutions to improve resource combinations. 8. Individual—how to predict future prices, maintain output and minimize risk, adjusting production over time. Society—extent of gains in resource efficiency possible from forward prices, crop insurance and credit policy.

more complex than presented here. The core of the "farm management problem" revolves largely around these two factors. Complex models exist which treat these adequately. However, because of the limited scope of this paper and since farm management research traditionally has been unable or made little attempt to make substantial progress on either problem, the remainder of this paper will be restricted to analysis of some techniques aimed at answering the less complex problems. Although the facets are different, the central problems of production are the same to the individual business unit and to society. This again emphasizes the need for double-barrelled objectives in farm management research or a coordinated attack on the problems.

DATA NEEDED FOR PERFECT ANSWERS

Were it possible to attain the ideal and provide the perfect answer to each of the farmer's production "problems," what information would be needed? On the one hand the list of basic data would include a complete inventory of input-output ratios or production coefficients. (Viz., rates of production, rates of transformation, etc.—ratio of livestock output to feed input for livestock fed at different levels; crop yields from all conceivable rotations, rates of fertilization, numbers of cultivations, varieties of seed, etc.; marginal rate of substitution of protein, carbohydrates and roughage feeds for each other in producing a given output of livestock; rate of substitution of machines and labor in producing a given amount of output; machinery depreciation, repairs and fuel requirements when used for varying acreages; time and motion studies indicating labor requirements for labor-saving as compared to labor-using techniques; etc.) Given this complete list of existing or yet-to-be-discovered physical data (the task of establishing input-output ratios per se is technology rather than economics) only one other type of data would be necessary for perfect solution to the individual farmer's production "problems." This is knowledge of future prices (and costs). Given these two sets of data, the perfect plan could be fashioned and on a research basis, two groups of investigators would be required: (1) the technologist to complete the list of production functions or input-output ratios and (2) the price specialist to provide knowledge of future prices. No other data would be necessary. Management economics would then simply involve the activity of combining these two sets of complete data. (Although with this knowledge the management function would be indeed minimized.) There would need be no field of farm management research. No new principle of profit maximization would be necessary. These are already given in economics. (A principle for giving the optimum answer for each of the simpler "problems" already exists, given the data, and can be proven by simple arithmetic, higher mathematics or common sense. The ninth problem would no longer exist.) Given unlimited capital the farm operator would, on the basis of the given physical and price data, increase crop yields per acre as long as marginal (additional) costs were greater than marginal returns. With limited capital he would also know exactly whether to increase crop yields via fertilizer or whether the marginal return of the same capital invested in protein feed or more or inherently higher producing dairy cows would be greater. A field of educational and extension farm management alone would be needed to teach principles of production economics or profit maximization. (Farm records would still be required to give an inventory of the individual's input-output ratios but these would not be necessary for research or between farm comparisons since the inventory of production functions or input-output ratios and price data would indicate the more profitable.)

The examples of basic data necessary for perfect answers to the "production problems" are extremes. Obviously, this complete inventory of data will never be available since the countless number of production functions yet to be discovered would require a gigantic army of research workers. Then why bother the imagination with this Utopian state of affairs? The reason is simple. It points the direction which research should move however slow the progress. It also suggests the futility of searching for "new principles" of profit maximization in farming when the need is obviously for the basic technological and price data necessary for existing principles. Lack of these perfect data is also suggestive of the type of substitute economic data needed in answering the specific problems.

EXAMINATION OF SOME TRADITIONAL PROCEDURES

The importance of research directed at guidance of the individual farm has already been pointed out. Probably more rather than fewer resources should be invested in this sector of economic research. But before more funds are invested stock should be taken of present procedures. To what extent do present research techniques result in findings which tell the farmer "the direction to adjust," "how far to go" and "how to get there?" To what extent do the findings correspond with known and established economic models and technical relationships?

Only a few research techniques can be explored in a paper such as this. Accordingly, the remaining space will be devoted mainly to techniques and studies which often result in findings contradictory to known economic relationships and conditions necessary for profit maximization. One of these is the factors-affecting-farm-profits type of study in which data are sorted into a few groups on the basis of one variable, mean income computed and then are sorted again on the basis of other variables. Labor, income, management return or other residual "profit" figures are related to each "independent" variable as a measure of the relative efficiency (profitability) of the specific resource combinations. It is the resulting findings which most often contradict known economic principles and technical relationships.

Some suggest increasing returns where it is well established that diminishing returns exist. Others imply no economic limit to the level which output should be raised or one factor substituted for another. Many overestimate the productivity of resource inputs throughout. On the following pages an attempt is made to uncover some of the inherent steps in research which may lead to distorted findings.

A common defect in farm management research has been the abuse given the commonly employed measures of efficiency. The labor, management or other residual income figure used as an index of efficiency is computed by charging part or all of the resources employed at market rates or prices. In principle this concept is acceptable if resources are charged at their actual productivity. Yet as used, this measure of efficiency may often lead to erroneous conclusions. If market rates are lower than the actual net productivity of the resources employed, the residual "profit" figure will include one component which is not due to efficiency of the given resource combination or farm practice but to the quantity of resources employed. In periods when the actual productivity of resources is above their market price, practices found on large farms will appear relatively too profitable as compared to practices found on farms employing small quantities of resources. In periods when the market price is greater than the productivity the reverse will hold true. It is undoubtedly true that the efficiency (or lack of) attributed to minor practices (or perhaps major resource combination) has often been due to scale of operations. Refinements can be made which at least partially eliminate these imperfections.[14] Although this weakness is generally recognized, research workers continue to "evaluate" minor practices on the basis of this imperfect criterion when the sample studied is small and includes large variations in the quantities of resources employed. It is also extremely doubtful that this technique is appropriate for determining the economic optimum milk output per cow or in studying resource combinations which vary with farm size.

The traditional factors-affecting-farm-profits study has attempted to get at the "level of output problem" by relating "profits" to the index of crop yields or rate of livestock production. The sample data are sorted into groups on the basis of (say) crop yield indices and the average "profits" for each group is computed. The results may show, for example, that three groups of farms with average crop yield indices of 75, 105, and 130 have labor incomes of $60, $75, and $650 respectively. These figures (as well as many published) imply increasing returns and no economic limit to level of output per unit of specialized resource. Yet it is common knowledge that diminishing returns

---

[14] See the article "Production Functions from a Random Sample of Farms," *Journal of Farm Economics* (November 1946). The note on efficiency is relevant. Another alternative is to include in a study only farms which employ approximately the same kinds and quantities of resources.

generally prevail in agriculture, and that returns will be lessened if inputs are extended beyond the point where marginal (additional) costs become greater than marginal (additional) returns. Finally, these data seldom provide the basis for action by the individual farmer in the sense that they tell the farmer "how to get there" or "how far to go." The farmer is told nothing about the components of these higher yields or profits. Should he simply try to attain the yields shown for the high profit farms in any manner whatsoever? The facts are interesting but there are no concrete data which the farmer can apply to his own farm. Information which is actually more useful on a specific farm is this: (1) Simple knowledge that (with unlimited capital) net return will be maximized if yields are increased as long as the value of the increased product is greater than the cost of the added input, and (2) data which show the added physical output in yield with variation in rates of fertilizer application, crop rotations, etc. (to which he can apply known or expected prices). These are the data and information which can be put into action.

FIGURE 1 FIGURE 2

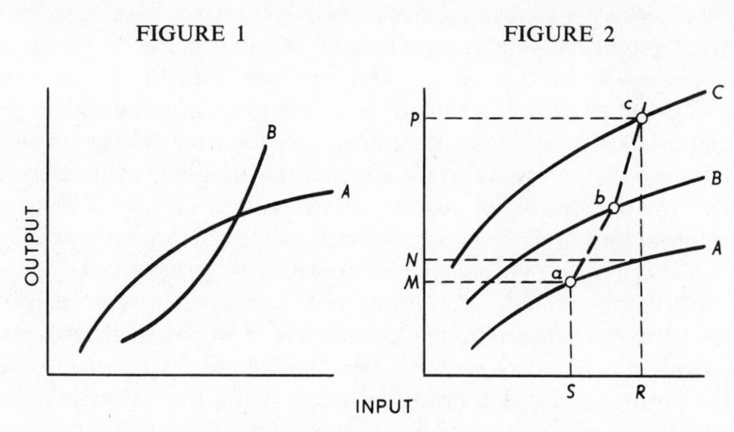

The farmer is interested in the relationship of input (or cost) to output (or profit) and only incidentally of output to profit. His control rests on inputs. Accordingly, input has been related to output in the following attempt to explain why traditional procedures may suggest distorted relationships and over estimate the productivity of specific inputs. (The basic reasoning is the same were output related to profit.) It is known that the existing production function or input-output curve for a specific resource applied to land (fertilizer crop rotation, etc.) follows, over the major portion, the nature of curve A in Figure 1.[15] Data of the nature presented above imply the curve B.

[15] Increasing returns does hold in a fairly narrow range of agriculture. It is well known, however, that the important range of production takes place largely in the range of decreasing returns. For this reason the details of an initial stage of increasing returns has not been incorporated into Figures 1 and 2.

Distorted findings relative to resource productivity and to relationships between input and output may be explained by several factors: one is the possibility that farms with high crop yields also are using large amounts of resources. Part of the returns to these resources are then attributed to crop yields. Another, one obviously expected, is that better farmers are on the high yielding crop land and part of the efficiency (profit) of other practices is being attributed to crop yields. However, another important economic concept and statistical or technological relationship is involved. It is the notion that a distinct production function or input-output curve exists for each quality of resource. That "low," "medium" and "high" crop yields will be found especially on sample farms with land of low, medium and high productivity respectively is almost certain. Figure 2 illustrates the expected outcome when this occurs. Curves A, B, and C represent the production function (yield of crop for varying levels of fertilizer input, rotation, etc.) on three soil types of "low," "medium" and "high" productivity respectively. The mean crop yield indices obtained by sorting farms into three groups have the partial effects of isolating the three points a, b, and c— one on each of the production functions. This gives the "apparent" input-output curve (and a corresponding profit curve) of abc. It is not a distinct production function in itself but instead connects three points on several separate input-output curves. Whereas it implies that if farmers with low yields (including those on soil of "low" productivity) increase inputs from OS to OR they will traverse curve abc, and crop yields (or profits) will increase from OM to OP. However, since farmers on soil of "low" productivity are faced with the true production function A, an input of OR gives a yield of not OP but only ON. Extension of inputs with the hope of getting yields of OP may result in less than maximum profits.

The nature of the "apparent" production function grows more out of substitution of one soil type for another in the process of data sorting (grouping of the farms on the basis of crop indices) as from inputs or practices which any one farmer may be able to control on his own farm. The analysis then not only distorts the nature of the relationship but overestimates the productivity of the input throughout the entire range. (This is true even if the apparent curve abc is a straight line or slopes to the right—constant or decreasing returns.) This is evidenced in the example since the rate of increase (slope) of the "apparent" production function is greater than for any one of the other three. Even the farmer on the most productive land would not realize an increase in output per unit of input as great as is implied by the "apparent" curve.

In a sample which is "sorted" by one variable (practice) then succeedingly by others and where the most (and least) productive practices tend to be grouped on farms, the figures of each sort will overestimate the productivity of the particular input. The overestimate of the productivity of any one input (practice) will then be compounded in proportion to the number of others investigated.

The findings of the agronomist based on a random (or block) sample of farms and relating yield to rate of fertilizer application would have little meaning: The effect of varying rates of fertilization would be confounded with differences in soil type, rotations, seed variety and a multitude of other factors. Similarly, the farm management research worker must consider the sampling or experimental design employed by the technologists if he is to investigate those problems in which the underlying technological relationships are largely expressed in their dollar-and-cents counterpart. Only then can the components of higher crop-yield profits be broken down such that individual farmers can take the data and apply the specific elements to their own farm.

The same approach is often employed in relating milk output per cow (or other rates of livestock production) to "profits." The problem of the most profitable level of milk output per cow can be broken down into two distinct elements: (1) The milk output of a cow of given inherent capacity can be increased by varying the rate of grain feeding or application of other inputs (problem 1). (2) A cow of one inherent capacity can be substituted for a cow of another inherent capacity in producing a given output of milk ("200 pound" cows can be substituted for "400 pound" cows or vice versa—problem 2). (In other words, feed can be substituted for cows or cows can be substituted for still other cows in obtaining a given output of milk.) The traditional findings ordinarily indicate no economic limit to which milk production per cow may be extended. Again a likely explanation is that of Figure 2: The means computed for the groups isolate only single points on different input-output curves and overestimate productivities throughout. Finally, there is little economic logic in attempts to establish that one level of milk output is most profitable since it is known that the most remunerative level of grain feeding depends on milk/feed price relationships.

We now pass to a clear-cut example of substitution—substitution of one resource for another in producing a given output of product (problem 2). Farm management research has sometimes been aimed at establishing the level of protein feeding for hogs (or similar practice that gives the greatest net "profit" or the greatest return per dollar fed). On the basis of experimental data for hogs of 35–75 pounds it is known that the product contour in producing 100 pounds of pork is of the general nature shown in Figure 3. The product contour or curve shown represents the alternative combinations of protein and corn that can be employed in producing 100 pounds of pork. The 100 pounds of pork can be produced with combination A of 330 pounds of carbohydrates and 45 pounds of protein, with combination B of 250 pounds of carbohydrates and 51 pounds of protein or with combination C of 64 and 225 pounds respectively. Again, there is little economic logic in attempts to establish that one protein-corn combination is always the most profitable.

The reason that farm sample or record data tends to indicate that one combination is always most profitable is partially explained by the illustration of Figure 4. Three assumed product contours are presented: A is representative of pork production which includes "disease-free lots," "high-fecundity sows," and "vitamin-complete ration." B represents production which includes only "disease-free lots" and C represents production which includes none of the three. (This is about what farm sample data indicates—individual practices on farms are highly associated.) The traditional procedure divides the farm sample data into (say) three groups—high, medium and low levels of protein feeding and computes means of feed requirements for each. The a

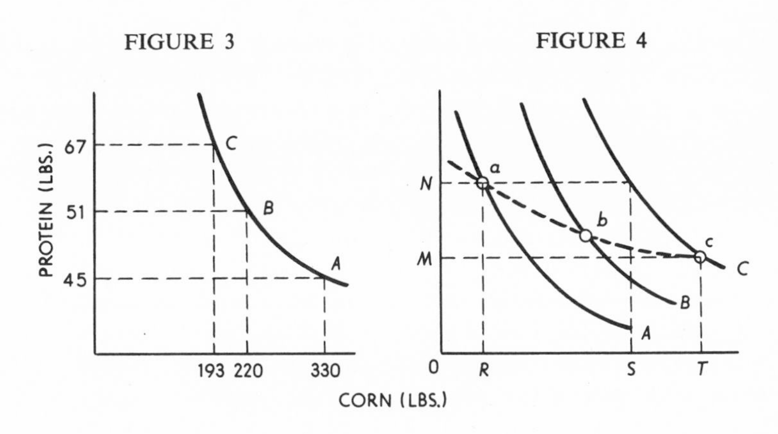

priori probability is nearly 1 that the group of farmers feeding small amounts of protein will include most of those who have diseased lots, vitamin-lacking rations, etc. In effect the three means will then be representative of single points on each of the three different curves (a, b, and c). This implies a product contour (curve showing the possible protein/carbohydrate combination in producing 100 pounds of pork) of the nature indicated by the line abc. On the basis of this curve, it appears that if farmers for which the average "c" is computed were to increase protein feeding from OM to ON they will reduce carbohydrate requirements from OT to OR. However, if they vary protein feed only they move not up the "apparent" product contour abc but up the real curve C. Corn requirements thus decrease only from OT to OS. The results of substituting high for low fecundity sows, disease-free for diseased-lots and mineral-complete rations are confounded with the substitution of protein for corn. The data overestimate the marginal rate of substitution of protein for corn. Again the warp and woof of the cloth are not segregated and isolated such that the farmer can apply the information in a meaningful manner in evaluating the economy of rations.

The farm management data are ordinarily presented in monetary terms—returns per $100 feed fed or as labor income. Yet the basic technological relationships and complexities still exist. They are not removed by attaching a dollar sign to the data.

Let us examine still another "production problem"—the selection of a haying method. This problem unfolds itself to the individual farmer mainly as "problem 2"—the substitution of capital for labor in putting up a given acreage of hay. But when the results are to be established on the basis of a farm sample, it also involves another economic concept which provides the hypothesis about the appropriate sample design and statistical analysis. This is the concept of a cost curve (problem 6) and unless recognized in designing

FIGURE 5

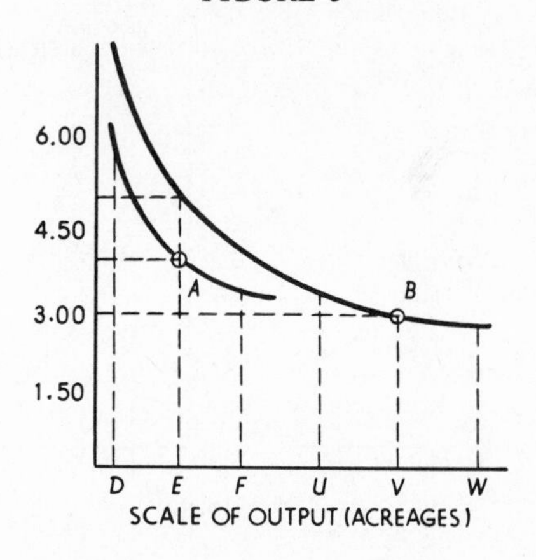

the investigation the published findings may lead to erroneous decisions. Figure 5 illustrates a likely outcome if this concept is ignored. The curve A represents unit costs for putting up hay by "loader." Curve B is representative of that for a "baler"—fixed outlay and high unit costs for small acreages. The "baler" is new while the "loader" is an old technique. Because of the high fixed or initial costs it can be expected that the "baler" will be found mainly on farms with a large hay output.

Various sampling and statistical techniques have been used in analyzing problems of this nature. In some instances an unstratified sample of all haying methods has been employed with the result that data is obtained for perhaps six choppers, sixty loaders, twenty balers, and two buck rakes. Means are then presented without indication of sampling errors or fiducial limits. Let us assume in our example that the efficiency of the overall sample has been increased at least to the extent that equal numbers of records are obtained for "loaders" and "balers." (No other sample or experimental design is employed.) Then suppose that we follow traditional procedures and compute the mean costs per ton of putting up hay with "loaders" and "balers." We thus get two means (assumed) of $3.87 and $2.80 respectively and on the basis of these the baler appears most efficient. But what have we? Because the balers are found on large farms, our "baler sample" includes mainly farms with acreages between U and W and the mean is representative of one point (V) on this curve. Our "loader" sample includes farms with acreages between D and F (with a mean of E). If farms with a hay acreage of E adopt a "baler," their per ton costs are not $2.80 as the computed mean suggests but $5.

The means are misleading. To provide a true basis for evaluating haying methods by farmers, the concept of the cost curve must be recognized and a sample designed accordingly. This requires not merely the simple stratification presented in our example above (which is more efficient than an unstratified sample drawn from the entire "haying" population). Rather the most efficient sample in this case is a purposive or objective sample (but still random) drawn separately for each the baler and loader. It must allow an estimate of the cost curve or its equivalent for each method. The sample would then include equal numbers of farms with hay acreages varying throughout the practical range of operations.[16]

We could cite other examples of research in which traditional procedures suggest erroneous courses of action because the underlying economic and physical relationships are not recognized or separated in designing the study. Farm management research directed at the individual firm has been too much concerned with obtaining "all-purpose" data—data which attempt to answer all the "production problems" in a single blow by sorting and resorting information from a given sample of records. The consequences often are that none are solved in a useful quantitative manner since experimental or sample controls are imperfect. True, the farm business is an entity and profits can be maximized only by equating marginal returns in the various alternatives. Yet these relative returns are not given by the traditional factors-associated-with-farm-profits study. It is because the fundamental economic models and underlying physical relationships are ignored that many of the so-called principles of farm management take on hollow or erroneous meaning at some point. (They imply no economic limits.) How can the farmer put into direct use the finding that "the higher the crop yield index the higher the farm profits"? It tells him nothing about the components of the higher yields found on some farms and whether he would profit by their adoption.

Our critique of the traditional findings which imply that input and substitution of resources should be extended indefinitely, has perhaps been too severe. To the extent that farmers generally apply inputs short of the rate

[16] Too, certain other problems of statistical and technological controls are present in haying studies and thus pose the possibility that more reliable data can be obtained through controlled experiments. The estimation of the pure physical relationship—the relative quantity of labor required per ton by various methods—may be distorted on a basis of farm data since (1) farms with the new technique have on the average, newer machines and fewer repair stops or (2) may have different kinds and yields of hay.

which is economically efficient then a blanket recommendation to this effect is not completely in error. Even then many farmers may have a rational explanation of their position. Farming is notably an industry short on capital. In this case and especially where much of the land is tenant-operated the problem of maximum returns may be more nearly one of applying a variable resource as capital to a fixed resource as land in a manner to give the greatest product per unit of the former rather than the latter resource. Too, studies which set out to establish *the one most profitable* level of crop or livestock output underestimate the mental ability of farmers. Statistics indicate that many farmers understand the elementary concept of diminishing productivity and vary the rates of grain-feeding dairy cattle, marketing weights of hogs and cattle and rates of fertilizer application in response to changes in commodity-price/resource-cost relationships.

There is an element of merit in the idea sometimes forwarded that the factors-affecting-farm-profits type of study is "qualitative" rather than "quantitative" (attempts to find "the presence of" factors affecting profits rather than the "numerical effect" of one variable or input on farm income). The contribution of these "qualitative findings" is also questionable where they contradict and are not qualified in terms of known economic and physical relationships. (The findings are often presented as graphs or regressions of "profit" on independent variables and thus express a quantitative relationship.) If this research is to be looked upon purely as qualitative, then the data might best be "sorted" by income and the values of other factors explained in terms of "the characteristics or description of high income farms" rather than "sorted" by values of independent variables, related to income and couched in terms of "the effect of these variables on farm profits." Finally, even if research along traditional lines is looked upon as "qualitative" rather than "quantitative," identical basic issues are at stake. It is mainly because the "presence of" erroneous relationships are "found" that errors in "numerical values" of relationships are "found" and vice versa. This can again be illustrated by Figure 4. The quantitative productivity of the resources is overestimated by curve abc only because the design in the assumed study is one which estimates the "presence of" a curve abc. Is it not as much an error to find "the presence" of a functional relationship which does not exist in a practical sense as to estimate magnitudes of this same relationship?

Without question, farm management research has made some important contributions in establishing the "quantitative" and "qualitative" productivity of farm resources. Perhaps even findings with the limitation outlined here have been of value as "persuaders." Yet as a maturing field of study, farm management should be capable of closing some gaps that still exist.

Ideally, the individual farm might best be guided in the use of its resources were a complete inventory of production functions available along with information on future prices. Even in this real world and in the absence of perfect price expectations, the individual can probably best be guided on levels of crop and livestock production, substitution of feeds and on similar problems from the results of controlled experiments (with some simulation of farm conditions) translated into economic terms. The notion that experiment stations should tomorrow attempt isolation of all these countless production functions is, of course, preposterous. It is unnecessary to go thus far. Even a few which allow extrapolation with a reasonable degree of accuracy would facilitate a better combination of farm resources and eliminate the need for at least part of the traditional farm surveys which probe in this area. (In addition to the Jensen production function for dairy cows of high capacity, for example, two or three more for typical farm cows of other capacities are needed and might suffice.) The professional interests of physical scientists have generally led to the establishment of only one or a few points on the upper reaches of the production function. Increasingly, there is a need for collaboration between economists and physical scientists in the experimental determination of the full practical range of the curve and in its economic interpretation.

Certain physical input-output ratios or production coefficients are not subject to feasible determination by "experimental plot" methods. But even though these are based on farm survey or record data, the experimental design techniques applicable in the "trial-plot" must be incorporated in the farm sample where the basic characteristics of the data are similar. The fact that physical data is gathered from a farm enumeration rather than from an experiment does not, by some magic, convert it from technology to economics. Neither does it change the nature of the appropriate statistical controls.

SAMPLE DESIGNS

Discussions of sampling procedures as applied to farm management have largely missed the crux of the problem. Most have centered around random samples versus block samples versus lack of scientific sampling procedure. The relative efficiency of different sampling methods is not a subjective phenomenon but can be measured quantitatively. It is true, however, that so much emphasis has been focused on the "random versus block" argument that the real core of farm production economics sampling has been bypassed. It is now common knowledge that if the main objective of the survey is estimation of such parameters as mean values or frequency distributions of a single population, the most efficient sample (statistically) is a random (or stratified random) sample. If the primary objective is the comparison of means (and related statistics) between two or more discrete populations (e.g., mean income for "owned" and "rented" farms) a random sample should be drawn from within each of the two populations. Although the appropriate size of sample will depend upon the variance of each population, a sample of equal size might, for example, be drawn from each. (This is in contrast with the procedure wherein a sample is drawn from the entire "haying population" such that one gets four "choppers," seventy "loaders" and fifteen "balers" when the real objective is to make comparisons between the distinct hay-making populations or techniques.)

Proponents of "block" sampling contend that they are not attempting to make population estimates but to establish relationships. (Most do use the sample data to enumerate certain characteristics of the area. This involves, of course, use of the means or other statistics as an estimate of the population parameter.) The fundamental issue, however, is not one of population estimates per se but this: A large number of studies are not directed at estimating the arithmetic or other mean of the population but are actually involved in estimating regression or functional relationships for the population. (Probably well over three-fourths of research based on farm data has been inherently concerned with the regression relationship between two or more variables.) Accordingly, it is true that the most efficient sample in these instances is only infrequently the one most efficient for estimating the arithmetic mean. Yet the appropriate or most efficient sample for estimating regression relationships is not given by a block sample. Neither is the role of the sample as an estimate of the population parameter eliminated. A population parameter is still being estimated but it is a regression coefficient rather than a mean. (This is true even though the statistical analysis employed is simple cross-tabulation.) A sample drawn such that each individual in the universe has the same probability of selection (or a block sample which is a complete census of a restricted population) will give a frequency distribution with the greatest number of cases concentrated around the mean or mode and with few at the extremes (a bell-shaped frequency curve if a normal distribution—although most farm data are skewed toward the upper limit). Obviously, this is not the most efficient sample for estimates of regression coefficients. Instead the appropriate sample is one which gives (approximately) an equal distribution of the independent variate throughout the entire range of the data (as many cases in the tails of the distribution as at the mean, mode or other point of the distribution). The sample is still random but it is stratified in the sense that an equal number of cases are drawn *at random* at each point (or within each interval) over the entire range of the data.

Here is the basic sampling problem of production economics. This is true not only for the studies which relate to the problems cited here but also for many other problems relating to resource efficiency. Empirical studies such as those concerned with returns to scale in agriculture and of the relationship between equity ratios and the willingness to accept risks would ideally be made on samples of this design. These samples are not easily established. Too few characteristics of individuals making up the population have been inventoried. Some possibilities do exist, however. List sampling, samples drawn from master samples and reconnaissance enumeration of the independent variable in question are a few. Yet this, the real problem of sampling in farm production economics research, has scarcely been scratched. It needs much greater attention.

Research in the economics of farm production is still far from fully developed. Too few resources have been devoted to fundamental research and development of methodology. The researcher has been too busy "getting out answers tomorrow." In the long run investigations will be more productive if a greater proportion of research funds are allocated to sample design, to statistical analysis, and to pilot studies which test given economic models.

COMMON PROBLEMS

The problems posed here are not necessarily those which should be given prior consideration in a research program. They are simply the ones which research must solve if it is to provide the "answers" which the individual farmer must have if he is to make a maximum use of his resources. However, an important problem area which has scarcely been scratched from the standpoint of empirical research is this: We previously stated that a basic "problem" is present in resource efficiency when the "existing" use of resources deviates from any theoretical or empirical "optimum" which can be established. More is known about the optimum than about the extent and cause of the gap between the "existing" and the optimum. Theory provides tools which explain the optimum scale of operations and combination of resources in general. Farm management has in a sense attempted to determine an empirical optimum in establishing the characteristics of the "most profitable farm." Obviously, there is some important and sound reasoning in the minds of farmers for not attaining this optimum even though it be what the "most profitable farm is doing." Otherwise the other "seventy-five" percent of the farmers would follow the recommendations of research. Numerous forces condition the use of resources on farms and explain this gap. Included in this list are lack of knowledge, uncertainty of the market, capital rationing and limitations, leasing and tenure imperfections, imperfect adjustments to price and production processes, sociological factors (family-farm relationships), psychological factors (inherent characteristics of individuals), consumption economic considerations (competition of household and business for funds) and general deviation in costs and returns between the specific farm and that outlined under the "optimum." Production economics research should probe further in exploring this gap as reflected on individual farms. Only then will attempts to bring about the most efficient use of farm resources become entirely realistic. Individual farmers can be better advised. But as important is the fact that a base will be laid for altering customs, institutions and programs which conditions the efficiency of farm production. Not all aspects of this "gap" are economic. Accordingly, there is need for cooperative studies with sociologists, psychologists and kindred scientists.

Again, we wish to emphasize the need for relating studies of the agricultural business firm to the economy as a whole. Contributions of research designed to guide the firm into profit equilibrium are real and important. Yet a large part of the research must consider or be justified in terms of the entire economy: 1. The outcome "apparent" from a study of a sample or small group of farms may be entirely misleading were large numbers of farms to make the adjustments and as market prices and costs change accordingly. 2. Recommendations based on sample data ordinarily cannot be brought about unless changes are made in other segments of the area or industry. (viz. adjustments in farm size, etc.) 3. Output—increasing adjustments by all farms must be justified mainly in terms of social welfare where commodity demands are inelastic, as is true for many agricultural products. (Increases in total output result in a smaller rather than a larger industry revenue in case of inelastic demands). 4. The conditions necessary for profit equilibrium are generally necessary for resource efficiency in terms of social welfare. Yet, research should aid in isolating and eliminating areas in which private profit maximization is inconsistent with long-run social objectives. Finally, if the only ends of farm production economics were extension of private profits, some of the more effective means would include output restriction, tariff legislation and other market manipulations on behalf of the farm operator.

13 Stress on Production Economics*

GLENN L. JOHNSON† ‡

This article was written at the invitation of the Editor of this *Journal*. In earlier correspondence the point was made that the author had been "having second thoughts on the decline of some departments of agricultural economics which were of a more applied nature" and that "this year will mark a decade since the emergence of Earl Heady's massive tome," *Economics of Agricultural Production and Resource Use,* Prentice-Hall, Inc. New Jersey, 1952. The suggestion was made to the author "that perhaps you could review developments in the field of production economics since the birth of the Heady *opus*."

Preferably, the article should be viewed as critical of certain developments in our profession, the origins of which extend back in history prior to the lives of any living person and horizontally in our society beyond the realms of production economics and, for that matter, far beyond the social science disciplines. The need is for criticism of a development and not for criticism of the people who participated in the development.

HISTORICAL BACKGROUND

In reviews of this type, it is extremely important to establish and interpret the historical context in which the developments under review take place. Therefore, the initial pages of this paper are devoted to establishing and interpreting the historical setting in which Heady's book was produced and used.

---

* *Australian Journal of Agricultural Economics,* Vol. VII, No. 1 (June 1963), pp. 12–26.

† Michigan State University, East Lansing, Michigan.

‡ The paper has benefited from criticisms and suggestions received from Lowell Hardin, Sam Engene, Dale Hathaway, Vernon Sorenson, L. L. Boger, James Bonnen, Carl Eicher, Karl Wright, Robert Jones, and others. The content, however, remains the sole responsibility of the author.

Historically, the discipline of agricultural economics grew out of an interest in farm management on the part of agricultural technical scientists. Those scientists became interested in the overall operation of farm businesses and proceeded to develop a discipline of farm management without relating the new discipline directly to economics.[1] Later, a number of agriculturalists trained in economics became interested in transferring theoretical economics into the emerging field of study, farm management. Important among these early U.S. contributors to the emerging discipline was Henry Taylor.[2, 3] Somewhat later, John D. Black took up the case for economics in the field of farm management. Black's early contributions were made at Minnesota. Later, as a professor at Harvard, he stressed the need for more economics both in farm management and in the emerging departments of agricultural economics which were beginning to address themselves to problems in marketing, agricultural policy and agricultural prices.[4]

As a Harvard professor, Black was able to make the case for more economics in agricultural economics. Workers in marketing, agricultural policy and price analysis quickly became allies of anyone propounding the use of more economics in a college of agriculture. However, workers in the field of farm management proper resisted. They had strong constituent support among the farmers they serviced well and academic support in the allied technical agricultural disciplines from whence they came. Though these workers employed very little economic theory, they contributed to the solution of many problems facing farmers with relevant information from their accounting and descriptive work and a substantial quantity of common sense. No one can deny that the earlier, non-theoretical farm management workers made real contributions to agriculture, contributions which developed much financial support for the merging discipline of agricultural economics, a debt not yet adequately recognized.

As just noted, the early descriptive, non-theoretical work in farm management was relevant for the solution of practical problems. The philosophy of science which guided these people was expressed in Karl Pearson's *Grammar of Science* and, as such, was essentially positivistic.[5] Though positivism avoids

---

[1] Walter Wilcox, Sherman Johnson, and Stanley Warren, *Farm Management Research 1940–41,* Social Science Research Council, New York, N.Y., Bulletin 52, 1943, pp. 1–4.

[2] J. R. Currie, "A Review of Fifty Years in Farm Management Research," *Journal of Agricultural Economics,* Vol. XI (1955) "... the first serious scientific studies of the economics of farming ... started in the United States of America."

[3] Wilcox, Johnson, and Warren, *op. cit.* p. 4.

[4] J. D. Black, *Introduction to Production Economics* (New York: Henry Holt & Co., 1926); and J. D. Black, and A. G. Black, *Production Organization* (New York: Henry Holt & Co., 1929).

[5] By positivistic, the author means, "the philosophic position that the highest form of knowledge is simple description." *The Dictionary of Philosophy—Ancient—Medieval—Modern,* D. D. Reeves, ed. (Patterson, N.J.: Littlefield, Adams & Co., 1961), p. 243. This position ordinarily holds that goodness and badness are not observable and, hence, not susceptible to description.

purpose and leads eventually to difficulty in defining and solving problems,[6] the charge of irrelevance could not be levelled validly at the early farm management workers. The closeness of these workers to farmers and their problems insured that the positivistic work they did involved the determination of facts which were relevant to the solution of problems facing farmers. However, with the passage of time, the interests of these workers and their successors became introverted instead of focused on problems.[7] Much of the descriptive work began to be done for its own sake, *i.e.,* it concentrated upon repetitive estimation of certain accounting ratios and on repetitive surveys and reports. Essentially, the same pattern of facts was gathered from account keepers and cooperators in surveys, while times and problems changed violently in the 1920's and 1930's.[8] This loss of relevance disturbed those desiring to make a greater place for economic theory in farm management work.

In 1939, T. W. Schultz added to the criticism.[9] He noted that farm management work failed to use economics to focus on the problems of the post-World War I and depression years. He also noted that static economic theory even where used, was not always appropriate and called attention to the theory of the managerial processes expounded by Frank Knight in his *Risk, Uncertainty and Profit.* Though the main impact of Schultz's work was to strengthen the case for theory in farm management, his observations about the inappropriateness of static production economic theory in solving certain problems were astute; they anticipate criticisms of production economics research to be advanced in later pages of this article. More specifically, these later pages will be concerned with lack of attention to problems not definable in terms of static disequilibria. Schultz also stressed that the work of departments and sections of farm management was vulnerable on another score. Attention had been concentrated on the individual farm firm at the expense of dynamic and more macro or aggregative studies of the agricultural economy.[10] Still further, serious questions existed about sampling technique.[11] Statistically trained agricultural economists, therefore, joined the chorus by criticizing the statistical methodologies and technique employed in both farm management survey and farm records work.

After World War II, the irrelevance of much of the positivistic farm management accounting and survey work was clearly apparent to agricultural

---

[6] Purpose is rejected as teleological and nonexplanatory.

[7] A similar situation developed in land economics when a pragmatic "problem-solving" approach competed with a positivistic approach. See L. A. Salter, *A Critical Review of Research in Land Economics* (Minneapolis: University of Minnesota Press, 1948), pp. 39ff.

[8] Wilcox, *et. al., op. cit.* Preface by T. W. Schultz. p, viii.

[9] T. W. Schultz, "Scope and Method in Agricultural Economics Research," *Journal of Political Economy,* Vol. 47 (1939), pp. 709ff.

[10] Wilcox, *et al., op. cit.* preface.

[11] *Ibid,* p. vii and last full paragraph continuing on p. viii.

economists and to administrators.[12] The older or "traditional" type of farm management fell in administrative esteem. Those pre-war departments of farm management, which had existed independently of departments of agricultural economics, were merged with those departments and, for the most part, lost their identity under administrators more fully committed to the use of economics in farm management.[13]

This submersion of farm management into agricultural economics continued to occur intellectually as well as administratively. In the North Central states, the Farm Foundation took steps in 1948 to organize a workshop at Land o'Lakes, Wisconsin. At that workshop, the earlier forms of farm management work were subjected to serious intellectual examination. The examination started at Land o'Lakes was continued at the Black Duck workshop a year later in Minnesota.

Though the issue at Land o'Lakes and Black Duck has often been interpreted as one between theorists and practitioners,[14] no person, to the writer's knowledge, has interpreted it as a difference between a positivistic philosophy, which tends eventually to preclude problem definition and problem solving as integral parts of the scientific method, and a more normative philosophy leading to work with value concepts, at least to the extent of assuming the existence of values in terms of which problems could be defined and solved.[15] However, it is easy to find quotations in the report of the Black Duck workshop which indicate that there was a concern at that conference with failures to define and solve problems.[16] These quotations contain clear evidence of a desire on the part of the theorists to focus farm management research in a "pin-point manner" on problematic questions rather than employing "buckshot" farm accounts and surveys which produce, repetitively, a stable pattern of data not focused on the solution of any particular problem. At the Black Duck conference, efforts were made to isolate problems which could be solved by finding the equilibria defined in static production economic theory. Such use of economic theory assumed purpose and, as compared with positivistic survey and accounting work, *increased ability both to*

---

[12] Farm accounting and surveys not focused directly on problems (either practical or academic) fell off. In Michigan, for instance, the number of farm accounts was reduced from 862 in 1948 to 501 in 1953.

[13] Glenn L. Johnson, "Agricultural Economics, Production Economics and the Field of Farm Management," *Journal of Farm Economics,* Vol. 39 (May 1957), pp. 441ff. Also, H. C. M. Case, and D. B. Williams, *Fifty Years of Farm Management* (Urbana, Ill.: University of Illinois Press, 1957), pp. 319ff.

[14] Case and Williams, *op. cit.* 359–63 and 366ff.

[15] Case and Williams, *ibid.,* come close to recognizing that the traditional approach was positivistic but do not really clarify the matter. See p. 360 for a discussion of "The emphasis on fact collection . . . inherited from the physical sciences."

[16] Report of the North Central Farm Management Research Workshop, August 22 to September 2, 1949. The focus on problems is clearly discernible in the discussion of the theory of research which produced an outline containing the following:

"*Selecting the Study.* The study should be selected with a view toward: (a) solving

define and recognize solutions to problems involving attainment of the assumed purposes. This, not theory per se, was what was attractive to those advocating the use of more theory. Such use of theory contrasted sharply with the endless, less *purposeful,* unchanging repetitive accumulation of farm survey and record data unfocused on the changing problems of farmers and society.

Though the new orientation concentrated on problems and, in this sense, differed significantly from the immediately preceding fact-finding research in the field of farm management, it contained a serious flaw to be discussed later. The flaw involved the narrowness of the problems considered which tended to be defined in terms of the disequilibria of static, production economic theory. This concentration made farm management a narrow problem-solving subfield of production economics which, in turn, was a subfield of general economics. Thus, even the initial problematic interests of the new theoretical farm management workers were narrower than those of the early, more traditional farm management workers whose interests had ranged from the technological and institutional through accounting to the sociological.[17]

The issue was carried back to the individual experiment stations and departments. In the years which followed, the older farm management members of the North Central Farm Management Research Committee retired and were replaced by persons with greater interest in economic theory and in statistics. Eventually, the North Central Farm Management Research Committee and much of the farm management research and teaching in Midwestern agricultural experiment stations developed an initial problem-solving orientation built around a substantial injection of economic theory into the field of farm management.

HEADY'S BOOK APPEARS

The historical perspective provided above indicates that agricultural economics (including the somewhat attenuated farm management groups) was well

---

specific, definable problems leading to purposeful action; (b) anticipating problems and discovering remedies before they arise . . .

The problem selected for study should be significant in terms of; (a) its own importance and/or acuteness and (b) its relationship to other problems . . .

Stating the Problem. The problem should be stated clearly and fully in terms of: (a) the nature and extent of the apparent situation; (b) the circumstances which give rise to it; (c) the limitations and presuppositions under which it will be pursued; (d) the application expected to be made of the results; and (e) the economic ends of the individual or society . . .

Determining the Evidence Needed. The evidence to be assembled should: (a) be relevant to the stated problem and hypotheses . . .

Presenting the Results . . . Forthright endeavours should be made to insure utilization of the findings: (a) by obtaining and maintaining contacts with press, radio, extension workers, and other outlets; (b) by presenting the findings to persons in strategic positions; (c) by sharing experiences with fellow workers through personal contacts, journal articles, correspondence, *etc.*"

[17] As evidenced by the number of rural sociology departments which grew out of the activities of administrators of the earlier, more traditional farm management departments, those departments having evolved earlier out of the technological departments.

prepared for and, in fact, demanding the kind of book which Heady produced. Heady sensed and filled that demand. The alacrity with which this reviewer and many others adopted it as a graduate text attests to the esteem in which it was and is still held. This alacrity also reflected the widespread concensus in the profession about the need for the book. In reviewing the book, David MacFarlane wrote, "Professor Heady has written a highly important book . . . which for the first time brings within the covers of one volume the 'revolution' that has occurred in the field of agricultural production economics over the past 15 years. A small group of able, venturesome workers in farm management and production economics, with the author (Heady) in the forefront, have brought the 'new economics' to bear on farm production problems in an original and most valuable manner."[18]

The book articulated, in a remarkably accurate way, the then prevalent mood of the members of the profession, most of whom viewed it as a means of bringing into use the powerful tools of economic theory in *defining* and *solving* the practical, important production *problems* of the agricultural economy, particularly at the individual farm level. This was the driving purpose, the *raison d'être,* of those who eagerly adopted the text and built courses around it and the related literature.

Ten years have now passed, and it is time to ask and answer the question "Is production economics playing its proper role in agricultural economics, including farm management?"

To answer this question requires that we also outline the main developments which have taken place since the appearance of the book, that data having significance *not* because a book was published at that time *but, instead, because* it more or less marks the triumph of a point of view started by Spillman and Taylor, nurtured by Black, and brought to triumph by Heady and others.

TRENDS SINCE THE TRIUMPH—A LOSS IN PRODUCTIVITY

Since 1952, the following trends have become evident in the United States:

1. The use of economic theory in farm management *research* has expanded many fold.
2. The use of advanced statistics, mathematics, and electronic computers in farm management *research* has expanded far beyond levels envisioned in the early fifties.
3. Farm management research with a "production-economics" orientation has become increasingly:

   (*a*) less focused on the practical problem of managing farms, and

---

[18] See David D. MacFarlane's highly complimentary review in the *Journal of Farm Economics,* Vol. 35 (August 1953), p. 445.

(*b*) more focused on methodological and theoretical issues of less and less relevance to the solution of practical farm management problems as exemplified by such studies as; joint input-output experiments in crop and livestock production;[19] studies of the managerial process, per se;[20] and budgeting and linear programming studies of farm organization.

4. The proportionate use of farm management research by extension workers has decreased as its production economics orientation has increased. This is associated with;
   (*a*) decreased relevance in practical farm management problem situations of much of the current production economics research in farm management; and
   (*b*) the failure to increase competence with respect to production economics as rapidly among extension as among research farm management workers.
5. Accompanying the above trends in farm management research toward methodological and theoretical research, at the expense of the practical, has been an expanded interest in macro and policy work on the part of the persons with specific training in production economics. There has also been an important but not comparable reciprocal interest of students of policy, prices, etc. in production economics. This macro and policy work has tended, in turn, to focus on the theoretical and methodological at the expense of the practical and applied,[21] and as such differs from a "natural" tendency of young farm management workers and others to develop an interest in policy.
6. "Production economics" oriented farm management workers have either largely ignored or been largely ignored by the editors of the Journal of Farm Managers and Rural Appraisers, whose supporting association and membership have maintained a keen interest in the practical problems of farmers.

Somehow or another, these trends are not in accord with the expectations accompanying the shift to problem-solving farm management research based on the use of more theory. There has been no major rush of farmers to obtain the results of agronomic-economic research or of similar research

[19] Compare E. L. Baum, *et al.* (eds.), *Methological Procedures in the Economic Analysis of Fertilizer Use Data* (Ames, Iowa: Iowa State University Press, 1955), with E. L. Baum, *et al.* (eds.), *Economic and Technical Analysis of Fertilizer Innovations and Resource Use* (Ames, Iowa: Iowa State University Press, 1957).

[20] Compare G. L. Johnson and C. B. Haver, *Decision-Making Principles in Farm Management,* Kentucky Agricultural Experiment Station Bulletin, January 1953, with G. L. Johnson *et al.* (eds.), *A Study of Managerial Processes of Midwestern Farmers* (Ames, Iowa: Iowa State University Press, 1961).

[21] Compare E. O. Heady, *et al.* (eds.) *Agricultural Adjustment Problems in a Growing Economy* (Ames, Iowa: Iowa State University Press, 1958), with E. O. Heady, *et al.* (eds.) *Agricultural Supply Functions—Estimating Techniques and Interpretations* (Ames, Iowa: Iowa State University Press, 1961).

in animal husbandry.[22] Production function and linear programming analyses of farm businesses have produced no major breakthrough.[23] T. W. Schultz has stated:

"It will be said that much progress has been made in production economics. Simple, old-fashioned budgeting has been replaced by sophisticated production functions. The journals runneth over with 'results' from linear programming, a new apparatus that is turning out thus far an undigested mixture of a few insights and many 'numbers' that do not make sense."[24]

The shifts to estimating supply responses from linear programmes and to stress on Leontief input-output studies have had little impact on policy makers.[25] In short, neither public nor private decision makers have had much direct help from production economists in solving problems. Lest this conclusion dismay production economists and farm management workers to the comfort of others, it is worthwhile noting that, in 1959, a Committee of the Social Science Research Council (S.S.R.C.) drew a similar conclusion about the profession as a whole when it stated:

"Agriculture in the United States is in a period of critical change. The forces of change include rapid technological advance, rapid growth and structural change in the industrial and commercial environment within which agriculture functions, and an accompanying intensification and realignment of political pressure impinging on agricultural policy.

. . . The economic and social consequences of these changes in agriculture are far-reaching and arouse widespread concern. These consequences include serious chronic distress within major sectors of agriculture itself, in spite of public remedial programmes that have grown to unmanageable proportions, and an accelerated movement of population out of agriculture that nevertheless appears to fall short of the rate needed for economic adjustment. Among families that remain in agriculture, the income gap widens between those able to adopt progressive technology and those lacking the necessary financial resources or personal capabilities. Successive

---

[22] R. F. Hutton and D. W. Thorne, "Review Notes on the Heady-Pesek Fertilizer Production Surface," *Journal of Farm Economics,* Vol. 37, (February 1955), pp. 117ff. Also see G. L. Johnson, "A Critical Evaluation of Fertilizer Research," *The Economics of Fertilizer Application,* Farm Management Research Conference of the Western Agricultural Economics Research Council, Report No. 1, June 1956, pp. 33ff.

[23] James S. Plaxico, "Problems of Factor-Product Aggregation in Cobb-Douglas Value Productivity Analysis," *Journal of Farm Economics,* Vol. 37 (November 1955), pp. 664ff. Also see Earl Swanson, "Determining Optimum Size of Business from Production Functions," in E. O. Heady, *et al.* (eds.), *Resource Productivity, Returns to Scale and Farm Size* (Ames, Iowa: Iowa State University Press, 1956), pp. 133ff.

[24] T. W. Schultz, "Reflections on Agricultural Production, Output and Supply," in E. O. Heady, *et al.* (eds.), *Economic and Technical Analysis of Fertilizer Innovations and Resource Use* (Ames, Iowa: Iowa State University Press, 1957), p. 335. In this same connection see *Farm Size and Output Research—A Study in Research Methods,* Southern Coop. Series Bulletin No. 56, June 1958, bottom of p. 118 and top of p. 119.

[25] See T. W. Schultz, "Output-Input Relationships Revisited," *Journal of Farm Economics,* Vol. 40 (November 1958), pp. 924ff., which is critical of an earlier article of Heady's published in the May 1958 issue of the same journal. Heady had, in turn, criticized a still earlier article by Schultz in the August 1956 issue of the same journal.

sectors of agriculture are being increasingly controlled by outside commercial interests. Areas of traditional economic leadership in agriculture are challenged by new areas of agricultural economic growth.

The concern with these consequences reaches all strata of the agricultural population and all groups concerned with agricultural welfare . . . .

There are, of course, no simple, easily applied, costless, yet effective remedies for agriculture's ills. But they are not beyond constructive approach. That comments are so often only doctrinaire and that arguments seem so repetitious suggest *failure on the part of agricultural economists to apply imagination, to depart from customary thought patterns, to break down the mental barriers that restrict their formulation of problems.*[26] (Italics mine.)

If we accept the truth of the S.S.R.C. committee statement and the earlier criticisms which were directed more specifically at production economists and their work, then all agricultural economists as well as production economists must ask, Why? Why has the increased theoretical and empirical competence of agricultural economists led to reduced instead of increased productivity in terms of ability "to apply imagination, to depart from customary thought patterns, and to break down the mental barriers that restrict their formulation of problems."?[27] Or more specifically, on the subject of this paper, why have the production economists' efforts to include more production economics theory and improved mathematical and/or statistical methods in farm management and in other phases of agricultural economics been accompanied by less rather than more productivity?

WHY

Two explanations for the irrelevance (and, hence, reduced ability to contribute to solutions of practical problems) of much current production economics research work in farm management and other phases of agricultural economics are to be found not in production economics itself, but instead in specialization in economics and a tendency to become more positivistic.[28]

---

[26] George K. Brinegar, Kenneth L. Bachman, and Herman M. Southworth, "Reorientations in Research in Agricultural Economics," *Journal of Farm Economics,* Vol. 41 (August 1959), pp. 600ff. Other more polite but nonetheless disturbing papers include those of W. W. Cochrane, "Agricultural Economics in the Decade Ahead," *Journal of Farm Economics,* Vol. 36 (December 1954), pp. 817ff. and Karl Brandt, "The Orientation of Agricultural Economics," *Journal of Farm Economics,* December 1955, pp. 793ff.

[27] *Ibid.* Brinegar, *et al. Journal of Farm Economics,* August 1959, pp. 600ff.

[28] *Ibid.* Brinegar, Bachman, and Southworth, advance an alternative explanation, that of compartmentalization, which some readers may want to pursue. This explanation does not seem to be a very useful explanation of the lack of productivity associated with departmentalizing (the opposite of compartmentalization) farm management by making it more a part of economics. Disagreement with the SSRC Agricultural Economics committee point of view is also found in *Management Strategies in Great Plains Farming,* Great Plains Council Publication No. 19. Published by the University of Nebraska College of Agriculture, August 1961, p. 97.

These two developments, as we saw earlier, are in part consequences of an environmental call for more emphasis on production economics and, as such, can hardly be regarded as consequences of that emphasis or as a sole responsibility of those who answered the call. It is likely that these developments explain the lack of productivity in general agricultural economics which concerned Brinegar and his co-authors in the S.S.R.C. committee report.

Specialization in economics has a tendency to result in concentration on problems of economic disequilibria to the exclusion of other kinds of problems.[29] In economic theory, disequilibria indicate that problems exist. Problems definable in terms of disequilibria are solvable with recommendations designed to establish equilibria. So long as the marginality conditions for an equilibrium are met, the problems which exist are not directly discernible or solvable solely within the theory and, hence, tend to be overlooked by persons concentrating on the use of such theory.

The theory, for instance, does not ask whether the equilibrium distribution of incomes resulting from a given initial asset ownership pattern constitutes a problem or not. Though the core of a Kentucky hill farmer's problem be that of getting ownership of enough property and command over enough skill to earn "a decent living," no purely "economic-problem" exists if his hill farm is organized to "equate returns at the margin in both his production and consumption activities." While there is an income problem solvable by helping the Kentucky hill farmer get control "by hook or by crook" over more property and skills, the focus of economic theory on disequilibria tends to distract its user's attention away from the really relevant problem of inadequate resources in a search for non-existent problems of disequilibria.

When the problem is one of changing the institutional structure of agriculture, problems of disequilibria, too, are likely to be present but often are not worth correcting until the institutional changes are made, at which time new disequilibria are likely to arise to render irrelevant the original problems of disequilibria. For instance, in recent decades the problems encountered in designing new farm credit institutions and in creating institutional arrangements for controlling soil erosion were not solely problems of disequilibria and were more likely to create new disequilibria than to cure old ones.

Similarly, a problem growing out of a need to discover or create new technology may exist whether or not a farm business is in equilibrium. And, the discovery or creation would, in turn, typically obviate any pre-existing equilibria or disequilibria, possibly leaving a still greater disequilibrium problem to be solved as a minor sub-consequence of the solution to the major farm management problem. The tendency to reduce farm management to a subfield of production economics, which is, in turn, a subfield of economic

---

[29] Glenn L. Johnson, "Agricultural Economics, Production Economics and the Field of Farm Management," *Journal of Farm Economics*, Vol. 39 (May 1957), pp. 441ff.

shows up in the work of J. D. Black who wrote in 1953, "When the economics of agricultural production is reduced to terms of the individual farm, it becomes what is ordinarily known as Farm Management. Any textbook in *real* (my italics) Farm Management is a treatise on the economics of production of the individual farm."[30]

These examples should be sufficient to make it clear that concentration on problems of economic disequilibria is not identical with concentration on important, relevant problems. In fact, it is argued here that the problems which dismayed the S.S.R.C. sub-committee were mainly of this variety and that they were being ignored by agricultural economists who had concentrated instead on problems of disequilibria.

In 1959, this author commented,

"The tendency of farm management workers to oversimplify by concentrating on static economic analysis . . . is of recent origin. Somehow or another we have become so concerned with technique and simplicity that we fail to face up to problems either practically or methodologically . . . We do repetitive applications of mechanistic techniques sometimes using hypothetical data. In short, we play with technique and underemphasize the descriptive as a basis for isolating problems and preparing an all out attack on them . . . we fail to face up to the non-Pareto-better aspects of technological advance, economic growth and uncertainty . . . and of changes in wants and preferences."[31]

We now turn to the tendency toward positivism as a second explanation of the irrelevance of much research work involving production economics. This tendency is, of course, the same one which led earlier, nontheoretical farm management away from the relevant to the irrelevant.

The *tendency toward positivism* has gone through several stages in economic investigations involving the use of theory.

Early, Pareto and Hicks recognized the problem of assessing gains conferred on some persons in terms comparable with assessments of losses imposed on others. Without such assessments, it is difficult to ascertain whether a proposed solution to a problem would result in a net gain or loss. Recognition of this measurement problem suggested the advisability of limiting conclusions about net gains to situations in which at least one person was made better off and *no-one* was made worse off. Use of "the compensation principle" made it possible to extend the conclusion to instances where compensation could be paid by those benefited to anyone damaged and still leave those benefited better off. This development reduced the number of decisions which economists were willing to make about which actions are "right" to take or recommend as solutions to practical problems. Solutions were precluded which involved the imposition of uncompensatable

---

[30] J. D. Black, *Introduction to Economics for Agriculture* (New York: The Macmillan Co., 1953), p. 120; also see Johnson, *Ibid.*

[31] *Management Strategies in Great Plains Farming, op. cit.* p. 89.

damages on one or more persons or groups in order to benefit others.[32] The preclusion of such solutions leads to avoidance of problems involving institutional changes, redistribution of property rights and income streams, technological advance, and education advances.

Pareto's and Hicks' recognition of the problem of obtaining interpersonally valid utility measurements prepared the ground for the acceptance of the still more drastic positivistic conclusion that nothing objective was knowable about purpose, about good and bad, or, for that matter, about right and wrong solutions to problems. The research methodologies implied by positivism were and are extremely productive in the physical sciences where normative questions are less obvious and immediate than in the applied and/or social science disciplines. In fact, animistic and teleological reasoning which are non-positivistic but, fortunately, not the only kinds of non-positivistic reasoning often hinder non-social science research by introducing purely imaginary "purpose" to distract and, hence, lower the productivity of investigators. From this point, it is easy, if erroneous, to conclude that positivistic methodologies should be embraced to the exclusion of the normative in order to gain for social science the productivity of the physical sciences.

It was a long way *from the pre-Pareto and pre-Hicksian point of view* that objective knowledge of good and bad exists and is attainable *to the positivistic point of view* that such knowledge does not exist and, hence, is unattainable. It is a road from having some confidence in an objective ability to define and prescribe the solution to problems, to making both the definition and the solution of problems matters of subjective opinion beyond the realm of objective inquiry. So viewed problem-solving research loses its dignity, and is referred to as applied (the slang term is "putting out brush fires"), while positivistic research is glorified as "basic and fundamental." Paradoxically, the probability of relevance for what is called basic and fundamental yet divorced from the problems of society, seems to approach zero as only a small part of the infinitely complex, real and imaginal world is relevant.

One of the intermediate stages on the road from problem-solving to extreme positivism involves the technique of assuming or taking as given what is good and bad and then defining problems as involving the maximization of the good or minimization of the bad. This technique, referred to elsewhere by this author as "conditional normativism,"[33] was more widely used by

---

[32] The work of the North Central Technical Committee (NC-28) on soil conservation concentrated on the Pareto-better aspects of conservation and missed the "real" problems which involve imposition of damages on the living to confer benefits on those yet unborn. See L. A. Bradford and Glenn L. Johnson, *Farm Management Analysis* (New York: John Wiley & Sons, Inc., 1953), p. 429, for a brief statement of this aspect of the soil conservation problem. Also see Glenn L. Johnson, *op. cit.* p. 14.

[33] Glenn L. Johnson, "Value Problems in Farm Management," *Journal of Agricultural Economics,* Vol. 14 (June 1962), pp. 13f. This article discusses conditional normativism in relation to modern welfare economics.

production economists formerly than now but is still followed extensively.

Kenneth Parsons has attacked conditionally normative research in a recent article.[34] Parsons feels that if researchers do not proceed under the proposition that knowledge of right and wrong is possible, they will become unproductive. Parsons' own specialized pragmatic philosophy holds that answers to normative and non-normative questions are inextricably interdependent and that to assume one while varying the other is impossible. In contrast to Parsons, Ciriacy-Wantrup urged production economists to become more positivistic.[35]

With or without Ciriacy-Wantrup's urging, the tendency has been for some production economists to be more positivistic. Distinctions are now being drawn between *supply functions,* which are defined as what profit maximizing farmers ought to do, and *supply response estimates,* which predict what farmers will actually do. The first are labelled normative, while the latter are dubbed positive or predictive. In commenting on an assignment to discuss normative supply functions, this author once wrote:

"The term 'Normative', which appears in the title, has unfortunately tended to become an opprobrious epithet reserved in certain circles for *inaccurate* supply estimates while accurate estimates are labelled 'predictive' or 'positive'. This unfortunate distinction arises from the desire of positivists to avoid purpose or ends as being animistic, teleological and, hence, non-scientific (in their opinion). The use of this distinction implies that the behaviour of producers can be accurately predicted without reference to desire for profit, liquidity preference, desires for security as reflected in risk discounts, and the desires for security as reflected in willingness to make long chance investments which condition the behaviour of producers. The author feels that appropriate handling of subjective matters involving purposes and ends will produce more accurate (in the positivistic sense) supply response estimates than attempts to eliminate consideration of such matters. Obviously, studies which assume entrepreneurs to maximize what they do not, in fact, try to maximize may produce at least as inaccurate estimates as studies which avoid all maximization. Human behaviour (and production decisions are a form of human behaviour) is often a compromise between the entrepreneurs, concepts about 'what ought to be' (values or norms) and concepts about 'what is or can be' (beliefs—facts or predicted facts). It seems obvious that more accurate predictions of facts about supply decisions and responses must, generally speaking, be obtained in studies which take both values and beliefs into account than by non-normative studies. In addition, of course, errors in the process by which 'right actions' are determined from value and belief concepts would have to be considered in order to arrive at still more accurate predictions. The point is that the behaviour of producers is in part a social

---

[34] In this attack, he specifically and emphatically disagrees with the conditional normativism of J. D. Black, and E. O. Heady. See, Kenneth Parsons, "The Value Problem in Agricultural Policy," in E. O. Heady, *et al.* (eds.) *Agricultural Adjustment Problems in a Growing Economy* (Ames, Iowa: Iowa State University Press, 1958), pp. 295–96.

[35] S. V. Ciriacy-Wantrup "Policy Considerations in Farm Management Research," *Journal of Farm Economics,* Vol. 38, pp. 1301ff.

phenomenon, 'a serious analysis' of which, in Knight's words, requires 'a quite complicated pluralism,' including but not limited to positivism . . ."[36]

On the relative objectivity of normative and non-normative concept formulation Boulding has written "Although I shall argue that the process by which we obtain an image of values is not very different from the process whereby we obtain an image of fact, there is clearly a certain difference between them."[37]

A conference of the Iowa Adjustment Center, recognized the inadequacy of positive research by focusing on goals and values. As Director of the Center for Agricultural and Economic Adjustment, Heady wrote; ". . . until it is recognized that progress to solution of the income problem rests on resolution of apparent conflicts in goals and values, progress in solving major structural problems of agriculture may be small."[38] The importance of normative considerations in defining and solving problems which Heady recognized in the above quotation has been underscored in a large number of recent reports,[39] even if not reflected in the nature and content of much current production economics research which has, instead, tended toward the positivistic at the expense of the conditionally normative and normative. This tendency toward positivism has led us away from relevant problem-solving work.

In summary, then, this long section supports the thesis that specialization and a tendency towards positivism are responsible for the lack of productivity (in terms of solving problems) noted in the previous section.

---

[36] Glenn L. Johnson, "Budgeting and Normative Analysis of Normative Supply Functions," in Earl O. Heady *et al.* (eds.) *Agricultural Supply Functions—Estimating Techniques and Interpretations* (Ames, Iowa: Iowa State University Press, 1961), pp. 170–71. Frank Knight's interesting but somewhat contradictory position on this is found in his book. *On the History and Method of Economics* (Chicago: University of Chicago Press, 1956), especially pp. 172–77.

[37] Kenneth E. Boulding, *The Image* (Ann Arbor, Mich.: University of Michigan Press, 1956), p. 11.

[38] Iowa State University Center for Agricultural and Economic Adjustment, *Goals and Values in Agricultural Policy* (Ames, Iowa: Iowa State University Press, 1961), p. vi. At this conference, many conflicting positions on how to work with values and goals were presented and noted, emphatically, to be inconsistent. In this connection, see pp. 254ff.

These conflicts, in turn, were still apparent at a subsequent conference of the Center which was devoted to the *problem* of land use; one-half of one out of 22 chapters reporting that conference was devoted to normative considerations. See, Iowa State University Center for Agricultural and Economic Adjustment, *Dynamics of Land Use—Needed Adjustment* (Ames, Iowa: Iowa State University Press, 1961). For a review of this effort, with emphasis on its normative shortcoming, see G. L. Johnson, "Dynamics of Land Use—Needed Adjustment—Review," *Journal of Farm Economics,* Vol. 44 (May 1962), pp. 643ff.

[39] Joseph Ackerman, *et al.* (eds.) *Land Economics Research,* Farm Foundation and Resources for the Future, Inc. (Baltimore, Md.: Johns Hopkins Press, 1962). See Chapters 1, 3, 9 and 11. Also see *Land and Water Planning for Economic Growth*, Western Water Resources Conference, University of Colorado Press, 1961, pp. 129–36 and pp. 177ff. and Glenn L. Johnson and Lewis K. Zerby, "Values in the Solution of Credit Problems," in F. L. Baum, *et al.* (eds.), *Capital and Credit Needs in a Changing Agriculture* (Ames, Iowa: Iowa State University Press, 1961), pp. 271ff.

As constructive criticism demands corrective suggestions, the next step is to examine some of the problems being neglected as a prelude to suggesting some needed redirection in the last section.

EXAMPLES OF THE KINDS OF PROBLEMS WHICH ARE NOT BEING HANDLED

As problem situations are dynamic and not static, a stable list of neglected problems cannot be produced. Thus, the following partial list of specific problems is necessarily ephemeral and only illustrative.

In the *problem area of farm management,* production economists can contribute to the solution of problems:

1. faced by technical researchers asking what kind of new technologies are needed;
2. faced by farmers unsure about the value to be placed on security, income, the "fringe benefits" of urban society, education, public facilities, research etc.[40]
3. faced by farmers in different regions when changes are proposed which would influence their comparative advantages. Such changes include modifications of transportation, technology, production control and price support schemes, credit institutions, international trade arrangements, *etc.*
4. faced by farmers without command over enough resources to enable them to earn acceptable incomes in equilibrium. Here the need may be for access (right) to more credit, outright ownership of more property, command (ownership) of more skills, use (right to, ownership of) more public or semi-public property such as roads, schools, market facilities, research agencies, and accounting systems. The production economist can help predict the consequences of such changes and contribute substantially to conclusions about their desirability even when the changes under consideration are obviously non-Pareto-better;
5. faced by farmers locally, seasonally and chronically short of labour or priced out of the labour market. In this connection, work is needed (a) on institutional arrangements affecting the seasonal and geographical supply of labour, (b) on farm reorganization plans affecting labour utilization (such plans involving far more than shifts on given subproduction functions), and (c) by technical researchers on what kinds of labour saving technology are needed.

Without exploring all the ramifications of these and other farm management problems, some attention should be given to the kinds of marketing

[40] Dynamic production economists interested in the managerial process clearly have an interest in the "good judgment of managers." Judgment is asserted here to depend on knowledge of the value of income, security, *etc.*

problems which production economists can help solve. Roughly, these parallel those in farm management and, like those in that area, are often not definable in terms of initial disequilibria. In fact, marketing situations in initial equilibrium may often call for drastic changes.

1. In both factor and product markets, situations reach static impasses where drastic action is required. Present product markets are not characterized by widespread disequilibria, given existing government controls, yet there is an active search for new market arrangements and mechanisms. In Michigan, for instance, the Farm Bureau actively seeks, through its farm service organization, new bargaining rights for farmers producing processing apples, pickles and sugar beets. Elsewhere in the U.S., bargaining rights are sought by a new major farm organization, the National Farmers Organization, for livestock products and for food grains. What are production economists doing with respect to problems involving new ways of producing marketing services, reorganizing markets and devising new marketing mechanisms?
2. The labour market, too, is characterized by demands for new arrangements for handling foreign and domestic migrant labourers to meet seasonal, local and regional shortages of labour. Production economists have much to offer in predicting the consequences of alternative solutions and in estimating the disequilibria which would be created by various proposed changes.
3. In marketing, too, there is great interest in new physical layouts and technologies to reduce labour requirements. What production economists have really become creative and aggressive in developing such layouts and in indicating to engineers and architects the kind of equipment and buildings required?

Economic development and growth has always been a major concern of agricultural economists. Farm economies, stagnating in near static equilibria are characteristic of many of the underdeveloped countries. People can be starving and going without the elemental requirements for supra-animal existence in "penny capitalistic" economies which are in equilibria.[41] The problems here involve changes in land tenure, additional ownership of capital, new skills, and rights to new services. Introduction to these changes, in turn destroys old equilibria whose existence paralyzes the thoughts of economists trying to find infinitesmal problems of disequilibria while walking over mountains of problems involving human suffering, injustice and hopeless despair. Especially in economic development, normative work is badly needed to clarify and establish (by experience and logic) the workability of various concepts of the goodness and badness of such things as income, medical facilities, lawfulness, disorderliness, justice, work, education, *etc.*

[41] Sol. Tax, *Penny Capitalism: A Guatemalan Indian Economy* (Chicago: University of Chicago Press, 1963).

Agricultural policy also presents a wide range of problems, only part of which involve disequilibria and most of which involve serious normative questions. Here we have problems involving public investment in agricultural research; the creation of institutions to stabilize production and prices, public investment in roads, irrigation and drainage facilities, and education; the procurement and/or maintenance of rights to services such as electricity, telephones, markets, schools, *etc.,* as size of farms increases and population densities decrease. We also have problems of devising new institutional ways of controlling resource flows into and out of agriculture. The production economist has much help to offer in estimating and evaluating the output effects of such alternative policies and programmes if he will face up to such problems.

NEEDED REDIRECTIONS

All of the above has noted two current tendencies:

1. of production economics researchers (and others acquiring increased theoretical and empirical competence) to specialize in problems of disequilibria to the *exclusion* of problems involving technical, political, social and other changes; and
2. of production economics researchers to become increasingly positivistic to the *exclusion* of normative investigations.

Fortunately, neither tendency has become completely dominant though both have reduced the relevance of the research work of production economist and others stressing theoretical and empirical competence. The needed redirections do not involve either a change in or a diminished total role for production economics. Instead, they involve:

1. the use of production economics in conjunction with data and concepts from a wide range of academic disciplines to attack a wide range of practical problems going far beyond conventional economic disequilibria;
2. the avoidance of the sterilizing impacts of highly specialized philosophies of inquiry, particularly positivism, with its presumption that objective knowledge of purpose, of good and bad, or of right and wrong is unobtainable;
3. recognition that the wide range of problems to be attacked by production economists which is beyond economic disequilibria requires related research in the physical and social sciences and in the humanities; thus, the contribution of production economists to problem-solving research needs to be recognized as *partial* within problematic areas much broader than production economics or, for that matter, all of economics.

So directed, the contribution of production economics can fulfill the hopes of that "small group of able and venturesome workers in farm management and production economics, with the author (Heady) of this volume in the forefront" who ". . . brought the new economics to bear on farm production problems in an original and most valuable manner."[42] At the time Heady's book was written, the reviewer just quoted also wrote, "Our definition and understanding of problems is more revealing; and our tools sharper. For these advances we owe a tremendous debt to Professor Heady." Now, over ten years later, I would write instead, "Professor Heady's book has increased our capacity to understand and find problems and has sharpened our tools. For this we owe Professor Heady a tremendous debt. Whether or not we use this capacity to understand and find and help *solve* the important problems of private and public decision makers depends upon *our* ability to use these tools without being confined to them and without becoming unduly positivistic as our account keeping and/or surveying forebears did before us. This performance we came dangerously close to repeating during the last half of the decade which has passed since Professor Heady made his truly great contribution to agriculture."

---

[42] MacFarlane, *op. cit.* p. 444.

14 Hybrid Corn: an Exploration in the Economics of Technological Change*[1]

ZVI GRILICHES†

1. INTRODUCTION

The work presented in this paper is an attempt to understand a body of data: the percentage of all corn acreage planted with hybrid seed, by states and by years. By concentrating on a single, major, well defined, and reasonably well recorded development—hybrid corn—we may hope to learn something about the ways in which technological change is generated and propagated in U.S. agriculture.

The idea of hybrid corn dates back to the beginning of this century and its first application, on a substantial commercial scale, to the early thirties. Since then it has spread rapidly throughout the Corn Belt and the rest of the nation.[2]

---

* *Econometrica,* Vol. XXV, No. 4 (October, 1957), pp. 501–22.

† University of Chicago, Chicago, Illinois.

[1] This research was begun during my tenure as a Research Training Fellow of the Social Science Research Council. It has been supported by the Office of Agricultural Economics Research at the University of Chicago and is being supported by a generous grant from the National Science Foundation. I am indebted to Professor T. W. Schultz for arousing my interest in this problem and for encouraging me in my work, to Professors H. G. Lewis and A. C. Harberger for their valuable advice and guidance, and to the members of the Public Finance Workshop and other members of the Department of Economics at the University of Chicago, both faculty and students, for their suggestions and criticisms. I owe to the generosity of the Field Crop Statistics Branch of the Agricultural Marketing Service a large part of the unpublished data used in this paper. I also want to acknowledge and thank the people directly connected with hybrid corn, both in the Agricultural Experiment Stations and in the private seed companies, for their complete cooperation. This article is based on my unpublished Ph.D. dissertation, "Hybrid Corn: An Exploration in Economics of Technological Change," on file at the University of Chicago Library.

[2] A popular history of hybrid corn can be found in A. R. Crabb, *The Hybrid Corn Makers: Prophets of Plenty* (Rutgers University Press, 1948). See also F. D. Richey, "The Lay of the Corn Huckster," *Journal of Heredity*, Vol. 39(1), (1946), pp. 10–17; P. C. Mangelsdorf, "The History of Hybrid Corn," *loc. cit.*, Vol. 39, (1948), pp. 177–80; G. F. Sprague, "The Experimental Basis for Hybrid Maize," *Biological Reviews*, Vol. 21, (1946), pp. 101–20; M. T. Jenkins, "Corn Improvement," *U.S. Department of Agriculture Yearbook*, (1936), pp. 455–522; and H. A. Wallace and W. L. Brown, *Corn and Its Early Fathers* (Michigan State University Press, 1956).

There have been, however, marked geographic differences in this development (see Figure 1). Hybrid corn was the invention of a method of inventing, a method of breeding superior corn for specific localities.[3] It was not a single invention immediately adaptable everywhere. The actual breeding of adaptable hybrids had to be done separately for each area. Hence, besides the differences in the rate of adoption of hybrids by farmers—the "acceptance" problem—we have also to explain the lag in the development of adaptable hybrids for specific areas—the "availability" problem.

FIGURE 1
PERCENTAGE OF TOTAL CORN ACREAGE PLANTED WITH HYBRID SEED

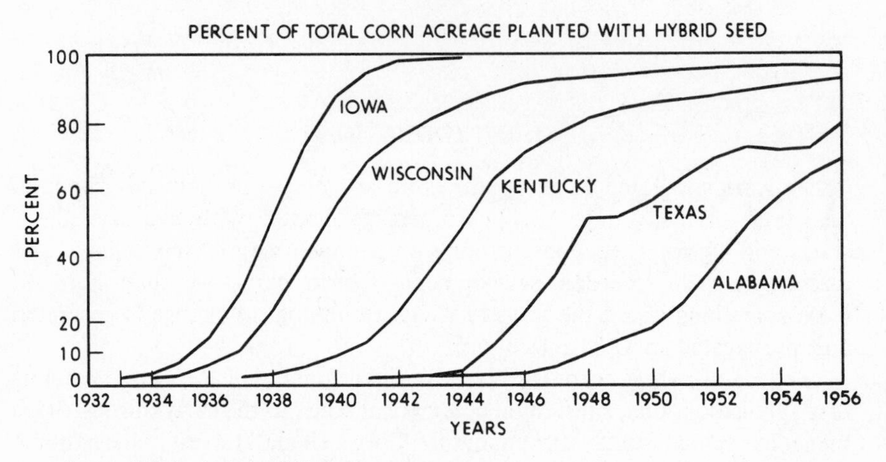

Source: USDA, *Agricultural Statistics*, various years.

In the following sections I shall first outline a method used to summarize the data. Essentially it will consist of fitting trend functions (the logistic) to the data, reducing thereby the differences among areas to differences in the values of a few parameters. Then I will present a model rationalizing these

[3] "Hybrid corn is the product of a controlled, systematic crossing of specially selected parental strains called 'inbred lines.' These inbred lines are developed by inbreeding, or self-pollinating, for a period of four or more years. Accompanying inbreeding is a rigid selection for the elimination of those inbreds carrying poor heredity, and which, for one reason or another, fail to meet the established standards." "[The inbred lines] are of little value in themselves for they are inferior to open-pollinated varieties in vigor and yield. When two unrelated inbred lines are crossed, however, the vigor is restored. *Some* of these hybrids prove to be markedly superior to the original varieties. The development of hybrid corn, therefore, is a complicated process of continued self-pollination accompanied by selection of the most vigorous and otherwise desirable plants. These superior lines are then used in making hybrids." First quote is from N. P. Neal and A. M. Strommen, "Wisconsin Corn Hybrids," Wisconsin Agricultural Experiment Station, Bulletin 476, February 1948, p. 4; and the second quote is from R. W. Jugenheimer, "Hybrid Corn in Kansas," Kansas Agricultural Experiment Station, Circular 196, February 1939, pp. 3–4. See also the references in the previous footnotes.

differences and illustrate it with computational results. Finally, I shall draw some conclusions on the basis of these results and other accumulated information.

2. THE METHOD AND THE MODEL

A graphical survey of the data by states and crop reporting districts along the lines of Figure 1 led to the conclusion that nothing would be gained by trying to explain each observation separately, as if it had no antecedent.[4] It became obvious that the observations are not points of equilibrium which may or may not change over time, but points on an adjustment path, moving more or less consistently towards a new equilibrium position. Hence we should phrase our questions in terms of the beginning of the movement, its rate, and its destination. This led to the decision to fit some simple trend functions to the data and concentrate on the explanation of the cross-sectional differences in the estimates of their parameters.

The choice of a particular algebraic form for the trend function is somewhat arbitrary. As the data are markedly S-shaped, several simple S-shaped functions were considered. The cumulative normal and the logistic are used most widely for such purposes. As there is almost no difference between the two over the usual range of data,[5] the logistic was chosen because it is simpler to fit and in our context easier to interpret. While there are some good reasons why an adjustment process should follow a path which is akin to the logistic, I do not want to argue the relative merits of the various S-curves.[6] In this work the growth curves serve as a summary device, perhaps somewhat

---

[4] This conclusion was also supported by the results of an attempt to fit a model in which the year-to-year changes in the percentage planted to hybrid seed were to be explained by year-to-year changes in the price of corn, price of hybrid seed, the superiority of hybrids in the previous year or two, etc. The trend in the data was so strong that, within the framework of this particular model, it left nothing of significance for the "economic" variables to explain.

[5] For a comparison, see C. P. Winsor, "A Comparison of Certain Symmetrical Growth Curves," *Journal of the Washington Academy of Sciences*, Vol. 22 (1932), pp. 73–84, and J. Aitchison and J. A. C. Brown, *The Lognormal Distribution* (Cambridge University Press, 1957), pp. 72–75.

[6] It may be worthwhile to indicate why it is reasonable that the development should have followed an S-shaped growth curve. The dependent variable can vary only between 0 and 100 percent. If we consider the development to be an adjustment process, the simplest reasonable time-path between 0 and 100 percent is an ogive. While the supply of seed can increase exponentially, the market for seed is limited by the total amount of corn planted, and that will act as a damping factor. Also, if we interpret the behavior of farmers in the face of this new, uncertain development as if they were engaged in sequential decision making, the ASN curve will be bell-shaped, and the cumulative will again be S-shaped. See also H. Hotelling, "Edgeworth's Taxation Paradox and the Nature of Demand and Supply Curves," *Journal of Political Economy*, Vol. 40, (October, 1932). The argument for the logistic is given by R. Pearl, *Studies in Human Biology* (Baltimore, 1924), pp. 558–83, and S. Kuznets, *Secular Movements in Production and Prices* (Boston: Houghton Mifflin Co. 1930), pp. 59–69.

more sophisticated than a simple average, but which should be treated in the same spirit.

The logistic growth curve is defined by $P = K/1 + e^{-(a+bt)}$, where P is the percentage planted with hybrid seed, K the ceiling or equilibrium value, t the time variable, b the rate of growth coefficient, and a the constant of integration which positions the curve on the time scale. Several features of this curve are of interest: It is asymptotic to 0 and K, symmetric around the inflection point, and the first derivative with respect to time is given by $dP/dt = - b/(P/K)(K-P)$.[7] The rate of growth is proportional to the growth already achieved and to the distance from the ceiling. It is this last property that makes the logistic useful in so many diverse fields.[8]

There are several methods of estimating the parameters of the logistic.[9] The method chosen involves the transformation of the logistic into an equation linear in a and b. By dividing both sides of the logistic by $K-P$ and taking the logarithm, we get its linear transform, $\log_e [P/(K-P)] = a + bt$, allowing us to estimate the parameters directly by least squares.[10] The value of K, the ceiling, was estimated crudely by plotting the percentage planted to hybrid seed on logistic graph paper and varying K until the resulting graph approximated a straight line. After adjusting for differences in K, the logistic was fitted to the data covering approximately the transition from 5 to 95 percent of the ceiling. The observations below 5 and above 95 percent of the ceiling value were discarded because they are liable to very large percentage errors and would have had very little weight anyway in any reasonable weighting scheme. The period included in the analysis, however, accounts for the bulk of the changes in the data.

---

[7] For a more detailed description of the logistic and its properties, see Pearl, *op. cit.*

[8] Perhaps the simplest interpretation of the logistic is given by A. Lotka, *Elements of Physical Biology* (Baltimore: Williams and Wilkins, 1925), p. 65. We are interested in the general adjustment function, $dP/dt = F(P)$. Using a Taylor Series approximation and disregarding all the higher terms beyond the quadratic we get a function whose integral is the logistic. The logistic is the integral of the quadratic approximation to the adjustment function.

[9] See Pearl, *op. cit.*; H. T. Davis, *The Theory of Econometrics* (Principia Press, 1941), chapt 2; and G. Tintner, *Econometrics* (New York: John Wiley & Sons, Inc., 1952), pp. 208–11, and the literature cited there.

[10] This is a simplification of a method proposed by Joseph Berkson. Berkson's method is equivalent to weighted least squares regression of the same transform with $P(K - P)$ as weights. J. Berkson, "A Statistically Precise and Relatively Simple Method of Estimating the Bioassay with Quantal Response, Based on the Logistic Function," *Journal of the American Statistical Association*, Vol. 48 (1953), pp. 565–99, and "Maximum Likelihood and Minimum Chi-square Estimates of the Logistic Function," *loc. cit.*, Vol. 50 (1955), pp. 130–62. Berkson proposed this procedure in the context of bio-assay. It is not clear, however, whether the bio-assay model is applicable in our context, nor is it obvious, even in bio-assay, what system of weights is optional. See also J. Berkson, "Estimation by Least Squares and by Maximum Likelihood," *Proceedings of the Third Berkeley Symposium on Mathematical Statistics,* Vol. I (University of California Press), pp. 1–11. Hence no weights were used. In view of the excellent fits obtained, it is doubtful whether alternative weighting systems would have made much difference.

The procedure outlined above was used to calculate the parameters of the logistic for 31 states and for 132 crop reporting districts within these states.[11] The states used account for almost all of the corn grown in the U.S. (all states except the West and New England). Out of a total of 249 crop reporting districts only those were used for which other data by crop reporting districts were readily available. Districts with negligible amounts of corn and unreliable estimates of hybrid corn acreage were also left out.[12]

The results of these calculations are presented in Tables 1 and 2. Table 1 summarizes the state results, Table 2 the results by crop reporting districts. Time is measured from 1940, and $(-2.2-a)/b$ indicates the date at which the function passed through the 10 percent value. This date will be identified below with the date of *origin* of the development. Several things are noteworthy about these figures: the high r^2's indicate the excellent fits obtained.[13] The b's, representing the slope of the transform or the rate of adjustment, are rather uniform, becoming lower as we move towards the fringes of the Corn Belt. The values of $(-2.2-a)/b$, the dates of *origin*, indicate that the development started in the heart of the Corn Belt and spread, rather regularly, towards its fringes.[14] The ceiling—K—also declines as we move away from the Corn Belt.

In this section we have succeeded in reducing a large mass of data to three sets of variables—*origins, slopes,* and *ceilings*. "Thus on the basis of three numbers we are prepared, in principle, to answer all the questions the original data sheet can answer provided that the questions do not get down to the level of a single cell . . . . . This is saying a great deal."[15]

The economic interpretation of the differences in the estimated coefficients will be developed in the following sections. The values of the different parameters are not necessarily independent of each other, but for simplicity will be considered separately. Variations in the date of origin will be identified

[11] Each state is usually divided into nine crop reporting districts numbered in the following fashion:

		N		
	1	2	3	
W	4	5	6	E
	7	8	9	
		S		

[12] It should be noted that the sum of logistics is not usually a logistic. However, the logistic is also valid for an aggregate, as long as the components are similar in their development. See L. J. Reed and R. Pearl, "On the Summation of Logistic Curves," *Journal of the Royal Statistical Society*, Vol. 90 (New Series, 1927), pp. 729–46. How good the approximation is in fact is indicated by the results below.

[13] These r's should be taken with a grain of salt. They are the r^2's of the transform rather than of the original function and give less weight to the deviations in the center. Also, they do not take into account the excluded extreme values. Nevertheless, an examination of the original data indicates that they are not a figment of the fitting procedure.

[14] *Origin* is measured from 1940. Hence, the *origin* in Iowa is placed approximately in 1936, and in Georgia in 1948.

[15] R. R. Bush and F. Mosteller, *Stochastic Models for Learning* (New York: John Wiley & Sons, Inc., 1955), p. 335.

with supply factors, variations in slopes with factors affecting the rate of acceptance by farmers, and variations in ceilings with demand factors affecting the long-run equilibrium position. In each case we shall consider briefly the implicit identification problem.

TABLE 1
HYBRID CORN LOGISTIC TREND FUNCTIONS BY STATES

States	*Origin* $\frac{-2.2-a}{b}$	*Rate of acceptance* b	*Ceiling* K	r^2
N.Y.	−.89	.36	.95	.99
N.J.	−1.48	.54	.98	.90
Pa.	−1.29	.48	.95	.98
Ohio	−3.35	.69	1.00	.97
Ind.	−3.13	.91	1.00	.99
Ill.	−4.46	.79	1.00	.99
Mich.	−1.44	.68	.90	.98
Wisc.	−3.52	.69	.91	.99
Minn.	−3.06	.79	.94	.99
Iowa	−4.34	1.02	1.00	.99
Mo.	−3.32	.57	.98	.98
N.D.	−.65	.43	.65	.96
S.D.	−.40	.42	.85	.95
Neb.	−.60	.62	.97	.99
Kan.	.42	.45	.94	.97
Del.	.21	.47	.99	.98
Md.	−.73	.55	.98	.97
Va.	1.60	.50	.92	.97
W. Va.	−.23	.39	.85	.98
N.C.	5.14	.35	.80	.89
S.C.	5.72	.43	.60	.96
Ga.	7.92	.50	.80	.99
Fla.	2.89	.38	.90	.93
Ky.	.08	.59	.90	.99
Tenn.	2.65	.34	.80	.97
Ala.	7.84	.51	.80	.99
Miss.	4.75	.36	.60	.98
Ark.	1.46	.41	.78	.99
La.	4.89	.45	.53	.99
Okla.	3.57	.56	.80	.98
Tex.	3.64	.55	.78	.98

Notes: $P = \frac{K}{1+e^{-(a+bt)}}$; $\log_e\left(\frac{P}{K-P}\right) = a + bt$; $t_{1940} = 0$; $N = -6$ to 16; Max $S_b = .06$; *Origin* = Date of 10 percent = $\frac{-2.2-a}{b}$, measured from 1940, e.g., −4.0 = 1936, + 7.0 = 1947; *Rate of acceptance* = Slope = b; and *Ceiling* = K

TABLE 2

HYBRID CORN LOGISTIC TREND FUNCTIONS BY CROP REPORTING DISTRICTS*

State and C.R. District	Origin	Rate of Acceptance	Ceiling	r^2
Pa. 1	.15	.41	.85	.99
2	1.16	.49	.90	.99
3	.76	.46	.91	.98
4	.44	.47	.92	.99
5	.11	.62	.95	.98
6	−1.02	.55	.95	.99
7	−.63	.40	.90	.98
8	−1.04	.54	.96	.99
9	−2.35	.60	.98	.97
Ohio 1	−3.22	1.25	1.00	.99
2	−2.73	.99	1.00	.98
3	−1.77	.75	.95	.98
4	−3.00	.90	1.00	.98
5	−3.19	.77	1.00	.98
6	−3.14	.69	.95	.94
7	−2.69	.88	1.00	.98
8	−1.78	.60	.95	.99
9	−1.80	.73	.95	.97
Ind. 1	−3.82	1.15	1.00	.99
2	−3.60	1.10	1.00	.99
3	−3.12	1.15	1.00	.99
4	−3.24	.95	1.00	.99
5	−2.85	1.07	1.00	.99
6	−2.63	1.12	1.00	.99
7	−1.67	.87	1.00	.96
8	−1.57	.82	1.00	.98
9	−1.88	.76	1.00	.98
Ill. 1	−4.81	1.13	1.00	.99
3	−4.59	.98	1.00	.99
4	−4.16	1.08	1.00	.99
4a	−2.65	1.09	1.00	.99
5	−4.68	1.17	1.00	.99
6	−4.25	1.18	1.00	.99
6a	−2.46	.91	1.00	.99
7	−.81	.64	1.00	.97
9	−.58	.78	1.00	.97
Mich. 7	−1.12	.77	.92	.97
8	−1.04	.89	.92	.98
9	−1.70	.78	.92	.98
Wisc. 1	−2.17	.81	.85	.99
2	−2.22	.97	.70	.99
3	−2.42	.93	.60	.99
4	−3.24	.67	.95	.96
Wisc. 5	−2.54	.61	.90	.98
6	−3.03	.87	.78	.99
7	−4.16	.89	.98	.99
8	−3.55	.88	.95	.99
9	−3.21	.72	.95	.98
Minn. 7	−3.08	1.36	1.00	.99
8	−3.66	1.14	1.00	.99
9	−3.04	1.01	1.00	.99
Iowa 1	−4.39	1.01	1.00	.99
2	−4.78	1.05	1.00	.99
3	−4.46	1.00	1.00	.99
4	−3.71	1.12	1.00	.99
5	−4.70	1.13	1.00	.99
6	−5.15	1.09	1.00	.99
7	−2.74	1.25	1.00	.99
8	−3.61	1.07	1.00	.99
9	−4.15	1.10	1.00	.99
Mo. 1	−1.37	1.19	1.00	.97
2	−1.33	1.15	1.00	.95
3	−1.27	1.15	1.00	.96
4	−1.51	.66	.95	.98
5	−.64	.78	.93	.99
6	−1.11	.72	.97	.97
7	.16	.46	.90	.99
8	.63	.63	.87	.99
9	−.94	.64	.97	.99
N.D. 9	.40	.74	.85	.96
S.D. 3	−.53	.57	.90	.99
6	−.71	.85	.93	.99
9	−1.72	.75	.95	.99
Neb. 3	−2.48	.90	1.00	.99
5	.36	.82	.93	.99
6	−2.18	.85	1.00	.99
7	2.33	.90	.95	.99
8	1.60	.94	.95	.99
9	−.77	.91	1.00	.97
Kan. 1	2.68	.41	.95	.95
2	1.52	.66	1.00	.98
3	−.88	.72	1.00	.99
6	−.88	.68	.92	.99
9	.73	.41	.95	.99

TABLE 2—(*Continued*)

State and C.R. District		*Origin*	*Rate of Accept-ance*	*Ceiling*	r^2
Md.	1	2.92	.37	.97	.94
	2	−1.12	.64	1.00	.97
	8	.88	.48	.98	.98
	9	.40	.60	1.00	.93
Va.	2	.87	.68	1.00	.99
	4	1.51	.61	.98	.93
	5	2.37	.68	.95	.99
	6	2.06	.63	.97	.96
	7	1.21	.29	.80	.85
	8	2.18	.40	.85	.90
	9	1.04	.50	.95	.96
Ky.	1	.67	.89	.95	.97
	2	−.42	.72	.98	.99
	3	.49	.61	.90	.97
	4	−.36	.83	.92	.99
	5	−.77	.78	.90	.99
	6	1.94	.62	.60	.98
Tenn.	1	.76	.29	.85	.97
	2	1.88	.33	.55	.99
	3	2.64	.39	.70	.97
	4	2.53	.43	.75	.96
	5	3.43	.35	.80	.91
	6	2.94	.33	.70	.95
Ala.	1	7.73	.56	.60	.98
	2	6.33	.57	.99	.99
	2a	8.80	.45	.90	.97
	3	7.68	.54	.95	.98
	4	7.45	.42	.50	.95
	5	8.08	.49	.70	.95
	6	8.15	.39	.60	.95
	7	7.84	.58	.85	.97
	8	8.24	.45	.70	.97
	9	8.53	.55	.90	.99
Ark.	1	.41	.37	.75	.97
	2	1.98	.40	.82	.98
	3	.68	.50	.85	.99
	4	2.24	.42	.77	.94
	5	1.89	.35	.85	.95
	6	1.54	.35	.80	.99
	7	1.66	.32	.55	.93
	8	2.41	.37	.70	.92
	9	1.88	.33	.85	.99
Okla.	3	2.61	.49	.80	.97
	5	3.62	.55	.90	.97
	6	3.17	.52	.88	.93
	7	4.05	.39	.80	.97
	8	4.85	.67	.90	.98
	9	4.08	.52	.75	.95

* I am indebted to the Field Crop Statistics Branch of the Agricultural Marketing Service for the unpublished data by crop reporting districts.

3. THE SUPPLY OF A NEW TECHNIQUE

There is no unique way of defining the date of *origin* or of "availability." Hybrid corn was not a single development. Various experimental hybrids were tried until superior hybrids emerged. After a while, these were again superseded by newer hybrids. Nor is there a unique way of defining *origin* with respect to growth curve. The logistic is asymptotic to zero; it does not have a "beginning." Nevertheless, it is most important to distinguish between the lag in "availability" and the lag in "acceptance." It does not make sense to blame the Southern farmers for being slow in acceptance, unless one has taken into account the fact that no satisfactory hybrids were available to them before the middle nineteen-forties.

I shall use the date at which an area began to plant 10 percent of its ceiling acreage with hybrid seed as the date of *origin*.[16] The 10 percent date was chosen as an indicator that the development had passed the experimental stage and that superior hybrids were available to farmers in commercial quantities. The reasonableness of this definition has been borne out by a survey of yield tests in various states and it has been supported by conversations with various people associated with developments in hybrid corn in the experiment stations and private seed companies.[17]

"Availability" is the result of the behavior of agricultural experiment stations and private seed companies. If we include the growers of station hybrids in the general term "commercial seed producers," then availability is the direct result of the actions of seed producers with the experiment stations affecting it through the provision of free research results and foundation stocks. The activities of the experiment stations serve to reduce the cost of innovation facing the seed producers but the entry decisions are still their own. The date at which adaptable hybrids became available in an area is viewed as the result of seed producers ranking different areas according to the expected profitability of entry and deciding their actions on this basis.[18] The relative profitability of entry into an area will depend on the size of the eventual market in that area, marketing cost, the cost of innovating for that area, and (given a positive rate of interest) the expected rate of acceptance.[19]

It is extremely difficult to define "market size" operationally. The definition is not independent of marketing cost or of the particular characteristics of the innovation (the area of adaptability of a particular hybrid) and is complicated by the arbitrariness of the political subdivisions used as the geographic units of analysis. The problem of the "right" geographic unit of analysis, however, will be postponed to the end of this section. As an approximation to the size of the market I used the average corn acreage in the area at about

---

[16] The date at which the fitted logistic passes through 10 percent is given by $Y = (-2.2 - a)/b$. As the variation of b is small relative to that of a, small changes in the definition of Y will be in the nature of an additive constant and will rarely change the ranking of the data of *origin* in different areas.

[17] This is essentially a definition of "commercial" availability. An attempt was made to measure the date of "technical" availability by going through yield tests and other official publications and noting the first year in which hybrids clearly outyielded the open pollinated varieties. The rank correlation between this technical definition and the "10 percent" definition was .93. The average lag between the technical and the commercial availability was approximately 2 years. Also, preliminary explorations with 1 and 5 percent definitions, and with the rank of an area rather than the absolute date, indicated that the results are not very sensitive to changes in definition.

[18] Implicitly, we have assumed here that the lag between the entry decision and actual availability is approximately constant or at least independent of other variables under analysis.

[19] Throughout the paper it is assumed that the price of hybrid seed is given and approximately uniform in different areas. This is a very close approximation to reality and a result of a very elastic long-run supply curve of seed.

the time of the date of entry, adjusted for differences in ceilings. That is, the average corn acreage was multiplied by .9 if that was the estimate of the fraction of the corn acreage which would be ultimately planted with hybrid seed. Because the political subdivisions are of various and sundry sizes, to make them more comparable the adjusted corn acreage was divided by total land in farms. The resulting variable—X_1 = (Average corn acreage) × K ÷ Total land in farms—is a measure of "market density" rather than of "market size."[20] If the areas are not too different in size and in the range of adaptability of their hybrids, market density will closely approximate a relevant measure of market size. Also, in its own right, it is important as a measure of marketing cost, the relative cost of selling a given supply of seed in different areas. Under the name of "market potential," such a variable was, in fact, used by at least one major seed company in its decision making process. The importance of a variable of this sort was strongly emphasized, in private conversations, by executives of the major seed companies.

The importance of marketing cost is underscored by the striking differences in marketing methods of hybrid seed in different parts of the country. While almost 90 percent of all the seed in the Corn Belt is sold by individual salesmen who call on each farmer, almost all of the seed in the South is sold through stores where the farmer must come and get it. The small size of the corn acreage per farm, the relative isolation of the small farm, and the large proportion of corn on noncommercial farms make the type of marketing used in the Corn Belt prohibitively expensive in the South. The cost of selling a given amount of seed is quite different in various parts of the country, as many more farmers have to be reached in one area than in another. As a measure of "average size of sale," I used average corn acres per farm reporting corn, X_3.

The estimated slope coefficient, b, was used as a measure of the expected rate of acceptance in different areas. This assumes that producers were able to predict reasonably well the actual rate of acceptance.

There is no good way of estimating the relative costs of innovation. It is probably true that there are no substantial differences in the cost of developing a hybrid from scratch for any corn-growing area of the country and, if there were some, they would be swamped by the large differences in returns. A difficulty arises, however, from the fact that a hybrid may be adaptable in more than one area, allowing the cost of innovation to be spread over several areas, and because the experiment stations have borne a substantial part of the innovation cost by developing and releasing inbred lines and whole hybrids. That is, the actual cost of innovating for an area will depend on whether or not hybrids which have already been developed for other

[20] Differences in seeding rates have been disregarded here. There is, however, some evidence that the results would have been somewhat better if X_1 were adjusted for these differences.

areas prove adaptable in this area, and on whether or not the experiment stations have produced and released inbred lines or hybrids adaptable to this area.

Since most of the early research was done for the area known as the "Corn Belt," other areas benefited from the availability of these research results to a varying degree, depending on the adaptability of Corn Belt inbred lines to those areas. A measure of the degree to which other areas are different from the Corn Belt with respect to the adaptability of Corn Belt lines can be approximated by taking the published pedigrees of the recommended hybrids in different areas in 1956 and computing the percentage of all inbred lines represented by "Corn Belt" lines. An index of "Corn Beltliness," X_4, was defined as the number of Corn Belt inbred lines in the pedigrees of the recommended hybrids for that area, divided by the total number of lines.[21]

To take other aspects of the "complementarity" problem into account, another variable, X_{10}, was defined as the earliest date of entry (*origin*) in the immediate (contiguous) neighborhood of the area under consideration.[22] X_{10} was introduced on the assumption that it may be cheaper, both from the point of view of the additional research needed and from the point of view of setting up a marketing organization, to enter an area contiguous to an area already entered even though the "market potential" there may be lower than in some other area farther away.

Using either the number of released inbred lines or hybrids or the reported research expenditures, several unsuccessful attempts were made to measure the relative contribution of the various experiment stations. To some extent, however, the impact of this variable is already accounted for by our measures of the "market." The contribution of the various experiment stations is strongly related to the importance of corn in the area. In the "good" corn areas the stations did a lot of work on hybrids and in the marginal areas, less.[23]

The simple correlation coefficients between these variables, on the state level and on the crop reporting district level, are presented in Tables 3 and 4 respectively. All of the correlation coefficients with Y have the expected sign and most of them are also significantly different from zero.

---

[21] On the state level, a published list of recommended hybrids and their pedigrees was used, with Iowa, Illinois, Indiana, Ohio, and Wisconsin lines defined as "Corn Belt" lines. See C. B. Henderson, "Inbred Lines of Corn Released to Private Growers from State and Federal Agencies and Double Crosses Recommended by States," Champaign, (2d rev. Illinois Seed Producers Association, April 15, 1956). On the crop reporting district level, I used unpublished data from the Funk Bros. Seed Co., listing their hybrids by "maturity groups" and giving coded pedigrees.

[22] This is analogous to the introduction of a lagged value of the dependent variable into the regression in time series analysis. Except that the "lag" here is spatial rather than a time lag.

[23] There are a few exceptions to this statement. In the North, Connecticut, Wisconsin, and Minnesota contributed more than their "share," and so did Texas and Louisiana in the South.

The inter-correlation among the independent variables, however, prevents us from successfully estimating their separate contributions from these data. Almost all sets and subsets of independent variables in these tables were tried without yielding more than one significant coefficient in each multiple regression.[24] These results are disappointing, particularly because the highest correlations are with the rather artificial variables X_4 ("Corn Beltliness") and X_{10} (the "spatial trend").[25] Hence, another approach to the problem was sought.

TABLE 3

CORRELATION COEFFICIENTS ON THE STATE LEVEL—N = 31

	X_1	X_3	b	X_4	X_{10}
Y	−.44	−.35	−.62	−.89	.82
X_1		.52	.77	.55	−.39
X_3			.46	.28	−.36
b				.68	−.51
X_4					.79

Note:

Y = Date of *origin*. The date an area reached 10 percent, computed. See Tables 1 and 2.

X_1 = Market density. For states: average corn acreage 1937–46 times K, divided by land in farms in 1945. Similar for crop reporting districts but averaged over different periods, depending on the availability of data. Source: *Agricultural Statistics, Census of Agriculture,* and published and unpublished materials from state agricultural statisticians.

X_3 = For states, average corn acres per farm, 1939. Source: *Census of Agriculture.* By crop reporting districts: the same average corn acreage as in X_1, divided by the 1939 or 1945 census number of farms reporting corn, depending on availability of data.

b = The slope of the logistic transform, computed.

X_4 = "Corn Beltliness." The proportion of all inbred lines accounted by "Corn Belt" lines in the pedigrees of recommended hybrids by areas. Source: C. B. Henderson, "Inbred Lines of Corn Released to Private Growers from State and Federal Agencies and Double Crosses Recommended by States," 2d rev., Champaign Illinois Seed Producers Association, April 15, 1956); and unpublished data from the Funk Bros. Seed Co., Bloomington, Ill.

X_{10} = Earliest date of origin in the immediate neighborhood.

TABLE 4

CORRELATION COEFFICIENTS ON THE CROP REPORTING DISTRICT LEVEL—N = 132

	X_1	X_3	b	X_4	X_{10}
Y	−.56	−.35	−.70	−.73	.95
X_1		.69	.73	.57	−.57
X_3			.54	.40	−.36
b				.67	−.73
X_4					−.76

See *Note* at bottom of Table 3.

[24] Similar results were obtained when the logarithms rather than the actual values of the independent variables were used.

[25] The good performance of X_{10} is not surprising. The smaller the geographic unit of analysis, the better will be the relationship between Y and X_{10}. This can be seen by comparing the correlation coefficients on the state and crop reporting district levels. There is, however, another way of rationalizing the performance of X_{10}. See footnote 27.

The trouble with the above approach is that it does nothing about the problem of the "right" geographic unit of analysis. Considering only the "market density" variable, it is obvious that it does not always measure what we want. Markets are continuous. While some areas are poor by themselves they may be a part of a larger market. Also an area may be entered because it is a springboard to other areas rather than on its own grounds. One way of taking these considerations into account is to define the "market potential" of an area as a weighted average of the "market densities" in *all* areas, densities in other areas weighted inversely to the distance from the area under consideration.[26] Given more than a few areas, however, the calculation of such a variable becomes impracticable.[27]

The trouble with our geographic units arises because states are too large while crop reporting districts are too small and neither corresponds either to technical regions of adaptation of particular hybrids nor to the decision units of the private seed companies. It is possible, however, to ask a more modest question: What were the characteristics of the areas entered in a particular year as compared with the characteristics of areas entered in another year? It is possible to aggregate areas according to the year of entry and test the "market potential" hypothesis on these aggregates. I shall define areas according to the year of entry, i.e., all districts with the *origin* in 1939 will make up one such area, and aggregate the data by crop reporting districts into such areas. Given our "10 percent" definition of *origin*, we have 16 such areas, 1935 to 1950. Alternatively, we would like to define areas according to the adaptability of particular hybrids. However, most hybrids overlap geographically and there are almost no data on the geographical distribution of particular hybrids, but there are breakdowns of the country into "maturity regions." A major seed company breaks down the U.S. and its line of hybrids into 11 "maturity groups," locating the areas of adaptation of these groups on a map. It is possible to aggregate the crop-reporting districts into these "technical" regions and ask whether high market areas were entered earlier than others.

The results of these calculations are presented in Table 5-A. In the aggregation by year of origin, to simplify the calculations, the actual "10 percent or more" year rather than the calculated date from the logistic was

---

[26] See W. Warnz, "Measuring Spatial Association with Special Consideration of the Case of Market Orientation of Production," *Journal of the American Statistical Association*, Vol. 51 (December 1956), pp. 597–604.

[27] It does suggest, though, a reason for the good performance of X_{10}. Consider a simple model in which the date of origin is a function of the "true" market measure, the "true" measure being a weighted average of the densities in all areas, weights declining with distance. This "true" measure can be approximated by the actual density in the area and the "true" measure in the immediate neighborhood. But the date of origin in the immediate neighborhood is a function of the "true" density there and can serve as its measure. This implies that X_{10} is another measure of the "market!" For a similar approach in a different context, see M. Nerlove, "Estimates of the Elasticities of Supply of Selected Agricultural Commodities," *Journal of Farm Economics*, Vol. 38 (May 1956), pp. 500–503.

used. For the technical regions the computed origins by districts were used, weighted by the average corn acreage in the district and adjusted for differences in ceilings. That is, aggregate $Y = \sum Y\ A\ K / \sum\ A\ K$, where A stands for average corn acres. Aggregate X_1 was defined as $\sum\ A\ K / \sum\ L$, where L stands for total land in farms. Because of the simplicity of the computations involved in this particular approach, 90 more crop reporting districts were added at this point to the analysis, raising the number of included districts to 222. Where separate logistic curves were not computed, Y was estimated by linear interpolation. As the technical regions overlap, each of the aggregates includes a few districts also included in the neighboring aggregates.[28]

TABLE-5A

CORRELATION COEFFICIENTS BETWEEN THE AGGREGATES OF Y, X_1, X_4 AND X_{10}

Aggregation by		X_1	X_4	X_{10}
"Date of Origin": All areas $N = 16$				
	Y	−.82	−.98	.95
	X_1		.82	−.64
	X_4			−.93
"Date of Origin": All areas except the Southeast $N = 13$				
	Y	−.94	−.97	.96
	X_1		.90	−.86
	X_4			−.97
"Technical Regions": $N = 12$				
	Y	−.69	−.82	.95
	X_1		.90	−.59
	X_4			−.78

To make the results comparable with those presented in Table 4, similar calculations were also performed on X_4 and X_{10}. For the aggregation procedure by "date of origin," X_{10} was defined as the earliest date of origin in the immediate neighborhood of the area defined by the procedure, and X_4 as a simple unweighted average for the districts included in the aggregate. For the aggregation by "technical regions," X_{10} was defined as the lowest weighted average date of origin among the neighboring "technical regions." No aggregation had to be performed on X_4, as it had been originally defined and computed for these regions.

The results presented in Table 5-A indicate a strong association between the date of *origin* and average market density in the area, and suggesting that

[28] Because one of the "maturity" areas is much larger than the others, it was divided into two on a north-south basis. Hence, we have 12 technical regions in our analysis.

the market density variable is much more important than is indicated by the results in Tables 3 and 4. The association is higher if we exclude the Southeast from the aggregation procedure. This is explained by the relative lateness of the research contributions of the southeastern experiment stations and by the various obstacles put in the way of private seed companies there. Also, after we come down to a certain low level, it does not really pay to discriminate between areas on the basis of X_1 because the differences are too small, and other factors predominate. This is brought out when we ask the same question about the association of Y with X_1 within each technical region separately. When regressions of Y on log X_1 were computed for each of the technical regions separately, 9 had the expected sign and were significantly different from zero, while the other 3 were not significantly different from zero. This result is significant on a sign test alone. But more interestingly, the r^2's were .66 rank correlated with the mean value of X_1, indicating that the explanatory power of this variable declined for areas with low average X_1 values.

The aggregation procedure, besides indicating that X_1 is a better variable than is implied by Tables 3 and 4, also helps us with the collinearity problem. Before aggregation, the partial correlation coefficient of Y with X_1, holding X_{10} constant, was $-.24$ on the state level and only $-.08$ on the crop reporting district level. Now it becomes $-.90$ for the aggregates by date of origin, $-.84$ when we leave out the Southeast, and $-.64$ for the data by technical regions. The regressions of Y on X_1 and X_{10} are presented in Table 5-B. The coefficient of X_1 has the expected sign and is significantly different from zero for the aggregates by "date of origin" and is almost twice the size of its standard error for the aggregates by technical region. This indicates that it is possible to separate the contributions of X_1 and X_{10} if we define our area units correctly.

While these results may not be too conclusive, together with information gathered in conversations with executives in the industry and a graphical

TABLE 5-B

REGRESSIONS OF Y ON X_1 AND X_{10}

Aggregation by	*Coefficients of* X_1	*Coefficients of* X_{10}	R^2
"Date of Origin": All areas	−17.8 (2.5)	1.02 (.07)	.982
"Date of Origin": All areas except the Southeast	−16.5 (3.4)	1.03 (.07)	.077
"Technical Region":	−10.5 (5.6)	.88 (.12)	.925

Note: Figures in parentheses are the calculated standard errors.

survey of the data, they leave little doubt in my mind that the development of hybrid corn was largely guided by expected pay-off, "better" areas being entered first, even though it may be difficult to measure very well the variables entering into these calculations.

4. THE RATE OF ACCEPTANCE

Differences in the *slope* or adjustment coefficient b will be interpreted as differences in the rate of adjustment of demand to the new equilibrium, and will be explained by variables operating on the demand side rather than by variables operating on the supply side.[29] Actually, the path traced out is an intersection of short-run supply and demand curves. It is assumed, however, that while shifts on the supply side determine the origin of the development, the rate of development is largely a demand, or "acceptance," variable.[30] The usefulness of this assumption is due to a very elastic long-run supply of seed and is supported by the fact that only local and transitory seed shortages were observed. On the whole, the supply of seed was not the limiting factor.[31]

Differences in the rate of acceptance of hybrid corn, the differences in b, are due at least in part to differences in the profitability of the changeover from open pollinated to hybrid seed. This hypothesis is based on the general idea that the larger the stimulus the faster is the rate of adjustment to it.[32] Also, in a world of imperfect knowledge, it takes time to realize that things have in fact changed. The larger the shift the faster will entrepreneurs

[29] The dimension of b, the adjustment coefficient, may be of some interest. b indicates by how much the value of the logistic transform will change per time unit. A value of $b = 1.0$ implies that the development will go from, e.g., 12 to 27 to 50 to 73 to 88 percent from year to year; i.e., the distance from 12 to 88 percent will be covered in four years. A value of $b = 0.5$ would imply a path: 12, 18, 27, 38, 50, 62, 73, 82, 88, etc., i.e., it would take twice the time eight years, to transverse the same distance. If one thinks in terms of the cumulative normal distribution positioned on a time scale, which is very similar to the logistic, then b is approximately proportional to $1/\sigma$. A low standard deviation implies that it will take a short time to go from, e.g., 10 to 99 percent, while a higher standard deviation implies a longer period of adjustment.

[30] Implicitly, we have the following model: the potential adjustment path of supply is an exponential function, which after a few years rises quickly above the potential adjustment function of demand. The demand adjustment function has the form of the logistic. The actual path followed is the lower of the two, which, after the first few years, is the demand path.

[31] "Clearly it would have been physically impossible for a large percentage of operators to have planted hybrids in the early thirties. There simply was not enough seed. It seems likely, however, that this operated more as a potential than an actual limitation upon the will of the operator, and that rapidity of adoption approximated the rate at which farmers decided favorably upon the new technique." B. Ryan, "A Study in Technological Diffusion," *Rural Sociology*, Vol. 13 (1948), p. 273. Similar views were expressed to the author by various people closely associated with the developments in hybrid corn.

[32] E.g., "The greater the efficiency of the new technology in producing returns, . . . the greater its rate of acceptance."—"How Farm People Accept New Ideas," Special Report No. 15, Agricultural Extension Service, Iowa State College, Ames (November 1955), p. 6.

become aware of it, "find it out," and hence they will react more quickly to larger shifts.[33]

My hypothesis is that the rate of acceptance is a function of the profitability of the shift, both per acre and total. Per acre profitability may be defined as the increase in yield due to the use of hybrid seed, times the price of corn, and minus the difference in the cost of seed. As there is very little relevant cross-sectional variation in the price of corn, the seeding rate, or the price of seed, these will be disregarded and only differences in the superiority of hybrids over open-pollinated varieties taken into account.[34]

I shall use two measures of the superiority of hybrids over open pollinated varieties: (1) the average increase in yield in bushels per acre, based on unpublished mail questionnaire data collected by the Agricultural Marketing Service, X_7, and (2) the long-run average pre-hybrid yield of corn, X_8. The latter measure was used on the basis of the widespread belief that the superiority of hybrids can be adequately summarized as a percentage increase.[35] A variation in pre-hybrid yields, given a percentage increase, will also imply a variation in the absolute superiority of hybrids over open pollinated varieties. Twenty percent is the figure quoted most often for this superiority.[36] Average corn acres per farm, X_3, were used to add the impact of total profits per farm.

As the value of b depends strongly on the ceiling K, to make them comparable between areas, the b's had to be adjusted for differences in K. Instead

---

[33] This is analogous to the situation in Sequential Analysis. The ASN (average sample number) is an inverse function of, among other things, the difference between the population means. That is, the larger the difference between the two things which we are testing, the sooner we will accumulate enough evidence to convince us that there is a difference. See A. Wald, *Sequential Analysis* (New York: John Wiley & Sons, Inc., 1947).

[34] The apparent cross-sectional variation in the average price of hybrid seed is largely due to differences in the mix of "public" versus "private" hybrids bought by farmers. The "public" hybrids sell for about $2 less per bushel. The rank correlation between the price of hybrid seed and the estimated share of "private" hybrids in 1956 was .73.

[35] The data from experiment station yield tests indicate that this is not too bad an assumption. See Sprague, *op. cit.*, and the literature cited there. It is unfortunate that these data are not comparable between states and, hence, cannot be used directly in this study.

[36] "If an average percentage increase in yield to be expected by planting hybrids as compared to open pollinated varieties were to be computed at the present it would probably be near 20 percent. . . ."—J. T. Swartz, "A Study of Hybrid Corn Yields as Compared to Open Pollinated Varieties," Insurance Section, FCIC, Washington, April and May, 1942, unpublished manuscript.

"Experience in other corn-growing regions of the United States shows that increases of approximately 20 percent over the open pollinated varieties may be expected from the use of adapted hybrids. Results so far in Texas are in general agreement with this figure," J. S. Rogers and J. W. Collier, "Corn Production in Texas," Texas Agricultural Experiment Station, Bulletin 746, February 1952, p. 7.

"Plant breeders conservatively estimate increase in yields of 15 to 20 percent from using hybrid seed under field conditions. They expect about the same relative increases in both low—and high—yielding areas," USDA, *Technology of the Farm* (Washington, 1940), p. 2.2.

of b, $b' = bK$ was used as the dependent variable, translating the b's back into actual percentage units from percentage of ceiling units. Alternatively, one should have adjusted the independent variables to correspond only to that fraction of the acres which will eventually shift to hybrids. But there are no data for making such an adjustment; hence b was adjusted to imply the same actual percentage changes in different areas.[37]

Linear and log regressions were calculated for the date from 31 states and 132 crop reporting districts. The results are presented in Table 6.[38] The figures speak largely for themselves, indicating the surprisingly good and uniform results obtained. The log form and X_8 rather than X_7 did somewhat better but not significantly so. The similarity of the coefficients in comparable regression is striking. For example, compare the coefficients of X_8 and X_7 in the log regressions and all the coefficients in the similar regressions on the state and crop reporting district levels. These results were also similar to those obtained in preliminary analyses using b rather than b' as the dependent variable[39] (see Table 7).

An attempt was made to incorporate several additional variables into the analysis. Rural sociologists have suggested that socioeconomic status or level-of-living is an important determinant of the rate of acceptance of a new technique.[40] The United States Department of Agriculture level-of-living index for 1939, when added to the regressions by states, had a negative coefficient in the linear form and a positive coefficient in the logarithmic form. In neither case was the coefficient significantly different from zero.

A measure of the "importance" of corn—the value of corn as a percentage of the value of all crops—was added in the belief that the rate of acceptance may be affected by the relative importance of corn within the farmer's enterprise. However, its coefficient was not significantly different from zero. Nor was the coefficient of total capital per farm significantly different from zero. The latter variable was introduced in an attempt to measure the impact of "capital rationing."[41]

The rate of acceptance may be also affected by the "advertising" activities

---

[37] This adjustment affects our results very little. See Table 7, below.

[38] X_7 was not used on the state level because it was felt that the aggregation error would be too large. We want an average of differences while I could get only a difference between averages. For some states this difference exceeded the individual differences in all the crop reporting districts within the state.

[39] These were calculated for subsamples of 65 and 32 crop reporting districts.

[40] See "How Farm People Accept New Ideas," *op. cit.*, and E. A. Wilkening, "The Acceptance of Certain Agricultural Programs and Practices in a Piedmont Community of North Carolina," (unpublished Ph.D. thesis, University of Chicago, 1949), and "Acceptance of Improved Farm Practices in Three Coastal Plain Counties," Tech. Bull. No. 98, North Carolina Agricultural Experiment Station, May 1952.

[41] The failure of the last two variables is due largely to their strong intercorrelation with the included variables. "Importance" is highly correlated with average yield and capital with corn acres per farm. When used separately, these two variables did as well on the state level as yield and corn acres per farm.

TABLE 6
REGRESSION OF *SLOPES* ON "PROFITABILITY" VARIABLES

Regression	Coefficients of			
	X_3	X_7	X_8	R^2
By states—N = 31:				
$b' = c_0 + c_3X_3 + c_8X_8$	.006 (.002)		.017 (.005)	.66
$\log b' = c_0 + c_3 \log X_3 + c_8 \log X_8$	.30 (.08)		.66 (.11)	.67
By crop reporting districts—N = 132:				
$b' = c_0 + c_3X_3 + c_7X_7$	.0073 (.0008)	.079 (.009)		.57
$b' = c_0 + c_3X_3 + c_8X_8$	.0076 (.0007)		.016 (.002)	.61
$\log b' = c_0 + c_3 \log X_3 + c_7 \log X_7$	.44 (.04)	.70 (.09)		.61
$\log b' = c_0 + c_3 \log X_3 + c_8 \log X_8$	.44 (.03)		.57 (.05)	.69

Notes:
Figures in parentheses are the calculated standard errors.
X_3—Average corn acres per farm reporting corn.
X_7—The average difference between hybrid and open pollinated yields by districts tabulated only from reports showing both and averaged over 4 to 10 years, depending on the overlap of the available data with the adjustment period (10 to 90 percent). Based on unpublished AMS "Identicals" data.
X_8—Pre-hybrid average yield. Usually an average for the 10 years before an area reached 10 percent in hybrids. Sometimes fewer years were used, depending on the available data. Source: for states, *Agriculture Statistics*; for crop reporting districts, various published and unpublished data from the AMS and from state agricultural statisticians.

TABLE 7
REGRESSION OF UNADJUSTED *SLOPES* ON "PROFITABILITY" VARIABLES

Regression	Coefficients			
	X_3	X_7	X_8	R^2
$b = c_0 + c_3X_3 + c_7X_7$ ($N = 65$)	.005 (.001)	.06 (.01)		.40
$b = c_0 + c_3X_3 + c_8X_8$ ($N = 32$)	.005 (.001)		.022 (.002)	.75

of the extension agencies and private seed companies. There are no data, however, which would enable us to take this into account. There is also some evidence that the estimated rate of acceptance will be affected by the degree of aggregation and the heterogeneity of the aggregate. Heterogeneous areas imply different component growth curves and hence a lower aggregate slope coefficient. This is exhibited by the lower state values for b as compared to the values for the individual crop reporting districts within these states. No way has been found, however, to introduce this factor into the analysis.

Nevertheless, our results do suggest that a substantial proportion of the variation in the rate of acceptance of hybrid corn is explainable by differences in the profitability of the shift to hybrids in different parts of the country.

5. THE EQUILIBRIUM LEVEL OF USE

I am interpreting the *ceilings* as the long-run equilibrium percentages of the corn acreage which will be planted to hybrid seed. Differences in the percentage at which the use of hybrid seed will stabilize are the result of long-run demand factors. It is assumed that in the long run the supply conditions of seed are the same to all areas, the same percentage increase in yield over open pollinated varieties at the same relative price. However, this same technical superiority may mean different things in different parts of the country.

The ceiling is a function of some of the same variables which determine b, the rate of acceptance. It is a function of average profitability and of the distribution of this profitability. With the average above a certain value no farmer will be faced with zero or negative profitability of the shift to hybrids. With the average profitability below this level some farmers will be facing negative returns and hence will not switch to hybrids. In marginal corn areas, however, "average profitability" may become a very poor measure. Its components lose their connection with the concepts they purport to represent. Yield variability may overshadow the average increase from hybrids. The relevance of the published price of corn diminishes. In many marginal corn areas there is almost no market for corn off the farm. The only outlet for increased production is as an input in another production or consumption process on the farm. But on farms on which corn is a marginal enterprise, with little or no commercial livestock production, the use of corn is limited to human consumption, feed for draft animals, a cow and a few chickens. The farmer is interested in producing a certain amount of corn to fill his needs, having no use for additional corn. It will pay him to switch to hybrid corn only if he has alternative uses for the released land and other resources which would return him more than the extra cost of seed. But in many of these areas corn is already on the poorest land and uses resources left over from other operations on the farm. Also, there may already be substantial amounts of idle land in the area. All these factors may tend to make hybrids unprofitable although they are "technically" superior. Similarly, in areas where capital rationing is important the recorded market rate of interest will be a poor measure of the opportunity costs of capital. While the returns to hybrid corn may be substantial, if corn is not a major crop, the returns to additional investments in other branches of the enterprise may be even higher.

Ceilings are not necessarily constant over time. Even without any apparent change in the profitability of the shift from open pollinated to hybrid corn, a change in the relative profitability of corn growing, an improvement in the functioning of the market for corn, or an increase in storage facilities may change them. Also, in areas where there are large year-to-year changes in the corn acreage, the percentage planted to hybrid seed may fluctuate as a result of the differential exit and entry in and out of corn of farmers using hybrid or open pollinated seed. These changes may occur without any "real" changes in the relative profitability of hybrids or in farmers' attitudes towards them. It is very difficult to deal statistically with a development composed of a series of adjustments to shifting equilibrium values.[42] As a first approximation I shall ignore this problem. Only in the marginal corn areas is this a problem of some importance. For most of the Corn Belt the assumption of an immediate ceiling of 100 percent is tenable. In the fringe areas ceiling values somewhat lower than 100 percent fit very well. There are some indications that in the South ceilings may have shifted over time, but I doubt that this is important enough to bias seriously our results.

In spite of all these reservations and the crudeness with which the ceilings were estimated in the first place, it is possible to explain a respectable proportion of their variation with the same "profitability" variables that were used in the analysis of *slopes*. Because there is a ceiling of 1.00 to the possible variation in K, the logistic function was used again, giving us logit $K = \log_e [K/(1 - K)]$ as our dependent variable. As there were a substantial number of areas with $K = 1.0$, a value not defined for the transform, two approximations were used. On the state level all values of $K = 1.0$ were set equal to .99, while on the crop reporting level, where there was no problem of degrees of freedom, these values were left out of the analysis. X_3, average corn acres per farm, and X_8, pre-hybrid yield, were used as "profitability" measures, and X_{11}, capital per farm, was added to take "capital rationing" into account. The results of these calculations are presented in Table 8. They indicate that differences in measures of average profitability, differences in average corn acres and pre-hybrid yields, can explain a substantial proportion of the variation in *ceilings*, the long-run equilibrium level of hybrid seed use. The proportion of the variation explained on the state level is substantially higher, indicating that additional variables which may be at work at the crop reporting district level may cancel out at the state level. For example, the coefficient of capital investment per farm, a measure of "capital rationing," is significant at the crop reporting district level but not at the state level. Undoubtedly this analysis could be improved by the addition of other

---

[42] I am aware of only one attempt in the literature to deal with this kind of problem. See C. F. Roos and V. von Szelisky, "Factors Governing Changes in Domestic Automobile Demand," particularly the section on "The Concept of a Variable Maximum Ownership Level," pp. 36–38, in General Motors Corporation, *Dynamics of Automobile Demand* (New York, 1939).

variables but I would not expect it to change the major conclusion appreciably.

6. LIMITATIONS, SUMMARY, AND CONCLUSIONS

The above analysis does not purport to present a complete model of the process of technological change. Rather the approach has been to break down the problem into manageable units and to analyze them more or less separately. I have concentrated on the longer-run aspects of technological

TABLE 8
REGRESSIONS OF LOGIT *K* ON "PROFITABILITY" VARIABLES

Regression	*Coefficients of*			
	X_3	X_8	X_{11}	R^2
By states—N = 31:				
$c_0 + c_3X_3 + c_8X_8$	.03	.11		.71
	(.01)	(.02)		
$c_0 + c_3 \log X_3 + c_8 \log X_8$	1.94	5.88		.71
	(.56)	(.80)		
$+ c_{11} \log X_{11}$	1.55	5.25	.71	.72
	(.84)	(1.30)	(1.14)	
By crop reporting districts— N = 86:				
$c_0 + c_3 \log X_3 + c_8 \log X_8$ $+ c_{11} \log X_{11}$	1.09	2.22	1.35	.39
	(.48)	(.61)	(.64)	

Notes:
Figures in parentheses are the calculated standard errors.
X_3—Average corn acres per farm.
X_8—Pre-hybrid yield.
X_{11}—On the state level, value of land and buildings per farm, 1940. Source: *Statistical Abstract of the United States*, 1948, p. 600. On the crop reporting district level, total capital investment per farm, 1949. Computed from Table 11, E. G. Strand and E. O. Heady, "Productivity of Resources Used on Commercial Farms," USDA, Technical Bulletin No. 1128 (Washington, D.C., November 1955), p. 45.

change, interpreting differences in the pattern of development of hybrid corn on the basis of the long-run characteristics of various areas, and ignoring the impact of short-run fluctuations in prices and incomes. This limitation is not very important in the cases of hybrid corn because the returns from the changeover were large enough to swamp any short-run fluctuations in prices and other variables.[43] It might, however, become serious were we to consider other technical changes requiring substantial investments, and not as superior to their predecessors as was hybrid corn. Nor can we transfer the particular numerical results to the consideration of other developments. Nevertheless, a cursory survey of trends in the number of cornpickers and tractors on farms, and of trends in the use of fertilizer, does indicate that it

[43] Estimates made for Kansas data indicate returns from 300 to 1000 percent on the extra cost of seed.

might also be possible to apply a version of our approach to their analysis.

I hope that this work does indicate that at least the process of innovation, the process of adapting and distributing a particular invention to different markets and its acceptance by entrepreneurs, is amenable to economic analysis. It is possible to account for a large share of the spatial and chronological differences in the use of hybrid corn with the help of "economic" variables. The lag in the development of adaptable hybrids for particular areas and the lag in the entry of seed producers into these areas can be explained on the basis of varying profitability of entry. Also, differences in both the long-run equilibrium use of hybrids and in the rate of approach to that equilibrium level are explainable, at least in part, by differences in the profitability of the shift from open pollinated to hybrid varieties.

Looking at the hybrid seed industry as a part of the specialized sector which provides us with technological change, it can be said that both private and public funds were allocated efficiently within that sector.[44] Given a limited set of resources, the hybrid seed industry expanded according to a pattern which made sense, allocating its resources first to the areas of highest returns.

The American farmer appears also to have adjusted rationally to these new developments. Where the profits from the innovation were large and clear cut, the changeover was very rapid. It took Iowa farmers only four years to go from 10 to 90 percent of their corn acreage in hybrid corn. In areas where the profitability was lower, the adjustment was also slower. On the whole, taking account of uncertainty and the fact that the spread of knowledge is not instantaneous, farmers have behaved in a fashion consistent with the idea of profit maximization. Where the evidence appears to indicate the contrary, I would predict that a closer examination of the relevant economic variables will show that the change was not as profitable as it appeared to be.[45]

---

[44] Some minor quibbles could be raised about the allocation of public funds, but the returns to these funds have been so high that the impact of the existing inefficiencies is almost imperceptible.

[45] In this context one may say a few words about the impact of "sociological" variables. It is my belief that in the long run, and cross-sectionally, these variables tend to cancel themselves out, leaving the economic variables as the major determinants of the pattern of technological change. This does not imply that the "sociological" variables are not important if one wants to know which *individual* will be first or last to adopt a particular technique, only that these factors do not vary widely cross-sectionally. Partly this is a question of semantics. With a little ingenuity, I am sure that I can redefine 90 percent of the "sociological" variables as economic variables. Also, some of the variables I used, e.g., yield of corn and corn acres per farm, will be very highly related cross-sectionally to education, socio-economic status, level-of-living, income, and other "sociological" variables. That is, it is very difficult to discriminate between the assertion that hybrids were accepted slowly because it was a "poor corn area" and the assertion that the slow acceptance was due to "poor people." Poor people and poor corn are very closely correlated in the U.S. Nevertheless, one may find a few areas where this is not so. Obviously, the slow acceptance of hybrids on the western fringes of the Corn Belt, in western Kansas, Nebraska, South Dakota, and North Dakota was not due to poor people, but the result of "economic" factors, poor corn area.

Part V Aggregative Analysis of Production and Supply

15 The Nature of the Supply Function for Agricultural Products*

D. GALE JOHNSON†

It is generally believed that the total output of farm products responds little if any to changes in the average price of farm products. For example, most farmers believe this to be true for downward movements in real prices; the willingness of farmers and their representatives to accept direct control of output and marketing clearly reflects their belief that downward movements in real prices will not substantially reduce farm output. Though this belief is apparently based on the depression experiences of 1919–22 and 1929–33, it is applied without hesitation to a period when resources are generally fully employed.[1]

The best published discussion of the responsiveness of agricultural output to price changes is by Professors Galbraith and Black.[2] Their analysis is restricted to depression conditions and lacks preciseness largely because it fails to distinguish between those conditions relevant to the decision process within firms and those relevant to the nature of the factor markets, *i.e.*, the supply conditions of factors. No systematic attempt has been made, to my knowledge, to make a similar analysis for non-depression conditions.

This paper attempts to fill these gaps by analyzing the reaction of aggregate output (1) to falling relative prices under depression conditions, and (2) to

---

* *American Economic Review,* Vol. XL, No. 4 (September, 1950), pp. 539–64.

† University of Chicago, Chicago, Illinois. The author expresses appreciation to Milton Friedman, F. V. Waugh, T. W. Schultz, and O. H. Brownlee for suggestions and criticisms.

[1] See Secretary of Agriculture Brannan's *Statement before a Subcommittee of the Committee on Agriculture and Forestry, U.S. Senate, Eighty-First Congress, First Session, on S. 1882 and S. 1971 (July 7, 11, 12, 13, 14, 15, 18, and 19, 1949)*, pp. 50–52.

[2] See J. K. Galbraith and J. D. Black, "The Maintenance of Agricultural Production during Depression: The Explanations Reviewed," *Journal of Political Economy*, Vol. 46 (June 1938), pp. 305–23.

changing relative prices when resources are fully employed in the economy. These two sets of conditions are chosen to simplify the discussion and because they represent the important empirical conditions.

I. AGRICULTURAL OUTPUT DURING A DEPRESSION

Aggregate farm output has repeatedly failed to decline during depressions. Numerous explanations have been offered for this phenomenon; such as high fixed costs in agriculture, the length of the production process, and the competitive structure of agriculture. Several such explanations are reviewed and analyzed in this section and an attempt is then made to outline a more general explanation.

A. The Facts

Much of the evidence usually presented on the behavior of agricultural output has been interpreted as indicating that agriculture's output response during major cyclical declines is peculiar to it. Table 1 presents data of the

TABLE 1
INDEXES OF PRODUCTION FOR AGRICULTURE, MANUFACTURING, AND MINING, 1927–1947
(1935–39=100)

Year	Agri-cultural Output	Manu-facturing	Durable Manu-facturing	Non-durable Manu-facturing	Iron and Steel	Machinery	Mining
1927	95	94	107	83	108	99	97
28	99	99	117	85	121	106	95
29	97	110	132	93	133	130	103
30	95	90	98	84	97	100	91
31	104	75	67	79	61	66	82
32	101	57	41	70	32	43	72
33	93	68	54	79	54	50	80
34	79	74	65	81	61	69	83
35	96	87	83	90	81	83	89
36	85	104	108	100	114	105	99
37	108	113	122	106	123	126	109
38	105	87	78	95	68	82	99
39	106	109	109	109	114	104	105
40	109	126	139	115	147	136	114
41	114	168	201	142	186	221	122
42	128	212	279	158	199	340	125
43	125	258	360	176	208	443	132
44	130	252	353	171	206	439	145
45	129	214	274	166	183	343	143
46	133	177	192	165	150	240	142

Source: *Statistical Abstract, 1947*, p. 816, and *Agricultural Statistics, 1947*, p. 533.

type usually considered rather conclusive. In 1933, agricultural output was only 6 percent below its 1929 level, and that decline was in substantial part due to poor weather in the Great Plains area. In 1932, farm output was actually higher than in 1929. Manufacturing output as a whole declined by more than a third, while iron and steel output declined by 70 percent and machinery, by 60 percent.

But any theory explaining agriculture's behavior must also be consistent with another set of facts, namely that there were other important segments in the economy which produced almost as much in 1932 and 1933 as in 1929. The following tabulation shows 1933 annual output as a percentage of 1929 output:[3]

Meat packing	95
Shortening	98
Canned milk	98
Cheese	95
Butter	110
Cotton goods	87
Woolen and worsted goods	87
Knit goods	100
Shoes, leather	94
Beet sugar	151
Canned fruits and vegetables	88
Clothing, women's	91
Soap	98
Petroleum refining	86

Employment in agriculture in 1929 was 8,323,000 family workers and 2,984,000 hired workers; in 1933, 8,590,000 and 2,433,000, respectively. Total employment declined roughly 2 percent, from 11,289,000 to 11,023,000. Employment in manufacturing as a whole declined by 30–35 percent and employment in certain types of manufacturing (automobiles, for example) by more than 40 percent and hours worked, by even more. On the other hand,

---

[3] Source: Solomon Fabricant, *The Output of Manufacturing Industries, 1899–1937* (New York: National Bureau of Economic Research, 1940). The reader may object that output behavior of the manufacturing groups included in the tabulation do not support the statement that output in some segments of the economy behaved much the same as agricultural output. Each of the industries, except the last, processes an agricultural product and since agricultural output did not decline, it seems evident at once that the output of the specified processing groups would not decline. The output behavior of the processing groups can be explained by the theory developed below, namely by the shifting of the supply functions of factors or by the price inelasticity of the supply functions for one or more of the factors. Inspection of the list will disclose several industries for which the cost of the agricultural raw material represents only a small fraction (less than a fifth) of the total manufacturing cost. In these instances, the supply prices of other factors declined sufficiently to permit the firms to maintain output.

employment in food manufacturing declined only 15 percent from 1929 to 1932 and rose from 1932 to 1933.

B. A Review of the Explanations

Roughly a half-dozen explanations of the cyclical behavior of agricultural output have been put forward. This section examines each of them; the next presents a general theory constructed to explain those characteristics of agricultural output under discussion.

1. *High Fixed Costs.* The belief that high fixed costs are responsible for the failure of farmers to reduce output during a depression has achieved more general acceptance than any other explanation.

It is generally argued that farm firms have fixed costs because the labor supply is so closely related to the firm. Labor is viewed as a resource that is fixed to the firm because the operator and family members constitute roughly three fourths of total farm workers. The same considerations are frequently alleged to apply to land.

This argument seems invalid. The employment of hired labor in agriculture is almost as constant as family employment.[4] Yet hired labor is certainly not considered a fixed resource by the firm. Hired workers are apparently willing to offer their services at prices which the firms believe are no higher than the value of the marginal product and so continue to be employed.

In many cases, the land operated is one of the assets of a firm in the sense that the firm owns the land. Most farm firms have the alternative of renting the land to another firm to operate, even during a depression. Only in the exceptional case would such an alternative not be available. Even if farmers who own land are unwilling to consider this alternative, the behavior of firms renting land cannot be explained by treating land as a fixed cost. There was roughly as much land rented during the thirties as was owned by the farm firms. Presumably operators continued to use the land because the price of land fell enough to equalize demand and supply at a level of "full" employment.

Table 2 is pertinent to the present argument. It indicates changes in gross income, net operator income, and production expenses from 1929 to 1932. Most of the changes in expenditures are due to changes in prices rather than quantities.[5] Net operator income represents the returns to all resources owned or controlled by the operator, including labor, land, and capital. Of the total production expenses, only taxes and farm mortgage interest would have continued to be claims on current income even if no output had

---

[4] Between 1929 and 1933, hired labor employment declined by 15 percent, but an unknown fraction of this decline was due to the shift from the hired to the unpaid family labor category.

[5] See below, pages 257–58.

been planned. These two items represented, in 1929, only 15 percent of total production expenses and only 9 percent of the value of gross output.

TABLE 2
EXPENSES OF FARM PRODUCTION AND FARM INCOME
(millions of dollars)

	1929	*1932*	*1947*
Gross income	13,824	6,406	34,705
Net operator income	5,654	1,715	17,087
Total production expenses	8,170	4,691	17,618
Feed purchased	919	348	3,783
Livestock purchased	461	164	1,302
Fertilizer and lime	293	125	685
Operating motor vehicles	509	384	1,505
Hired labor	1,284	584	2,791
Miscellaneous current expenses[a]	1,146	814	1,768
Taxes	641	504	705
Farm mortage interest	582	534	222
Rent (net)[b]	1,062	343	2,300
Depreciation[c]	1,273	890	2,579

[a] Includes such items as electricity, twine, ginning fees, dairy supplies, seeds, containers, etc.
[b] Gross rents were as follows: 1929—$1,621,474,000; 1932—$668,935,000; and 1947—$3.1 billion. About the same amount of land was rented in 1932 as in 1929, while perhaps 10 percent less was rented in 1947.
[c] Gross investment: 1929—$1,414,000,000; 1932—$290,000,000; 1947—$3,682,000,000.
Source: Department of Agriculture, Bureau of Agricultural Economics, "Net Farm Income and Parity Summary 1919–41" (mimeo.) and *Farm Income Situation, August–September, 1948.*

Even if one were willing to assume that labor is a fixed cost to the farm firm, nothing is gained by so doing. High fixed costs are not an adequate explanation of the relative stability of hired labor employment nor of the constancy of the amount of land rented. Nor can one, on this basis, explain the constancy of the output of livestock products, particularly hogs. Farm management studies indicate that 75 percent of the average cost of producing hogs is feed cost. Hog output is maintained only because feed prices fall, and fall as much or more than hog prices during the downswing of a major depression.

The constant employment of factors apparently reflects not high fixed costs but either (a) inelastic supply curves together with highly flexible factor prices or (b) changes in the marginal opportunity costs of the factors with the business cycle. The first explanation is pertinent to physical capital assets and land; the second to labor, feed, and livestock. Since most feeds are durable, why do feed prices fall low enough during a depression to clear the market of all of the current output? Given existing cost conditions during a depression, farmers are maximizing their position by producing crops, but they have the alternatives of feeding or storing the feed crops in anticipation of higher prices later. In this way, livestock output could be contracted during depression. Constancy of output of livestock implies that the supply curve of feed grains for current use has shifted far to the right. I shall consider this point later.

2. *Farmers Try to Offset Lower Prices by Increased Output.* The explanation that agricultural output is maintained (or even increased) by farmers as a means of offsetting lower prices may have a certain validity. Over certain ranges, the supply curve of operator and unpaid family labor may be backward sloping; *i.e.,* individuals work more at a lower than a higher wage. This statement implies that as income falls, the marginal utility of income increases relative to the marginal utility of leisure. Since the employment of some inputs do decline during a depression because their prices are not as flexible as product prices, farm output is probably maintained by a small increase in the quantity of labor supplied by a given number of workers.

3. *Subsistence Production is Important in Agriculture.* If production is largely for the consumption of the operator family and few of the inputs are purchased, relative prices have little effect upon the firm under any circumstances. Production decisions will be based largely on resources owned or controlled (mostly land and labor), and consumption preferences.

In 1939, about one quarter of all farms had household use as the major source of income, and in 1944, roughly 22 percent.[6] These farms produced less than 4 percent of the total farm output in 1944.[7] Roughly three quarters of what was produced on these self-sufficient farms was consumed in the household. In 1944, the rest of the farm operators consumed only about 8 percent of what they produced.[8] Consequently, the production of the bulk of the agricultural output is so commercialized that constancy of subsistence production cannot explain constancy of aggregate production.

4. *Technological Factors Inhibit Response to Price Changes.* The production process in agriculture is relatively long. Consequently, a decline in prices may not be followed at once by a reduction in output. Farmers will find it advantageous to complete the production process as long as price equals or exceeds the marginal cost of completing the production process as of any moment of time. This explanation can apply only to cycles of short duration when prices fall for a year or 18 months and then start to increase. It cannot apply to the 1929 to 1933 downswing. Here farmers did have time to change their production plans and yet failed to do so.

5. *Agriculture Has a More Competitive Structure Than the Rest of the Economy.* The belief that agricultural output is maintained during depressions because agriculture is competitive, is strongly held in many quarters.

---

[6] *United States Census of Agriculture, 1945.* Volume II, *General Report,* chap. 10, Table 4. Data based on 1945 classification by type of farm.

[7] *Ibid.,* chap. 10, Table 26.

[8] *Ibid.*

The belief that output in many sectors of the nonfarm economy is highly variable during a business cycle because of enterprise monopoly is also strongly held.

The data on page 249 suggest that monopoly by no means always leads to large output variations during a business cycle. By measures ordinarily used to measure degree of concentration (percentage of output controlled by a few firms), canned milk, meat packing, soap, and beet sugar are rather noncompetitive; the rest of the industries, relatively competitive. Yet all had highly stable output.

In addition, it should be noted that several competitive industries produced much smaller outputs in 1933 than in 1929. Among these were all branches of mining and lumber and most products of lumber.[9]

An enterprise monopolist would restrict output and maintain prices during a depression in two sets of circumstances. First, if the supply functions for all factors were perfectly elastic *and* if the supply functions did not shift from the peak to the trough of the business cycle. In these circumstances the monopolist would find it in its interest to maintain prices in the face of declining demand.[10] Without knowing the exact nature of the shift in demand, it cannot be said with certainty that no price change would occur but it is reasonable to assume that the change in price would be relatively small and most of the adjustment would be in output.

A competitive industry in the same circumstances would react in the same fashion. Since marginal cost did not decline, price could not fall for any period of time.

Second, an enterprise monopolist producing a durable product would be more likely to maintain prices during a depression if it believed that an

---

[9] See Solomon Fabricant, *The Output of Manufacturing Industries, 1899–1937*, Appendix B and Harold Barger and Sam H. Schurr, *The Mining Industries, 1899–1939*, Appendix A. (New York: National Bureau of Economic Research, 1944). Walter F. Crowder summarized an analysis of the output behavior of 407 products from 1929 to 1933 and 1933 to 1937. He concluded as follows: "If eight or ten products which decreased more than 90 percent are not given undue weight, the logical inference would seem to be that the changes in quantity output of the great mass of manufactured products between 1929 and 1933 were not related to the concentration ratios of the products." For the 1933–37 period, he stated, ". . . it cannot be said that manufactured products in the 'low' concentration group exhibit any outstandingly different behavior pattern from that of products in the 'high' concentration group." (T.N.E.C. Monograph No. 27, *The Structure of Industry*, pp. 350–51 and 354.)

[10] This seems to be the assumption made by several writers who have discussed the relation between enterprise monopoly and cyclical price rigidity. Boulding, for example, assumed a relatively flat marginal cost curve and then argued that a decline in demand during a downturn of the business cycle would lead to price maintenance and output restriction. This explanation fails to indicate why the marginal cost curve does not shift during the cycle. If the cost curve shifted downward, regardless of how flat it is, price would be permitted to fall unless the demand curve shifted in a very peculiar manner (See Kenneth Boulding, *Economic Analysis* [20 ed.; New York: Harper & Bros, 1948], p. 557.) For an analysis similar to that contained in this paper, see T. De. Scitovszky, "Prices under Monopoly and Competition," *Journal of Political Economy*, Vol. 49 (October 1941), pp. 663–86.

extra unit sold during a depression at a lower price would otherwise be sold later at a higher price during the subsequent prosperity. A policy such as this is not without costs and it is by no means certain that if such a monopolist realized lower marginal costs during the depression that it would maintain prices at the pre-depression level. A competitive industry producing a similar product with the same demand relationship in time would not react as the monopolist does for obvious reasons.

The degree of competition in the factor markets is probably more important than the degree of competition in the product market in explaining output response during a depression. It would be difficult to distinguish between the price and output behavior during a depression of an enterprise monopolist that buys factors in a competitive market and a competitive firm. Food processors did not contract output because the supply functions for at least one important factor, farm products, shifted, and the factor price fell sharply. The output behavior of the firms did not seem to have been affected by the extent of monopoly and one should not have expected that it would be.

But if the factor markets are not competitive and the supply functions for the factors do not shift during the depression, both an enterprise monopolist and a competitive firm would be unable to maintain output, if demand for the product declined.

The important unanswered question about price and output reactions during the 1929–33 depression is found in the urban labor market, why the hourly earnings of production workers in manufacturing declined so little (from $0.566 in 1929 to $0.442 in 1933) despite the drastic decline in employment.[11] Unions were not then sufficiently important in manufacturing to have had much influence. Given the small decline in wages, manufacturing industries which did not use an important factor, or input having a flexible price, could not react in the same way as agriculture.

6. *Summary of the Explanations.* Most of the preceding explanations of the difference between the behavior of output in agriculture and in non-agriculture must be rejected. High fixed costs, the importance of subsistence production, and technological conditions are clearly invalid explanations. The differences in the competitive structure of agriculture and industry in the degree of enterprise monopoly is a superficially more plausible explanation, yet I believe it, too, is invalid. An enterprise monopoly faced with the same factor supply conditions as agriculture would, in my view, react in much the same way as a competitive firm.

The belief that farm workers may work harder during periods of low income cannot be rejected on the basis of existing data, and this hypothesis is consistent with actual behavior.

---

[11] Farm wage rates declined more than 50 percent in the same period. See *Statistical Abstract, 1947*, pp. 199 and 210.

C. A Possible Theory

Any theory purporting to explain the constancy of agricultural output during a depression should explain also similar behavior in the rest of the economy; it should be consistent also with the fact that agricultural output increases when the relative price of agricultural products increases, and that farmers shift from one product to another as the relative prices of different products vary.

It is my view that a theory meeting these requirements is provided by the usual economic analysis of farmers as profit-maximizing entrepreneurs and that the special characteristics of the behavior of agricultural output can be explained by the characteristics of the supply functions of factors to agricultural firms.

The supply function for agricultural products is sometimes expressed as a simple relation between the quantity of output and the price of the output. However, the use of this relation obscures the complexity of the supply process determining the supply of agricultural products. The supply of agricultural products depends on: (1) Production conditions—the technological relations between inputs and outputs; (2) Supply conditions of the factors of production; (3) Price or demand conditions for output; and (4) The behavior of firms, including the objective of the entrepreneur.

The explanations provided in this paper of the behavior of agricultural output assume that firms maximize profits and that the demand for factors of production is determined solely on this basis unless a contrary assumption is made. The assumption of profit maximization implies that output behavior will be determined by the relationship between output and factor prices. For example, a greater relative increase in product than factor prices will result in increased output, and vice versa. Further, a rise in the price of one factor relative to another will decrease the employment of the first factor relative to the second. It is not necessary for our purpose that farmers actually maximize profits, but it is important, of course, that reliable predictions can be made by using the assumption of profit maximization.

Attention must be given to the supply conditions for the factors of production. These are spelled out in some detail at the relevant points in this article, but some comment on the labor supply function is required at this point. It is assumed that there is a labor supply function including all farm labor. To do this requires a strict separation of the farm firm and the labor function of the operator and other family members. This separation is required if confusion is to be avoided.

A firm is a business unit under single control within which productive resources are combined in order to produce goods and services for sale and use as a means of achieving some objective. A firm may consist solely of entrepreneurship, a business opportunity, and liquid capital. The farm operator is both an entrepreneur and a laborer. He accepts this dual rôle in the belief that he can thereby achieve a larger return from his energies. Otherwise, he would forego his entrepreneurial activities and hire out as a laborer. Analytically, we can divorce the supply of labor by the operator and his family to the farm firm from the farm firm itself, *i.e.*, we need not assume that this labor is a part of the firm.

During a depression, the supply function of land for use in agriculture has a price elasticity of nearly zero for a period of five to ten years. The response in quantity supplied following a price decline is related to disinvestment in land and failure to provide for maintenance. The supply function for capital equipment—to agriculture as a whole—is very inelastic whenever the demand price is below the price of new equipment. The supply function is then related solely to the existing supply of old equipment. Since such equipment does not have alternative uses outside of agriculture, there is no reservation price above the depreciation cost. Since this cost can be postponed, it may not represent an effective lower limit. The supply function of labor shifts with the level of income and employment in the rest of the economy. The marginal opportunity cost of labor falls rapidly as unemployment increases and rises similarly as unemployment declines. As the marginal opportunity cost approaches zero, the supply curve for agricultural labor becomes very inelastic. Farm workers are willing to accept lower rates of pay rather than be unemployed.

These conditions of supply would mean that during a major prolonged decline in business activity (1) farm prices, farm wage rates, and land rents would fall in about the same proportion and (2) the employment of land, labor, and machinery would not change appreciably. Condition (2) might prevail without (1) if the resources had to be used in fixed proportions or if one of the resources had a fixed coefficient of production, conditions that seem less plausible than the conditions of supply outlined above.

Tables 3 and 4 are not inconsistent with the above conclusions, except for the behavior of wage rates between 1919 and 1921. In part, this is explained by the fact that the peak in prices received came in May, 1920; the minimum, in June, 1921. Actually, no serious drop in farm prices came until the 1920 harvest, after wage bargains had largely been made.

The 1920–22 depression did not result in any significant decrease in crop acres planted. Labor employment was roughly constant. Employment of power and machinery increased slightly. Absolute farm prices fell 42 percent between 1919 and 1921, and relative farm-nonfarm prices by 22 percent. Because of the shortness of the time period, the 1920–22 depression cannot be considered as good a verification of our hypotheses as one might like.

The 1930–33 depression is a much better test. The period was four years, sufficiently long to permit farmers to revise their production plans completely. For employment of resources, the experience and hypotheses match very well. Acres planted may have increased slightly. Total labor employment remained almost constant (decreasing only 3 percent), while hired labor

TABLE 3

CROPS PLANTED, LABOR EMPLOYED AND POWER AND MACHINERY USED ON FARMS AND RELATIVE FARM PRICES, 1919–39

Year	Crops Planted[a] (in millions)	Labor Employment[b] Total (in millions)	Labor Employment[b] Hired (in millions)	Power and Machinery[c]	Relative Farm Prices[d]
1919	363	11.1	2.78	468	112
20	359	11.4	2.88	477	121
21	358	11.4	2.90	505	88
22	354	11.4	2.92	496	85
23	353	11.4	2.89	454	101
24	353	11.4	2.87	455	101
25	364	11.4	2.97	458	106
26	359	11.5	3.03	460	100
27	358	11.3	2.95	463	99
28	367	11.4	2.96	463	102
29	363	11.3	2.98	466	101
30	368	11.2	2.85	471	106
31	372	11.2	2.69	468	73
32	376	11.1	2.50	452	62
33	372	11.0	2.43	416	67
34	339	10.9	2.33	391	73
35	360	11.1	2.43	389	86
36	360	11.0	2.56	391	91
37	364	10.9	2.63	403	90
38	356	10.8	2.62	419	78
39	344	10.7	2.60	428	78

[a] 1924–1939, *Agricultural Statistics, 1940*, p. 542; 1919–23, estimate by the author.

[b] Department of Agriculture, Bureau of Agricultural Economics, *Farm Wage Rates, Farm Employment, and Related Data, 1943*, p. 155.

[c] Martin R. Cooper, Glen T. Barton, and Albert P. Bradell, *Progress of Farm Mechanization*, Department of Agriculture Misc. Pub. No. 630 (1947), p. 81. An index number with volume measured in terms of 1935–39 average dollars, 1870 = 100.

[d] Calculated from *Agricultural Statistics, 1945*, pp. 430–31. Based on ratio of prices received by farmers to wholesale prices of all commodities. Index equals 100 in 1910–14.

employment declined about 15 percent. Part of this decline resulted from a shift for workers related to the employer from the hired to the unpaid category.

As shown in Table 4, prices received and rent paid moved down together from 1929 to 1932 and 1933, with rent falling slightly more than prices.[12]

[12] The following tabulation indicates the relationship more clearly than Table 4:

Year	Prices Received	Cash Farm Income	Wage Rates	Wages Paid	Gross Rent Paid
1929	100	100	100	100	100
1930	86	80	93	88	81
1931	60	56	72	66	56
1932	46	42	53	45	41
1933	48	48	47	40	49

TABLE 4

FARM PRICES AND WAGE RATES, FARM WAGES AND RENTS PAID, AND CASH FARM INCOME, 1919–39

Year	Prices Received by Farmers[a]	Wage Rates[b]	Wages Paid[c] (millions of dollars)	Gross Rent[d] (millions of dollars)	Cash Farm Income[e] (millions of dollars)
1919	215	207	1,515	2,226	14,602
20	211	242	1,780	1,645	12,608
21	124	155	1,159	1,208	8,150
22	132	151	1,122	1,347	8,594
23	143	169	1,219	1,501	9,563
24	143	173	1,224	1,651	10,221
25	156	176	1,243	1,585	10,995
26	146	179	1,326	1,518	10,564
27	142	179	1,280	1,648	10,756
28	151	179	1,268	1,640	11,072
29	149	180	1,284	1,621	11,296
30	128	167	1,134	1,315	9,021
31	90	130	847	906	6,371
32	68	96	584	669	4,743
33	72	85	512	793	5,445
34	90	95	601	953	6,780
35	109	103	740	1,101	7,659
36	114	111	880	1,187	8,654
37	122	126	1,039	1,218	9,217
38	97	125	1,000	1,080	8,168
39	95	123	982	1,170	8,684

[a] *Agricultural Statistics, 1945,* p. 430, 1910–14 = 100.

[b] Bureau of Agricultural Economics, Department of Agriculture, *Farm Wages Rates, Farm Employment, and Related Data, 1943,* pp. 3–4, 1910–14 = 100.

[c] Bureau of Agricultural Economics, Department of Agriculture, *Net Farm Income and Parity Report, 1943* (1944), pp. 26 and 18.

[d] *Agricultural Statistics, 1943,* p. 412.

In the absence of an important change in the marginal physical productivity of land, the employment of land would not have been expected to decline, and it did not do so.

Wage rates tended to lag behind prices, and employment of hired labor might therefore have been expected to decline slightly, as indeed it did.

The net income attributable to land, capital, and labor accounts for roughly 70 percent of gross agricultural income.[13] The remainder is attributable to products and services purchased (about 15 percent),[14] taxes (about 4 percent), and depreciation and maintenance (about 11 percent). Of these, only taxes requires a net outlay regardless of the level of output or prices.

[13] D. Gale Johnson, "Allocation of Agricultural Income," *Journal of Farm Economics,* Vol. 30 (November 1948), p. 742.

[14] Includes only products and services purchased from nonfarmers.

Current outlay for depreciation and maintenance in agriculture can be postponed almost in its entirety for as long as four years.

Current purchases of products and services from the nonagricultural sector of the economy are not made under supply conditions comparable to the supply conditions for land, labor and capital. During depressions, prices of these products and services do not decline as rapidly as prices received by farmers. Consequently, except for products and services that are limitational in character, purchases of such items should fall considerably. And this was the case. Fertilizer prices decreased 35 percent.[15] Fertilizer consumption declined more than 45 percent.[16] Farm machinery prices declined less than 10 percent. Expenditures on motor vehicles and machinery, including repairs for machinery, declined more than 70 percent. Building material prices fell 20 percent, and expenditures about 80 percent.

Other current inputs of a highly varied nature, such as the cost of operating motor vehicles, electricity, twine, ginning fees, and seeds apparently declined only moderately in price and in quantity purchased. Many of these inputs such as seed, twine, ginning fees, and containers are in the category of inputs having fixed coefficients of production. Consequently, farmers would not decrease their use of these items as long as they continued to stay at full production.

Two other categories of expenses to the individual farmer need consideration, namely, feed and livestock purchases. Though data on quantities of feed and livestock purchased are not available, the data on expenditures and prices indicate that quantities of feed and livestock purchased decreased by roughly 10 percent. The prices of feed and livestock declined slightly less than farm prices in general, perhaps 5 percent less. Because of the slightly smaller relative price declines in feed and livestock for feeding purposes, one would expect that interfarm sales of these items would decline some but not much.

The theory that we have outlined rests on certain presumptions about the supply functions of labor, capital, and land. This theory is not complete. Certain important aspects of output behavior, such as the constancy of livestock output, are not explained by the assumptions. The theory explains why all crop land is utilized during a depression, but it is insufficient to explain why farmers sell the output of durable products or transform the feed into livestock. Why do the farmers not store such products as wheat, corn, and oats during periods of absolute and relative price declines during a major cycle?

Tables 5 and 6 present the data indicating the constancy of livestock output. Table 5 requires no comment; farmers kept on producing livestock. Table 6 indicates that falling prices led to only minor increases in the stocks of corn and wheat. Most of the wheat stocks were held by the government.

---

[15] *Agricultural Statistics, 1945,* p. 429.

[16] *Ibid.*, p. 467.

TABLE 5
PRODUCTION OF FEED GRAINS, HAY, AND PASTURE, PRODUCT ADDED BY LIVESTOCK AND HOGS

Year	Production of Feed[a] Grains, Hay, and Pasture	Product Added by Meat Animals and[a] Animal Products	Product Added by Hog Production[b]
1919	106	83	14.0
20	116	80	13.5
21	108	84	14.1
22	107	89	16.5
1927	107	95	16.3
28	108	96	16.2
29	103	97	15.6
30	94	99	15.2
31	103	101	16.5
32	113	101	16.4
33	96	103	16.6

[a] 1935–39 = 100. Source: Glen T. Barton and Martin R. Cooper, *Farm Production in War and Peace*, USDA, BAE, F.M. 53, p. 74.
[b] In billions of pounds. Source: *Agricultural Statistics, 1940*, p. 370.

The increase in corn stocks should be seen in their proper perspective; from 1929 through 1932, more than 10 billion bushels of corn were produced. Of this total, hogs consumed at least 4 billion bushels.

It is necessary to specify the nature of the supply function for current use or sale of the durable farm products in order to explain this behavior on the part of the farmer. The supply function for current use or sale of durable farm products shifted to the right roughly as far as did the output curve for these products. In other words, the demand for inventories by farmers or others did not increase to result in a significant difference between the physical output of the products and the quantities offered for sale or used as inputs for further production; supply prices of factors used in producing livestock fell proportionately as much as the prices of livestock, and as one would expect, livestock output was maintained.

Two explanations seem relevant for the failure of the demand for inventories to increase during depressions. First, farmers do not believe that they can estimate anticipated prices very accurately. What I feel to be the best model available to them, namely, that next year's price will be the same as this one, is consistent with not holding stocks in any large volume.[17] Second, most farmers have never had enough capital to be able to forego the current

[17] See D. Gale Johnson, *Forward Prices for Agriculture* (Chicago: University of Chicago Press, 1947), chap. 6.

TABLE 6

PRICES AND TOTAL STOCKS OF CORN AND WHEAT IN U.S.

Year	Total Stocks (millions of bushels) Corn	Wheat	Corn Price (previous marketing year) (cents per bushel)	Wheat Price
	(Oct. 1)	(July 1)		
1919		85		205
20		170		216
21		124		183
22		96		103
23		132		97
1927	217	109	75	122
28	92	113	85	119
29	148	227	84	100
30	136	291	80	104
31	168	313	60	67
32	270	375	32	39
33	386	378	32	38

Source: *Agricultural Statistics 1940*, pp. 10, 23, 46 and 54.

income required by a definite storage policy or to permit them to accept the large risks that arise from storage.[18]

If private storage has not acted to stabilize somewhat the price of the durable products over the cycle through storage operations, we may find that public storage will do so. If this occurs, agricultural output will behave quite differently from the way it has in the past. The output of livestock products will decline during the depression and so will aggregate agricultural output. However, government policy may also involve subsidization of the output of livestock products. If this is done, total output would be maintained.

The theory propounded above is consistent with the behavior of the nonagricultural firms that maintained output during the depression. Most of the firms—in meat packing, butter, evaporated milk, cheese, shortening and beet sugar—had one input that was extremely important from a cost standpoint, and this input had a supply function similar to that ascribed to land or to labor in agriculture. This input was an agricultural product. Since the

[18] *Ibid.*, chap. 10, esp. pp. 156–61. The path of price movements during and following the 1929–33 depression indicates that farmers were relatively wise in not accumulating stocks. For example, if a farmer had stored wheat in 1930 and if the costs of storage were 10 cents a year, he would have been unable to have made a profit at any time until the present. If he had stored wheat in 1931, he would have realized a substantial gain within two years. The same circumstances were true in corn. But what basis would a farmer have had for knowing that he should have stored in 1931 but not in 1930?

alternative cost of these products fell sharply, the same volume of product would be available for processing at a much lower price and at a price that would clear the market.

Since other factors used by these industries did not have the same type of supply curves for other inputs, total output in any real sense probably fell. The data seem to indicate that hours worked declined more than output. Output is usually measured for such industries as a linear function of agricultural input.

II. AGRICULTURAL OUTPUT DURING PERIODS OF FULL EMPLOYMENT

The movement of farm prices relative to nonfarm prices appears to have no important influence on total agricultural output during periods of recession or depression. The reasons for this behavior have been outlined above. It is sometimes assumed that agricultural output would be equally unresponsive to a decline in relative farm prices under full-employment conditions. This statement, however, cannot be empirically verified by the experience of the United States. There is no period in our history for which we have reasonably accurate data—which means since 1900—when high levels of employment coincided with declining relative farm prices.[19] One such period may now be emerging—starting in 1949.

Consequently those individuals who rely solely upon empiricism and eschew the use of theoretical models can find no support for the contention that farm output is not responsive to declining relative farm prices when employment opportunities are readily available in the rest of the economy. It may well be that under dynamic conditions aggregate agricultural output would not actually decrease despite a fall in relative farm prices, but such a statement is certainly not the same as the statement that relative prices do not affect the level of output. If clarity of thought is considered important, the two statements should not be confused.

Since 1900 there have been three periods of sustained full employment. During two of these periods—1900 to 1919 and from 1940 to 1948—real farm prices were rising. The only other period of sustained full employment—1923 to 1929—was a period of relatively stable real farm prices.

A. Implications of the Theory

The theory by which we have sought to rationalize the behavior of farm output during depressions has important implications for the behavior to be expected under full employment conditions. These implications can best be

[19] The late twenties does not seem to constitute such a period. As indicated in Table 3, except for the single year 1925, relative farm prices were stable from 1923 through 1929.

outlined by considering, first, the effect of changes in relative prices under given production conditions, and second, the modifications introduced by changes in production conditions.

Under given production conditions, output of agricultural products can change only as a result in the quantity factors of production employed—to speak broadly, in the quantities of land, labor, or capital employed. An increase in the real price of output will raise the marginal product of factors to farmers, and therefore lead them to demand a larger quantity at previous prices. Under given conditions of supply of factors, this will lead to an increased employment of factors—unless their supply prices are perfectly inelastic—and hence to an increase in output.

A decline in the price of real output will lower the marginal products of the factors. At previous prices of the factors, farmers will demand smaller quantities of the factors. For downward movements in factor prices, the supply function for land is almost perfectly inelastic in the short run. Land is an asset with no alternative use outside of agriculture and its quantity will be affected only as depreciation and depletion exceed maintenance expenditure. A protracted decline in prices would lead to the former exceeding the latter and thus to a decline in the quantity of land supplied.[20] Capital equipment of a durable nature also has an inelastic supply function for downward price movements in the short run. A given quantity of such equipment exists, and its quantity can be reduced only by depreciation since it has no alternative use outside of agriculture. The value of the existing assets would decline and new purchases from the nonfarm sector would be reduced. The marginal product of labor would decline and the demand for labor would decrease. Given flexible wage rates in agriculture, labor employment would decrease as a result of migration though unemployment would not emerge.

In a period of three to five years of declining real output prices, the reduction in farm output will depend largely upon the reduction in farm labor employment. The supply of labor to agriculture is a function of its wage in agriculture, of the wage for comparable labor in nonagriculture, of the level of unemployment, and of the growth of the farm labor force due to the excess of additions (individuals living on farms reaching working age) over withdrawals (from death or retirement). If the elasticities of the quantity of labor supplied with respect to the farm wage rate, the nonfarm wage rate and unemployment are relatively small, the reduction in labor supplied produced by a decline in relative prices may be fairly small. These are likely to be the conditions when the price decline is assumed to be temporary. If the price decline is assumed to be permanent, the elasticities of the quantity of labor supplied with respect to the relevant variables are likely to be

---

[20] Unless the government subsidizes maintenance through payments for "soil conservation" or increases the available supply of land through irrigation and reclamation projects.

relatively large, and the adjustment in labor supply would occur more rapidly.

In the above paragraphs, it has been assumed that the production function remains unchanged. The production function in agriculture does change as new techniques become available. Though the availability of new techniques of production is probably unrelated to the level of farm prices, the rate of adoption of new techniques requiring significant investments might be. Many types of new techniques have not, however, required important investments by farmers adopting them in the past; for example, new seeds, new feeding methods and rations, and disease control methods. Thus it may be assumed that the production function shifts at a slow rate under any circumstances and that this rate may be increased somewhat by high real output prices.[21]

If real farm prices were constant, agricultural output would gradually increase due to the autonomous shifts in the production function. The employment of farm resources in a growing economy could increase, decrease, or remain constant depending upon the annual change in demand for farm products, the technological change in agriculture, and the technological change in the rest of the economy.[22] If the annual change in demand were equal to the technological change in agriculture, which in turn was equal to the technological advance in the rest of the economy, resource employment in agriculture would remain unchanged. However, if technological change occurred more rapidly in the rest of the economy than in agriculture, constant real prices of farm products would result in a decline in relative returns to resources in agriculture and some reduction in resource use, particularly of capital and labor. In this case, constant real prices would not represent a long-run equilibrium situation.

Given technological change, falling real farm prices need not produce a decline in aggregate output in agriculture. The autonomous shift in the production function may increase the marginal physical productivity of each of the resources sufficiently to counteract the decline in resource use. In consequence, the failure of aggregate output to decline would

---

[21] The evidence on the relation between output prices and technological change is admittedly conjectural. It cannot be assumed that because output per worker rises more rapidly during periods of high or rising prices than during periods of low or falling farm prices, the production function is shifting more rapidly in the former period than in the latter. High or rising prices induce more investment per worker, which is not the same thing as a technological change. It is argued below that the rate of technological change in agriculture has been much less than is generally assumed. The same may be true in the rest of the economy. Increased capital per worker over the years may be as important, if not more important, than technological change in increasing output per worker.

[22] The change in the demand for farm products is assumed to be a function of the change in per capita income and of the change in population. Technological change is measured by the increase in output from a fixed quantity of resources.

not be inconsistent with long-run equilibrium in the factor markets.[23]

We have so far taken no account of either uncertainty or capital rationing. A change in relative farm prices for one or two years may not affect the level of resource employment because entrepreneurs do not expect such change to be permanent. Consequently, actual plans may be made in terms of expected prices either higher or lower than the market prices. Capital employment is not determined solely by profit maximization; in addition, as has been argued elsewhere, capital use in agriculture is subject to capital rationing.[24] Consequently, new investment in agriculture is a function of the liquidity position of farmers as well as of current and expected returns. However, this factor will not reverse the general direction of movement of capital employment, though the amount of investment would obviously be affected thereby.

In testing the above propositions in any empirical situation, one specific caution must be noted. The conditions stated and conclusions following therefrom are based on the assumption that the economy has been operating at a high level of employment for some time. In other words, it is assumed that labor unemployment in the nonfarm sector of the economy has not been acting as a deterrent to the migration of labor out of agriculture. At the beginning of the period of rising real farm prices if there is much unemployment of labor in the nonfarm economy, farm labor will be earning less than comparable *employed* nonfarm labor. Consequently, if the rise in real farm prices is associated with a decline in unemployment, the supply function of agricultural labor will shift to the right; farm labor employment will decline even though the return to labor in agriculture rises relative to the return to employed labor in nonagriculture.[25]

B. Tests of the Theory

1. 1900–1920. The period 1900 to 1920 was one of almost continuous high levels of employment. According to Douglas, unemployment in manufacturing and transportation—two cyclically volatile industries—exceeded 6 percent in only four years out of the 22.[26] And only two of these were consecutive years—1914 and 1915.

---

[23] The share of total national output produced by agriculture would decline.

[24] See D. Gale Johnson, *Forward Prices for Agriculture,* chaps. 4 and 5.

[25] There is, of course, an increase in real farm prices that would increase the demand for farm labor by more than the supply decreased and thus result in an increase in farm employment. The argument in the text implies only that an increase in real farm prices and in farm labor returns (wages of hired labor and labor income of unpaid workers, including the operator) relative to the wages of employed nonfarm workers need not be inconsistent with a decline in farm employment in a specific situation.

[26] Paul Douglas, *Real Wages in the United States* (Boston: Houghton Mifflin Co., 1930) p. 445.

Real farm prices apparently rose 25 to 30 percent,[27] and farm output, 25 percent[28] or roughly 1 percent per year.

The increased farm output was associated with increased employment of all resources except labor—labor employment was roughly the same in 1920 as in 1900.[29] The employment of other resources, however, increased sharply. Total cropland increased from 319 million acres in 1900 to 402 million in 1920—an increase of 26 percent. However, the land added was less productive (produced less rent per acre) than existing cropland. The net increase in the production capacity of the land was probably of the order of 15 percent. The quantity of farm power, machinery and equipment increased from an index of 295 in 1900 to 477 in 1920—an increase of 62 percent.[30] Livestock, exclusive of horses and mules, increased 12 percent. Total capital inputs probably increased 30 percent. Current operating expenses must have increased at least 100 percent, perhaps considerably more.[31]

The increased employment of resources was sufficient to account for most of inputs, the increased output,[32] and the changing relative prices of output and to account for the increased employment of land, capital and current inputs.[33]

---

[27] See Bureau of Agricultural Economics, *1949 Agricultural Outlook Charts,* p. 1.

[28] Martin R. Cooper, Glen T. Barton, and Albert P. Brodell, *Progress of Farm Mechanization*, Department of Agriculture Misc. Pub. No. 630, p. 81.

[29] Barton, Cooper and Brodell estimate farm employment at 11.4 million in 1900 (*ibid.*, p. 5). The Bureau of Agricultural Economics estimates the 1920 farm employment as 11.4 and 1910 as 12.1 (*Farm Wages, Employment and Related Data, 1943*).

[30] See Barton, *et al., op. cit.*, p. 7.

[31] From 1910 to 1920, total current operating expenses, excluding feed and livestock purchased and short-term interest, deflated by the index of prices paid by farmers for items used in production, except feed, increased 69 percent. Similar data are not available for 1900 to 1909.

[32] We do not have data that would permit an accurate estimate of the production function for agriculture. However, a crude estimate of changes in the function is possible if we assume (a) that there are constant returns to scale for agriculture as a whole, and (b) that the marginal productivities of resources are equal to the average net productivities. (As defined by Joan Robinson, *Imperfect Competition* [London: Macmillan, Co., Ltd., 1934], p. 239.)

Using estimates of average productivities for 1910–14 (See Johnson, "Allocation of Agricultural Income," p. 742) and assuming two different functions that meet the requirement of constant returns to scale (one linear and one linear in the logs), the following functions were obtained:

(1) Log output = .44 log labor + .27 log land + .17 log capital + .12 log current expenses.

(2) Output = .44 labor + .27 land + .17 capital + .12 current expenses.

All variables were 100 in 1900, while the 1920 values were 100 for labor, 115 for land, 130 for capital and 200 for current inputs. Substituting these values in the functions gave 1920 estimates of output of 118 for the log function and 121 for the linear function. Actual output was 125. Roughly three fourths or more of the increase seems to have been explained by increased inputs.

[33] Between 1910 and 1920, the average price inputs increased from 100 to 188, while farm prices increased from 102 to 211. Comparable data are not available for 1900 through 1910, but during this period the wholesale price of farm products increased 47 percent and the wholesale price of nonagricultural products increased 17 percent.

In consequence, no substantial change in technology can be inferred from the increase in output.

Why did farm labor employment fail to increase? The evidence available is inconclusive in indicating what rational conduct would have been for farm workers. Farm labor income per worker rose relative to the income of employed industrial workers between 1910 and 1919. The absolute difference between annual earnings, however, increased from about $335 in 1910–14 to $570 in 1919, and to $820 in 1920. A rise in relative earnings when the absolute differences increase may nor may not indicate that real returns to farm workers increased relatively. When the absolute difference is actually larger than the farm labor return, as it was in 1910–14, possible differential changes in the cost of a fixed level of living and changes in the content of the level of living made it impossible to infer with certainty whether the real returns to farm labor kept pace with the real returns to nonfarm labor.

2. 1923–29. The period from 1923 through 1929 was one of stable relative farm prices (in the aggregate). The parity index—a measure of relative farm prices—had the following values starting with 1923—86, 86, 92, 87, 86, 90, 89.

Our theory would indicate reasonable stability in the employment of all inputs, except perhaps labor. With respect to capital and land, actual experience does not contradict the expectations. Net investment in horses and mules, machinery, motor vehicles, including tractors, trucks, and the farm share of autos, and service dwellings was zero or perhaps negative.[34] The estimate made by Cooper, Barton and Brodell of farm power and machinery also indicated no change.[35] The current inputs purchased from nonagriculture increased, in real terms, about 22 percent. This increase was associated largely with the shift from farm produced to mechanical power.[36]

It is not clear how labor employment should have been expected to behave. If it is assumed that the labor market was in long-run full-employment equilibrium in 1923, there should have been no appreciable change in labor employment. And this is what actually happened according to Bureau of Agricultural Economics estimates. Total farm employment declined less than 1 percent.[37]

Between 1923 and 1929, the labor income of farm workers increased somewhat relative to the income of employed industrial workers—from about 30 percent as much in 1923 to about 35 percent in 1929.[38] During the

---

[34] Based on values expressed in 1910–14 dollars. Data taken largely from Bureau of Agricultural Economics, *Net Farm Income and Parity Report, 1943.*

[35] *Op. cit.*, p. 81. The index was 454 in 1923 and 466 in 1929.

[36] *Ibid.*, p. 90. The cost of farm produced power which is payment for inputs produced by farmers, declined by $300 million measured in dollars of constant purchasing power. Costs of operating mechanical power increased $390 million.

[37] See Bureau of Agricultural Economics, *Farm Wages, Farm Employment, and Related Data*, p. 155.

[38] Based on estimates of labor income by writer, "Allocation of Agricultural Income," p. 738 and Bureau of Agricultural Economics, *1949 Agricultural Outlook Charts*, p. 7.

seven-year period, there was a net movement of 4,260,000 people off farms—an annual average of 630,000 or roughly 2 percent of the population.[39] This movement, large as it was, was sufficient only to stabilize the quantity of labor supplied.

The changes in farm production and in resource use are not inconsistent with an essentially unchanged production function. Calculations similar to those in footnote 32 indicate that one half of the approximate 8 percent increase in farm output can be explained by increased inputs. The rest of the increase could be due to weather and other natural changes, though there seems to be no evidence that weather changes were important.[40]

3. 1940–48. Following 1940, real farm prices rose rapidly—from 80 to a peak of 121 in 1946 and then fell slightly to 115 in 1948. It seems clear that the demand for all inputs would rise in these circumstances. And such increases in demand did occur. More capital was employed and net investment would have been even greater had items been available at quoted prices. Between January, 1940 and January, 1948, the quantity of power and machinery increased about 40 percent. Acreage of land harvested increased about 10 million or 3 percent. Current operating expenses (except livestock and feed purchased and short-term interest) increased 60 percent. Farm output increased 20 percent.

The farm population declined from 30.3 millions to 27.8 millions by January 1, 1949, and the level of farm employment by slightly more than 4 percent.

The change in farm employment is consistent with our theory. It is quite clear that labor in agriculture was not in a position of long-run equilibrium in 1940. The supply of labor was large in agriculture because of the heavy rate of unemployment that had prevailed previously in the rest of the economy. As unemployment declined, the supply of labor to agriculture also decreased. The differential in earnings was such as to induce movement out of agriculture at a given level of unemployment. Agriculture had a net migration during the last half of the thirties of 2,770,000 or 555,000 per annum,[41] despite unemployment ranging from 14 to 20 percent.[42]

Agriculture would have lost more of its labor force had it not been for the rapid rise in returns to agricultural resources. During the early part of the period, labor income in agriculture rose more rapidly than labor income in the rest of the economy, yet the movement out of agriculture was at a fantastic rate—net civilian migration of 1,920,000 in 1942 and 1,146,000 in 1941.

---

[39] Bureau of Agricultural Economics, *Farm Population Estimates, 1910–1942*, pp. 1 and 2.

[40] See U.S. Department of Agriculture, *Crops and Markets*, 1949 edition, p. 6 for estimates of yields per acre. Yields for field crops were identical in 1923 and 1929.

[41] Bureau of Agricultural Economics, *Farm Population Estimates, 1910–1942*, p. 2.

[42] Bureau of Agricultural Economics, *1949 Agricultural Outlook Charts*, p. 4.

This was due to the large absolute difference in real earnings that still persisted. In 1941, labor returns per worker on commercial farms was $700 less than the wage income of employed workers—a difference of slightly less than 50 percent. By 1946 the absolute difference had narrowed to $450 and the relative difference to 20 percent,[43] and these differences remained roughly the same in 1947 and 1948.

In the three years 1946, 1947, and 1948—there was probably a rough equilibrium in the allocation of labor to commercial farms. Consequently, no significant change in farm population or labor force was to be expected during these years, except from the return of veterans. Apparently about one half of the farm veterans returned to the farm and stayed there.

The change in the production function between 1940 and 1948 was probably not as spectacular as is frequently believed. A large fraction of the increased output—perhaps half—can be attributed to increases in resource inputs. The remainder can be attributed to changes in the production function and natural factors, such as weather.

C. Conclusions

On the whole, the simple theory that we have used gives a reasonably accurate indication of the response of resource employment and output to changes in relative farm prices during periods of high-level employment, at least as judged by the three "tests" we have been able to make.

The attempt to judge the shift in the production function in the periods surveyed is significant in understanding the probable response of farm output to falling relative prices during periods of high-level employment. If during a period of rising relative prices, a considerable fraction of the increased output reflects increased inputs, a subsequent period of falling prices may well result in an actual decline in output. As farm prices decline, net investment will fall, the level of current inputs will diminish, and labor migration will increase. The decline in output may not be large, but it does not need to be in order to reestablish equilibrium in the factor markets because of the price inelasticity of demand for agricultural output.

An important policy conclusion can be drawn from this analysis. Maintaining farm price returns at levels above market prices during periods of high-level employment will make farm output higher than it would otherwise be.[44] Such induced increases in output will increase the difficulty of maintaining farm price returns, necessitating direct controls of output if governmental expenditures are not to exceed the amounts that even a "generous"

---

[43] See Johnson, "Allocation of Agricultural Incomes," pp. 740 and 745, and Bureau of Agricultural Economics, *1949 Agricultural Outlook Charts,* p. 7.

[44] The term "farm price returns" is used in this paragraph instead of farm prices because farm prices can be supplemented by direct subsidies to farmers.

Congress is willing to appropriate. In fact, it can be argued that increasing farm price returns by governmental action during periods of full employment does a real disservice to farm people, unless agriculture is to be permanently subsidized. If the price props are withdrawn (or a depression occurs), returns to agricultural resources would be lower than otherwise because too many resources have been retained in agriculture.

The attainment of equilibrium in the factor markets in agriculture during a period of generally falling prices or after the establishment of a lower level of agricultural prices may take longer than seems desirable. If this is so, the appropriate policy action would not seem to be higher support prices *which would prevent the resource adjustments from occurring*. Rather, the slowness of the adjustment process would seem to call for direct measures to increase the outmovement of labor.[45]

SUMMARY

The theory presented in this article to explain the output behavior of agriculture rests on two major assumptions: (1) That farmers are profit-maximizing entrepreneurs and (2) that the supply functions of factors to agriculture have certain characteristics. These characteristics are: (a) The labor supply function shifts with changes in the general level of business activity and unemployment (reflecting the alternatives to farm employment) and for any level of business activity, unemployment and nonfarm wage rates, the price elasticity with respect to labor returns in agriculture is small enough to lead to essentially full employment of labor. (b) The land supply function has a very low price elasticity in the short run, in part, due to the lack of alternative uses outside of agriculture and due to small changes that can be made in the quantity of land through investment and disinvestment. (c) The supply function of capital assets has a very small price elasticity for downward movements in prices since the quantity of such assets existing at any one time can achieve higher returns in agriculture than elsewhere; in response to upward movements in prices, the price elasticity is higher as new investment becomes profitable to farmers.

This theory, simple as it is, seems to be consistent with the observed

---

[45] Walter Wilcox has indicated a contrary view in "High Farm Income and Efficient Resource Use," *Journal of Farm Ecomonics*, Vol. 31 (August 1949), pp. 555–57. He argues that farm migration is increased by high farm family incomes due to increased mechanization and the aid high incomes give to migration. He used population changes for Iowa, South Carolina and Tennessee for 1930 to 1940 in support of his position. A more detailed study of farm migration for the same decade made under the direction of the writer indicates that state differences in migration rates were unrelated to the level of farm income. The two factors which were most closely associated with migration were a measure of population pressure (the excess of new entrants to the farm labor force over deaths) and changes in the level of farm income from the late twenties to the thirties. The changes in farm population in the Pacific Coast States since 1930 clearly contradict Wilcox's position, as well.

phenomena. The theory seems much more useful in understanding the behavior of agricultural output under various sets of circumstances than other explanations that have been offered. The high fixed cost explanation of constancy of output during a depression not only has the defect of being inconsistent with the observed behavior of the employment of hired labor and rented land, but high fixed costs are not an explanation at all of output responses to rising real output prices. Nor does the competitive structure of agriculture seem to have much relevance to output behavior. Other explanations—the length of the production process and the importance of subsistence production—have been found to be unsatisfactory. The effect of the real wage upon the amount of effort a given labor force will exert is an explanation of behavior that seems consistent with observed phenomena. It is a hypothesis that deserves further investigation. The hypothesis is not inconsistent with the theory expounded here. If we knew more of its relevance and significance, it would be possible to specify with greater accuracy the nature of the labor supply function.

16 Reflections on Agricultural Production, Output and Supply*

THEODORE W. SCHULTZ† ‡

Tell me what the supply of farm products will be five or ten years from now, and I shall give you meaningful answers to the more important economic problems of agriculture. This is not an idle promise. Most of the relevant knowledge of consumption and demand is at hand and the important economic problems of agriculture call primarily for adjustments in production. One is not asking for the impossible. It is not like asking for a fulcrum with which to move the world. There are, of course, many who talk and act in the research they undertake as if the U.S. farm problem could be resolved by adjustments in the demand. They are climbing a mole hill, not the mountain awaiting to be scaled.

It will be said, however, "Surely much progress has been made in production economics." It is true that simple, old-fashioned budgeting has been replaced by sophisticated production functions, and the journals run over with "results" from linear programming, a new apparatus that is turning out, thus far, an undigested mixture of a few insights and many "numbers" that do not make sense. These particular studies in production economics, however, tell us very little about the supply of farm products. They contribute little for two reasons. Many are about things that are trivial. Those that take a larger bite concentrate on conventional inputs. These, it so appears, can tell us comparatively little about changes in the supply. As a qualification, there is some research work that is in a way an exception: most of it

---

* *Journal of Farm Economics,* Vol. XXXVIII, No. 3 (August, 1956), pp. 613–31.

† University of Chicago, Chicago, Illinois.

‡ I have benefited from a number of comments and suggestions that I received on an earlier draft of this paper from D. Gale Johnson, A. C. Harberger, and Zvi Griliches.

was formerly in the old BAE and now in the Agricultural Research Service.[1]

The unresolved problem of the "inputs" explaining the increase of the supply goes far beyond agriculture, however. It is indeed a fundamental matter, at the heart of any approach to explain economic growth. How is growth in output, for example, achieved? Theorizing based on savings and capital formation, on disguised unemployment or on industrialization, has not proven fruitful. Each of these notions flounders on the increase in production and for the same reason, so it would appear, as in agriculture; namely, *growth in output cannot be explained satisfactorily by an analysis which is based on conventional inputs.*

Moreover, our farm problem of too much agricultural production, and that in poor countries of too little, are basically of the same species, because both are problems pertaining to economic growth. In our case the task may be one of adjusting to a rapid growth of output which, if we understood it, could be checked or taken in stride by planning to adjust to it. Whereas in poor countries the task is usually one of living with too little growth in output —importantly, in most cases, in agriculture, which, if understood, could be made to increase at a more rapid rate. The nature of economic growth in both cases turns out to be the unresolved problem of explaining the additional output with which we started.

I. DEMAND AND SUPPLY COMPARED

In the case of demand, we analyze particular activities of households, and in the case of supply, activities of firms. For households we seek to determine the underlying consumption functions, and for firms the production functions. Both concepts are based on received theory of long standing. Why is it, then, that the knowledge we have been able to amass about the demand, say, for food is on a much stronger footing empirically than is the equivalent knowledge about the supply of farm (food) products? We know, for instance, that the demand for food of consumers at retail has relatively low price and income elasticities. We are quite confident that both of these elasticities will continue to be relatively low; and that five or ten years from now they will have about the same values they have at present with one minor qualification; namely, that as we become somewhat richer as a people these elasticities are likely to become a little more inelastic over time. We also know, in addition

[1] A number of titles come to mind at once: *Technology on the Farm, Changes in American Farming, Changes in Farm Production and Efficiency,* and the older *Farm Production Practices, Costs and Returns,* and others. In an earlier draft of this paper I had included some results from data made available to me by Dr. Wylie D. Goodsell, drawn from the studies of *Farm Costs and Returns of Commercial Family Operated Farms by Type and Location.* As I proceeded, however, it became clear to me that these data go beyond the task at hand; and I shall, therefore, come back to them on another occasion.

to these price and income elasticity values, that the aggregate demand for food is some function of the number of consuming units. Thus the growth of the demand can be linked to growth of population.

By comparison we know much less about the supply of farm foods. We have no meaningful estimates of the price elasticity of the supply. We theorize that for a large sector like agriculture the supply is likely to be quite inelastic in the short run, because it is difficult to shift many resources out of or into agriculture, and that the supply is more elastic, given time to make such inter-sector shifts and given time for producers to convert the relatively fixed inputs into variable inputs. There once were some fairly useful "farmer response to price" studies and the well known "corn-hog ratio" studies that cast some light on the supply of particular farm products.

Presently, however, the main effort is to determine the underlying production functions of farms. This leads one to ask: Suppose we knew the production functions of each and every farm, could one with this knowledge indicate even approximately what the aggregate supply of farm foods is likely to be five or ten years hence? The answer appears to be in the negative, because, as I shall show later, these functions are based on a *set of conventional inputs* and only a minor part of the shift of the supply to the right that occurs in agriculture comes from such additional inputs.

The striking difference in what we know about demand and what we know about supply has not come about because one has received our attention while the other has been neglected. The difficulty runs much deeper than this. For a function to be useful it must either be stable over time, or we must be able to predict how it will change. The stability of the function underlying the demand is dependent upon what happens to "tastes" and in the case of supply upon "technology." We observe, however, whereas tastes remain fairly constant, technology does not. Therefore, unless we can predict the changes in technology it follows that production functions, linear programming models and input-output models are all comparatively "useless" in a logical, positivistic sense.[2]

There are, therefore, two basic factors that go a long way in accounting for the wide disparity in our present knowledge about demand and supply. Both of these factors indicate that the demand concept with which we work rests on a fairly stable foundation, whereas the supply concept stands on

---

[2] If this statement is a valid characterization of what is happening in production, one may easily overrate the value of these observed functions to farmers as useful farm management information. How can a farmer benefit from knowledge about yesterday's or today's production functions if they are obsolete tomorrow? The information which he would find valuable would consist of knowledge about the nature of the change of the production function that is underway, applicable to his farm.

shifting sand.[3] First there is the fact that in the case of households, the tastes underlying consumption, on which the price elasticity of the demand for food depends, have stayed remarkably constant for consumers at retail for five or ten years and longer.[4] In the case of farms, on the other hand, the technology employed in production, on which the price elasticity of the supply of farm products depends, have been subject to many important changes during a decade and less. Secondly, and closely related, when it comes to determining the way the demand and supply schedules shift over time, the consuming unit has been a relatively stable institution for consumption. This stability has made it possible and comparatively easy to take account of growth in population by simply adding the appropriate number of additional consuming units. For many purposes even a per capita demand multiplied by the size of the population, while quite rough and ready, has proved fairly useful. On the supply side, however, the producing unit in farming, and in other sectors as well, is not on a comparable footing. From a change in the number of firms one cannot infer changes in output; nor can one proceed the other way around. The supply schedule of farm products needs not and has not been riding to the right on the backs of more farms. Then, too, useful knowledge about the scale of firms having any predictive value is not at hand. Scale considerations that may be sufficient for our purposes are still among the unknowns. Nor can one get far on the supply side (at any given relative supply price) by taking the additional inputs of the conventional type to determine additional output, as we shall show.

---

[3] This statement about the demand does not imply that we can predict either the growth in population or the rise or fall in per family or per capita income. But it is not the task of a theory of demand to explain population and income. Our statement, however, does imply that for a particular population; namely, for the consumers of the United States buying food at retail, there are observable price and income elasticities that have remained fairly stable.

In the case of supply, we also need to point out that this statement does not imply that we can predict the growth of the labor force, the additions to the stock of reproducible capital and the further "discoveries" of non-reproducible factors; this is not the task of a theory of supply. What our statement does say, however, is that with a particular set of such resources at hand we are not able to observe any dependable price elasticities for the supply, or with particular increases in such resources, we are not able to observe any stable relations between such increases in resources and increases in production.

[4] As already noted in the demand for food, the income effects on which the income elasticity depends also appear to be remarkably stable. The demand, however, is not free of uncertainty considerations which, of course, also abound in the case of the supply. The recent advance in distinguishing between the "permanent" and "transitory" components in income adds further to our understanding of the demand. The theoretical underpinning of this advance and its relevance in organizing consumption and savings data will appear in Professor Milton Friedman's book, *A Theory of the Consumption Function,* to be published by the National Bureau of Economic Research.

The possibility remains that developments can take place at some future time that could alter substantially the now existing price and income elasticities of this demand. Such possibilities are not ruled out in what has been said here.

II. ADDITIONAL OUTPUT AND ADDITIONAL CONVENTIONAL INPUTS

At what supply price will a substantial increase (let this be 20 percent) in output be forthcoming over a span of a decade?[5] There are studies with estimates showing that the returns to scale in farming are approximately constant. Suppose, also, no limitational inputs would come into play in increasing output by no more than a fifth. Diminishing returns would not show its ugly head. But of what use is such knowledge? Surely no one who has even a casual acquaintance with agriculture would be foolhardy enough to predict that it will take a fifth more inputs to achieve a 20 percent increase in output during the decade. An engine of analysis that is restricted *to conventional inputs* simply does not have the power to tell us what the supply of farm products will be in future periods. Additional inputs of the kind that are commonly placed in our conceptual boxes—labor, land, other capital, and current production items—account for only a part and, as it appears, for a declining part of the increase in agricultural output.

The estimates in Table 1 are based on two different methods for determining changes in aggregate input. The output data, however, are essentially the same: either "agricultural production for sale and home uses on farms," or "farm output," as these indexes have been prepared by the USDA. The particular base period is not of as much concern for the output index as for the input index because changes in the relative prices of farm products have not been so important. In the case of the aggregate input, the "I" estimates are those of Johnson[6] based on production functions for agriculture assuming constant returns to scale and marginal productivities of resources equal to average net productivities.[7] Estimates "II" were derived by aggregating eight sets of production inputs using 1935–39 input prices for the periods 1910–20, 1923–29 and 1930–40, during which time the relative changes in these input prices were not considered to be of major importance.[8] Later, as the price of labor rose sharply relative to most other inputs, 1946–48 input prices were

---

[5] In putting this question we assume that the increases in total labor force, in the stock of reproducible capital and in the nonreproducible factors have been or may be estimated and that one proceeds to determine the answer with such estimates at hand.

[6] D. Gale Johnson, "The Nature of the Supply Function for Agricultural Products," *American Economic Review*, Vol. 40 (September 1950).

[7] *Ibid.*, p. 559, See fn. 32 for a procedural note giving two different functions, one linear and the other linear in the logs. The estimate for linear in logs indicated that the input increased 18 percent from 1900 to 1920. The changes in marginal products with 1900 = 100, if product prices had not changed, imply the following changes in marginal physical products: labor + 18 percent, land + 3 percent, capital − 9 percent, and current inputs − 41 percent.

[8] The eight sets of inputs appear in Table 7-5 of my book, *The Economic Organization of Agriculture* (New York: McGraw-Hill Book Co., 1953), using 1946–48 price weights. The data using 1935–39 input prices as weights have not been published. Source of these data is set forth in Chapter 7 of author's book.

TABLE 1

RECENT CHANGES IN OUTPUT AND INPUT IN AGRICULTURE IN THE UNITED STATES

Period	*Output (Percent)*	*Input (Percent)*	*Proportion of Additional Output Accounted for by Additional Input*[e] *(Percent)*
(1)	(2)	(3)	(4)
1900–1920[a]	25	18 to 21	72 to 84
1910–1920[b]	15	17	100[f]
1923–1929			
I[a]	7	4	57
II[b]	7	3.7	53
1930–1940[b]	16	−5	0
1940–1948			
I[a]	25	6.5[d]	26
II[c]	25	5	20
1930–1950[c]	39	1	4
1950–1955	12	n.a.[g]	n.a.[g]

[a] D. G. Johnson's estimates in "The Nature of the Supply Function for Agricultural Products," *American Economic Review,* Vol. 51 (September 1950). For 1900–1920, the output is based on "agricultural production for sale and home use on farms"; for the other periods the recent estimates of "farm output" are presented here.

[b] My estimates based on data obtained in preparing Chapter 7 of *Economic Organization of Agriculture* (New York: McGraw-Hill Book Co., 1953), using, however, 1935–39 prices for the weights. The input series based on these weights has not been published.

[c] Same source as in footnote b above, using 1946–48 input prices as weights. This input series appears in Table 7-5 of author's book.

[d] Johnson's input estimates for 1940–48 were based on the old labor input series, which substantially understated the decline of this input in agriculture and which for 1940–48 indicated an increase in input of 10 percent or less. Using census estimates of farm labor that are now available, however, the increase in input becomes 6.5 percent, as is shown here.

[e] With "constant" returns for additional inputs.

[f] Implies diminishing returns for the additional inputs.

[g] Not available.

used to weight the several inputs. The similarity in the magnitudes obtained by using these two methods in determining the change in input in agriculture is noteworthy. The two estimates do not appear to be inconsistent one with another; on the contrary, they reinforce each other.

The estimates in Table 1 may be interpreted as follows: From 1900 to 1920 all—or virtually all—of the increase in output may have been achieved by additional inputs. There may even have been some diminishing returns for the additional inputs against nonreproducible factors. See column (4). From 1923 to 1929, only about one half—or a little more—of the increase in output appears to have been achieved by additional inputs. During the depression years, 1930 to 1940, none of the increase in output seems to be explained by additional inputs. One observes that although output increased 16 percent, the input fell by 5 percent. The war years called forth substantially more output, yet from 1940 to 1948 perhaps only about a fifth to a fourth of the increase in output can be accounted for by additional inputs.

The declining importance of additional inputs in the expansion of agricultural production in the United States is the outstanding fact that emerges from these data.

Moreover, this observed "declining importance of additional inputs" in achieving additional agricultural output is not unique to the circumstances of the United States or to other highly developed countries. Moore's studies, although based on less satisfactory data, even so, convince one that Brazil and Mexico have been experiencing supply developments similar to our own. Table 2 indicates that in Brazil and Mexico only about one half of the large increases in output from 1925–29 to 1945–49 have come from additional inputs. Ballesteros' study of the Argentine goes deeper and makes clear that from 1908 to 1920 about seven tenths of the rise in output in agriculture may be explained by additional inputs, this being not unlike the experiences of U.S. agriculture at the same time. However, only a fourth or less of the big increase in output from 1920 to 1940 came from additional inputs of the conventional types. Then came the great impairment of the economy of the Argentine: from 1940 to 1952 the output of agriculture fell more than a tenth while the input appears to have dropped about as much.[9]

We also now have from Johnson's study comparable data for the U.S.S.R.

TABLE 2
RECENT CHANGES IN OUTPUT AND INPUT IN AGRICULTURE IN BRAZIL, MEXICO AND ARGENTINA

Country and Period	*Increase in* Output (Percent)	Input (Percent)	Proportion of Additional Output Accounted for by Additional Input[f] (Percent)
(1)	(2)	(3)	(4)
Brazil[a]			
1925–29 to 1945–49	54[c]	30[d]	55
Mexico[a, b]			
1925–29 to 1945–49	60	27[e]	45
Argentina[g]			
1908–1920	24	17	71
1920–1940	55	12	22
1940–1952	−12	−7	—

[a] Clarence A. Moore's estimates. For Brazil, "Agricultural Development in Brazil" (unpublished Discussion Paper No. 54–044, Room 417, Social Sciences, University of Chicago) growing out of the TALA studies. For Mexico, "Agricultural Development in Mexico," *Journal of Farm Economics*, Vol. 37 (February 1955).
[b] Restricted to agricultural crop production.
[c] Moore's output index I, based on 1937 prices. His output index II rose 56 percent.
[d] Moore's input index II, based on 1940 input prices. His input index I rose 28.7 percent.
[e] Moore's input index II, based on 1940 input prices. His input index I rose 24.7 percent.
[f] With "constant" returns for additional inputs.
[g] Marto Ballesteros' study, *The Economic Development of Agriculture in Argentina, 1908–1954* (in process). These data are from Table 6-3 of his paper, No. 55–035, Room 417, Social Sciences, University of Chicago.

[9] The input data, however, present difficulties of a kind that make one believe that the drop may have been somewhat greater than this.

TABLE 3

RECENT CHANGES IN OUTPUT AND INPUT IN AGRICULTURE IN THE U.S.S.R.[a]

	Increase in		*Proportion of Additional Output Accounted for by Additional Input*[b] *(Percent)*
Period	*Output (Percent)*	*Input (Percent)*	
(1)	(2)	(3)	(4)
1913–1928	8	4	50
1928–1938	15	0	0
1938–1952	20	20	100

[a] Source: D. Gale Johnson, *A Study of the Growth Potential of Agriculture of the U.S.S.R.*, RM-1561 (October 1955), The Rand Corporation, Santa Monica, Calif.
[b] With "constant" returns for additional inputs.

Agriculture in the U.S.S.R. achieved very little increase in production from 1913 to 1928; about one half of this increase may be explained by additional input. During the next decade, however, the rise in output was about 15 percent and this was achieved without additional input, thus, not unlike our own experience from 1930 to 1949. Johnson's estimates indicate, however, that since then, that is from 1938 to 1952, the additional output has not exceeded the additional input.

To maintain one's bearing, it may be helpful to take a brief look at what has been happening to the U.S. economy as a whole on the score of its input and output. Solomon Fabricant,[10] drawing upon the wealth of data of the National Bureau of Economic Research, has reported that during the eight decades from 1868–1873 to 1949–1953, the growth in per capita output in the United States increased about fourfold, which represents an annual rate of 1.9 percent compounded. By adjusting for the increase in population, and for the relatively small increase in input per capita, one finds that the implied output rose from 100 (for 1869–73) to 1,950 (for 1949–53), while the additional input rose from 100 to about 468 during the same period. Accordingly, the additional inputs, assuming "constant" returns, account for only about one fifth of the additional output.[11]

[10] Solomon Fabricant, *Economic Progress and Economic Change,* a part of the 34th Annual Report of the National Bureau of Economic Research, New York, May, 1954. In deriving the aggregate input from Fabricant's per capita data, population was taken at 38.5 million for the first period and at 150 million in the second, and the per capita input was increased as reported by Fabricant.

[11] Since this was written, a paper by Moses Abramovitz has been made available to me. This paper, "Resources and Trends in the United States since 1870" was read at meetings of the American Economic Association, New York City, December 1955, and appeared in the *Proceedings* of the Association, *American Economic Review,* Vol. 46, No. 2 (May 1956).

The data appearing in Table 1 of the Abramovitz paper are calculated for 1869–78 and 1944–53. They, however, show the same result, namely that only about one fifth of the growth in output can be explained by additional conventional inputs:

Net national product rose 12.25 times
Index of total inputs rose 2.61 times

From these data and the production experiences they represent, several inferences about the supply appear plausible. Additional inputs of the conventional types have accounted for most of the additional output during some periods, for example, during the early part of this century in agriculture in the United States. Such a close relationship between additional outputs and inputs has been the exception, however, rather than the rule, for we find that much, and probably most, of the more recent expansion in agricultural production has not come from additional inputs of the conventional types. In the main, additional output has not been dependent upon such additional inputs. The link between such conventional inputs and output is, therefore, very weak, too weak to bear the analytical burden of determining the supply. We thus repeat the following statement: If we had known the production functions of each and every farm, say as of 1930 or as of some other recent date, as these are now being determined, that kind of knowledge, along with estimates of the increases of the quantity of conventional inputs employed, would not have given us even a rough approximation of the aggregate supply of farm products that has been produced.[12]

III. IN SEARCH OF A THEORY OF OUTPUT GROWTH

We would like to know: To the extent that growth in output does not come from additional conventional inputs, *where does it come from?* The facts are strong and stubborn in supporting the inference that much, and probably most, of the growth in output cannot be explained by increases in the size of the labor force and in the stock of reproducible inputs. We have cited Fabricant and Abramovitz who found *four fifths* of the remarkable economic growth of the United States of the last eight decades unexplained by additional inputs. Fabricant explained it by an appeal to "improvements in national efficiency." But what is that?

The question remains: Where does all of this unexplained increase in output come from? Is the four fifths beyond economics? If that is the case, in

[12] I do not wish to imply that we should forego working with production functions even though these functions are as a rule subject to important changes. Research based on the assumption that they remain unchanged has made some useful contributions. There are some situations in production where technology and the marginal rates of transformation have stayed fairly constant. Under these particular circumstances useful estimates are possible as to the effects of changes in the relative prices of inputs upon production (or what should be produced), and as to the effects of changes in relative price of outputs upon production where one or all inputs can be used in producing the several outputs. Glenn L. Johnson has given us an excellent statement of these results. These achievements in production economics should not be underrated or lost sight of, especially in view of the important changes that have been occurring in the relative prices of inputs used in farming. These achievements, however, cast little or no light on the expansion of the supply of farm products where incremental output substantially exceeds incremental input. See Glenn L. Johnson, "Results From Production Economics Analysis," *Journal of Farm Economics,* Vol. 37 (May 1955).

view of the importance that countries and individuals attach to more output, it is high time students in other fields took over. If economic analysis, however, can explain a substantial part of this growth, why has it failed to do so?

Clearly some stock taking is called for. The idea of economic progress is not wholly new: John Stuart Mill devoted all of Book IV of his famous synthesis of classical economics, *Principles of Political Economy,* to this topic. Allyn A. Young's well-known paper dealt with "Increasing Returns and Economic Progress." More recent theorizing about economic development, in the main, has been tied either to savings and the formation of conventional capital (items), or to that of disguised unemployment. These views of the problem have been part and parcel of the intellectual aftermath of the mass unemployment of the thirties. Neither of them appears to have much relevance to the kind of economic growth that one observes in most countries; that is, to the growth in output where the link between incremental input and incremental output has become tenuous.

There are, so it would appear, four developments at work changing the supply that are not represented among the supply variables in current studies. They are either omitted or viewed as ad hoc developments beyond the reach of economic analysis. First, there are the production effects of the greater division of labor dependent upon the extent of the market. This is most certainly not a new concept. On the contrary, the launching of "systematic economics" by Adam Smith was keyed to the division of labor. The concept, nevertheless, has continued to remain surprisingly vague and no one to my knowledge has used it as an analytical tool in empirical research. Secondly, there is the improvement of the *quality* of people as productive agents. Adam Smith gave much credit to the role of specialization in improving the dexterity and skill of workers. He thus related this development mainly to the division of labor. Marshall rated new knowledge very high and considered it the most powerful engine of production. The rise in knowledge of workers and of entrepreneurs (let me add also the advance in knowledge of those important civil servants who administer the monetary and fiscal and other economic controls of government) is nowhere taken into account. Changes in the labor force are measured by the size of the labor force, either by taking the numbers of people doing "productive" work or by calculating the numbers of hours that they work (altogether). All changes in "quality" of this, the most important input of them all, have been completely neglected.[13]

Thirdly, we come to inventions and all manner of new and better techniques of production. This development has become known as advance in technology. Adam Smith, again, saw it (mainly) as a function of the division of labor. Marshall included it under knowledge that was useful. A vast literature

[13] The changes that occur in the quality of inputs represented by reproducible capital are, also, not taken into account fully, although the consequence of this neglect is probably less important than that in the case of "labor."

has appeared in recent decades ascribing most of the rise in "output per unit of input" to advances in technology. Surprising little analysis has been undertaken, however, to determine the (economic) developments related to a particular new technique. No one, as far as I know, has ventured to treat new techniques in such a way that one might predict their appearance, their adoption, or the economic effects once they have been adopted.[14] Fourthly, there remains the concept of diminishing returns, old and revered, of additional inputs against whatever nonreproducible factors exist. If all factors were reproducible, the observed expansion in output (per additional input) would have been somewhat greater than it has been. Diminishing returns is, in this sense, a drag on economic growth varying from country to country and from sector to sector in a particular economy, depending upon the nature and magnitude of the nonreproducible factors. This concept, old as it is, has been put to little use in supply analysis.

These exploratory observations would seem to indicate that several important factors have been neglected in studying economic growth and the increases in production on which such growth rests. It is clear that output linked to conventional inputs does not provide us with a satisfactory scheme for analyzing this kind of a development.

The analytical task, as I see it, is to reestablish a strong and satisfactory linkage between input and output over time. In our efforts to do this, we would do well to place before us and keep in mind the characteristics of an *ideal input-output formula* for this purpose. It would be one where *output over input,* excluding of course, changes in their quality stayed at, or close to, one. The closer we come to a one to one relationship in our formulation the more complete would be our (economic) explanation.[15]

Our belief is that we can approximate this ideal formulation by introducing two important changes in inputs, changes that are being neglected. We shall treat these changes in inputs, when we consider the economy as a whole, as two neglected inputs. Let us then start with the economy, leaving the firm for later, and proceed to represent these two neglected inputs and say a word or two about the activities that are required to "produce" them.

The two neglected inputs may be represented (1) by the new techniques that are adopted in production, and (2) by improvements in the labor force, that is, in the quality of the people who engage in production. We therefore need to examine the activities that come into play in "producing" these two inputs. Let us assume that it takes capital and effort to improve the quality of the labor force and to "discover" and develop new techniques of production. The particular activities are fairly apparent. They are, for example,

---

[14] Such a study is now underway at the University of Chicago. Zvi Griliches is concentrating his research on developments related to hybrid corn in the United States.

[15] The author is indebted to Zvi Griliches for viewing the problem before us in this way.

education, training to impart skills some of which may be acquired on the job, and facilities and services related to health and so on, for the one. In the case of the other, we have centers where scientists work, research institutes, agricultural experiment stations and such similar "agencies." It is not necessary that the allocative process committing capital and effort to these activities have a strong economic orientation. Where they are so oriented, however, one would expect to find the rates of return in these activities over the long run to become about the same as they are on capital and effort allocated to produce the conventional inputs. Whether these rates of return are high or low, relative to those realized from capital and effort used to produce the conventional types of inputs, is, however, strictly a question of fact.[16] If there are observable inequalities in these rates of return, the opportunity would exist to increase the national product by appropriate reallocations of the available resources.

There can be no doubt that these particular activities exist and that in the United States a substantial quantity of capital and effort is being allocated to them. To analyze them as production activities presents no new analytical problems. In practice, however, there are some difficulties, especially in identifying and evaluating the "product." In the case of those activities that are organized to produce new techniques of production, it is helpful to think of them as one would of drilling for oil where most holes turn out to be dryholes. The economics of such drilling operations is, nevertheless, straightforward when they are viewed as producing firms working on some probability bases. So it is with organized research.

Let us now look briefly at the firm where these two neglected inputs enter and play important roles in increasing output. The best way to represent the two inputs under consideration is to treat each of them as introducing a change in quality of one or more of the conventional inputs. In the case of improvements in the labor force, a change in quality is what we need to identify and evaluate. So too, in the case of a new technique; for example, the difference between a bushel of open-pollinated corn and a bushel of hybrid corn may be represented as a qualitative difference. And so it is with other new techniques.

We observe everywhere throughout the economy that the marginal (and average) productivity of the human agent has been rising. The human agent,

---

[16] From observations and study of the 20 Latin American republics and of Puerto Rico, the author would venture the guess that in these countries the marginal (and average) rates of return on capital and effort allocated to improve the quality of people and to raise the productive arts far exceeds that on reproducible capital of the conventional types. Moreover, it appears that those countries with strong economic growth characteristics are precisely the ones that have been "investing" their available capital and effort accordingly. See the author's lectures at Cornell University, March 1956, *The Economic Test in Latin America,* to be published by the School of Labor and Industrial Relations of Cornell University.

viewed as an input, has come to be worth increasingly more to the firm, in what the firm can and does pay for the services of this agent. This development in itself creates a strong presumption that the quality of this input has been improving. The traditional concept of labor in studying production of merely counting the number who work, or the number of hours worked, fails completely to take account of changes in quality of this most important input of all. The studies of Zeman[17] and Willett[18] of Negro workers represent a major advance in research to determine the "market value" of the variations in the quality of this input. Johnson's[19] earlier study of the nonfarm wages of recent farm migrants also comes to grips with an important aspect of this problem. In examining the income disparity among communities some time back, I gave much weight to the *conditions that determine the abilities of a population to produce.*[20, 21]

In the case of a new technique of production, we may look upon it as another particular input and as an input that is qualitatively better than the one it replaces. We have already suggested this possibility by comparing a bushel of open-pollinated corn with a bushel of hybrid corn.

Whereas the direction and even the magnitude of the economic effects of a new technique upon the price of the product, and upon other input prices, present no new analytical problems, there remains a most difficult index number problem in pricing the improvement in the quality of this input. Take, for example, the introduction of hybrid corn. Let us assume that farmers know from their past experiences that they can "count on" say $1.10 of returns on each $1 of open-pollinated corn that they may plant. There now is available to them an alternative input, the hybrid corn. Farmers in some places, say in the heart of the corn belt, find that it will contribute as much as $10 per $1 of this (new) input. Farmers in other places, however, find that this alternative input will not produce for them per $1 expended any more than they have been realizing by using open-pollinated corn. In still other areas the rate of return on the hybrid corn available to them may turn out to be less than on the established open-pollinated varieties. The direction of the implications of these differences in returns, to the decisions and the activities of these firms, is clear enough. One also may trace such effects of hybrid corn upon the relative price of corn, upon the value of land in the

---

[17] Morton Zeman, "A Quantitative Analysis of White-Nonwhite Income Differentials in the United States" (to be published by the University of Chicago Press).

[18] Joseph W. Willett, "An Analysis of the Incomes of White and Negro Commercial Farm Operators in the Southern States," a manuscript at the University of Chicago.

[19] D. Gale Johnson, "Functioning of the Labor Market," *Journal of Farm Economics,* Vol. 33 (February 1951).

[20] See the author's *The Economic Organization of Agriculture* (New York: McGraw-Hill Book Co., 1953), chap. X.

[21] In a recent paper "Agriculture's Advancing Productivity" read before the National Farm Institute, Des Moines, Iowa, on February 17, 1956, Sherman E. Johnson stressed the importance of basic education in the transformation of American agriculture (see page 5).

different places used to produce corn, and upon the redistribution of the corn acreage among these places, by traditional partial equilibrium theory and process analysis. But the index number problem of assigning weights to this (new) input in the various places requires major analytical attention.[22]

CONCLUSION

From these reflections we are prepared to say that our knowledge about demand is on a much stronger footing than is our knowledge about supply. Our analysis of supply fails because so much of the increase in output in agriculture and, alas, in the rest of the economy, cannot be explained by additional inputs of the conventional types. This failure to explain much, and probably most, of the additional output that we have been enjoying is strongly supported by data now at hand. The analytical task is to reestablish, if we can do so, a firm link between additional output and additional input. The ideal input-output formula would be one where output over input stayed at or close to one. Our proposal is that we can approximate this ideal formulation by introducing two major neglected inputs, namely, the improvement of the quality of the people as productive agents and the raising of the level of the productive arts. In studying the functioning of the economy as a whole, both of these "neglected inputs" require capital and effort and, therefore, the activities that create them may be analyzed as production activities. At the level of the firm the way to bring these changes in inputs into the analysis is to treat them as improvements in the quality of what we have called the conventional inputs. The index number problem, in this case, of determining the weights for these qualitative differences in the inputs will demand major analytical attention.

---

[22] After a new equilibrium has become established in the places where hybrid corn turned out to be qualitatively better (more productive) than the open-pollinated corn, the additional productivity would be redistributed and presumably exhausted in a relatively lower product price and in a redistribution of the rewards among inputs more favorable to the nonreproducible factors with the new input "earning" no more than its cost. But this would not be the case at the outset when the hybrid corn was being introduced. A difficulty in determining a "price weight" in measuring the new input may be seen in a comment that Zvi Griliches has made: namely, suppose that instead of a competitive hybrid corn seed industry we had had a perfect discriminatory monopoly, and that as a consequence the price of the hybrid corn in each place had been set at a level that would have made it just profitable to shift to hybrid corn. This would make the measure (the price weight) of the new input depend upon the monopoly (or competitive) characteristics of the market.

17 Optimum Resource Allocation in U.S. Agriculture*

FRED H. TYNER and LUTHER G. TWEETEN†

Elasticities of production for nine input categories in U.S. agriculture were estimated with the assumption that factor shares adjust to the production elasticity with a distributed lag. A Cobb-Douglas production function was formulated from the estimated production elasticities and used to show the economically optimum level and combination of aggregate resources in U.S. agriculture. Adjustment to the least-cost input combination which would produce the actual average 1952–1961 output would have reduced the actual input dollar volume by $1.9 billion, or 5.6 percent. Adjustment of farm resources to an equilibrium level, with all resources earning an opportunity-cost return would have entailed a reduction of 4.2 billion 1947–1949 dollars, or 12.5 percent of the actual input volume. The cost of excess capacity was approximately $2.2 billion or 6.6 percent of the resource volume; the cost of a nonoptimal input mix was $2.0 billion or 5.9 percent of the resource volume. Two-fifths of agricultural labor was estimated to be in excess supply in the 1952–1961 period.

Overcapacity in U.S. agriculture was defined by the authors in an earlier article [13] as the excess of production over utilization at socially acceptable prices. Excess production is symptomatic of the more fundamental problem of excess resources committed to agriculture.[1] The finding [13, p. 28] that agricultural production capacity in recent years had exceeded market utilization by 7 percent also means that agricultural resources were in excess.

It is apparent that certain resources such as labor have been overcommitted to a greater extent than cash operating inputs. The purpose of this

* *Journal of Farm Economics,* Vol. XLVIII, No. 3, Part I (August, 1966), pp. 613–31.

† Louisiana State University, Baton Rouge, Louisiana; and Oklahoma State University, Stillwater, Oklahoma, respectively.

[1] The term "excess" does not necessarily imply a connotation of an *unneeded* or *undesirable* gap between production capacity and utilization. It has been emphasized that the "excess" may be highly valued by society as insurance or as a hedge against unforeseen future food and fiber needs. In fact there may be many in society who feel that the excess is not large enough. Cf. Tweeten [11].

article is to show the optimum level and combination of resources in U.S. agriculture that would have (1) minimized the cost of production, and (2) made marginal value products for all resources equal to their earnings in alternate uses. The optimum resource allocation is oriented to an historic rather than a future perspective. The assumption is that resources are mobile and that knowledge of both cost-minimizing and equilibrium resource allocation is a useful norm for public policy. This by no means implies that efficiency is the only objective of public policy and that justice, equity, security, and other goals are unimportant—in fact the latter goals may take precedence over efficiency.

A method for estimating the elasticities of production for aggregate agricultural inputs has been presented in another article by the authors [14].[2] Elasticity estimates were obtained for nine input groups by decades since 1910 and are employed in this article to determine the optimum resource allocation in U.S. agriculture. As the initial step in this analysis, the elasticity estimates were used to synthesize a series of aggregate production functions—one for each decade beginning with 1912. The production functions were then used to study the following: (a) minimum-cost input levels for specified outputs, (b) equilibrium output and resource levels, (c) changes in factor-substitution relationships, and (d) factor-demand and product-supply elasticities.

Table 1 presents the input groups used and their respective elasticity estimates by decades. The productivity of the fertilizer-and-lime input appears to be underestimated. This may have resulted from one or more of several causes. One possible cause was our failure to account fully for the interdependence of fertilizer with improved inputs such as pesticides and seed varieties. Introduction of the latter inputs raises the productivity and the optimum input levels of fertilizer and lime. Other factors or data inadequacies may also mask the productivity of fertilizer and lime.

Standard errors of the elasticity estimates in Table 3 are not available. Explanation of the methods used in the estimation of the elasticities [14] did not include measures of statistical reliability. Briefly, acceptance of the elasticity estimates was based on significance of the adjustment coefficient, g, and the autocorrelation coefficient, β. The elasticity estimate, E^*_t, was

---

[2] The method, briefly, is as follows. A factor is being used optimally under competitive conditions when its marginal product equals the factor–product price ratio, $\partial Y/\partial X_i = P_i/P_y$. Multiplying by X_i/Y gives the elasticity of production, E_i, on the left and the factor share, F_i (defined as the ratio of expenditure on an input to the value of output), on the right. Assuming a *disequilibrium* situation ($E_i \neq F_i$), we postulate a tendency towards equilibrium as typified in the following adjustment model: $F_{i,t} - F_{i,\,t-1} = g(E^*_{i,\,t} - F_{i,\,t-1})$, which says that the change in use of a factor is some proportion, g, of the divergence from equilibrium. The equilibrium elasticity estimate, E*, is obtained by using regular least squares or autoregressive least squares to estimate the coefficients in the above model and in several variations of the above model which allow for changing g and E*.

calculated from the constant term, A, in an autoregressive least-squares equation:

$$A = gE^*_t(1 - \beta)$$

$$\text{and } E^*_t = A/g(1 - \beta).$$

If β was not significant, a regular least-squares equation was used to obtain the estimate of E^*_t.

Sums of elasticities need not equal 1, since values of the factors used are necessarily equal to total receipts in agriculture only in equilibrium and with constant returns to scale (see footnote 2). Input and output data used in later sections are in million 1947–1949 dollars, except for labor, which is in million man-hours. Data and sources are described in the appendix.

Griliches [4, 6] derived production-elasticity estimates of aggregate inputs for 1939 in a cross-sectional study which may be compared with some of the results in Table 1. His estimates for land and buildings were considerably in excess of our average 1942–1951 estimate but about equal to the 1952–1961 average. The only other inputs grouped similarly are machinery and labor, with Griliches' machinery estimate more than double ours, and his labor estimate 0.449 (or 0.524) compared to our 0.345. According to the Griliches estimate, a 10 percent decrease in labor input would reduce farm output 5 percent. The production function Griliches used resulted in a sum of elasticities greater than the sum we estimated by about 0.35 (1.36 versus 1.01), so the factor-elasticity estimates are not strictly comparable.

THE PRODUCTION FUNCTION

The hypothesis used here is that the imputed elasticities of production in Table 1 express input–output relationships in a power (Cobb-Douglas) type of function. In general terms, the function is

$$Y = aX_1^{b_1}X_2^{b_2} \cdot\cdot\cdot X_9^{b_9}, \qquad (1)$$

where Y is output and the X_i's are inputs, with the b_i's the corresponding elasticities of production.[3]

---

[3] The following formula imputes the total output to the respective inputs $X_1, X_2, \cdots X_i, \cdots X_n$ where ξ is the degree of homogeneity of the production function. It is apparent from

$$Y = \sum_{i+1}^{n} \frac{\partial Y}{\partial X_i} \cdot \frac{X_i}{\xi} \qquad (a)$$

that two approaches are feasible to impute to factors the entire output over a period of time. One is to adjust upward the quantity series X_i for changes in productivity of the factor as technological changes occur, and to leave $\partial Y/\partial X_i$ unadjusted. See Zvi Griliches [5]. A second approach, which was used in the analysis of this article, is to leave quantity unadjusted for increased productivity, and to reflect increased productivity in the marginal product or elasticity of production through the process defined in footnote 2.

The function was selected for this analysis because of its frequency of occurrence in production economics literature and its relative simplicity of use, especially since a number of estimates of the b_i's (elasticities of production) are already available for comparison. This function also affords relative ease of manipulation for determination of the items studied. It is necessary, however, to assume that the production elasticities are independent of the level of use of any of the factors of production, an assumption which places a limitation on the usefulness of the elasticities for sizable changes in input levels.

The constant term *a* in (1) has yet to be determined. Its value may be estimated in two alternative ways, depending on whether the error is assumed to be additive or multiplicative. In the additive case, *a* may be estimated by considering $X_1^{b_1}X_2^{b_2} \cdots X_9^{b_9}$ as one variable, Z. Using constant-dollar data for Y and the X's, the relation

$$Y = aZ + u \tag{2a}$$

may be estimated by the least-squares method, using raw sums of squares and cross-products to force a zero intercept. That is, $\hat{a} = \sum YZ/\sum Z^2$.

If the error is assumed to be multiplicative, the function becomes

$$Y = aZu, \tag{2b}$$

and *a* is estimated from

$$\log Y = \log a + \log Z + \log u \tag{2c}$$

as

$$\hat{a} = \text{antilog}\,\frac{1}{n}\left(\sum \log Y - \sum \log Z\right).$$

The proper assumption can be selected by comparing the results, and choosing the method with the least unexplained residual, i.e., by selecting the equation with the higher R^2. On the basis of this criterion, the additive case (equation 2a) was the better assumption, though the margin for selection was slight. However, comparison of the *a*'s estimated both ways showed differences in size of less than 7 percent, so the choice of assumptions was not critical.

The $\hat{a}$'s obtained on the basis of equation (2a) were as follows:

1912–1921:	109.67675	1942–1951:	17.55649
1922–1931:	175.49798	1952–1961:	7.52389
1932–1941:	7.64468		

Data for estimating an elasticity of production for labor during 1912–1921 and 1922–1931 were not available. Consequently only eight inputs were used in forming the Z variable, and the $\hat{a}$'s are correspondingly large in these periods, since the effect of labor is incorporated. The larger $\hat{a}$ for 1942–1951 than for 1932–1941 and 1952–1961 is primarily due to the low productivity estimate obtained for real estate during the war and the immediate post-war period (Table 1).

Combining the elasticity estimates from Table 1 and the calculated *a*-values above in the Cobb-Douglas framework provides estimates of the production function for five 10-year periods.

TABLE 1
ESTIMATED PRODUCTION ELASTICITIES BY DECADES, NINE INPUT CATEGORIES, U.S. AGRICULTURE, 1912–1961

Input[a]	*1912–1921*	*1922–1931*	*1932–1941*	*1942–1951*	*1952–1961*
1. Fertilizer and lime	.02237	.02400	.02648	.02885	.04325
2. Feed, seed, and livestock	.03256	.03067	.06165	.08766	.08862
3. Labor	—[b]	—[b]	.34777	.34458	.28983
4. Machinery	.09100	.05833	.06056	.07768	.09408
5. Real estate	.34449	.30206	.23619	.14837	.23816
6. Machinery operating expenses	.02698	.04722	.06513	.06901	.10321
7. Miscellaneous current operating expenses	.08296	.08187	.07550	.05133	.07793
8. Crop and livestock inventory (interest)	.05605	.04560	.04587	.04441	.04112
9. Real estate taxes	.03200	.04682	.03861	.02112	.03542
Sum of elasticities	—	—	.95776	.87301	1.01162

[a] A description of the input categories and sources of data may be found in the appendix.
[b] Date not available prior to 1929.

1. MINIMUM-COST INPUT LEVELS

The preceding parameter estimates in the production function specified in (1) now provide the framework to determine the minimum-cost quantities of inputs which will provide a specified output, Y*. The cost function is

$$C = \sum P_i X_i, \tag{3}$$

the sums of input quantities times their respective prices.[4] To minimize costs subject to production of a specified output, Y*, the production-function restraint is added in

$$C^* = \sum P_i X_i + \lambda(Y^* - aX_1^{b_1} \cdots X_9^{b_9}), \tag{4}$$

[4] Since inputs except labor are measured in dollars, the prices of these inputs are assumed to be $1. The price level used for labor is the average wage of factory workers during the period, and 85 percent of the factory wage represents the opportunity cost to farm workers.

where λ is a Lagrangean multiplier. Costs are then minimized by taking partial derivatives of (4) with respect to each of the unknowns, equating the derivatives to zero, and solving the resulting system of equations simultaneously. The derivatives equated to zero are as follows:

$$\frac{\partial C^*}{\partial X_1} = P_1 - a\lambda b_1 X_1^{b_1-1} X_2^{b_2} \cdots X_9^{b_9} = 0, \tag{5}$$

$$\frac{\partial C^*}{\partial X_2} = P_2 - a\lambda b_2 X_1^{b_1} X_2^{b_2-1} X_3^{b_3} \cdots X_9^{b_9} = 0, \tag{6}$$

$$\vdots$$

$$\frac{\partial C^*}{\partial X_9} = P_9 - a\lambda b_9 X_1^{b_1} \cdots X_8^{b_8} X_9^{b_9-1} = 0, \tag{13}$$

and

$$\frac{\partial C^*}{\partial \lambda} = Y^* - X_1^{b_1} \cdots X^{b_9} = 0. \tag{14}$$

Minimum-cost combinations of inputs to produce the average outputs of the five periods were determined by first taking logarithms of equations (5)–(14), and then solving the system of simultaneous linear equations. Optimal input combinations were derived for the following situations:

A. All inputs variable:
   1. labor priced at the nonfarm wage rate,
   2. labor priced at 85 percent of the nonfarm wage rate.[5]
B. Real estate (X_5) fixed; other inputs variable:
   1. labor priced at the nonfarm wage rate,
   2. labor priced at 85 percent of the wage rate.
C. For 1952–1961 only, with real estate fixed, labor priced at 85 percent of the nonfarm rate, and average output reduced to $.95\bar{Y}$, $.93\bar{Y}$, and $.90\bar{Y}$, where $\bar{Y}$ is average production of the 1952–1961 period.

These combinations, as computed from the "equilibrium" elasticity estimates, are given in Tables 2–4. Actual averages are included for comparison.

Comments on the minimum-cost levels in Table 2 will be limited to the 1952–1961 period. Comparison of estimates (M-1) with actual levels indicates

---

[5] Hathaway [7, p. 37] suggests that this pricing allows for comparability between farm and nonfarm labor income after consumption of home-produced food and differences in family size are considered.

that a higher level of investment in machinery, increased operating expenditures for machinery, and about a doubling of the real estate input allowed a halving of the labor force. Other inputs remained approximately at their 1952–1961 levels. Pricing labor at a lower rate (M-2) brought a substitution of labor for real estate and machinery, though the level of real estate expenditure was still unreasonable. Real estate inputs remained very stable, since the land base is fixed and increases can occur only through land-improvement practices and buildings. For this reason it would have been desirable to have an estimate of productivity for land and improvements separately, though this was not practical. In lieu of separate estimates, the real estate input was held at actual levels for the estimates presented in Table 3.

Looking first at the M-1 estimates in Table 3 by input groups, we see that the use of fertilizer and lime tended only slowly toward the optimum until the 1950's, but actual use in 1952–1961 was only 18 percent under the estimated optimum. Feed, seed, and livestock purchases from the nonfarm sector were nearly optimum in 1912–1921 and above optimum in the unfavorable period of the 1920's; they have been below but tending strongly toward optimality since that time.

Unfortunately for long-term comparisons, no labor estimates were available for the first two periods. The ratio of estimated to actual levels has remained at about one half since 1932, though the absolute difference has declined considerably. The machinery estimate consistent with such a reduction in the labor force has been considerably in excess of the actual level for the periods since 1932, the estimated machinery shortage amounting to more than $1 billion from 1942 to 1961. Corresponding to increased machinery ownership, minimum-cost estimates of machinery operating expenses exceeded actual expenses. Miscellaneous current operating expenses would also need to increase to offset the decrease in labor input. Examples of such operating expenses might be the use of electrically powered and operated labor-saving equipment in feed-handling systems. Crop and livestock inventories were apparently being maintained at near-optimum levels. Tax increases on real estate were indicated. One interpretation is that this implies greater need for improved tax-supported services such as education for rural residents.

Based on results using the estimated production function for 1952–1961, with real estate fixed and labor priced at 85 percent of the nonfarm rate (the M-2 estimates), a labor reduction of 35 percent and increases in machinery stock, machinery operating expense, and miscellaneous operating expenses of 28, 49, and 34 percent, respectively, would have produced the average 1952–1961 output at the minimum cost to farmers. Average output for 1952–1961 in 1947–1949 dollars was $32,452.5 million. Input costs (actual average in 1947–1949 dollars with labor priced at the opportunity-cost level) were $33,512.6 million and estimated minimum costs (M-2) were

TABLE 2

ESTIMATED MINIMUM-COST LEVELS OF INPUTS REQUIRED FOR AVERAGE ACTUAL OUTPUT BY DECADES, 1912–1961, ALL INPUTS VARIABLE, TWO LABOR PRICES, WITH AVERAGE INPUTS FOR COMPARISON

Input	*Item*[a]	*Period* 1912–1921	1922–1931	1932–1941	1942–1951	1952–1961
		Million 1947–1949 Dollars[b]				
1. Fertilizer and lime	M-1	261.9	333.0	664.2	1,039.7	1,343.4
	M-2	—[c]	—[c]	626.0	975.0	1,282.0
	A	182.7	249.2	286.4	753.4	1,364.7
2. Feed, seed, and livestock	M-1	381.2	425.6	1,546.7	3,159.4	2,752.3
	M-2	—[c]	—[c]	1,457.8	2,962.0	2,627.3
	A	528.7	761.1	896.7	1,978.4	2,698.0
3. Labor	M-1	—[c]	—[c]	8,462.6	9,574.2	5,591.0
	M-2	—[c]	—[c]	9,388.6	10,566.0	6,280.6
	A	23,400.3	23,277.2	21,075.0	17,855.1	11,782.2
4. Machinery	M-1	1,065.6	809.5	1,519.2	2,799.6	2,922.1
	M-2	—[c]	—[c]	1,431.9	2,624.8	2,789.3
	A	1,000.1	1,187.8	1,066.2	1,606.8	2,642.4
5. Real estate	M-1	4,033.6	4,191.8	5,925.1	5,346.9	7,397.8
	M-2	—[c]	—[c]	5,584.7	5,014.2	7,060.0
	A	3,387.2	3,389.9	3,356.6	3,471.5	3,742.8
6. Machinery operating expenses	M-1	315.9	655.2	1,633.8	2,487.1	3,205.5
	M-2	—[c]	—[c]	1,539.9	2,331.8	3,059.9
	A	331.2	558.4	743.9	1,783.7	2,502.4
7. Miscellaneous current operating expenses	M-1	971.4	1,122.1	1,894.1	1,849.8	2,420.5
	M-2	—[c]	—[c]	1,785.2	1,734.6	2,310.5
	A	1,342.2	1,337.3	1,121.9	1,211.0	2,100.7
8. Crop and livestock inventory (interest)	M-1	656.3	632.8	1,150.5	1,600.3	1,277.0
	M-2	—[c]	—[c]	1,084.7	1,500.7	1,219.0
	A	1,106.5	1,079.2	1,102.7	1,314.7	1,441.4
9. Real estate taxes	M-1	374.7	649.7	968.5	743.9	1,100.3
	M-2	—[c]	—[c]	912.8	697.4	1,050.0
	A	546.7	853.5	825.1	643.1	902.2
Average output		17,882.7	19,791.4	20,737.5	27,291.7	32,452.5

[a] M-1 and M-2 are minimum-cost levels, with labor priced at the nonfarm wage rate and at 85 percent of nonfarm rate, respectively; A is the actual average for the period indicated.
[b] Except for input 3 (labor), which is in million man-hours.
[c] No elasticity estimate was obtained for labor for 1912–1921 and 1922–1931; therefore only one minimum-cost combination was obtained for each period.

TABLE 3

Estimated Minimum-cost Levels of Inputs Required for Average Actual Output by Decades, 1912–1961, Real Estate Fixed, Two Labor Prices, with Average Inputs for Comparison

Input	Item[a]	*1912–1921*	*1922–1931*	*1932–1941*	*1942–1951*	*1951–1961*
			Million 1947–1949 Dollars[b]			
1. Fertilizer and lime	M-1	312.0	417.7	800.0	1,135.8	1,656.9
	M-2	—[c]	—[c]	739.6	1,051.2	1,558.8
	A	182.7	249.2	286.4	753.4	1,364.7
2. Feed, seed, and livestock	M-1	454.2	533.8	1,863.0	3,451.5	3,395.5
	M-2	—[c]	—[c]	1,722.3	3,193.8	3,194.5
	A	528.7	761.1	896.7	1,978.4	2,698.0
3. Labor	M-1	—[c]	—[c]	10,193.0	10,459.0	6,896.0
	M-2	—[c]	—[c]	11,099.0	11,392.0	7,636.6
	A	23,400.3	23,277.2	21,075.0	17,885.1	11,782.2
4. Machinery	M-1	1,269.4	1,015.3	1,829.8	3,058.4	3,604.2
	M-2	—[c]	—[c]	1,691.6	2,830.1	3,390.8
	A	1,001.0	1,187.8	1,066.2	1,606.8	2,642.4
5. Real estate (fixed)	A	3,387.2	3,389.9	3,356.6	3,471.5	3,742.8
6. Machinery operating expenses	M-1	376.4	821.9	1,967.9	2,717.1	3,954.6
	M-2	—[c]	—[c]	1,819.3	2,514.2	3,719.6
	A	331.2	558.4	743.9	1,783.7	2,502.4
7. Miscellaneous current operating expenses	M-1	1,157.2	1,407.7	2,281.4	2,020.7	2,985.4
	M-2	—[c]	—[c]	2,108.6	1,870.3	2,808.7
	A	1,342.2	1,337.3	1,121.0	1,211.0	2,100.7
8. Crop and livestock inventory (interest)	M-1	781.8	793.8	1,385.8	1,748.3	1,575.1
	M-2	—[c]	—[c]	1,281.1	1,618.1	1,481.8
	A	1,106.5	1,079.2	1,102.7	1,314.7	1,441.4
9. Real estate taxes	M-1	446.4	814.9	1,166.5	812.6	1,357.1
	M-2	—[c]	—[c]	1,078.4	752.0	1,276.4
	A	546.7	853.5	825.1	643.1	902.2

[a] M-1 and M-2 are minimum cost levels with labor priced at the nonfarm wage rate and at 85 percent of the nonfarm rate, respectively; A is the actual average for the period indicated.

[b] Except for input 3 (labor), which is in million man-hours.

[c] No elasticity estimate was obtained for labor for 1912–1921 and 1922–1931; therefore only one minimum-cost combination was obtained for each period.

$31,620.3 million, a difference of $1,892.3 million. It is apparent that the comments on the M-1 estimates apply in general to the M-2 estimates. The lower charge for labor, of course, increased the optimum level of that input, and resulted in substitution of labor for some quantity of each of the other inputs, especially the machinery-related inputs.

Excess capacity has been estimated by the authors [17] for the period 1955–1962 (based on Commodity Credit Corporation net acquisitions, subsidized exports from commercial stocks, and production averted through government land-withdrawal programs) to range from 5.3 to 11.2 percent of probable production in the absence of the programs in effect. We arbitrarily select levels of 5, 7, and 10 percent excess production for demonstrating adjustment in input use to reduce production by stated amounts. The criterion used is that production costs to farmers be minimized. The minimum-cost input levels are calculated for outputs of 95, 93, and 90 percent, respectively, of the 1952–1961 average. Other restrictions placed on these estimates include holding the real estate input constant and pricing labor at 85 percent of the nonfarm wage rate. The solution values and actual values are shown in Table 4.

TABLE 4

MINIMUM-COST LEVELS OF INPUTS FOR OUTPUT LEVELS REDUCED 5, 7, AND 10 PERCENT BELOW ACTUAL AVERAGE, 1952–1961, REAL ESTATE FIXED, LABOR PRICED AT 85 PERCENT OF NONFARM RATE, WITH AVERAGE INPUT USE FOR COMPARISON

Input	*Actual Average Input*	*Output Level*			
		Percent of Average for 1952–1961			
		100	*95*	*93*	*90*
	Million 1947–1949 Dollars[a]				
1. Fertilizer and lime	1,364.7	1,558.8	1,458.8	1,419.7	1,360.5
2. Feed, seed, and livestock	2,698.0	3,194.5	2,988.8	2,908.1	2,787.4
3. Labor	11,782.2	7,636.6	7,146.7	6,951.8	6,663.5
4. Machinery	2,642.4	3,390.8	3,173.2	3,087.4	2,959.5
5. Real estate (fixed)	3,742.8	3,742.8	3,742.8	3,742.8	3,742.8
6. Machinery operating expenses	2,502.4	3,719.6	3,481.0	3,386.8	3,246.4
7. Miscellaneous current operating expenses	2,100.7	2,808.7	2,628.4	2,516.4	2,451.3
8. Crop and livestock inventory (interest)	1,441.4	1,481.8	1,386.8	1,349.0	1,293.0
9. Real estate taxes	902.2	1,276.4	1,194.8	1,162.2	1,114.0

[a] Except for labor, which is million man-hours.

Estimated minimum-cost levels for output reduced 10 percent are very similar to actual average input use except for labor, the machinery-related inputs, and miscellaneous operating expenses. A reduction of the labor input from 11.8 billion to 6.7 billion hours is associated with an increase in quantity of machinery from $2.6 to $3.0 billion, an increase in expenses for operation and repair of machinery from $2.5 to $3.2 billion, and an increase in miscellaneous operating expenses from $2.1 to $2.5 billion. The comparatively small amount of disequilibrium is consistent with the results shown previously,[6] that the adjustment rate of factor shares to the equilibrium value is quite high.

2. Equilibrium Output and Resource Levels

The preceding sections have emphasized the finding of optimum input combinations under conditions where the level of output was specified. No mention has been made of the impact of changing output on prices received by farmers. This study would be incomplete without giving attention to the effect of prices received by farmers on their demand for inputs and the resultant effect on output.

To state the problem in other words, what output could be expected if the use of all inputs was at equilibrium, and what would be the effect of changing levels of prices received? As in the foregoing analysis, input supply (except real estate) is assumed to be perfectly elastic, so that changes in input and output levels have no perceptible influence on input prices.

The supply function based on equilibrium factor use is derived as follows: Since the competitive equilibrium condition for use of X_i is $MPP_i = P_i/P_y$, the first derivatives of the production function are set equal to P_i/P_y. Adding the production function to the system and solving simultaneously gives the desired values of the X_i and Y for a given P_y. Output price P_y can be varied and the system re-solved to generate a set of values of Y, thus locating a supply function. The intersection of an aggregate demand curve with the supply curve then will indicate the output and price level necessary for production—consumption equilibrium and for factor-use equilibrium.

The S_e line in Figure 1 is the supply function based on equilibrium factor use, showing the calculated values of Y for different levels of P (index of prices received by farmers, 1947–1949 = 100) given the condition that $MPP_i = P_i/P_y$. Since P_y is $1 per unit initially (output is in constant-dollar-value terms) the system was solved with P_y = $0.70, $0.75, · · · , $1.25, and these prices were converted to the prices-received index, with $1 corresponding to the average index for the period.

The elasticity of demand for agricultural products has been estimated frequently as approximately—0.25. Given the elasticity of demand, the only additional requirement for locating a demand schedule is one point on the curve. One coordinate of this point is the average level of prices received, $\bar{P}$, during the 1952–1961 period, 90.4. The second coordinate would be the average value of farm output, $\bar{Y}$, except that this figure overestimates the market demand (*i.e.*, it includes government purchases for price support,

[6] The rapid adjustment rates, around 0.5 for many resources, were not consistent with the fixed-resources hypotheses [14].

etc.). We adjust this average output downward by 5 percent, which is greater than the government diversions in the first part of the period but is less than our previous estimate [13] of a 7 percent excess of "probable" production in the absence of government programs in effect.

The D curve is constructed by using the adjusted average output, $\bar{Y}^*$, of 30,933 million 1947–1949 dollars, an average price index of 90.4, and the

FIGURE 1
AGGREGATE FARM DEMAND AND SUPPLY, SHOWING EQUILIBRIUM PRICE P_e AND OUTPUT Y_e FOR THE 1952-1961 PERIOD

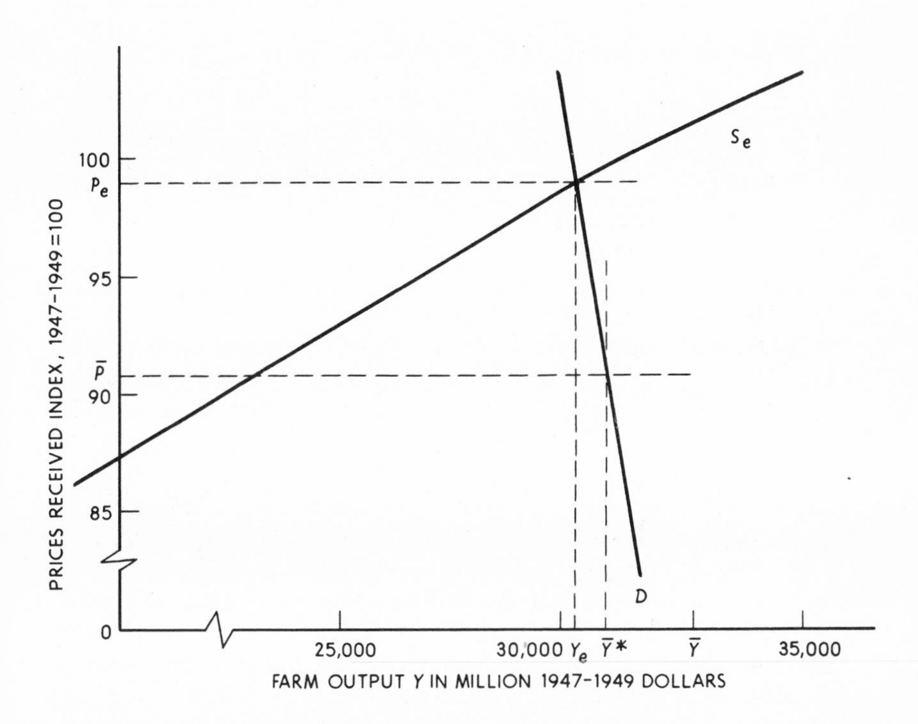

elasticity of demand, −0.25. Intersection of the D and S_e curves is at approximately Y_e = \$30,300 million and P_e = 98.5. The average index of prices paid by farmers during 1952–1961 was 115.1, and the parity-ratio average was 78.9, with both indexes based on 1947–1949 = 100 (1910–1914 = 100 index averages were 288 and 86, respectively). If production had been sufficiently reduced during this period to maintain an average of prices received of 98.5, and if the changing combination of inputs had not altered the prices-paid index appreciably, then the equilibrium parity ratio would have been approximately 86 (1947–1949 = 100), or 93 (1910–1914 = 100).

Table 5 contains the equilibrium input levels associated with the equilibrium product price and quantity in Figure 1. At the indicated input levels, all resources would have received earnings equal to their opportunity cost, and the total cost of producing the equilibrium output would have been minimized. As expected, labor was in oversupply, by approximately 40 percent.

TABLE 5

ESTIMATED EQUILIBRIUM AGGREGATE INPUT LEVELS FOR 1952–1961[a]

Input	*Actual Average Input*	*Equilibrium Input*	*Actual Input as Percentage of Equilibrium Input*
	Million 1947–49 Dollars[b]		*Percent*
1. Fertilizer and lime	1364.7	1431.9	95
2. Feed, seed, and livestock	2698.0	2932.3	92
3. Labor	11,782.2	7009.7	168
4. Machinery	2642.4	3112.4	85
5. Real estate (fixed)	3742.8	3742.8	—
6. Machinery operating expenses	2502.4	3394.0	74
7. Miscellaneous current operating expenses	2100.7	2578.1	81
8. Crop and livestock inventory (interest)	1441.4	1360.2	106
9. Real estate taxes	902.2	1171.9	77

[a] See text and Figure 1 for definition of "equilibrium." Real estate is fixed at the 1952–1961 average volume. All inputs except real estate are assumed to be variable and perfectly elastic in supply. All variable inputs are valued at opportunity-cost levels. Labor is valued at 85 percent of the average hourly factory wage.

[b] All farm inputs are in 1947–1949 constant dollars except labor, which is in million man-hours.

The results do not support the hypothesis that farmers have purchased excess amounts of machinery and other capital items. However, it is possible that additional capital items optimally would have been reduced in amount, if labor had been fixed at the average 1952–1961 level (in recognition of the inelastic response of labor to price changes), and the equilibrium then computed. The substantial reduction in labor inputs more than compensates for the 17 percent indicated increase in capital inputs (all inputs except real estate and labor), and the total input volume falls from the actual $33,513 million to the equilibrium $29,313 million—a drop of 12.5 percent. The equilibrium output is 6.6 percent less than the 1952–1961 average; hence approximately 6.6 percent of the input reduction was imputed to a contraction of the agricultural plant and 5.9 percent was imputed to input savings from a recombination of inputs into the least-cost mix in Table 5.

3. Changes in Factor-substitution Relationships

There are several elasticity estimates other than the elasticity of production which are of interest and which can be derived from the Cobb–Douglas production function. These are (a) the elasticity of substitution between factors, (b) the elasticity of demand for a particular factor, and (c) the elasticity of output supply.

The elasticity of substitution between factors i and j is here defined as the percentage change in X_i associated with a 1 percent change in X_j, given that output is unchanged [9, p. 54; 8, pp. 144–45].[7] With a two-factor production function,

$$Y = aX_1^{b_1}X_2^{b_2}, \tag{15}$$

the marginal rate of substitution of X_1 for X_2 in the production of Y is

$$\frac{dX_2}{dX_1} = -\frac{\dfrac{\partial Y}{\partial X_1}}{\dfrac{\partial Y}{\partial X_2}}, \tag{16}$$

the negative ratio of the marginal products of the two factors. The marginal rate of substitution is converted into an elasticity by multiplying by the ratio of factors, X_1/X_2, giving

$$E_{1:2} = \frac{dX_2}{dX_1}\cdot\frac{X_1}{X_2} = -\frac{\dfrac{\partial Y}{\partial X_1}}{\dfrac{\partial Y}{\partial X_2}}\cdot\frac{X_1}{X_2} = -\frac{b_1}{b_2}. \tag{17}$$

A comparison of all the substitution elasticity changes among the nine input categories would be both lengthy and unnecessary. There are, however, several relations of considerable interest, especially changes in substitution elasticities between fertilizer materials and land (real estate) and between labor and machinery.

Elasticities of substituting fertilizer for real estate ($-b_1/b_5$) for each decade since 1912 are −0.06494, −0.07945, −0.11211, −0.19445, and −0.18160. Machinery-for-labor substitution elasticities ($-b_4/b_3$) for each decade since 1932 are −0.17414, −0.22543, and −0.32460. The rate at which fertilizer substitutes for real estate is now 2.8 times as great as in

[7] This definition is different from that given by R. G. D. Allen [1, pp. 340–43].

1912–1921 and the machinery-for-labor substitution rate is more than 1.5 times as great now as in the decade 1932–1941.

4. Factor-Demand and Product-Supply Elasticities

The demand for specific factors of production is related to the price of the factor and the price of the product. The percentage change in factor use associated with a 1-percent change in the factor price (or product price if only one factor is variable) is the elasticity of input demand. The demand elasticity with respect to factor price is usually referred to simply as "elasticity of demand" (E_d) and with respect to product price as "cross elasticity of demand"[8](E_{cd}).

To maximize profit, each input is employed at the level at which marginal value product equals marginal factor cost, i.e., $(\partial Y/\partial X_1)\, P_y = P_i$. Thus the implicit-demand function for X_1 (with X_2 fixed) in a 2-factor Cobb–Douglas function[9] is

$$X_1 = [P_y a b_1 X_2{}^{b_2} P_1{}^{-1}]^{1/1-b_1}. \qquad (18)$$

In the Cobb–Douglas framework the elasticities of direct and cross demand (as derived from equation 18) bear the relationship $E_{d_1} = -E_{cd_1}$, so only one set needs to be presented. Table 6 gives the cross elasticities of demand for the nine input groups under the assumption that inputs other than the *i*th are fixed.

Supply elasticity is a measure of the percentage change in output associated with a 1 percent change in product price. Comparison of "simple" supply elasticities in Table 7 indicates the effect of product supply associated with a change in only the *i*th input, which in turn is due to a change in the product price. Inputs other than the *i*th are assumed to be fixed. (This input-fixity assumption gives rise to the term "simple.") Inclusion of the simply supply elasticities is not meant to imply that the sole response to a change in product price would be to change one input, but to indicate the effects *if* this were the sole change. Also, the simple supply elasticities are definitionally related to the *aggregate* supply elasticity in Table 8. Another assumption is that the supply of inputs is perfectly elastic. This assumption is significantly violated for an expansion in real estate, which is therefore fixed at actual levels.

---

[8] "Cross elasticity of demand" is used to refer to (1) factor with respect to price of competing factor and (2) factor with respect to product price in Heady and Tweeten [9 p. 52].

[9] *Prices* of variable inputs are included in the demand function but only *quantities* of fixed inputs are included [9, p. 48]. For the Cobb–Douglas function, fixing the level of other factors excludes "other" prices from the demand equation in order to meet the requirements of the conventional definition of an input-demand elasticity. Equation 18 is derived from $(\partial Y/\partial X_1)\, P_y = P_1$, where $Y = aX_1{}^{b_1}X_2{}^{b_2}$.

TABLE 6

CROSS ELASTICITIES OF DEMAND FOR NINE INPUT GROUPS BY DECADES, 1912–1961[a]

Input[b]	*Period*				
	1912–1921	*1922–1931*	*1932–1941*	*1941–1951*	*1952–1961*
1. Fertilizer and lime	1.02288	1.02459	1.02720	1.02971	1.04520
2. Feed, seed, and livestock	1.03366	1.03164	1.06570	1.09608	1.09724
3. Labor	—[c]	—[c]	1.53320	1.52574	1.40811
4. Machinery	1.10011	1.06194	1.06446	1.08422	1.10385
5. Real estate	1.52553	1.43279	1.30923	1.17422	1.31261
6. Machinery operating expenses	1.02773	1.04956	1.06967	1.07412	1.11509
7. Miscellaneous current operating expenses	1.09046	1.08917	1.08166	1.05411	1.08452
8. Crop and livestock inventory (interest)	1.05938	1.04778	1.04808	1.04647	1.04288
9. Real estate taxes	1.03306	1.04912	1.04016	1.02158	1.03672

[a] Elasticity of demand for *i*th input with respect to product price, *i.e.*,

$$E_{cd_i} = \frac{dX_i}{dP_y} \cdot \frac{P_y}{X_i} = -\frac{dX_i}{dPi}\frac{P_i}{X_i} = -E_{d_i}$$

[b] Corresponds to numbering in Table 1.

[c] No production elasticity was estimated for these periods.

For supply-elasticity estimates to have practical value they must relate to the length of time required for an input to be varied. The long-run elasticity of supply assumes that all inputs are variable. The nine inputs can reasonably be divided into four groups with respect to time required for variation: cash operating inputs—1, 2, 6, 7, durable capital—4, 8, labor—, and real estate—5, 9. Based on these groupings, supply elasticities relating to four lengths of run (short, intermediate, intermediate-long, and long) can be estimated. These estimates for 1952–1961 are presented in Table 8. The short-run period is the length of time required for adjustments in the use of inputs 1, 2, 6, and 7 (fertilizer and lime; feed, seed, and livestock purchases; machinery operating expenses; and miscellaneous current operating expenses). The interpretation of the supply-elasticity estimate is that a 1 percent increase in product price would increase production 0.46 percent.

Given time also for adjustments in the inventories of machinery, livestock, and crops (inputs 4 and 8), the percentage change in output per 1 percent change in product price would be 0.84 percent. Labor is presumed to be almost as fixed as real estate, because most farm labor is provided by the operator's family. Given time also for labor (input 3) to react to adjustment stimuli, the percentage change in output occasioned by a 1 percent change in price would be 3 percent. It is quite unlikely, however, that such a

TABLE 7

SIMPLE SUPPLY ELASTICITIES FOR EIGHT INPUT GROUPS BY DECADES, 1912–1961[a]

Input[b]	*Period*				
	1912–1921	*1922–1931*	*1932–1941*	*1942–1951*	*1952–1961*
1. Fertilizer and lime	.02288	.02459	.02720	.02971	.04520
2. Feed, seed, and livestock	.03366	.03164	.06570	.09608	.09724
3. Labor	—[c]	—[c]	.53320	.52574	.40811
4. Machinery	.10011	.06194	.06446	.08442	.10385
5. Real estate	—[d]	—[d]	—[d]	—[d]	—[d]
6. Machinery operating expenses	.02773	.04956	.06967	.07412	.11509
7. Miscellaneous current operating expenses	.09046	.08917	.08166	.05411	.08452
8. Crop and livestock inventory (interest)	.05938	.04778	.04808	.04647	.04288
9. Real estate taxes	.03306	.04912	.04016	.02158	.03672

[a] Considering quantities of only the *i*th input variable. Thus

$$E_{s_i} = \frac{dY}{dP_y} \cdot \frac{P_c}{Y} = E^c{}_{d_i}(-E_{pi}) = \frac{b_i}{1 - b_i}$$

where

$$E_{cd_i} = \frac{dX_i}{dP_y}\frac{P_y}{X_i} \quad \text{and} \quad E_{pi} = \frac{\partial Y}{\partial X_i}\frac{X_i}{Y.}$$

[b] Corresponds to numbering in Table 1.

[c] No production elasticity was estimated for these periods.

[d] Real estate is held constant.

phenomenon would ever be observed, because of the changes occurring in "short-run" variables.

As in the case of simple demand and supply elasticities, the estimates in Table 8 provide primarily for a comparison of relative sizes of elasticities between varying lengths of run. The Cobb–Douglas-derived supply elasticities are the maximum potential response and overestimate the true response, but the proportion of increase in intermediate and succeeding lengths of run may not be significantly affected. Heady and Tweeten [9, pp. 433–34] have estimated a short-run supply elasticity of approximately 0.1.[10]

CONCLUSIONS AND LIMITATIONS

Following are some of the conclusions and limitations of the study.

1. Adjustment to a least-cost input combination to produce the actual average 1952–1961 output would have reduced the input dollar volume by $1.9 billion, or 5.6 percent.

---

[10] Griliches [3, pp. 309–22] estimates that the short-run elasticity of supply is about 0.3 and the long-run elasticity is about 1.3. Estimates of short-run supply elasticities published a year later are 0.1 to 0.2 both for the aggregate and for all crops, and 0.2 to 0.3 for livestock and livestock products [2].

TABLE 8

SUPPLY ELASTICITIES FOR FOUR LENGTHS OF RUN, DERIVED FROM 1952–1961 COEFFICIENTS[a]

Length of run	*Inputs Variable*	*Supply elasticity*
Short	1, 2, 6, 7	0.45562
Intermediate	4, 8 (plus above)	0.84386
Intermediate—long	3 (plus above)	2.96024
Long	All	Large[b]

[a] E, (for more than one input variable) $= \Sigma b_i / 1 - \Sigma b_i$. For a general proof see the appendix to Luther Tweeten and Earl Heady [11].

[b] The long-run supply elasticity derived from the Cobb–Douglas production function is ∞ for constant ($\Sigma b_i = 1$) or increasing ($\Sigma b_i > 1$) returns to scale. Σb_i in this case is 1.01162.

2. Adjustment of farm resources to an equilibrium level, with all variable resources earning an opportunity-cost return, would have entailed a reduction of 4.2 billion 1947–1949 dollars, or 12.5 percent of the actual input volume. The cost of excess capacity was approximately $2.2 billion, or 6.6 percent of the resource volume; the cost of a nonoptimal input mix was $2 billion, or 5.9 percent of the resource volume.

3. Labor was estimated to be in excess supply by two fifths in the 1952–1961 period. The marginal product of labor was positive, however. Two limitations in the labor series are apparent. First, labor input was based on man-hour requirements and not on total employment in farming. The labor estimate was essentially a conditionally normative concept, rather than the positive kind of concept used in the other input series. The result is a rate of adjustment to equilibrium for labor that is too high, although the production-elasticity estimate retains much validity as an indicator of the equilibrium man-hour productivity. Man-hours rather than the conceptually more relevant employment series were used because the former contain less error and are used by the USDA in constructing the input-output indices. The second limitation of the labor series, which affects the results for other inputs also, is inadequate recognition of the structural changes that accompany a reduction in the labor force. We hypothesize that when changes in farm size, capital, and management stemming from labor outmovement are incorporated adequately into the model, the "net" marginal product of farm labor is negative, except perhaps in the Southeast. This statement need not invalidate the Cobb–Douglas labor estimate used in the study—the Cobb–Douglas function unfortunately does not allow the MPP's to change sign. A reduction of the labor input by the amount indicated in this article would be likely to lead to a positive marginal product of labor. Further study of this hypothesis is needed.[11]

[11] For an analysis supporting a positive marginal product of labor for agriculture, see Gale Johnson [10].

4. Elimination of the disequilibrium discussed above would not necessarily imply economic equality for agriculture in the dynamic sense. While the results suggest that agricultural adjustments in equilibrium are much more rapid than we had previously supposed, disequilibrium is constantly being created by the forces of education, research, weather, and changes in prices and technology originating in the nonfarm sector. These forces impose on agricultural firms higher production elasticities than the inputs considered in this study. In fact, the sum of elasticities often is sufficiently high to cause decreasing costs (increasing returns) on farms. As a result, even with equilibrium in the variable-resource markets (MVP's equal to factor prices), average costs exceed both marginal costs and revenue, and farms continue to lose money if all costs are included. This concept, too, needs further analysis.

5. Capital inputs supplied by the nonfarm sector are not generally used in excess by farmers, according to the results of this study. In equilibrium, a substantial reduction in labor costs would be accompanied by a substantial rise in capital inputs.

6. The ERS input and output series were accepted in a very uncritical manner as data for this study. The limitations of the series have been discussed before. It was entirely beyond the scope and resources of this study to construct more accurate and meaningful series, even if such an effort had been thought necessary.

The foregoing analysis can serve as a guideline for public policy by indicating the magnitude of resource adjustments needed to achieve economic equilibrium, and the economic cost of maintaining nonoptimal resource levels and combinations in agriculture. Against the gains must be balanced the social and economic cost of public policies designed to speed the adjustment process. Also the analysis gives some measure of the cost of excess capacity to be balanced against the possible benefits of holding a strategic reserve of excess production capacity in agriculture. The analysis also provides an approach that might be used at the firm or industry level to determine production parameters and optimum resource allocation.

REFERENCES

1. Allen, R. G. D. *Mathematical Analysis for Economists,* London: Macmillan & Co., Ltd., 1947.
2. Griliches, Zvi. "The Aggregate U.S. Farm Supply Function," *Journal of Farm Economics*, Vol. 42 (May 1960), pp. 282–93.
3. ———."The Demand for Inputs in Agriculture and a Derived Supply Elasticity," *Journal of Farm Economics*, Vol. 41 (May 1959), pp. 309–22.
4. ———. "Estimates of the Aggregate Agricultural Production Function from Cross-Sectional Data," *Journal of Farm Economics,* Vol. 45 (May 1963), pp. 419–28.

5. ———. "Measuring Inputs in Agriculture: A Critical Survey," *Journal of Farm Economics*, Vol. 42 (December 1960), pp. 1411–27.
6. ———. "Research Expenditures, Education, and the Aggregate Agricultural Production Function," *American Economic Review*, Vol. 54 (December 1964), pp. 961–74.
7. Hathaway, Dale E. *Government and Agriculture.* New York: Macmillan Co., 1963.
8. Heady, Earl. *Economics of Agricultural Production and Resource Use.* Englewood Cliffs, N. J.: Prentice-Hall, Inc., 1952.
9. Heady, Earl, and Luther Tweeten. *Resource Demand and Structure of the Agricultural Industry.* Ames: Iowa State University Press, 1963.
10. Johnson, D. Gale. "Income and Output Effects of Reducing the Farm Labor Force," *Journal of Farm Economics*, Vol. 47 (November 1960), pp. 779–82.
11. Tweeten, Luther. "Discussion: Comparing Effects of U.S. and Canadian Farm Policies," *Journal of Farm Economics,* Vol. 47 (December 1965), pp. 1152–59.
12. Tweeten, Luther, and Earl Heady, "Short-run Corn Supply Functions and Fertilizer Demand Functions," Iowa Agr. Exp. Sta. Res. Bul. 507 (1962).
13. Tyner, Fred H., and Luther G. Tweeten, "Excess Capacity in U.S. Agriculture," *Agricultural Economics Research*, Vol. 16 (1964), pp. 23–31.
14. ——— and ———, "A Methodology for Estimating Production Parameters," *Journal of Farm Economics,* Vol. 47 (December 1965), pp. 1462–67.
15. U.S. Department of Agriculture, *Changes in Farm Production and Efficiency*, ERS Stat. Bul. 233, revised July 1964.
16. U.S. Department of Agriculture, *Farm Income Situation*, July 1965 and earlier issues.
17. U.S. Department of Agriculture, unpublished worksheets, Production Adjustment Branch, ERS.

APPENDIX: DATA DESCRIPTION AND SOURCES

(Data, unless otherwise indicated, are from unpublished, USDA worksheets, Production Economies Branch, ERS.)

1. Fertilizer and lime. Expenditures in million 1947–1949 dollars.
2. Feed, seed, and livestock. Purchases from the nonfarm sector (essentially marketing charges) in million 1947–1949 dollars.
3. Labor. Million man-hours of labor used for farm work. From U.S. Department of Agriculture [15].
4. Machinery. Charges in million 1947–1949 dollars for interest on investment in machinery, plus depreciation.
5. Real estate. Charges in million 1947–1949 dollars for interest on investment in real estate, plus building depreciation, accident damage, repairs, and maintenance.
6. Machinery operating expenses. Charges in million 1947–1949 dollars

for fuel, operation, and repairs. Current-dollar series from U.S. Department of Agriculture [16] deflated by index of prices paid for motor supplies, 1947–1949 = 100.

7. Miscellaneous current operating expense. Expenses in million 1947–1949 dollars. Current-dollar series from U.S. Department of Agriculture [16] deflated by index of prices paid for farm supplies, 1947–1949 = 100.
8. Crop and livestock inventories. Charges in million 1947–1949 dollars for interest.
9. Real estate taxes. Taxes in million 1947–1949 dollars.

Part VI Economic Development

18 Effects of Increased Productivity upon the Ratio of Urban to Rural Population*

BY HERBERT A. SIMON†

A wide range of economic forces have cooperated to produce a steady increase in the ratio of urban to rural population in the United States and most Western European countries during the past several centuries. It is the purpose of this paper to enumerate briefly these various forces, and then to explore formally the theory of one of them—increasing economic productivity.

While the conclusions that will be reached confirm existing economic theories as to the reasons for the increase in urban population, it will be of interest to show how this result can be rigorously derived from rather simple economic models. The models, in turn, will help to reveal the anatomy of the mechanisms that are responsible for the shift.

The urban-rural population ratio depends upon the proportion of the occupied population in nonagricultural and agricultural occupations, respectively. The relation between these two ratios is not quite direct, however. The rural population includes, in addition to those engaged in agriculture and their families, a large number of other persons who are located in rural areas either because they are engaged in occupations oriented toward farm markets (distributors and those occupied in market-oriented industries), or because they are engaged in occupations oriented toward the source of raw materials (e.g., cotton gins and cheese factories). Moreover a considerable part of the time of the farmer may be devoted to nonagricultural activities, particularly in a subsistence economy.

Throughout the analysis it will be assumed that disparities between incomes

* *Econometrica,* Vol. XV, No. 1 (January, 1947), pp. 31–42.
† Carnegie-Mellon University, Pittsburgh, Pennsylvania.

of those engaged in agriculture and those in nonagricultural pursuits will be removed by migration of occupied persons from the one type of occupation to the other. As is well known, there are in fact substantial lags in this migration, and of these the analysis will take no account. It will be strictly an "equilibrium" analysis. It will also be assumed that the length of the average work week remains unchanged.

I

In studying the urban-rural population ratio for any country or area two aspects of the problem must be considered: the international and the internal. International trade may affect the ratio in two distinct ways:

1. Changes in comparative advantage between agricultural and industrial production. Whether a nation will have net imports or net exports of agricultural products will depend upon its comparative advantage in producing such commodities relative to industrial commodities. A shift toward a greater comparative advantage for agriculture will increase the proportion of the population engaged in agriculture, while an opposite shift of comparative advantage in favor of industry (which has been characteristic of the United States almost throughout its history, and certainly since the Civil War) will reduce the proportion engaged in agriculture.

2. Changes in the costs of international trade. By "costs" here are meant transportation costs and the costs imposed by governmental trade policies—tariffs and the like. Reduction in these costs will, of course, stimulate international trade and encourage geographical specialization. Hence a country whose agriculture has a comparative advantage will undergo an increase in the percentage of its population engaged in agriculture if costs of international trade are reduced.

The explanation of changes in the rural-urban ratio in a relatively self-contained economic area is an entirely different question. Among the causative economic factors that have been generally recognized here are: increased specialization in economic activities, and increased productivity.

3. Increased specialization in economic activities. The economies of large-scale production, reinforced and partly made possible by reduction in transportation costs and improved transportation methods, encourage specialization in order to take advantage of locations that possess low raw-material, manufacturing, or marketing costs. There results, too, greater aggregation in order to realize the economies of size, and a consequent separation of manufacturing processes from the place of raw-material production (milling, for example) or from the place of consumption (e.g., baking). In both cases, although there may be no change in the percentage of persons engaged in agriculture, many activities which had previously been carried on in rural areas, near to the raw materials or farm markets, will move to urban areas. Hence, the ratio of nonfarmers to farmers in rural

areas will probably decrease, and the rural-urban population ratio decrease correspondingly.

4. Increased productivity. Increased productivity in any segment of the economy will have a positive income effect and a positive substitution effect (barring from consideration inferior goods) upon the consumption of that commodity. When we consider not the quantity demanded, but the quantity of resources that go into the production of the commodity, these two effects are opposed by the resource-saving resulting from the increased productivity. As a rule, a decrease, rather than an increase, in the resource use may be expected. (This statement will be justified later.) Where increased productivity takes place in both the agricultural and industrial zones of the economy, the opposing substitution effects will tend to cancel out, and resource-saving will tend to balance the income effect. Hence no general conclusion can be reached about the proportion of resources devoted to each zone without a consideration of the relative income-elasticities of demand for the two types of commodities. A major part of this paper will be devoted to a more exact analysis of the effects of an increase in agricultural and industrial productivity.

It is a somewhat more complicated problem to trace the effects of increased productivity in the production of capital goods upon the use of resources in agriculture and industry. This is, however, a highly important part of the explanation of the rural-urban population ratio, because of the large-scale substitution of mechanical power, an industrial product, for horse power, a consumer of agricultural products, during the past generation. The last portion of the paper will be devoted to this problem.

II

The analysis will be undertaken by means of simplified models of the economy. It will be assumed that there are two consumption goods: agricultural commodities (A), and industrial commodities (M). In the first model no explicit consideration will be given to capital goods, but it will be assumed that the quantities of consumption goods produced depend solely on the quantities of labor (X) employed.[1]

Consider commodities A and M of which the quantities q_a and q_m are produced by the use of quantities x_a and x_m, respectively, of labor:

$$q_a = \xi(x_a); \qquad q_m = \eta(x_m). \tag{1}$$

The total supply of labor is assumed to be fixed:

$$x_a + x_m = X = \text{constant}. \tag{2}$$

[1] A fuller justification of models of the type used here, and a description of their properties, will be found in G. C. Evans, "Maximum Production Studied in a Simplified Economic System," *Econometrica,* Vol. 2 (January 1934), pp. 37–50; F. W. Dresch, "Index Numbers and the General Economic Equilibrium," *Bulletin of the American Mathematical Society*, Vol. 44 (February 1938), pp. 134–41; R. W. Shephard, "A Mathematical Theory of the Incidence of Taxation," *Econometrica,* Vol. 12 (January 1944), pp. 1–18.

The utility of consumers is given by an index of the form $\phi = \phi(q_a, q_m)$. The profits, π_a and π_m, of producers of A and M, respectively, are:

$$\pi_a = q_a p_a - x_a; \qquad \pi_m = q_m p_m - x_m; \tag{3}$$

where p_a, p_m are the prices of A and M, and the wage of labor is taken as the *numéraire*. (Since we are concerned only with equilibrium under full employment, any one price may be taken as *numéraire*. In line with our original assumption of perfect mobility of labor, the wages of labor in the two types of production must be equal.)

Finally, the total money value of product, I, is

$$I = q_a p_a + q_m p_m. \tag{4}$$

Consumer rationality requires the maximization of ϕ with prices given, and subject to the restriction that I is constant. The necessary condition for a maximum with this side relation is:

$$d\phi = \left(\phi_a - \frac{p_a}{p_m}\phi_m\right) dq_a = 0, \quad \text{or} \tag{5}$$

$$\phi_a = \frac{p_a}{p_m}\phi_m, \qquad \text{where } \phi_a = \frac{\partial\phi}{\partial q_a},\ \phi_m = \frac{\partial\phi}{\partial q_m}. \tag{6}$$

The sufficient condition for a maximum is that $d^2\phi/dq_a^2 < 0$. Differentiating (5) totally with respect to q_a, we require:

$$\frac{d^2\phi}{dq_a^2} = K = \left(\phi_{aa} - 2\frac{p_a}{p_m}\phi_{am} + \frac{p_a^2}{p_m^2}\phi_{mm}\right) < 0. \tag{7}$$

The producers will strive to maximize profits. Taking prices as given (pure competition), we get as necessary conditions:

$$d\pi_a = (p_a\xi_x - 1)dx_a = 0; \qquad d\pi_m = (p_m\eta_x - 1)dx_m = 0; \tag{8}$$

or

$$p_a\xi_x = 1; \qquad p_m\eta_x = 1, \qquad \text{where } \xi_x = \frac{\partial\xi}{\partial x_a},\ \eta_x = \frac{\partial\eta}{\partial x_m}. \tag{9}$$

As sufficient conditions, we require:

$$\frac{d^2\pi_a}{dx_a^2} = L = p_a\xi_{xx} < 0; \qquad \frac{d^2\pi_m}{dx_m^2} = M = p_m\eta_{xx} < 0, \tag{10}$$

$$\text{where } \xi_{xx} = \frac{\partial^2\xi}{\partial x_a^2},\ \eta_{xx} = \frac{\partial^2\eta}{\partial x_m^2}.$$

Suppose now that the production of A and M becomes technologically more efficient. Designate by $\bar{q}_a$, $\bar{q}_m$, $\bar{x}_a$, $\bar{x}_m$, etc., the new quantities of the several variables. Suppose, also, that the new production functions are of the form:

$$\bar{q}_a = (1 + \rho)\xi(\bar{x}_a), \qquad \bar{q}_m = (1 + \sigma)\eta(\bar{x}_m), \tag{1'}$$

where ρ and σ are small positive fractions. This is not, of course, the most general assumption possible, for we might have instead:

$$\bar{q}_a = \xi(\bar{x}_a) + \rho(\bar{x}_a), \qquad \bar{q}_m = \eta(\bar{x}_m) + \sigma(\bar{x}_m), \tag{1''}$$

where ρ and σ are now arbitrary functions. However, we shall assume that the new production functions can be sufficiently approximated by (1′), i.e., that the increase in marginal productivity is a constant fraction.

The other equations of the system remain unchanged in form:

$$\bar{x}_a + \bar{x}_m = X, \tag{2'}$$

$$\bar{\pi}_a = \bar{q}_a\bar{p}_a - \bar{x}_a; \qquad \bar{\pi}_m = \bar{q}_m\bar{p}_m - \bar{x}_m, \tag{3'}$$

$$\bar{I} = \bar{q}_a\bar{p}_a + \bar{q}_m\bar{p}_m. \tag{4'}$$

The conditions for equilibrium become:

$$\bar{\phi}_a = \frac{\bar{p}_a}{\bar{p}_m}\,\bar{\phi}_m, \tag{6'}$$

$$\bar{\phi}_{aa} - 2\frac{\bar{p}_a}{\bar{p}_m}\,\bar{\phi}_{am} + \frac{\bar{p}_a^{\,2}}{\bar{p}_m^{\,2}}\,\bar{\phi}_{mm} < 0, \tag{7'}$$

$$(1 + \rho)\bar{p}_a\bar{\xi}_x = 1; \qquad (1 + \sigma)\bar{p}_m\bar{\eta}_x = 1, \tag{9'}$$

$$(1 + \rho)\bar{p}_a\bar{\xi}_{xx} < 0; \qquad (1 + \sigma)\bar{p}_m\bar{\eta}_{xx} < 0. \tag{10'}$$

We now wish to calculate the changes in the equilibrium values of the variables, and in particular x_a, x_m. We define:

$$\delta q_a = \bar{q}_a - q_a; \qquad \delta q_m = \bar{q}_m - q_m, \quad \text{etc.,} \tag{11}$$

From (1) and (1′), for example, we get:

$$\begin{aligned} \delta q_a &= (1 + \rho)\xi(\bar{x}_a) - \xi(x_a) \\ &= (1 + \rho)\ [\xi(x_a) + \xi_x\delta x_a] - \xi(x_a) \\ &= \xi_x\delta x_a + \rho\xi \end{aligned} \tag{12}$$

(expanding by Taylor's theorem and dropping all terms of order above the first). Similarly:

$$\delta q_m = \eta_x\delta x_m + \sigma\eta, \tag{13}$$

$$\delta x_a = -\,\delta x_m, \tag{14}$$

$$\delta\phi = \phi_a\delta q_a + \phi_m\delta q_m, \tag{15}$$

$$\delta I = q_a\delta p_a + p_a\delta q_a + q_m\delta p_m + p_m\delta q_m, \tag{16}$$

$$\phi_a\delta p_m + p_m\delta\phi_a = p_a\delta\phi_m + \phi_m\delta p_a \qquad \text{[from (6) and (6′)],} \tag{17}$$

$$\delta p_a = -p_a^{\,2}\xi_{xx}\delta x_a - p_a^{\,2}\rho\xi_x, \tag{18}$$

$$\delta p_m = p_m^{\,2}\eta_{xx}\delta x_a - p_m^{\,2}\sigma\eta_x \ \text{[from (9) and (1), using (14)],} \tag{19}$$

$$\delta\phi_a = \phi_{aa}\delta q_a + \phi_{am}\delta q_m, \tag{20}$$

$$\delta\phi_m = \phi_{ma}\delta q_a + \phi_{mm}\delta q_m. \tag{21}$$

Substituting (12) and (13) in (20) and (21), and the resulting expressions for $\delta\phi_a$, $\delta\phi_m$ in (17), and substituting (18) and (19) in (17), we find for δx_a:

$$\delta x_a = \frac{[\rho\xi(\phi_{ma}p_a - \phi_{aa}p_m) + \sigma\eta(\phi_{mm}p_a - \phi_{am}p_m)] + \phi_a p_m^2 \sigma\eta_x - \phi_m p_a^2 \rho\xi_x}{\dfrac{p_m}{p_a}\left\{\phi_{aa} - 2\dfrac{p_a}{p_m}\phi_{ma} + \dfrac{p_a^2}{p_m^2}\phi_{mm}\right\} + \phi_m p_a^2 \xi_{xx} + \phi_a p_m^2 \eta_{xx}}. \tag{22}$$

The denominator of (22) is:

$$D = \frac{p_m}{p_a} K + \phi_m p_a L + \phi_a p_m M < 0 \qquad \text{[by (7) and (10)]}. \tag{23}$$

In the numerator of (22), however, we find four terms. The signs of the first two are unknown, the third is positive, and the fourth negative. In the next section, these terms will be interpreted, and the sign of δx_a evaluated for certain special cases.

III

We will write the numerator of (22): $N_1 + N_2 + N_3 + N_4$, where the N's represent the successive terms. N_1 and N_2 can be evaluated if it is assumed that neither A nor M is an inferior commodity. By an inferior commodity is meant one whose consumption will decrease as money income increases and prices remain fixed. Suppose I, in (4), to be increased by Δ, and q_a, q_m, ϕ_a, ϕ_m to undergo resulting variations of $\delta q_a'$, $\delta q_m'$, $\delta\phi_a'$, $\delta\phi_m'$, respectively. (The primes are added to emphasize that these variations are not the same as those defined in II.)

From (4) and (6), we obtain

$$p_a\delta q_a' + p_m\delta q_m' = \Delta, \tag{24}$$

and

$$\phi_{aa}\delta q_a' + \phi_{am}\delta q_m' = \frac{p_a}{p_m}(\phi_{ma}\delta q_a' + \phi_{mm}\delta q_m'). \tag{25}$$

Solving for $\delta q_a'$ and $\delta q_m'$, we get

$$\frac{\delta q_a'}{\Delta} = \frac{(p_a\phi_{mm} - p_m\phi_{am})}{p_a^2\phi_{mm} - 2p_a p_m\phi_{am} + p_m^2\phi_{aa}}, \tag{26}$$

$$\frac{\delta q_m'}{\Delta} = \frac{(p_m\phi_{aa} - p_a\phi_{ma})}{p_m^2\phi_{aa} - 2p_m p_a\phi_{am} + p_a^2\phi_{mm}}. \tag{27}$$

Since, by (7), the denominators of (26) and (27) are negative, the condition that A and M, respectively, *not* be inferior goods is that:

$$\alpha = (p_a\phi_{mm} - p_m\phi_{am}) < 0; \quad \beta = (p_m\phi_{aa} - p_a\phi_{ma}) < 0. \tag{28}$$

Hence N_1 is positive, while N_2 is negative.

Thus far our equations are completely symmetrical with respect to A and M—no assumptions have been introduced to distinguish the economic properties of agricultural commodities from those of industrial commodities. We now introduce such an assumption. We assume that the income-elasticity of demand for agricultural products is less than for industrial products. That is, for fixed prices,

$$\left| \frac{\delta q_m'}{\delta q_a'} \right| > \frac{q_m}{q_a}. \tag{29}$$

Since $\delta q_m'$ and $\delta q_a'$, for fixed prices, have already been evaluated in (26) and (27), we may substitute in (29):

$$\left| \frac{(p_m\phi_{aa} - p_a\phi_{ma}}{(p_a\phi_{mm} - p_m\phi_{am})} \right| = \left| \frac{\beta}{\alpha} \right| > \frac{\eta}{\xi}, \tag{30}$$

or

$$\xi\beta - \eta\alpha < 0 \qquad \text{[by (30) and (28)]}. \tag{31}$$

Next let us examine N_3 and N_4. Simplifying, we get:

$$N_3 + N_4 = \phi_a p_m(\sigma - \rho). \tag{32}$$

Hence, when $\sigma = \rho$, $(N_3 + N_4)$ vanishes. But under this same condition we find for $(N_1 + N_2)$:

$$N_1 + N_2 = \rho(\eta\alpha - \xi\beta). \tag{33}$$

Therefore, by (31),

$$N_1 + N_2 > 0, \quad \text{or} \quad \delta x_a < 0. \tag{34}$$

Thus we have proved that equal percentage increases in the efficiency of production of A and M will lead to a decrease in the quantity of labor employed in agriculture, and an increase in the quantity employed in manufacturing. This result follows from the assumption that the income elasticity of demand for agricultural goods is greater than for industrial goods. It would hold a fortiori if agricultural commodities were inferior commodities, i.e., if N_2 were positive.

In general, we let $(\sigma - \rho) = \tau$. Then (22) becomes:

$$\delta x_a = \frac{1}{D}\{-\rho(\xi\beta + \eta\alpha) + (\eta\alpha + \phi_a p_m)\tau\}. \tag{35}$$

We see that if τ is sufficiently small, the quantity of labor employed in agriculture will decrease, and this same result will hold, however large is τ, provided $|\eta\alpha| < |\phi_a p_m|$. The first term in the right-hand side of (35) might be interpreted as the income effect upon the demand for agricultural labor, the second term as the price, or substitution, effect.

IV

Thus far no account has been taken of the use of factors other than labor in the production of agricultural and industrial commodities. In the present section it will be assumed that the amount of agricultural commodities produced depends upon the quantity of labor employed, the quantity of agricultural goods used as capital goods in agriculture (horses and their pasture), and the quantity of industrial goods used as capital goods in agriculture (equipment such as tractors). The introduction of the tractor will be represented by an increase in the marginal productivity of industrial goods used as capital goods in agriculture. To simplify the analysis, the effects of substitution between agricultural and industrial consumption due to changes in relative price will be disregarded (but *not* shifts due to changes in real income).

Let q_a be the quantity of agricultural goods produced; q_m the quantity of industrial goods produced; x_a and x_m the quantities of labor employed in agriculture and industry, respectively; q_{a1} and q_{m1} the quantities of agricultural goods and industrial goods, respectively, used as agricultural capital; and q_{a2} and q_{m2} the quantities of agricultural goods and industrial goods, respectively, consumed. π_a, π_m, and I have the same meanings as before. Our new model will be given by the following equations:

$$q_a = \xi(x_a, v), \qquad \text{where } v = q_{a1} + \alpha q_{m1}. \tag{2.1}$$

In giving the production function for A this particular form we assume perfect substitutability between agricultural goods and industrial goods used as capital in agriculture, i.e., between the tractor and the horse.

$$q_m = \eta(x_m), \tag{2.2}$$

$$q_a = q_{a1} + q_{a2}, \qquad q_m = q_{m1} + q_{m2}. \tag{2.3}$$

$$x_a + x_m = X = \text{const.} \tag{2.4}$$

We now introduce the simplifying assumption mentioned above that the demand for q_{a2} and q_{m2} depend only upon the real income, and not upon relative prices, i.e., that a given real income will be divided in a determinate way between q_{a2} and q_{m2}. This assumption may be written:

$$q_{a2} = \gamma(q_{m2}). \tag{2.5}$$

Consequently, the utility function, ϕ, may be written $\phi = \phi(q_{m2})$. It is assumed that $dq_{a2}/dq_{m2} = \gamma_m$ is positive—that neither commodity is inferior.

We have for π_a, π_m, and I:

$$\pi_a = q_a p_a - x_a - p_m q_{m1} - p_a q_{a1}, \tag{2.6}$$

$$\pi_m = q_m p_m - x_m, \tag{2.7}$$

$$I = q_{a2} p_a + q_{m2} p_m. \tag{2.8}$$

Consumer behavior does not present any problem, since consumers will divide their income, I, between q_{a2} and q_{m2} in a manner consistent with (2.5).[2] For maximization of producer profit, taking x_a, q_{a1}, and q_{m1} as the independent variables in (2.6), and x_m in (2.7), we have:

$$\frac{\partial \pi_a}{\partial x_a} = p_a\xi_x - 1 = 0, \qquad \frac{\partial \pi_a}{\partial q_{a1}} = p_a\xi_v - p_a = 0,$$
$$\frac{\partial \pi_a}{\partial q_{m1}} = p_a\xi_v\alpha - p_m = 0, \qquad \frac{\partial \pi_m}{\partial x_m} = p_m\eta_x - 1 = 0, \tag{2.9}$$

whence

$$p_a\xi_x = 1, \quad \xi_v = 1, \quad \alpha = \frac{p_m}{p_a}, \quad p_m\eta_x = 1. \tag{2.10}$$

For sufficient conditions for a maximum, we have:

$$\frac{\partial^2 \pi_a}{\partial x_a^2} = p_a\xi_{xx} < 0, \quad \frac{\partial^2 \pi_a}{\partial q_{m1}^2} = \alpha^2 \frac{\partial^2 \pi_a}{\partial q_{a1}^2} = \alpha^2 p_a\xi_{vv} < 0,$$
$$\frac{\partial^2 \pi_m}{\partial x_m^2} = p_m\eta_{xx} < 0, \tag{2.11}$$

$$\frac{\partial^2 \pi_a}{\partial x_a^2}\frac{\partial^2 \pi_a}{\partial q_{a1}^2} - \left(\frac{\partial^2 \pi_a}{\partial x_a \partial q_{a1}}\right)^2 = p_a^2(\xi_{xx}\xi_{vv} - \xi_{xv}^2) > 0. \tag{2.12}$$

Now suppose α to be increased by a small amount, ϵ. Equations (2.1)–(2.8) become:

$$\bar{q}_a = \xi(\bar{x}_a, \bar{v}), \qquad \text{where } \bar{v} = \bar{q}_{a1} + (\alpha + \epsilon)\bar{q}_{m1}, \tag{2.1'}$$

$$\bar{q}_m = \eta(\bar{x}_m), \tag{2.2'}$$

$$\bar{q}_a = \bar{q}_{a1} + \bar{q}_{a2}, \qquad \bar{q}_m = \bar{q}_{m1} + \bar{q}_{m2}, \tag{2.3'}$$

$$\bar{x}_a + \bar{x}_m = X, \tag{2.4'}$$

$$\bar{q}_{a2} = \gamma(\bar{q}_{m2}), \tag{2.5'}$$

$$\bar{\pi}_a = \bar{q}_a\bar{p}_a - \bar{x}_a - \bar{p}_m\bar{q}_{m1} - \bar{p}_a\bar{q}_{a1}, \tag{2.6'}$$

$$\bar{\pi}_m = \bar{q}_m\bar{p}_m - \bar{x}_m, \tag{2.7'}$$

$$\bar{I} = \bar{q}_{a2}\bar{p}_a + \bar{q}_{m2}\bar{p}_m. \tag{2.8'}$$

[2] Consumer behavior in this model does not involve a maximum problem. The intersection of (2.5) with (2.8), for given I, determines the quantities of q_{m2} and q_{a2} demanded. By the assumption of no price substitution, the slopes of the indifference curves are supposed not to be continuous, hence the position of equilibrium is not a true maximum.

As before, denote the changes in the variables by $\delta x_a = \bar{x}_a - x_a$, etc. Then we obtain:

$$\delta q_a = \xi_x \delta x_a + \xi_v \delta v, \tag{2.13}$$

$$\delta v = \delta q_{a1} + \alpha \delta q_{m1} + \epsilon q_{m1}, \tag{2.14}$$

$$\delta q_m = \eta_x \delta x_m, \tag{2.15}$$

$$\delta q_a = \delta q_{a1} + \delta q_{a2}, \tag{2.16}$$

$$\delta q_m = \delta q_{m1} + \delta q_{m2}, \tag{2.17}$$

$$\delta x_a = - \delta x_m, \tag{2.18}$$

$$\delta q_{a2} = \gamma_m \delta q_{m2}, \tag{2.19}$$

where subscripts, as before, denote partial differentiation, i.e., $\xi_x = \partial \xi / \delta x_a$, $\xi_v = \partial \xi / \partial v$, etc. From (2.10) and the corresponding equations for the new equilibrium, we get:

$$p_a \xi_{xx} \delta x_a + p_a \xi_{xv} \delta v + \xi_x \delta p_a = 0, \tag{2.20}$$

$$\xi_{vx} \delta x_a + \xi_{vv} \delta v = 0, \tag{2.21}$$

$$p_a \epsilon + \alpha \delta p_a = \delta p_m, \tag{2.22}$$

$$p_m \eta_{xx} \delta x_m + \eta_x \delta p_m = 0. \tag{2.23}$$

When δx_m, δq_a, δq_m, δp_m, δv, δq_{a2}, are eliminated, there remain five equations in the variables δx_a, δq_a, δq_{m1}, δq_{m2}, δp_a:

$$\left(\xi_x - \frac{\xi_v \xi_{vx}}{\xi_{vv}} \right) \delta x_a - \delta q_{a1} - \gamma_m \delta q_{m2} = 0, \tag{2.24}$$

$$- \frac{\xi_{vx}}{\xi_{vv}} \delta x_a - \delta q_{a1} - \alpha \delta q_{m1} = \epsilon q_{m1}, \tag{2.25}$$

$$- \eta_x \delta x - \delta q_{m1} - \delta q_{m2} = 0, \tag{2.26}$$

$$\left(\xi_{xx} - \frac{\xi_{vx}^2}{\xi_{vv}} \right) \delta x_a + \xi_x^2 \delta p_a = 0, \tag{2.27}$$

$$p_m \frac{\eta_{xx}}{\eta_x} \delta x_a - \alpha \delta p_a = p_a \epsilon. \tag{2.28}$$

The determinant of the coefficients on the left-hand side of these equations is:

$$D = (\alpha + \gamma_m) \left\{ - \alpha \left(\xi_{xx} - \frac{\xi_{vx}^2}{\xi_{vv}} \right) - \xi_x^2 p_m \frac{\eta_{xx}}{\eta_x} \right\} > 0 \tag{2.29}$$

[from (2.11), (2.12)]. Solving the equations by Cramer's rule we obtain:

$$\frac{\delta x_a}{\epsilon} = -\frac{\xi_x}{D}(\alpha + \gamma_m) < 0, \tag{2.30}$$

$$\frac{\delta q_{a1}}{\epsilon} = \frac{\gamma_m q_{m1} p_m \xi_x}{D}\left\{\left(\xi_{xx} - \frac{\xi_{vx}^2}{\xi_{vv}}\right) + \xi_x \frac{\eta_{xx}}{\eta_x}\right\} \tag{2.31}$$

$$+ \frac{\xi_x^2 p_a}{D}\left\{\frac{\xi_{vx}}{\xi_{vv}} - \xi_x\right\}(\alpha + \gamma_m),$$

$$\frac{\delta q_{m1}}{\epsilon} = \frac{\xi_x \gamma_m \eta_x + \xi_x^2}{D} + \frac{q_{m1}}{D}\left\{\alpha\left(\xi_{xx} - \frac{\xi_{vx}^2}{\xi_{vv}}\right) + \xi_x^2 p_m \frac{\eta_{xx}}{\eta_x}\right\} \tag{2.32}$$

$$= \frac{\xi_x \gamma_m \eta_x + \xi_x^2}{D} - \frac{q_{m1}}{(\alpha + \gamma_m)},$$

$$\frac{\delta q_{m2}}{\epsilon} = \frac{q_{m1}}{(\alpha + \gamma_m)} > 0, \tag{2.33}$$

$$\frac{\delta p_a}{\epsilon} = \frac{p_a}{D}\left(\xi_{xx} - \frac{\xi_{vx}^2}{\xi_{vv}}\right)(\alpha + \gamma_m) < 0. \tag{2.34}$$

If we assume ξ_{vx} positive, a plausible assumption, it follows from (2.31) that $\delta q_{a1}/\epsilon < 0$. The sign of $\delta q_{m1}/\epsilon$ is not determinate, the first term being positive, the second negative. An interpretation can be made of this equation if we treat αq_{m1}, rather than q_{m1}, as the quantity of industrial capital employed in agriculture. (The increase ϵ is then a decrease in the unit cost of such capital.) Then:

$$\frac{(\alpha + \epsilon)\bar{q}_{m1}}{\epsilon} - \frac{\alpha q_{m1}}{\epsilon} = \frac{\alpha \delta q_{m1}}{\epsilon} + q_{m1} \tag{2.35}$$

$$= \frac{\alpha \xi_x}{D}(\gamma_m \eta_x + \xi_x) - \frac{\alpha q_{m1}}{(\alpha + \gamma_m)} + q_{m1}$$

$$= \frac{\alpha \xi_x}{D}(\gamma_m \eta_x + \xi_x) + \frac{\gamma_m q_{m1}}{(\alpha + \gamma_m)} > 0.$$

The effect, then, of an increase in the marginal productivity of industrial capital employed in agriculture will be to decrease the amount of labor employed in agriculture, and the price of agricultural goods. The quantity of consumption goods will, of course, be increased. With one additional assumption, ($\xi_{vx} > 0$), it can be shown that the quantity of agricultural capital used in agriculture (horses) will decrease. Industrial capital employed in agriculture (tractors) will increase.

V

It has been shown in this paper that a shift of labor from agricultural to nonagricultural occupations, and consequent shifts in the rural-urban population ratio, will result, under certain assumptions, from increases in productivity. In Sections II and III it was shown that such a shift will take place when there is an increase in industrial productivity as great (or nearly so) as in agricultural productivity. This result stems from the greater income-elasticity of demand for industrial as compared with agricultural goods.

In Section IV it was shown how the invention of the tractor would reduce the use of horses and pasture land and cause a shift in labor from agricultural to industrial occupations.

19 Reflections on Poverty within Agriculture*[1]

THEODORE W. SCHULTZ†

There is room for a lament on the state of ideas held and cherished with regard to poverty within agriculture. There is the widely held belief of farm people, many of whom are well up the income ladder, and of their leaders, that poverty is basically not a concern of the public but of the farm family that is poor. Thus by-passing the issue, agricultural policy is left free to concentrate on the economic problems of farmers who are substantially above the poverty rung. The chronic problem of poverty of long standing in many parts of agriculture is viewed by many as being mainly a private and personal affair of the families who are poor and as having no social roots or major social implications. There is also the belief, now firmly established among many industrial-urban people, that most farm people are poor most of the time. The lament becomes deep and mournful when one sees the formation of agricultural policy proceed as if all farm families were poor and when one observes the failure of agricultural programs to come to grips with the poverty that actually exists within American agriculture.

Poverty—the state of being in need—is an acceptable state socially; the poor have always been with us (and, of course, respectable, for it is not an unknown academic state!). It is neglected in research about agriculture, since thinking on this issue is usually not received with favor; and it is ill conceived in the formulation of agricultural policy and misused in seeking public support for agricultural programs. Poverty within agriculture is acceptable, for it is looked upon as natural. It is natural (1) because poor farmers gravitate

* *Journal of Political Economy,* Vol. LVIII, No. 1 (February 1950), pp. 1–15.

† University of Chicago, Chicago, Illinois.

[1] This paper was prepared for, and presented at, the meetings of the American Farm Economics Association, held at Laramie, Wyoming, August 17–20, 1949.

to poor land, and there is much poor land in the United States; (2) because many farm people prefer to stay poor rather than make adequate effort to improve their lot; (3) because in farming, although people may be poor in dollars, they are nevertheless rich in those valuable appurtenances that go with being close to nature and with the free independent living of farm life; and (4) because the Negro and the Mexican, of whom there are many in agriculture, are naturally poor. So run the mythology and folklore of our day, making poverty not only acceptable but necessary.

The neglect of the study of poverty within agriculture is understandable because the poor in agriculture are politically impotent. Although political influence may gradually come to them, such influence is still in the distant future; and those who administer research are necessarily sensitive to the immediate political repercussions of such research. If they were inclined otherwise, they would do well to look back and reflect on the fate that befell the rural sociologists, on the fire that was directed against the Bureau of Agricultural Economics, and on the frigidity of Congress toward proposals to help the poor in agriculture no longer ago than the early forties. But this neglect runs deeper, for those who do research are not prone passively to accept political coercion curtailing their freedom of thought when they feel strongly on the issues at stake. The inference is that they do not believe that poverty in agriculture is an important social problem. This belief may exist because, for the most part, agricultural research workers have been trained in an intellectual climate that gives little emphasis to the strong, liberal, and humanitarian currents that have characterized our Western culture; because their research problems have not brought them into close contact with the poor in farming; and, probably most important of all, because they have been inclined to accept the prevailing folklore about poverty in agriculture. Thus, since thinking and ideas must precede social action to diminish poverty, it should surprise no one that the formation of policy with regard to poverty is ill conceived and misapplied.

I. PRELIMINARY CONSIDERATIONS

To analyze the economic aspects of the poverty that has gradually become imbedded in agriculture, it is necessary to have some conception of economic development. The classical economists had a theory of economic growth and progress, which, however, as I shall show, does not have sufficient generality to deal with the type of economic development that has come to characterize the history of the United States. The task at hand consists of three parts. The first entails an attempt to describe the salient characteristics of the poverty that has emerged. This characterization is presented in the form of a series of propositions. Next, there is the task of selecting an analytical framework sufficiently comprehensive to include conditions under which economic progress can give rise to increasing disparity of income. And, finally, there is the difficult undertaking of determining the conditions that are necessary for increasing disparity in income to occur. It is my belief that the results of this approach are meaningful in the formation of policies to diminish poverty in American agriculture. The policy implications, however, are left for another occasion.

In this paper I take the American scene as it has developed during the comparatively few decades that have elapsed since the settlement of this continent as the empirical setting of the problem. I neglect, for the most part, the effects of sudden changes in the main economic magnitudes of either world war or of the great depression. Accordingly, in order to make my task manageable, I abstract from short-run fluctuations in the basic argument. I take poverty to mean being too poor to afford the level of living[2] that has

---

[2] The concept of "level of living" refers to the possession of goods, services, and opportunities. It consists in what people have, that is, the opportunities available to them and the goods and services that they use and consume. For the distinction between "level of living" and "standard of living" see Carl C. Taylor *et al., Rural Life in the United States* (New York: Alfred A. Knopf, 1949), chap. 17.

Margaret Jarman Hagood, of the Bureau of Agricultural Economics, has made a number of studies concentrating on the level of living of farm people. Her study, *Farm Operator Family Level of Living Indexes for Counties of the United States 1940 and 1945* (May 1947), is exceedingly instructive. With the United States county average for 1945 equal to 100, one finds that her indexes of the level of living for the ten lowest counties in Kentucky range from 5 to 16, as follows:

1945 Level of Living

Counties	*Index (10 Lowest Counties in Kentucky)*
Breathitt	5
Leslie	6
Elliott	9
Knott	12
Owsley	13
Magoffin	13
Clay	14
Lawrence	15
Lee	15
Knox	16

Her data for the 10 highest counties in Iowa show indexes ranging from 188 to 196, as follows:

1945 Level of Living

Counties	*Index (10 Highest Counties in Iowa)*
Ida	188
Buena Vista	189
Hamilton	189
Cherokee	190
Marshall	190
Wright	191
O'Brien	192
Sac	192
Benton	194
Grundy	196

become generally established and that most people can afford. I am not, however, concerned with the poverty of any particular farm family but, instead, with that of an aggregate consisting of all the families located in a given community or neighborhood.[3] More specifically, whenever I refer to "level of living" or to "income," I mean the average level of living or the per capita income of the community. Accordingly, this study does not focus upon isolated farm families, no matter how poverty-stricken they may be, but upon a group of families comprising a community or neighborhood. Thus in any given community one or more families may be beset by poverty as compared to the average level of living of the community. This *within*-community poverty is not, however, the object of this study. The analysis is restricted to *between*-community comparisons. It follows, therefore, that not all the families in a poor community are necessarily equally poor and that some families in such a community may be better off than are many families located in a comparatively rich community.

In order to simplify the problem, let me treat one of the empirical propositions as an assumption at this point. Let it be assumed that these communities had about the same distribution in wealth and natural endowments at the time of settlement or at the time that the developments associated with the industrial revolution began to make their impact. This means that within a community some families had more than average talents while others fell below that mark; for, even at the outset of settlement, it is only reasonable to suppose that some families were poorer than others both in natural endowments and in material possessions, including the "investment" that had already been made in themselves in ways that enhanced their productive capacity. I take it to be a rough approximation of the facts that the distribution of "talents" and "capital" within most, if not all, communities at the time of settlement or at the time that industrialization began to make itself felt was probably not significantly different from one community to another. Meanwhile, they have moved far apart in income, and therefore, on that score, the distributions of families have come to differ greatly. Whether, however, a similar drift has occurred in the case of the endowments of people within communities is a disputed point. Although the evidence is tenuous, it may be held that, whereas there are now poor and rich communities in agriculture, they are still essentially more alike than they are unlike one another, in the distribution of natural human endowments.[4]

---

[3] The author is inclined to follow fairly closely the idea of a community (or neighborhood) as it is set forth in Taylor *et al.*, *op. cit.*, chap. 4. For most of the conditions under consideration, the rural neighborhood can be used instead of the community. Accordingly, he will use the two terms "neighborhood" and "community" as being quite interchangeable.

[4] Dorothy S. Thomas, in reviewing the research that has been done on selective migration, finds that four conflicting hypotheses have emerged as to the direction of this selection and its effects upon rural areas:

"1. City migrants are selected from the superior elements of the parent population;
2. Cityward migrants are selected from the inferior elements;

II. SIMPLIFYING EMPIRICAL PROPOSITIONS

The propositions that follow are intended to direct attention to certain salient characteristics of our economic development. They are an attempt to describe one of the economic aspects of that development, namely, the differences between communities in the rates of growth or of progress, expressed in terms of per capita income or level of living. To isolate this aspect, it is necessary to simplify greatly and, in the process, to leave aside many other historical facts and issues. Nor is it my belief that no qualifications are required along the way. These propositions may be stated as follows:

1. In general, the differences in per capita income and level of living among communities were not so great at the time when people pioneered new areas or at the time industrialization began as they have become since then.[5] Poverty of whole communities did not generally exist under pioneering conditions because levels of living were in their essentials quite similar, although, if we look back, people were undoubtedly exceedingly poor by present-day standards.

2. The marked differences in level of living that have emerged within agriculture are not mainly the result of a deterioration on the part of those communities in which people are now living under conditions of poverty but largely the consequences of the increases in per capita incomes that have been realized by people in other communities.[6] This proposition means that families in some localities have been virtually stationary in their level of living. Others have advanced somewhat in their level of living, and still others have shown marked advances. The gap between the first and third types of community has become exceedingly wide, is becoming ever wider, and will continue to increase as long as the first type remains stationary or advances less rapidly than does the third.

3. These gaps, consisting of differences in level of living, are basically consequences of the way in which the economy of the United States has

---

3. Cityward migrants are selected from the extremes, *i.e.*, both the superior and the inferior elements; and
4. Cityward migration represents a random selection of the parent population."

Professor Thomas concludes that there is some evidence to support each of these hypotheses. Although the evidence is tenuous, it is nonetheless probable that "selection does operate positively, negatively, and randomly, at different times, depending on a variety of factors that, up to the present, have not been adequately investigated" (see "Selective Migration," *Milbank Memorial Fund Quarterly*, Vol. 16, No. 4 [October 1948], 403–7).

[5] Chester W. Wright, *Economic History of the United States* (New York: McGraw-Hill Book Co., 1941), discusses the agriculture of the late Colonial period in these words: "The outstanding feature that characterized colonial agriculture was the fact that the greater portion of the products raised was for the family's own consumption. This was typically the situation except in the regions such as the southern plantations where . . . [tobacco, rice, indigo] dominated" (p. 89). For an account of the level of living about 1770, covering housing, food, clothing, and medical care, see pp. 1010–22.

[6] A cogent study of this point is that of Mandel Sherman and Thomas R. Henry, *Hollow Folk* (New York: Thomas Y. Crowell Co., 1933).

developed and not primarily the results of any original differences in the cultural values or capabilities of the people themselves.

Each of these propositions is meaningful in the sense that it is possible, by making an appeal to empirical experience, to determine whether each is a valid statement about economic history. Actually, the first two are not essential to the argument proper; for they merely specify a particular set of conditions at the beginning of settlement and outline the changes that have occurred in the relative positions of neighborhoods since that time. It is the third of these that is central and most important to the argument, as may be seen when it is stated as follows: The differences in the per capita income and the level of living that have come to exist *among* neighborhoods in agriculture are basically the consequences of the way in which the economy of the United States has developed. The principal difficulty that arises in putting this statement to the test is largely in specifying the components that go to make up the way in which the economy has developed and in determining their effects upon the local fortunes of people. Before undertaking this task, however, it should be possible to clear away some underbrush by calling attention to several fairly obvious implications of this formulation of the problem of poverty in agriculture.

If poverty as herein defined is the result of economic development, it cannot be a consequence of the differences in the physical characteristics of land unless it can be shown that the differences in land per se are a significant factor in that development. It will become evident as I proceed that there are strong reasons for believing that the differences in land suitable for farming, in themselves, have not been an important factor in shaping the course of our economic development. The industrial "Ruhr" of the United States developed across the middle states to the north not because the farm land of the Corn Belt was better than that of the Cotton Belt generally, but for quite other reasons. The main effect has been the other way around, that is, the economy, essentially as an independent variable, has developed in such a way as to give some farm land a comparative advantage over other land in potential adjustments to economic progress. This statement means that people who settled on poor land located in or near the main stream of economic development have benefited from the economic progress growing out of that development as much as have people situated on highly productive land in or near this stream. On the other hand, people who settled on good land that was located away from the centers of active development, and thus at a disadvantage in terms of making the necessary social and economic adjustments, lost ground relative to those people who settled on either poor or good land located in or near the main stream. The term "disadvantage" in this context is not a matter of physical distances and therefore cannot be measured in miles. It must be expressed in terms of adverse effects upon efficiency and capacity of the entry and exodus of resources that can be transferred, especially of the human agent. The milk sheds are a case in point that firmly support these remarks regarding the role of farm land. The milk sheds are the closest of all farm land to the active centers of the main stream of economic development because of the overwhelming importance of the industrial-urban sectors in generating economic progress. The differences in the physical characteristics of land among major milk sheds is exceedingly great, some of it consisting of rough, hilly, poor land by any standards and some of level, highly fertile land. Yet nowhere within a milk shed, attached to a major industrial-urban area, can it be said that there exist whole communities of poverty-stricken farmers, as is the case in large parts of American agriculture located at a disadvantage relative to such areas.

The main import of these remarks on land is simply that studies concentrating on land may describe the location of poverty but cannot analyze its underlying causes, inasmuch as land is essentially passive in the process that has brought about the poverty under consideration.

Another implication of the argument set forth above pertains to the drift of prices. It may be stated thus: If poverty is the result of economic development and if this development is not incompatible with changes in the level of particular prices, the long-run decline (or rise) of a farm-product price is not necessarily a factor contributing to the poverty that has come to exist among communities in agriculture. Product upon product may be cited in which, over the years, the price has declined relative to other prices and the industry producing the product has prospered, in that it has attracted additional capital and labor into its productive effort. On the other hand, there are many cases in which a decline in price has necessitated less output, and the adjustment has been made without generating poverty. It can, therefore, be demonstrated both in theory and in practice that a decline in price is not incompatible with economic development; in fact, on the contrary, it has usually been an essential part of the process. This is not to argue that prices that fluctuate greatly are as efficient in guiding production as are steadier and more dependable prices.[7] Nor do I wish to imply that contraction is necessarily easy—certainly not in the short run. An appeal may be made to certain obvious empirical observations with regard to agriculture. Take any major farm product, and, regardless of whether the price has declined or risen over the years relative to other farm products, there are farmers—in fact, whole communities of farm families—who are distinctly well-to-do and who are mainly dependent for their income on that product. The view that I am advancing is simply that long-run price flexibility has not brought about the kind of poverty that is under consideration in this paper. It has, of course, enhanced greatly the efficiency and the size of the national product.

---

[7] The effects of variations in prices (in terms of the economic uncertainty that these impose upon farmers) on the production plans of farmers is the central subject of my article, "Spot and Future Prices as Production Guides," *American Economic Review, Papers and Proceedings,* Vol. 39 (May 1949), pp. 135–49.

III. ECONOMIC PROGRESS CAN BRING ABOUT INCREASING DISPARITY IN INCOME

Progress that increases income may be viewed either in the aggregate or in per capita terms. The argument on which this paper rests presupposes an economy in which both are increasing and in which the per capita income in some communities seems to remain virtually stationary while that of others increases, although the rates of increase may vary. To gain perspective, it may be helpful to look afresh at the classical conception of economic progress. The older economists—Ricardo, Malthus, Mill—conceived of "the dynamics of political economy"[8] as a process in which the aggregate income increases under circumstances where per capita income tends to remain constant. Their analytical apparatus was built around the rates of change of two important magnitudes; they were inclined to call one of these the "power of production" and the other the "power of population."[9] Various rates of increases in production were considered, but, under their assumption, it did not matter whether production moved forward gradually or took a sudden spurt, since extra population soon took up the slack. Their theory in its main outlines is simple and remains powerful. Whenever conditions are such that the growth in population absorbs any increase in production to the point that per capita incomes tend to remain constant, it necessarily follows that the power of production becomes the limitational factor not only of the size of the population but also of economic progress expressed in terms of increases in aggregate income. The conditions on which this classical conception of dynamics rests are no longer generally applicable, but as a special case they continue to apply to much, perhaps even to most, of the world. And, where they do apply, a great deal of insight can be had by the use of this apparatus.

We need, however, a formulation with greater generality; for it is clear that, when the concept of economic progress is restricted to an increase in aggregate income, with per capita income remaining constant, it is conceived altogether too narrowly. The following statement is proposed: Economic progress consists of an increase in aggregate income with changes in per capita income unspecified, except that no community becomes worse off. Actually, the most important part of this undertaking is to specify and identify the conditions that are necessary in economic progress, that generate disparity in per capita incomes, and that perpetuate these inequalities functionally considered, once they have become established.

A few observations on the economic developments that have characterized

---

[8] This is John Stuart Mill's phrase in opening Book IV, "Influence of the Progress of Society on Production and Distribution," of his *Principles of Political Economy*.

[9] Best expressed in David Ricardo's *The Principles of Political Economy and Taxation* ("Everyman's Library" ed.), chap. 5.

the industrial revolution of western Europe suggest that there is a close parallelism between those developments and the central propositions underlying the main argument of this paper regarding poverty in American agriculture. There is no firm basis for believing that the level of living that existed in most of the communities (or neighborhoods) comprising the bulk of the population of western Europe prior to the events associated with the industrial revolution were as different one from another as they have become since then.[10] The level of living of the mass of the people was obviously very low everywhere compared to levels that emerged subsequently, if we neglect the courts and a few of the trading towns. The levels of living were, with few exceptions, low in virtually all communities and did not differ nearly so much from one community to another as they do at present. The way in which the economy developed by increasing overall production is noteworthy. The per capita income and level of living began to rise in the countries experiencing the increases in production. One should note also that, instead of a migration of people from other parts of the world toward these countries, attracted by the rising per capita incomes and levels of living, there occurred, in fact, an extraordinary migration out of western Europe not only to the United States but to Asia and to other countries overseas.[11] Was it the poor, the people in

[10] In *Review of Economic Progress,* Vol. I, No. 4 (April 1949), Colin Clark presents data that permit the following comparisons among countries in terms of levels of real national product per man-hour, showing the period when they reached a specified level (in international units).

At 0.03	*0.10–0.15*		*At about 0.30*	
France before 1800	Britain before 1800	(0.14)	Britain, 1890	(0.31)
Germany before 1800	France, 1850	(.10)	U.S.A., 1890	(.34)
India by 1860	Sweden, 1860	(.10)	Denmark, 1913	(.30)
Japan by 1890	Greece, 1880	(.13)	Germany, 1913	(.31)
China by 1930	Eire, 1880	(.11)	Netherlands, 1913	(.29)
	Belgium, 1890	(.11)	Norway, 1920	(.33)
	Italy, 1890	(.10)	Spain, 1920	(.31)
	Norway, 1890	(.14)	Sweden, 1920	(.30)
	Switzerland, 1890	(.15)	France, 1924	(.30)
	U.S.S.R., 1900	(.15)	Switzerland, 1925	(.31)
	Estonia, 1913	(.11)	Eire, 1926	(.30)
	Hungary, 1913	(.14)	Belgium, 1930	(.33)
	Portugal, 1913	(.11)	Argentina, 1935	(.35)
	Japan, 1922	(.10)	Finland, 1937	(0.32)
	Turkey, 1927	(.10)		
	Ecuador, 1940	(.11)		
	Brazil, 1946	(0.11)		

[11] Dudley Kirk in his book, *Europe's Population in the Interwar Years* (Geneva: League of Nations, 1946), chap. 3, puts the migration out of Europe as follows: "The number of Europeans living outside of Europe was negligible in 1650; it has been estimated that since that time some 60 million Europeans have sought homes overseas . . . . Millions more crossed the low barriers of the Urals to settle in Siberia and the Interior of Asia."

the communities that were being by-passed by the industrial revolution, who migrated abroad; and did they do so because they found it easier to go abroad than to participate in the growing fortunes of people generally in communities benefiting from economic progress?

This brief reference to the economic history of western Europe since about 1650 suggests that the advances in technology and in economic organization usually ascribed to the industrial revolution, gave rise (1) to a much larger aggregate production; (2) to an increase in per capita income and in level of living generally in Europe, despite the fact that the European population has multipled five times from 1650 to date;[12] (3) to an increasing disparity in per capita incomes and in levels of living between western Europe (certainly up to World War II) and those parts of the world that had not benefited from the process of industrialization;[13] and (4) to conditions which impeded the migration of non-Europeans into Europe, a development that would have equalized returns to human agents of European and non-European communities had it occurred in sufficient numbers. But what actually happened was a migration of millions of Europeans to other parts of the world.

IV. CONDITIONS NECESSARY FOR INCREASING DISPARITY IN INCOME

There can be no doubt that the economic progress that has characterized the industrial development of the Western world, including our own, has brought about a disparity in incomes. One observes that the disparity in per capita incomes between the advanced and the undeveloped industrial countries has become ever greater; and also, within a country like the United States, communities at or near centers of economic progress have pulled further and further away in terms of productivity and income per head from those communities situated less favorably.[14] I shall endeavor to indicate the conditions responsible for the increasing disparity in incomes.

The accumulation of capital that is put to productive uses will, of course, other things being equal, increase the income of those who are the recipients of such earnings. The concentration of productive assets in the hands of people of advanced industrial countries is a commonplace; the unequal distribution of such assets among families within a country is also well known. This aspect of the growth of capital and its effects on the distribution of income is certainly not new. Nor has it been neglected in economics. In the

---

[12] *Ibid.*, p. 17.

[13] The increasing disparity in income per head is documented by a wealth of data brought together by Colin Clark, *The Conditions of Economic Progress* (New York: Macmillan Co., 1940), esp. chap. 4. In my paper, "Food, Agriculture, and Trade," *Journal of Farm Economics*, Vol. 29 (1947), p. 7, the author drew upon Clark to show how rapidly this disparity had occurred since about 1870.

[14] It may be of interest to note that, taking Colin Clark's figures appearing in *Review of Economic Progress*, Vol. 1, No. 4, and assuming that his $0.03 per hour (in terms of his

formation of policy for agriculture, however, sight is often lost of the fact that many farm families possess valuable property that earns for them a very considerable income and that such families are not necessarily poor even when farm prices are low.

Abstracting from changes in income contributed by the growth of capital other than that "invested" in the human agent, there are three sets of conditions inherent in economic progress, each of which can bring about a disparity in income. A disparity will occur in favor of people in communities located at or near the centers of economic progress under each of the following conditions: (1) those that alter the proportion of the population engaged in productive work in one community relative to that of another; (2) those that change the abilities of a population to produce, of one community relative to that of another; and (3) those that impede factor-price equalization of comparable human agents between communities.

1. CONDITIONS DETERMINING THE PROPORTION OF A POPULATION THAT CONTRIBUTES TO INCOME

The ratio of contributors to noncontributors becomes larger as communities participate in economic progress. Obviously, this ratio is important; for, if only a few people are active at productive work, there will be less income per head than if many people in a given community are contributors, other things being equal. The conditions that determine this ratio arise out of a number of complex developments. There are (1) the changes in composition of the population associated with economic progress, (2) the changes in the continuity of employment and in the specialization permitted by the division of labor that emerge as a result of economic developments, and (3) differences that arise from the way in which income is measured and in which the income accounting is done.[15]

---

international unit) is the lowest level of real national product per man-hour, we get the following spread between the low and the high countries:

Year	*No. of Times Highest Country Is above Lowest*
Before 1800	5
1800–1825	7
1910	17
1930	25
1940	33
1947	39

The last figure, that for 1947, is obtained by assuming that China has not risen above the $0.03 reported for 1930 and relating it to the $1.19 reported for the United States. That the level-of-living index of farm operators in the United States in 1945 should also show Grundy County, Iowa, 39 times as high as Breathitt County, Kentucky (see n. 1) is a similarity that should not be dismissed too lightly.

[15] The author will not elaborate the third in this paper because it would take him somewhat afield and because it would require an entire paper to do it satisfactorily.

Probably the most important of these developments is the demographic evolution of the population of a community. Students of population have observed that there are, from a demographic point of view, basically three population types in the world at present.[16] The first of these is the *pre-industrial type,* with very high birth and death rates, with a large proportion of the population in the lower-age brackets of the population pyramid, and with a short life-expectancy. It fulfils the essential conditions of the Malthus-Ricardo-Mill idea of dynamics, inasmuch as the potential increase in population is such that it can readily absorb substantial increases in production should they occur and thus tends to keep the level of living constant. The basic consideration in this context, however, is the fact that a large proportion of the population consists of nonproducers. The second type of population is usually referred to as *transitional,* with its diminishing birth and death rates but with the death rate dropping first[17] and for a time faster than the birth rate, with a marked increase in population taking place as a consequence. The advanced *industrial type* comes into existence when the birth and death rates are again approaching a balance at rates about one third to one half as high as those that characterize the pre-industrial populations. Life expectancy becomes fully twice as high, and the age distribution characterizing the population pyramid is such that a large proportion of the people are in the ages where they can contribute to productive economic effort.

We are inclined to think of the United States as approaching a demographic stage characteristic of an advanced industrial country, but it is true that within agriculture the pre-industrial and the transitional demographic population types predominate. Moreover, one of the major consequences of these demographic differences is to be found in the proportion of the farm population that can contribute to production. For example, in comparing Grundy County, Iowa, with Breathitt County, Kentucky, we find that, in 1940, 62 percent of the farm population of the Iowa County was twenty-one years of age and over, as against 42 percent of the Kentucky county.[18] The farm population

---

[16] An excellent essay on this subject is that of Frank W. Notestein, "Population—the Long View," in *Food for the World,* ed. Theodore W. Schultz (Chicago: University of Chicago Press, 1945); see also Warren Thompson, *Population and Peace in the Pacific* (Chicago: University of Chicago Press, 1946), chap 2.

[17] To quote Notestein, *op. cit.,* pp. 39–40, on this point: ". . . Fertility was much less responsive to the processes of modernization. So far as we can tell from available evidence, no substantial part of the modern population growth has come from a rise in fertility. On the other hand, neither did fertility decline with mortality. The reasons why fertility failed to decline with mortality are clear enough in general terms. Any society having to face the heavy mortality characteristic of the premodern era must have high fertility to survive. All such societies are therefore ingeniously arranged to obtain the required births. Their religious doctrines, moral codes, laws, education, community customs, marriage habits, and family organizations are all focused toward maintaining high fertility. These change only gradually and in response to the strangest stimulation. Therefore, mortality declined, but a fertility high enough to permit survival in an earlier period began producing rapid growth."

[18] Based on data from the 1940 Census. Note that Grundy County had a level-of-living index of 196, while that of Breathitt was 5 in 1945, according to the Hagood study (*op. cit.*).

seventy years of age and over in both cases was slightly more than 2 percent.

A second development altering the proportion of the population that contributes to income arises out of changes in the continuity of employment and the specialization afforded by the division of labor as economic progress has proceeded. Again, it may be assumed that, until industrialization got under way, most communities were essentially alike in this respect; but they have drifted apart because some communities in agriculture have emerged with more continuous employment and with work more specialized than have the communities that have been by-passed in the course of economic development.[19] The result is fairly obvious; in the communities that have been favored, people who can work may do so more of the time during the year; and the division of labor has been carried further, thus permitting them to specialize to better account. Here, again, to illustrate the consequences one needs only to refer to farming in central Iowa compared to that in eastern Kentucky.[20]

---

[19] "Underemployment," which is unproductive employment in the sense that a person produces a smaller product than he could elsewhere in the economy, is not included here, for it properly belongs under the set of conditions that impede factor-price equalization.

[20] There are many clues in the available statistics, although the data are not on a county basis. One comparison may be cited. In the fall of 1945 an attempt was made by the Bureau of Agricultural Economics, by means of an enumerative survey, to ascertain the average hours that farm operators worked during the week September 16–22. These data by type of farming regions show that in the dairy areas farm operators worked nearly twice as many hours (59) as did those in the general and self-sufficing areas (31). For the Corn Belt, the equivalent figure was 57 hours. The following table has been taken from unpublished data made available by Louis J. Ducoff, of the Bureau of Agricultural Economics:

AVERAGE HOURS WORKED BY FARM OPERATORS

	Week of September 16–22, 1945	*Week of July 14–20, 1946*
Regional Areas:		
United States	43	48
General and self-sufficing areas	31	37
Cotton Belt	35	35
Western specialty-crop areas	48	50
Range and livestock area	53	58
Corn Belt	57	65
Dairy areas	59	65
Wheat areas	59	69
Type-of-Farming Areas:		
South, general and self-sufficing areas	25	29
South, Cotton Belt	35	34
North-central, general and self-sufficing areas	40	46
West, wheat areas	44	60
Western specialty-crop areas	48	50
Northeast, general and self-sufficing areas	48	59
Northeast, dairy areas	52	59
West, range and livestock areas	55	57
North-central, Corn Belt	58	65
North-central, dairy areas	64	67
North-central, wheat areas	65	76

We conclude this section with the observation that it would appear from even these brief explorations that the conditions which determine the proportion of a population of a community that contributes to income is a consequence of the social evolution of our society set in motion by the character of our economic development.

2. CONDITIONS THAT DETERMINE THE ABILITIES OF A POPULATION TO PRODUCE

It will be convenient to classify abilities into those with which people are naturally endowed and those which they acquire. As to the first, we have already indicated that it would seem plausible to state that most communities at the time that industrialization began or at the time of settlement were roughly the same in the distribution of native talents. Moreover, communities in agriculture at present may not differ substantially on this score.[21] However, as for the abilities that can be acquired, differences have arisen as a result of the way in which our economy has developed. We can achieve considerable insight into this matter by abstracting from certain social and physical aspects in order to isolate (1) the process by which capital is "invested" in human agents, (2) the amount of capital thus invested, and (3) the effect of this investment upon the productivity of a population.

An analysis of the formation of capital in this sphere is beset by many major difficulties. It is exceedingly hard to draw a line of demarcation between inputs for consumption and those that act as capital. Many of these inputs undoubtedly make contributions both ways; and, when it comes to measurement, the existing capital market gives us little or no information because it is not organized to finance "investments" that enhance the abilities of people as producers. Where men are not slaves but free, a mortage on capital which in the process of formation becomes imbedded in a person requires the kind of instrument that has had no appeal to financial institutions, even though the earnings on such investments in many cases would prove very attractive.[22] Consequently, as one would expect, the supply of capital employed to improve the abilities of a population have come from two major sources—from the family and from the community in which a person lives. Furthermore, with few exceptions, the capital is made available without recourse, that is, the individual is under no obligation to repay his family or community. In substance, then, we have, for all practical purposes, no capital market serving this need. The institutions that exist, namely, the family and the community, bear

---

[21] Howard W. Beers (*Mobility of Rural Population* [Bull. 505, Kentucky Agr. Exper. Sta., June 1947], p. 40) advances the hypothesis that rural-urban migration has selected the less able youths, leaving on farms those who are most capable. For a more comprehensive review see Thomas, *op. cit.* (discussed in n. 3 above).

[22] Earl Hamilton has called my attention to the excellent observations of Marshall on certain aspects of this problem (*Principles of Economics* [8th ed.; London: Macmillan & Co., Ltd., 1930], see esp. pp. 560–63).

the brunt of this function, and the results are all too evident. The amount that is invested per human agent is extremely unequal from one community to another. Where the community is poor, families are also poor, and therefore neither of them can afford to make these investments; the converse, of course, is true in a rich community. The implications of this process to our argument are clear; economic development has been uneven; some communities have been left behind; these communities and the families in them have few resources per head and fewer still per child at hand to train and rear their children, while the communities and families situated in the main stream of economic development have many resources available for these purposes.[23]

There is not much that one can say on the amount of capital that is invested in human agents except to express the belief that it has become very large indeed in countries with an advanced industrial economy and especially so in the best-situated communities in the United States. Any attempt to measure this outlay encounters major obstacles, for reasons already touched upon.

There remain, then, the effects of investments of this nature upon the productivity of a population. It will be useful to distinguish between (1) the effects that alter the comparability of human resources in terms of abilities to do a given type of work equally well and (2) the effects that express themselves in awareness of alternative opportunities, in the capacity to communicate, and in willingness to migrate. In the case of the first of these two effects—that pertaining to comparability—it is evident that where the investment consists of preparing an individual for a task that requires years of careful and systematic training, such as is necessary to become a doctor, a lawyer, a scientist, or a skilled technologist, the person who has received this training is no longer comparable to a person who has not had similar preparation. What about the bulk of the work in agriculture, where advanced technology is employed, and in industry generally? It appears that in the short run a significant difference in productivity exists between those who have had the advantages that go with this class of investment as compared to those who have not. To illustrate, a young migrant from eastern Kentucky would probably find himself at some disadvantage on a typical Iowa farm or in doing a given job in industry compared to a young migrant from a rich farming community and from a fairly prosperous family in western Kentucky; but this margin of disadvantage in most cases is likely to disappear rather rapidly. The two men would differ appreciably in the short run, that is, for a month or two or even for as long as a year. After that, they would be on about equal footing in terms of the abilities that are required to do such work. The second of these effects involving awareness of opportunities and a willingness to migrate, it seems to me, is by all odds the more important of the two

[23] In 1938, Mississippi allocated about 5.4 percent of its income to the support of secondary and elementary schools, while Iowa used about 3.9 percent of its income for this purpose; and yet the amount that was available per enrolled student was about $22 in Mississippi compared to $74 in Iowa.

in accounting for the unequal incomes earned per person within agriculture. These effects, however, are basic in getting at the imperfect factor-price equalization that exists and therefore takes us to the third set of conditions underlying the disparity in incomes under consideration.

3. CONDITIONS THAT IMPEDE FACTOR-PRICE EQUALIZATION

We have explored briefly the conditions that increase the proportion of the population contributing to income and that improve the abilities of a population to produce, and I have endeavored to show how the forces of economic development, expressing themselves through the existing family and community institutions, alter these conditions. There still remains a third set of conditions which appear to play an important role in contributing to the growing disparity in income among communities within agriculture.

Two questions may be helpful in putting certain aspects of the problem of achieving factor-price equalization into focus. Does economic progress, as we have known it, require a vast and unprecedented transfer of human agents? The answer is, I am sure, without qualification, in the affirmative. Does economic progress give rise to major impediments to migration? The answer to this query may seem to be less unequivocal. It will become evident, however, as we proceed that an equally affirmative reply is warranted. What happens in this connection is about as follows: We have seen how economic development sets the stage for the emergence of the advanced industrial demographic type of population alongside what was formerly a common form, that is, the pre-industrial demographic type. As the differences between these two types increase, the cultural impediments to migration become greater. It is these impediments to a transfer of the human factor that bring about a series of short-run equilibria, which, as time goes on, fall increasingly short of achieving an optimum in the allocation of resources.[24]

---

[24] When factor-price equalization is based upon given wants, the cultural differences under consideration are taken as attributes of the existing pattern of wants. When the problem is approached in this way, the cultural differences between a community that has been by-passed by economic growth and progress and a community located at or near the centers of industrialization are not impediments to factor-price equalization but a part of the existing wants of the people in the two communities. It follows from this formulation that the two communities may be in equilibrium in terms of resource allocation, although great differences in the level of living exist. Another approach, the one on which this analysis rests, proceeds on the assumption that wants are not given and constant but that they are the result of cultural developments which are not independent of industrialization. One may view the changes in wants that emerge as industrialization proceeds as a movement away from a pre-industrial pattern of wants toward new, more dominant industrial-urban patterns and that the differences in wants are the result of lags in this adjustment. It is better, however, in order to simplify the analytical problem, to introduce a value-judgment explicitly in this connection. This value-judgment is simply to the effect that the wants that characterize the communities that have been by-passed by industrial growth and progress are inferior to the wants which are emerging in the main stream of industrialization. Given this valuation, it follows that the cultural factors that isolate the backward community and press upon it the relatively inferior wants operate as cultural impediments and, as such, impede factor-price equalization.

Two aspects require further elaboration, namely, (1) the comparability of a typical human agent located in a poor, pre-industrial demographic-type community and the typical person situated in an advanced community, and (2) the nature of the cultural impediments and their role as costs to the economy. Before touching on these, an observation on factor-price equalization among pre-industrial communities may be instructive. Let us take two communities of this demographic type with the same cultural values, including similar standards of living, and let us assume, further, that the fortunes of the one improve. To make this concrete, let the increase in production come from an irrigation project without cost to the community. Is it necessary for people to migrate from the less fortunate community to the one that has the windfall afforded by irrigation in order to attain factor-price equalization? The answer is that, even without a common market for either factors or products —that is, *without either migration or trade*—factor-price equalization will occur as a consequence of the upward surge in population in the community with the new irrigation project under the assumptions as I have formulated them. Factor-price equalization, however, cannot occur when the community benefiting from a windfall is of the advanced industrial demographic type and the other a preindustrial community, unless a transfer of factors takes place.[25]

The question of comparability of human agents as factors in this context raises a number of issues which are exceedingly difficult to resolve. Entirely too little work has been done on this problem;[26] and, as is obvious, the answer must come, in the last analysis, from an appeal to empirical reality. All that one can do with the fragmentary materials now available is to express one's belief on the matter. It seems to me that most of the people located at present in poor communities within agriculture are essentially comparable to most of the people situated in rich communities in terms of their capacities to produce if allowance is made for the short-run acclimatization required for the improvement in abilities which I have already considered. If this is true, it follows that the cultural impediments are indeed a heavy burden because the income earned by these (human) factors is very unequal between communities. Is it possible that the cultural impediments can be so great and so costly? Here the researches of the sociologists are making important

---

[25] P. A. Samuelson in two recent articles in the *Economic Journal,* "International Trade and Equalization of Factor Prices" (Vol. 68 [June 1948]) and "International Factor-Price Equalization Once Again" (Vol. 69 [June 1949]), has attempted to show that free commodity trade will, under certain conditions, inevitably lead to complete factor-price equalization. The conditions that are specified in his analysis are, however, far removed from the hard realities that underlie the existing geographical inequalities.

[26] A major research program made possible by a grant from the Rockefeller Foundation on the malallocation of resources that characterize agricultural production is under way at the University of Chicago, being carried forward largely by Professor D. Gale Johnson. This research program has as one of its objectives the determination of the comparability of resources within agriculture and between agriculture and other sectors of the economy and in the connection focusing primarily on the human agent.

contributions, and their results indicate quite clearly that it is no easy matter for people to pull up their roots and leave the folk society, with its strong local-personal-informal relations, and transplant themselves into an impersonal-formal, less locally oriented, urban-minded community. The economist must leave it to the sociologist to isolate and identify the nature of these cultural impediments; the economist, however, can and should come to grips with the cost aspects. The burden of these impediments is obviously a continuing one. If anything, measured in terms of the unequal factor prices that exist, they have become greater over time. If the "price" of eliminating, or even only substantially diminishing, these impediments is a nonrecurring cost for any given migrant, then the probabilities are high that society could achieve a very considerable gain by taking positive actions to diminish the adverse effects of these impediments upon factor-price equalization and, in so doing, diminish significantly the disparity in incomes on which we have concentrated our attention in this paper.

•

20 The Impact of Urban-Industrial Development on Agriculture in the Tennessee Valley and the Southeast*

VERNON W. RUTTAN†

I. The Income of Both Farm and Nonfarm Families is Closely Related to Urban-Industrial Development

The close relation between economic development and the growth of the urban-industrial sectors of the economy has received increasing attention in recent years. In its most general form, this relationship is implied in the well-known Clark-Fisher hypothesis:

In every progressive economy there has been a steady shift of employment and investment from the essential "primary" activities, without whose products life in even its most primitive forms would be impossible, to secondary activities of all kinds, and even to a still greater extent into tertiary production.[1]

T. W. Schultz has stated the relationship somewhat more precisely in a series of three hypotheses:

(1) Economic development occurs in specific locational matrix; there may be one or more such matrices in a particular economy . . . (2) These locational matrices are primarily industrial-urban in composition . . . (3) The existing economic organization works best at or near the center of a particular matrix of economic development

* *Journal of Farm Economics,* Vol. XXXVII, No. 1 (February 1955), pp. 38–56. Portions of this paper were presented to the annual meeting of the Southern Economic Association, Biloxi, Mississippi, November 19, 1954, and to the Association of Regional Scientists, Detroit, December 27, 1954.

† University of Minnesota, St. Paul, Minnesota. The author is indebted to Lewis S. Sinclair of TVA, Government Relations and Economics Staff, and to George Schlipf and Jack Powell of TVA's Office of Power—for assistance with the statistical calculations and analyses. Frank A. Hanna, Duke University; F. W. Williams, University of Tennessee; D. Gale Johnson, University of Chicago; Donald May, Emory University; John V. Krutilla, John M. Peterson, and Henry Erlanger, TVA, Government Relations and Economics Staff; and Stephen C. Smith, Robert Hutton, and John Blackmore, TVA, Division of Agricultural Relations—have offered helpful comments and criticism.

[1] Allan G. B. Fisher, *Economic Progress and Social Security* (London: 1945), p. 6. See also, Colin Clark, *The Conditions of Economic Progress* (London: 1940).

and it also works best in those parts of agriculture which are situated favorably in relation to such a center . . . [2]

If the effectiveness of the existing economic system can be measured by its ability to produce income, there can be little doubt that these hypotheses are consistent with the general pattern of economic development in the United States.

A number of investigations, based largely on data available prior to publication of the 1950 censuses of *Population* and *Agriculture,* tend to substantiate the hypothesis that *the level of income achieved by nonfarm families and individuals in any given area is closely related to the level of urban-industrial development in the same general area.*[3] In his study of "Factors Influencing State Per capita Income Differentials," Fulmer pointed out that "the best single index of a region's or state's economic development is the extent of urbanization."[4] In an investigation of "Some Effects of Region, Community, Size, Color and Occupation on Family and Individual Income," Johnson concluded that "incomes of (nonfarm) white families in the South are approximately the same as for the rest of the nation if the influence of community size is eliminated."[5]

---

[2] T. W. Schultz, *The Economic Organization of Agriculture* (New York, McGraw-Hill Inc., 1953), p. 147. See also Schultz's article, "A Framework for Land Economics—the Long View," *Journal of Farm Economics,* Vol. 33 (May 1951), pp. 204–15.

[3] See for example, Herbert E. Klarman, "A Statistical Study of Income Differences Among Communities," *Studies in Income and Wealth,* Vol. 6 (New York: National Bureau of Economic Research, 1943), pp. 206–35; John L. Fulmer, "Factors Influencing State Per Capita Income Differentials," *Southern Economic Journal,* Vol. 16 (January 1950), pp. 259–78; S. C. Sufrin, A. W. Swinyard, and F. M. Stephenson, "The North-South Differential —A Different View," *Southern Economic Journal,* Vol. 15 (October 1948), pp. 184–90; Louis H. Bean, "International Industrialization and Per Capita Income," *Studies in Income and Wealth,* Vol. 8 (New York: National Bureau of Economic Research, 1946), pp. 119–41; D. Gale Johnson, "Some Effects of Region, Community, Size, Color and Occupation on Family and Individual Income," *Studies in Income and Wealth,* Vol. 15 (New York: National Bureau of Economic Research, 1952), pp. 51–75.

For comments on the above studies, see Henry M. Oliver, Jr., "Income, Region, Community-Size and Color," *Quarterly Journal of Economics,* Vol. 60 (August 1946), pp. 588–99; Harold F. Breimyer, "Some Comments on Factors Influencing Differences Between State Per Capita Incomes," *Southern Economic Journal,* Vol. 17 (October 1950), pp. 140–7; John L. Fulmer, "Reply to Breimyer on State Per Capita Income Differences," *Southern Economic Journal,* Vol. 17 (April 1951), pp. 470–77; Jesse W. Markham, "Some Comments Upon the North-South Differential," *Southern Economic Journal,* Vol. 16 (January 1950), pp. 279–83; J. M. Buchanan, "Note on the Differential Controversy," *Southern Economic Journal,* Vol. 17 (July 1950), pp. 49, 60; Jesse W. Markham, "The North-South Differential —A Reply," *Southern Economic Journal,* Vol. 17 (January 1951), pp. 339–41; Herman P. Miller and Edwin D. Goldfield, "Some Effects of Region, Community Size, Color and Occupation on Family and Individual Income: Comments," *Studies in Income and Wealth, op. cit.,* pp. 70–72.

Most of the comments object to the overemphasis of community size as compared to regions rather than to the hypothesis that community size is one of the factors associated with income differentials. For example, Oliver, *op. cit.,* states "complete rejection of the regional thesis is as mistaken as complete passing over of the relationship between income-height and community-size, . . . income differentials among regions, as well as among communities of varying size are significant." (p. 595)

[4] Fulmer, *op. cit.,* p. 266.

[5] D. Gale Johnson, *op. cit.,* p. 51.

Analysis of data from the *1950 Census of Population* indicates that variations in the level of local urban-industrial development, as measured by the percent of the population that is *nonfarm,*[6] continues to be associated with a substantial share of the variations in the median income of *nonfarm* families. The coefficient of correlation (r) between the median income of nonfarm families and the percent of the population that is nonfarm for the states of the United States is .66 (see table 1). The comparable figure for state economic areas in the Southeast is .69 and for counties in the Tennessee Valley, .75.

There appears to be fairly general agreement, then, in spite of a few dissenting voices, regarding the relationship between overall economic development and local urban-industrial growth. There has not, however, been the same level of agreement—or investigation—with respect to the proposition mentioned by Scultz in this third hypothesis: "The existing economic organization works best . . . in those parts of agriculture which are situated favorably in relation to such a (urban-industrial) center."[7, 8]

Examination of data from the *1950 Census of Population* indicates that at

---

[6] Use of the percent of the total area population nonfarm as an index of the relative level of urban-industrial development appears to have some advantages over definitions based on (a) absolute size of nonfarm or urban population, or (b) distance from selected urban concentrations in that it is a relative measure and in that it is better adapted to handling differences in the size of the area considered (states, state economic areas, or counties). See Kingsley Davis and Hilda Golden, "Urbanization and the Development of Pre-Industrial Areas," *Economic Development and Cultural Change,* Vol. 3 (October 1954), pp. 6–24.

[7] Schultz, *op. cit.,* p. 147.

[8] Most discussion of the relationship between agricultural and industrial development has dealt with the role of agriculture as a factor in the location of industry. Research in this area would tend to support the hypothesis that the regional distribution of agricultural activity largely determined the location and type of industrial activity in pre-industrial societies, but that this relationship has largely disappeared in areas which have felt the effect of the industrial revolution. (See for example, "Food and the Location of Economic Activity," in Pei-kang Chang, *Agriculture and Industrialization* (Cambridge, 1949), pp. 28–30; Bowden, Karpovich, and Usher, *An Economic History of Europe Since 1750* (New York, 1937), pp. 4–5; S. H. Robock, "Rural Industries and Agricultural Development," *Journal of Farm Economics,* Vol. 34 (August 1952), pp. 346–60. Among the studies dealing specifically with the impact of local urban-industrial growth on agriculture in the same area are A. W. Ashby, "The Effect of Urban Growth on the Countryside," *The Sociological Review,* Vol. 31 (October 1939), pp. 345–69; L. A. Parcher, "The Influence of Location on Farmland Prices," Oklahoma Agricultural Experiment Station Bulletin No. B-417 (Stillwater, March 1954); J. M. Stepp and J. S. Plaxico, "The Labor Supply of a Rural Industry, South Carolina Agricultural Experiment Station Bulletin No. 376 (Clemson, July 1948); Francis E. McVay, "Factory Meets Farm in North Carolina," North Carolina Agricultural Experiment Station Technical Bulletin No. 83 (Raleigh, October 1947); and C. E. Bishop and J. G. Sutherland, "Resource Use and Incomes on Small Farms, Southern Piedmont Area," North Carolina Agricultural Experiment Station, AE Information Series 30 (Raleigh, October 1947); and C. E. Bishop and J. G. Sutherland, "Resource Use and Incomes on Small Farms, Southern Piedmont Area," North Carolina Agricultural Experiment Station, AE Information Series 30 (Raleigh, February 1953). Except for the studies by Bishop and Parcher, these studies are, however, concerned almost entirely with the impact on farm population and resources which shift from the farm to the nonfarm category rather than the impact on population and resources remaining in agriculture.

the present time, in both the Tennessee Valley region, the Southeast, and the nation as a whole, *the* (*median*) *income level achieved by rural-farm families* (*from farm and nonfarm sources*) *does bear a direct and a positive relationship to the relative level of urban-industrial development in the same general area.* In the areas studied the median income of *farm* families is almost as closely related to the percent of the total population that is nonfarm as is the median income of *nonfarm* families (see table 1, 2 and 3).[8a]

While this relationship seems generally valid for most areas of the nation, the analysis does not support the conclusion that high levels of income in rural areas cannot be achieved without extensive local urban-industrial development or that extensive local urban-industrial development necessarily results in high levels of rural income. At the state level, we have the example of seven high-income northern Great Plains states where there is apparently little or no relationship between the median incomes of farm families and the intensity of local nonfarm development. Indeed, for the Northern Great Plains area, there seems to be some evidence that the level of income achieved by nonfarm families is a function of the level of income achieved in the agricultural sector.[9] For the state economic areas of the 11 southeastern states and the 201 counties of the Tennessee Valley region, there are no extensive areas which stand as clearly outside the general pattern as the Northern Great Plains states do in the national picture.[10] Only a few isolated areas, such as the Mountain counties of northeastern Georgia (economic area 2), the

[8a] D. Gale Johnson has suggested (in a letter) that the similar relationship between both the median incomes of nonfarm families and the median incomes of farm families and the percent of the population that is nonfarm may be due to the concentration of nonwhite families in areas that are least urbanized. An examination was made of the dot diagrams between (a) median income of *white nonfarm* families and unrelated individuals and the percent of the population that is nonfarm; (b) the median income of *nonwhite nonfarm* families and unrelated individuals and the percent of the population that is nonfarm; (c) the median income of *white farm* families and unrelated individuals and the percent of population that is nonfarm; and (d) the median income of *nonwhite farm* families and unrelated individuals and the percent of the population that is nonfarm for the 16 southern states for which data on the median incomes of nonwhite families are available. All of the relationships appear to be strongly positive. Thus, while the concentration of nonwhite population in the least urbanized areas may be one of the factors involved in accounting for the above relationship (see tables 4 and 5 and pp. 9 and 10), the evidence would seem to indicate that a strong positive relationship between the percent of the population that is nonfarm would continue to exist even after the influence of the nonwhite population is removed.

[9] This conclusion is based (a) on the fact that the median income of nonfarm families is much less closely related to the percent of the total population that is nonfarm in the northern Great Plains that it is in the rest of the U.S. (figure 1), and (b) on the close relationship between the median incomes of urban and rural nonfarm families and the median income of rural farm families (figure 2).

[10] The data presented in tables 1, 2 and 3 indicate that the relationship between the median income of rural farm families and unrelated individuals and the percent of total population nonfarm is generally not as close at the state economic area level as at either the state or the county level. This would tend to cast some doubt on the usefulness of the state economic area as an appropriate unit for the analysis of factors influencing income differentials.

TABLE 1. THE RELATIONSHIP BETWEEN THE MEDIAN INCOMES OF NONFARM FAMILIES AND UNRELATED INDIVIDUALS IN 1949 AND THE PERCENT OF TOTAL POPULATION NONFARM IN 1950 FOR SELECTED AREAS*

Area	Equation[a]	Coefficient of:		Standard	F Ratio[b]	
		Correlation	Determination	Error	Computed	Critical
U.S. (48 States)	$I_1 = 817.25382 + 27.44437X$	.659	.434	$364.72	37.03	4.068
U.S. (41 States)[c]	$I_1 = 58.44549 + 35.65931X$	.790	.624	314.03	67.27	4.089
Southeast (104 State Economic Areas)	$I_1 = 672.10304 + 17.32401X$	.694	.481	292.11	96.44	3.944
Tennessee Valley Region (201 Counties)	$I_1 = 622.41862 + 18.67613X$	.749	.562	295.05	257.42	<3.92

TABLE 2. THE RELATIONSHIP BETWEEN THE MEDIAN INCOMES OF NONFARM FAMILIES AND UNRELATED INDIVIDUALS AND THE MEDIAN INCOMES OF FARM FAMILIES AND UNRELATED INDIVIDUALS IN 1949, FOR SELECTED AREAS*

Area	Equation	Correlation	Determination	Standard Error	Computed	Critical
U.S. (48 States)	$I_2 = -1452.07861 + 1.14763I_1$	.89	.797	$280.94	181.51	4.068
Southeast (104 State Economic Area)	$I_2 = 262.69368 + .46749I_1$	.545	.297	288.19	44.55	3.944
Tennessee Valley Region (201 Counties)	$I_2 = 355.38343 + .44761I_1$	.697	.486	204.23	190.43	<3.92

TABLE 3. THE RELATIONSHIP BETWEEN THE MEDIAN INCOME OF FARM FAMILIES AND UNRELATED INDIVIDUALS, 1949, AND THE PERCENT OF TOTAL POPULATION NONFARM, 1950, FOR SELECTED AREAS*

Area	Equation	Correlation	Determination	Standard Error	Computed	Critical
U.S. (48 States)	$I_2 = -289.86123 + 28.71894X$	.53	.282	$527.22	19.43	4.068
U.S. (41 States)[c]	$I_2 = -1749.41241 + 44.63575X$	.81	.650	371.06	75.37	4.089
Southeast (104 State Economic Area)	$I_2 = 342.13014 + 11.72888X$	.55	.303	286.98	45.83	3.944
Tennessee Valley Region (201 Counties)	$I_2 = 515.55245 + 10.86746X$	.68	.463	208.80	173.66	<3.92

[a] I_1 = Median Income of Nonfarm Families, 1949; I_2 = Median Income of Farm Families, 1949; X = Percent of Total Population Nonfarm, 1950.
[b] Critical values of F are at the .05 level of significance and indicate that the hypothesis—that there is no relationship between the two variables—should be rejected.
[c] Encludes Northern Great Plains States—Idaho, Montana, Wyoming, North and South Dakota, Iowa and Nebraska.
* Ixcome data used in these relationships are for families only for the states of the U.S. and for families and unrelated individuals for counties and state economic areas.
Source: Basic data compiled from *U.S. Census of Population, 1950,* vol. 2, *Characteristics of the Population.*

southeastern Virginia Tidewater area around Norfolk and Newport News (economic area 9), and the area around Memphis, Tennessee (Shelby County), diverge sharply from the general pattern.

The fact that welfare levels in agriculture, as measured by the median incomes of farm families, are generally higher in those areas of the nation and the Southeast where urban-industrial development has advanced the farthest increases one's confidence in the Schultz "impact hypothesis." Simple correlations of this type do not, however, tell one very much about (a) why the agricultural sector of the economy does perform more effectively in areas of advanced urban-industrial development, or (b) through what channels the interactions between the urban-industrial and the agricultural sectors of the economy take place.

In general, the interactions between the farm and nonfarm sectors of the economy can be expressed in terms of four sets of market relationships: (a) *the labor market*—through which labor is allocated as among agricultural enterprises and between the agricultural and the nonagricultural sectors of the economy; (b) *the capital market*—through which purchases of capital assets and current working capital are financed; (c) *the product market*—the market(s) for the products produced by agriculture; and (d) *the current-input market*—the market(s) for current inputs consumed in the process of agricultural production.

In the following sections of this paper an attempt will be made to determine the relative magnitude of the influences which urban-industrial development exerts on the incomes of farm families and farm workers in the Tennessee Valley region through each of these markets. The analysis will involve the use of correlation and regression techniques and the analysis of variance. These techniques will be employed to determine the impact of factors associated with each of the four markets on variations of the median incomes of farm families (from all sources) and the average incomes of farm workers from farming. This analysis depends for its validity on a normal distribution of median incomes among counties. The analysis will, therefore, be limited by the extent to which the assumption of normality is violated.

II. Major Impact of Urbanization on Farm Family Incomes Exerted Directly Through the Labor Market

In an area such as the Southeast, including the Tennessee Valley, it seems reasonable to suspect that *the major income effects of local urban-industrial development are transmitted to the agricultural sectors of the local economy through the labor market*. This hypothesis rests on four observations:

1. *Rapid Decline in Farm Labor Requirements.* A combination of rapid technological advance, the substitution of land, nonland capital inputs and current inputs for labor, coupled with the relatively low income elasticity of demand for the major farm products produced in the region has permitted a

substantial decline in labor inputs in southeastern agriculture over the last two decades.[11]

2. *Insufficient Growth of Nonfarm Jobs.* Although urban-industrial development occurred at a more rapid rate in the Southeast, including the Tennessee Valley region, than anywhere else in the nation except the Far West during the 1940–50 decade,[12] the expansion in nonfarm employment was not sufficiently rapid to absorb much more than two thirds of the new entrants to the nonfarm labor force (a) from the younger age groups, (b) from workers leaving agriculture, and (c) from the backlog of unemployment which existed in 1940.[13]

3. *Reluctance to Migrate.* Even though large declines in farm employment have occurred in recent years, substantial underemployment—measured in terms of either average or marginal labor productivity—continues to exist in most sectors of southeastern agriculture. The greater reluctance of low-income farm families and workers to migrate substantial distances than to accept local nonfarm employment[14] has tended to concentrate the greatest underemployment in areas farthest from urban centers.

4. *Institutional Barriers to Migration.* In spite of heavy outmigration from the Southeast to other areas of the nation and heavy rural-urban migration within given labor market areas in the Southeast, there is a strong presumption that most labor markets within the Southeast are relatively local in character with little transfer of information or workers among areas.[15] The impact of local expansion of nonfarm employment could, therefore, be expected to exert an especially heavy "pull" on underemployed farm workers in the local area while the impact of changes affecting the other three markets would be spread more widely throughout the region. This is not to argue that

---

[11] See Charles E. Bishop, "Economic Development and Adjustments of Southern Low-Income Agriculture," *Journal of Farm Economics* (forthcoming, December 1954). Also, Vernon W. Ruttan, "Comparative Data on Farm Income and Employment, 1929–51," Report No. 1 of the Project on Research on Agricultural Development in the Tennessee Valley Region, TVA, May 1953.

[12] Donald J. Bogue, *Population Growth in Standard Metropolitan Areas, 1900–1950* (Washington, D.C.: Housing and Home Finance Agency, 1953), p. 26.

[13] Stefan H. Robock, "Industrialization and Economic Progress in the Southeast," *Southern Economic Journal,* Vol. 20 (April 1954), p. 322.

[14] See C. E. Bishop and J. G. Sutherland, *op. cit.,* for documentation of this point.

[15] One factor contributing to this localization is the apparent failure of State Employment Service officials to develop staff cooperation in effecting interoffice employment clearance. Another factor is the lesser extent of unionization in the Southeast than in most other areas of the nation. See, for example, George R. Koons, "Regional Characteristics of Industrial Relations in Southern Industry," (an address to the Southern Economic Association, Atlanta, Ga., November 14, 1953). Even outside of the Southeast it seems likely that the labor market is probably more "local" in character than most other major markets. See for example, Lloyd G. Reynolds, *The Structure of Labor Markets* (New York: Harper & Bros., 1951), pp. 41–2, 77–86, 241–48, and Clark Kerr, "The Balkanization of Labor Markets," *Labor Mobility and Economic Opportunity* (Cambridge, Mass.: Technology Press, 1954), pp. 92–110. Kerr's discussion is limited by his excessive concentration on the role of craft unions.

TABLE 4

AN ANALYSIS OF FACTORS INFLUENCING THE MEDIAN INCOMES OF FARM FAMILIES IN THE TENNESSEE VALLEY REGION: 1949

(*Part 1*)

	Arithmetic Mean $\overline{X}_i$	Standard Deviation of the Mean σ_i	Coefficient of Simple (total) Correlation r_{11}	*Equation (1)—Seven Variables* Partial (Net) Regression Coefficient b_i	"Beta" Coefficient β_i	Coefficient of Separate (direct) Determination $\beta_i r_{11}$	*Equation (2)—Six Variables** Partial (Net) Regression Coefficient b_i	"Beta" Coefficient β_i	Coefficient of Separate (direct) Determination $\beta_i r_{11}$
X_1	1028.76	284.39	1.0	—	—	—	—	—	—
X_2	1039.30	319.37	.511	.360	.404	.206	.360	.405	.207
X_3	21.53	4.92	−.536	11.738	.202	−.108	11.185	.193	−.104
X_4	1386.62	416.85	.497	.011	.016	.008	—	—	—
X_5	9.60	4.35	.726	45.494	.695	.505	44.938	.687	.499
X_6	47.22	17.87	.683	2.356	.148	.101	2.537	.159	.109
	89.71	16.82	.460	2.194	.131	.060	2.194	.130	.060
						$R^2 = .772$			$R^2 = .771$
						$\overline{R}^2 = .764$			$\overline{R}^2 = .765$
						$\overline{R} = .874$			$\overline{R} = .875$
						$\sigma R = .016$			$\sigma R = .016$
						$\overline{S} = \$145.87$			$\overline{S} = \$138.25$

(Part 2) Coefficients of Simple (total) Correlation—Seven Variables

	r_1	r_2	r_3	r_4	r_5	r_6	r_7
r_1	1.0	.511	−.536	.497	.726	.683	.460
r_2		1.0	−.020	.238	.069	.293	.123
r_3			1.0	−.401	−.842	−.570	−.402
r_4				1.0	.504	.697	.098
r_5					1.0	.709	.471
r_6						1.0	.218
r_7							1.0

(Part 3) The Regression Equations

(1) $X_1 = -358.77 + .36X_2 + 11.74X_3 + .01X_4 + 45.55X_5 + 2.36X_6 + 2.19X_7$

(2)* $X_1 = -334.84 + .36X_2 + 11.19X_3 + 44.94X_5 + 2.54X_6 + 2.19X_7$

* An analysis of variance indicates that each of the variables except X_4 adds significantly (at the .05 level) to the coefficient of multiple determination (R^2). However, $R^2_{1.52} = .740$; $R^2_{1.527} = .747$; $R^2_{1.5\cdot76} = .760$; and $R^2_{1.52763} = .771$. (The order of subscripts indicates the order in which each variable was added.) Also, $X_1 = 163.86 + .41X_2 + 45.46X_5$ with $\sigma R = .018$ and $\bar{S} = 145.87$.

Source: X_1—Median income of rural farm families and individuals in 1949, estimated from data presented in U.S. Bureau of the Census, *U.S. Census of Population: 1950*, vol. 2, *Characteristics of the Population*, part 42, chap. B (Washington, D.C.: U.S. Government Printing Office, 1952).

X_2—Average income per farm worker from farming in 1949, estimated by TVA, see V. W. Ruttan, "Differentials in Farm Income and Employment in the Tennessee Valley Region Counties," Report No. 2 of the Project on Research in Agricultural Development in the Tennessee Valley Region, TVA, July 1953, for data and estimation procedures.

X_3—Percent of farm population employed in agriculture in 1950, *U.S. Census of Population: 1950, op. cit.*

X_4—Average income per production worker in manufacturing in 1947, U.S. Bureau of the Census, *U.S. Census of Manufacturers, 1947*, Vol. 2, *Statistics by States* (Washington, D.C.: U.S. Government Printing Office, 1950).

X_5—Percent of farm population employed in nonfarm work in 1949, U.S. Bureau of the Census, *U.S. Census of Population, 1950, op. cit.*

X_6—Percent of the total population nonfarm in 1950, U.S. Bureau of the Census, *U.S. Census of Population, 1950, op. cit.*

X_7—White farm operators as a percent of the total in 1949, U.S. Bureau of the Census, *U.S. Census of Agriculture: 1950*, Vol. 1, *Counties and State Economic Areas* (Washington, D.C.: U.S. Government Printing Office, 1952).

Tennessee Valley Authority
Government Relations & Economics Staff

the functioning of the other three markets, especially the capital market, may not also be related to the level of local urban-industrial development. I would argue however that localization of labor markets in the Southeast is especially important in the absence of a rate of growth in nonfarm employment sufficiently large to absorb the growth in the region's labor force.

An attempt has been made to test the labor market hypothesis stated above by examining the relationship among the following seven variables for the Tennessee Valley region (table 4).

X_1—The median income of rural farm families and unrelated individuals in 1949. The median income includes the income from both farm and nonfarm sources (but not from home consumption) and can be regarded as a crude indicator of rural welfare.

X_2—Average income per full-time farm worker from farming in 1949. This can be regarded as an index of the relative level of labor productivity in agriculture. The assumption is made that the effect of variations in capital and current inputs per worker on the median income of farm families can be summarized in a single figure representing the average income per farm worker.

X_3—Percent of farm population employed in agriculture in 1950. This represents an index of the relative importance of agricultural employment.

X_4—Average income per production worker in manufacturing in 1947. This can be regarded as an index of the relative level of labor productivity in nonfarm employment.

X_5—Percent of farm population employed in nonfarm work in 1949. This represents an index of the relative importance of nonfarm employment to the rural farm population. X_3 and X_5 together account for the proportion of the total farm population that is employed.

X_6—Percent of the total population that was nonfarm in 1950. The figure is employed as an index of relative urbanization.

X_7—White farm operators as a percent of the total in 1949. This is used to reflect the economic impact of racial discrimination in education and employment in rural areas.

Two of these variables—average income per farm worker from farming (X_2) and percent of farm population employed in nonfarm work (X_5), were associated with a major share ($R^2_{1\cdot 25} = .74$; $R_{1\cdot 25} = .86$) of the variation in the median income of farm families in the Tennessee Valley region in 1949. Of these two variables, the percent of the farm population employed in nonfarm work (X_5) is of considerably greater importance than the level of labor productivity within agriculture (X_2) ($B_5 = .687$; $B_2 = .405$).

Three other variables—the percent of the population employed in agriculture (X_3), the percent of the total population that was nonfarm (X_6), and white farm operators as a percent of the total (X_7)—are associated with a relatively small but statistically significant share of the variation in the median income of rural farm families. Variations in the level of nonfarm income, as reflected by the income of production workers in manufacturing (X_4), either exert no significant influence on the median income of farm families or its influence is obscured by its high intercorrelation with the percent of the farm population employed in nonfarm work and the percent of the total population nonfarm ($r_{45} = .504$; $r_{46} = .697$).

How are these results to be interpreted? *First,* it is clear that the major impact of urban-industrial development on the median incomes of farm families is exerted directly through the participation of members of farm families in nonfarm employment. The direct impact of job availability appears to be far more important than either (a) the direct impact of the level of earnings in nonfarm employment, or (b) the other influences of urbanization measured by the percent of the total population nonfarm. This is clearly consistent with our hypothesis (p. 5) that *the major income effects of local urban-industrial development are transmitted to the agricultural sectors of the local economy through the labor market.*

Second, the racial composition of the farm population appears to be relatively unimportant in explaining variations in the median incomes of farm families. This result should not have been entirely unexpected, in view of the results of Professor Fulmer's analysis of 1940 data.[16] However, while racial characteristics are relatively unimportant, they do exert a statistically significant influence. Furthermore, there is a strong presumption that the nonwhite farm operators are concentrated most heavily in areas furthest from urban centers ($r_{67} = .218$) with the result that the *"true"* relationship may be slightly underestimated as a result of this bias.[17] Even so, the data are consistent with the following proposition: *For any given level of urbanization, a high percentage of nonwhite farm operators is generally associated with a higher proportion of the farm population engaged in agriculture* ($r_{37} = .402$) *and a lower proportion engaged in nonfarm employment* ($r_{57} = .471$) *than would be the case if nonwhite farm operators represented a relatively low percentage of the total farm population.*

Third, the impact of urban-industrial development on labor productivity in agriculture—on the average income per farm worker from farming—is much less pronounced than its influence on the median incomes of farm families ($r_{15} = .726$; $r_{16} = .683$; $r_{25} = .293$, see Tables 5 and 6). Furthermore, the direct impact of urbanization, as measured by the percent of the farm population employed in nonfarm work (X_5), appears to exert a negative influence on average income per farm worker from farming; while the other influences of urbanization, as measured by the percent of the population nonfarm (X_6), appear to exert a positive influence on the average income per farm worker

---

[16] Fulmer, *op. cit.*, p. 263.

[17] This is consistent with data indicating considerable differentials in average and median incomes between white and nonwhite farm operators. See for example, Lewis Jones and Ernest Neal, "Negro Farmers in the Tennessee Valley," Tuskegee, Ala., Tuskegee Institute Rural Life Council, 1954 (mimeographed).

(see table 5).[18] It is clear, however, that the net effect of the two indicators of urban-industrial development is positive ($B_5 = -.337$; $B_6 = .469$) even though they together account for only about 12.5 percent of the variation in average income per farm worker ($R^2_{1.56} = .125$). While these results are consistent with the urban impact hypothesis the size of the impact of local urban-industrial development on labor productivity in agriculture is disappointingly small. Either the impact is small or it is so broadly diffused that its full impact on labor productivity does not show up in the form of county differentials.

One's first reaction to the existence of a negative relationship between average income per farm worker from farming and the percent of the farm population employed in nonfarm work is one of doubt. High intercorrelation between the percent of the farm population working off the farm and the percent of the total population nonfarm ($r_{56} = .709$) may tend to reinforce this doubt. A rationale for acceptance of the observed relationship can be developed, however. Information on the employment practices of plants using rural workers indicates that nonfarm employment of members of farm families is selective toward the younger and median age groups.[19] As a result, it is reasonable to suspect that an increase in the proportion of the farm population employed in nonfarm work (i.e., a decline in the proportion employed in agriculture) could result in a decline in the productivity, and hence the average income per worker from farming of those workers remaining in agriculture.

In the next section an attempt will be made to determine the extent to which this residual impact that does result from urban-industrial development is exerted through the capital market, as compared to the impact which is exerted through the markets for farm products and current inputs.

III. Functioning of the Capital Market Also Closely Related to Urban-Industrial Development

Along with the labor market, the capital market is regarded by many students as functioning rather inefficiently in allocating resources among farm firms and even more inefficiently in allocating resources among rural areas

[18] Using 1940 data on gross farm income per farm and average annual wages per worker in manufacturing, Gale Johnson concluded: "There does not seem to be any relation, either in the South or the North Central States between the level of nonfarm income and farm income, if countries are used as a basis of comparison" ("Functioning of the Labor Market," *Journal of Farm Economics,* Vol. 33 (February 1951), p. 81). Our results are apparently consistent with Johnson's. Although $r_{24} = .238$, average income per production worker in manufacturing (X_4) does not add significantly to coefficient of multiple determination (R^2).

[19] B. M. Wofford and T. A. Kelly, "The Sources and Efficiency of Working Forces in Selected Mississippi Industrial Plants" (mimeographed), Mississippi State College Business Research Station; N. A. Beadles, "Some Myths About the Character of the Southern Labor Force" (paper presented to the annual meeting of the Southern Economic Association, Biloxi, Mississippi, November 19–20, 1954).

TABLE 5
An Analysis of Selected Factors Influencing the Average Income per Farm Worker from Farming in the Tennessee Valley Region: 1949

(Part 1)

	Arithmetic Mean $\bar{X}_i$	Standard Deviation of the Mean σ_i	Coefficient of Simple (total) Correlation r_{2i}	Equation (3)—Six Variables: Partial (Net) Regression Coefficient b_i	Equation (3): "Beta" Coefficient β_i	Equation (3): Coefficient of Separate (direct) Determination $\beta_i r_{2i}$	Equation (4)—Four Variables*: Partial (Net) Regression Coefficient b_i	Equation (4): "Beta" Coefficient β_i	Equation (4): Coefficient of Separate (direct) Determination $\beta_i r_{2i}$
X_2	1039.30	319.37	1.000	—	—	—			
X_3	21.53	4.92	−.020	5.433	.084	−.002			
X_4	1386.62	416.85	.238	.072	.094	.022			
X_5	9.60	4.35	.069	−24.751	−.337	−.023	−29.676	−.404	−.028
X_6	47.22	17.87	.293	8.390	.469	.138	9.588	.537	.157
X_7	89.71	16.82	.123	3.868	.204	.025	3.727	.196	.024
						R^2 = .160			R^2 = .153
						$\bar{R}^2$ = .138			$\bar{R}^2$ = .140
						$\bar{R}$ = .373			$\bar{R}$ = .374
						σR = .060			σR = .060
						$\bar{S}$ = \$297.14			$\bar{S}$ = \$306.56

(Part 2) *The Regression Equations*

(3) $X_2 = 316.77 + 5.43X_3 + .07X_4 - 24.75X_5 + 8.39X_6 + 3.87X_7$

(4) $X_2 = 537.09 - 29.68X_5 + 9.59X_6 + 3.73X_7$

Note: See table 4 for intercorrelation coefficients and description of variables.

* An analysis of variance indicates that (at the .05 level) the addition of X_2 and X_4 does not significantly increase the coefficient of multiple determination (R^2). However, $R^2_{2.56}$ = .125; $R^2_{2.567}$ = .153; $R^2_{2.4567}$ = .159 and $R^2_{2.34567}$ = .160. The variables were added in order of their relative importance as indicated by the "beta" coefficients computed from equation (3).

Tennessee Valley Authority
Government Relations & Economics Staff

and between farm and nonfarm uses.[20] Schultz has argued that the efficiency with which the capital market allocates capital among farm firms is closely related to the level of local urban-industrial development.[21]

If this hypothesis is correct, we would expect to find in any area that: (a) *average income per farm worker is positively related to the level of capital inputs per worker;* (b) *the level of capital inputs per farm worker is positively related to the level of urbanization in the same general area;* and (c) *to the extent the functioning of the product markets and the market for current inputs is associated with urbanization, the percent of the total population nonfarm would also be positively related to the average income per farm worker.*

In an attempt to test this hypothesis, the relationships between the following six variables have been examined:

X_1—Average income per farm worker from farming in 1949.

X_2—Average acres of cropland per farm worker in 1950, and

X_3—Average value of land and buildings per farm worker in 1950. X_2 and X_3 act as indicators of the level of land and long-term capital inputs.

X_4—The average number of tractors per 100 farm worker in 1950. This is used as a crude indicator of the level of mechanization.

X_5—Average value of livestock per farm worker in 1950. X_4 and X_5 together are assumed to measure level of intermediate capital inputs.

X_6—Percent of the total population nonfarm in 1950. This figure is employed as an index of relative urbanization.

An examination of the patterns of agricultural output in the Valley region seemed to indicate that the counties of the region could be divided into at least two major areas depending on the relative importance of cotton and tobacco in each county. There were only six counties in the entire region in which cotton and tobacco each accounted for more than 5 percent of total sales of farm products.[22] Analysis of the differences between means of the several variables for 88 cotton and 107 tobacco-livestock counties indicated significant differences (at the 5 percent level) between the level of investment in land and buildings per farm worker (X_3), number of tractors per 100 farm workers (X_4), and value of livestock per farm worker (X_5). No statistically significant differences were observed in average income per farm worker (X_1) average acres of cropland per worker (X_2), or the percent of the total

---

[20] T. W. Schultz, "Factor Markets and Economic Development," *The Economic Organization of Agriculture, op. cit.*, pp. 283–312; Walter W. Wilcox, "Effects of Farm Price Changes on Efficiency in Farming," *Journal of Farm Economics,* Vol. 33 (February 1951), pp. 55–65; C. E. Bishop, "Underemployment of Labor in Southeastern Farms," *Journal of Farm Economics,* Vol. 36 (May 1954), pp. 264–68.

[21] Schultz, *op. cit.*, pp. 366–67.

[22] Reexamination of the county production patterns indicates that it might have been desirable to divide the Valley region into three groups: (a) cotton, (b) tobacco-livestock, and (c) subsistence farming areas.

population nonfarm (X_6). A decision to analyze the relationships between the six variables separately in each area was made on the basis of the significant difference obtained for the three capital input items.

In the *cotton counties* (table 6) the only statistically significant variable is the number of tractors per 100 farm workers (X_4). The coefficient of correlation (r) between average income per farm worker from farming and number of tractors per 100 farm workers is .687. Variations in the average value of land and buildings per farm worker (X_3), the average acres of cropland per farm worker (X_2), and the average value of livestock per farm worker (X_5) do not exert a statistically significant influence on average income per farm worker nor do variations in the percent of the total population nonfarm (X_6).

In the *tobacco-livestock* (table 7) counties there are two statistically significant variables. They are the average value of livestock per farm worker (X_5) and the percent of the total population nonfarm (X_6). Of these two variables, the average value of livestock per farm worker is the more important factor. Neither the average acres of cropland per farm worker (X_2), the average value of land and buildings (X_3), nor the number of tractors per 100 farm workers (X_4) contributed significantly (at the 5 percent level) to the average income per farm worker.

Before going on to present an interpretation of these results, a word of caution should be noted. The regression equations which express the relationship between average income per farm worker from farming and the several capital input items for the cotton and tobacco-livestock counties should not be regarded as agricultural production functions. These equations are quite different than the functions used in farm management analysis: (a) they are based on county averages rather than on data for individual farms; (b) even though the cotton and tobacco-livestock areas have been treated separately the data for each area are drawn from counties with rather large differences in farming systems; and (c) both production theory and the results of empirical investigations would lead us to suspect that relationships between factor inputs and outputs are curvilinear rather than linear. In this study only linear relationships have been employed. The analysis does permit a test of the hypothesis listed above in spite of its deficiencies from the point of view of production theory.[23]

[23] The analysis should also be useful in identifying areas for special analytical purposes. It would be very interesting, for example, to analyze the factors which permit certain counties to achieve exceptionally high levels of income per farm worker for given levels of capital inputs and extent of urbanization. An examination of the several dot diagrams indicates, for example, that the four northern delta counties (Fulton, Kentucky, and Dyer, Obion and Lake, Tennessee) each has achieved substantially higher incomes per farm worker than could be expected on the basis of X_2, average acres of cropland per farm worker; X_3, average value of land and buildings per worker; and X_5, average value of livestock per farm worker. This is true in spite of the fact that these counties do not depart significantly from the relationship between the median income of farm families and the percent of the total population nonfarm.

TABLE 6. AN ANALYSIS OF THE RELATIONSHIP BETWEEN AVERAGE INCOME PER FARM WORKER FROM FARMING AND CAPITAL INPUTS IN 88 TENNESSEE VALLEY REGION COTTON COUNTIES

(Part 1)

			Equation (1)—Six Variables				Equation (2)—Two Variables		
	Arithmetic Mean $\overline{X}_i$	*Standard Deviation of the Mean* σ_i	*Coefficient of Simple (total) Correlation* r_{11}	*Partial (Net) Regression Coefficient* b_i	*"Beta" Coefficient* β_i	*Coefficient of Separate (Direct) Determination* $\beta_i r_{11}$	*Partial (Net) Regression Coefficient* b_i		*Coefficient of Determination* r_{11}
X_1	1040.11	323.02	1.0	—	—	—	—	—	—
X_2	32.00	8.53	.471	11.06	.292	.138	—	—	—
X_3	4113.30	2631.41	.391	.02	.167	.065	—	—	—
X_4	20.44	8.68	.687	18.70	.503	.346	25.59	—	.472
X_5	562.50	246.69	−.002	−.40	−.346	.001	—	—	—
X_6	45.74	17.57	.247	−1.56	−.085	−.021	—	—	—

Equation (1): $R^2 = .529$; $\overline{R}^2 = .501$; $\overline{R} = .708$; $\sigma R = .052$; $\overline{S} = \$220.00$

Equation (2): $r^2 = .472$; $\overline{r}^2 = .466$; $\overline{r} = .683$; $\sigma r = .057$; $\overline{S} = \$237.40$

(Part 2) Coefficients of Simple (total) Correlation—Six Variables

	r_1	r_2	r_3	r_4	r_5	r_6
r_1	1.0	.471	.391	.687	−.002	.247
r_2		1.0	.324	.688	.623	.352
r_3			1.0	.488	.263	.427
r_4				1.0	.194	.450
r_5					1.0	.223
r_6						1.0

(Part 3) The Regression Equations

(1) $X_1 = 516.03 + 11.06X_2 + .02X_3 + 18.70X_4 - .40X_5 - .15X_6$

(2) $X_1 = 517.05 + 25.59X_4$

Source: X_1—Average income per farm worker from farming in 1949, estimated by TVA. See Vernon W. Ruttan, "Differentials in Farm Income and Employment in the Tennessee Valley Region Counties," Report No. 2 of the Project on Research in Agricultural Development in the Tennessee Valley Region, TVA, July 1953, for data and estimation procedures.

X_2—Average acres of cropland per farm worker in 1950, U.S. Bureau of the Census, *U.S. Census of Agriculture: 1950*, Vol. 1, *Counties and State Economic Areas* (Washington, D.C.: U.S. Government Printing Office, 1952) for county totals; *Ibid.*, for estimates of the number of farm workers.

X_3—Average value of land and buildings per farm worker in 1950; *Ibid.*

X_4—Number of tractors per 100 farm workers in 1950, *Ibid.*

X_5—Value of livestock per farm worker in 1950, *Ibid.*

X_6—Percent of the total population nonfarm in 1950, U.S. Bureau of the Census, *U.S. Census of Population, 1950.*

Tennessee Valley Authority　　Government Relations & Economics Staff

TABLE 7

AN ANALYSIS OF THE RELATIONSHIP BETWEEN AVERAGE INCOME PER FARM WORKER FROM FARMING AND CAPITAL INPUTS IN 107 TENNESSEE VALLEY REGION TOBACCO AND LIVESTOCK COUNTIES

(Part 1)

	Arithmetic Mean $\overline{X}_i$	Standard Deviation of the Mean σ_i	Coefficient of Simple (Total) Correlation r_{1i}	Equation (1)—Six Variables: Partial (Net) Regression Coefficient b_i	Equation (1): "Beta" Coefficient β_i	Equation (1): Coefficient of Separate (Direct) Determination $\beta_i r_{1i}$	Equation (2)—Three Variables: Partial (Net) Regression Coefficient b_i	Equation (2): "Beta" Coefficient β_i	Equation (2): Coefficient of Separate (Direct) Determination $\beta_i r_{1i}$
X_1	1041.18	320.10	—	—	—	—	—	—	—
X_2	32.92	13.63	.340	3.21	.137	.047	—	—	—
X_3	5202.99	2165.03	.325	.005	.035	.011	—	—	—
X_4	15.54	10.03	.341	1.14	.036	.012	—	—	—
X_5	832.06	359.67	.469	.27	.308	.144	.35	.397	.186
X_6	48.65	18.18	.377	4.41	.250	.094	4.78	.271	.102

Equation (1):
$R^2 =$ .308
$\overline{R}^2 =$ .273
$\overline{R} =$ .523
$\sigma R =$ .069
$\overline{S} =$ \$274.80

Equation (2):
$R^2 =$ .288
$\overline{R}^2 =$ .274
$\overline{R} =$ .524
$\sigma R =$ .070
$\overline{S} =$ \$274.05

(Part 2) Coefficients of Simple (total) Correlation—Six Variables

	r_1	r_2	r_3	r_4	r_5	r_6
r_1	1.0	.340	.325	.341	.469	.377
r_2		1.0	.019	.790	.487	.099
r_3			1.0	.443	.443	.572
r_4				1.0	.357	.309
r_5					1.0	.266
r_6						1.0

(Part 3) The Regression Equations

(1) $X_1 = 448.89 + 3.21X_2 + .005X_3 + 1.13X_4 + .27X_5 + 4.41X_6$

(2) $X_1 = 515.36 + .35X_5 + 4.78X_6$

Source: See table 6 for sources and definition of terms.
Tennessee Valley Authority
Government Relations & Economics Staff

The hypothesis that average income per farm worker is positively related to the level of capital inputs per worker is consistent with the data for at least one capital input item in both areas. Nevertheless, some of the results of the analysis are rather surprising.

a) In spite of the small number of acres of cropland per farm worker (about 32 acres in each area) and the small investment in land and buildings per farm worker—averaging $4,133 in the cotton counties and $5,203 in the tobacco counties—the analysis does not reveal a significant relationship between either of these two indexes of long-term capital inputs and average income per farm worker in either the cotton or the tobacco counties. A number of other studies, including the studies by Hughes in east Tennessee,[24] Johnson in western Kentucky,[25] and Heady and Shaw in north Alabama,[26] have indicated a low marginal productivity of investment in land and buildings in parts of the same area covered by this study. It has been suggested that a combination of the relatively low level of managerial ability of farm operators and extremely low level of capital and land inputs is responsible for a statistical conclusion that may not have too much meaning for the future.[27]
b) In the cotton counties, the only statistically significant variable is the number of tractors per 100 farm workers. This result would certainly not lend support to proponents of grassland-livestock agriculture in the cotton counties. Livestock apparently did not represent a profitable enterprise on most farms even during 1949, a period of relatively high livestock prices.
c) In the tobacco-livestock counties, the number of tractors per 100 farm workers did not exert any statistically significant influence on average income per farm worker. However, this result does not appear unreasonable in view of the high value output per acre in tobacco production and the small size of tobacco allotments.

The hypothesis that the level of capital inputs per farm worker is positively related to the level of urbanization in the same general area is consistent with the data for both areas. All of the coefficients of simple (total) correlation between capital input items ($X_2 \ldots X_5$) and the index of urbanization (X_6) are positive. This result tends to substantiate Schultz's hypothesis that the capital market functions more efficiently in area near developing urban-industrial complexes.

---

[24] R. B. Hughes, "Marginal Returns on Agricultural Resources in a Southern Mountain Valley," *Journal of Farm Economics,* Vol. 36 (May 1954), pp. 334–39.
[25] Glenn L. Johnson, *Sources of Income on Upland Marshall County Farms,* progress Report 1, Kentucky Agricultural Experiment Station, University of Kentucky, Lexington (see also the reports for other western Kentucky counties).
[26] Earl O. Heady and Russell Shaw, "Resource Returns and Productivity Coefficients in Selected Farming Areas," *Journal of Farm Economics,* Vol. 36 (May 1954), pp. 243–57.
[27] Heady and Shaw, *Ibid.,* p. 253.

IV. Functioning of the Product and Current Input Markets Less Closely Related to Urban-Industrial Development

The hypothesis that urbanization exerts an independent impact on income per farm worker, over and above the impact exerted through the capital market, is consistent with the data for the tobacco-livestock counties but is not consistent with the data for the cotton counties. In the cotton counties, the percent of the total population that is nonfarm does not exert a statistically significant influence on average income per farm worker.

It seems likely that the positive association between average income per worker and the percent of the total population that is nonfarm in the tobacco-livestock counties reflects the more efficient functioning of the markets for products and current inputs in areas near urban centers. The tobacco-livestock counties are heavily concentrated in the upland areas of the Valley region where, until fairly recently, travel and communication have been fairly difficult. In these circumstances, it seems reasonable to believe that the efficiency of the product and current input markets would be related to the level of local urban-industrial development.[28] Even in the tobacco-livestock counties the analysis would seem to indicate that the impact on income per farm worker exerted through the product and current input markets is less important than the influence exerted through the capital market alone. This conclusion is especially interesting in view of the relatively large agricultural research funds being devoted to improving the product and current input markets and the relatively small funds being devoted to improving the capital and labor markets.

V. Summary and Conclusions

The results of this study can be summarized in five steps.

First, the level of income achieved by *nonfarm* families and individuals in any given area is closely related to the level of urban-industrial development in the same general area.

Second, the median income level achieved by *farm* families in the areas studied was almost as closely related to the level of local urban-industrial development as was the median income of *nonfarm* families in 1949.

Third, in the Tennessee Valley region the labor market appears to be the major channel through which the impact of local urban-industrial development is transmitted to farm families. Increased off-farm jobs by members of farm families were more important in raising the income level of farm families than even increased labor productivity in agriculture.

---

[28] For a discussion of some of the product market effects, see John L. Fulmer, "Urbanization and Agriculture," in *Agricultural Progress in the Cotton Belt Since 1920*, Chapel Hill, N.C., 1950, pp. 123–29. and W. E. Christian, "Impact of Industrialization upon the Marketing Outlets for Locally Produced Farm Products," (Paper presented at the annual meeting of the Southern Economic Association, Biloxi, Miss., November 19–20, 1954).

Fourth, the direct impact on labor productivity in agriculture (on income per farm worker from farming) of increased nonfarm employment by members of farm families appears to be negative. This negative influence is, however, more than offset by the positive influences of local urban-industrial development which is exerted through the markets for capital, current inputs, and farm products.

Fifth, in the 88 cotton counties of the Tennessee Valley region, the impact of local urban-industrial development which is not exerted directly through the labor market seems to be exerted almost entirely through the capital market. In the 107 tobacco-livestock counties, there appears to be a residual impact exerted through the markets for farm products and current inputs as well as through the labor and capital markets.

21 The Role of Agriculture in Economic Development*

BRUCE F. JOHNSTON and JOHN W. MELLOR†

The present article deals with issues that have too often been discussed in terms of the false dichotomy of agricultural vs. industrial development. The approach adopted here is to examine the interrelationships between agricultural and industrial development and to analyze the nature of agriculture's role in the process of economic growth.

Diversity among nations in their physical endowment, cultural heritage, and historical context precludes any universally applicable definition of the role that agriculture should play in the process of economic growth. Nevertheless, certain aspects of agriculture's role appear to have a high degree of generality because of special features that characterize the agricultural sector during the course of development. The nature of agriculture's role is, of course, highly relevant to determining the appropriate "balance" between agriculture and other sectors with respect to (1) direct government investment or aids to investment, (2) budget allocations for publicly supported research and education-extension programs, and (3) the burden of taxation levied on different sectors.

I. Special Characteristics of the Agricultural Sector in the Process of Economic Development

Two important and related features distinguish the agricultural sector in an underdeveloped country and its role in the process of economic growth.

* *American Economic Review,* Vol. LI, No. 4 (September, 1961), pp. 566–93.

† Stanford University, Stanford, California, and Cornell University, Ithaca, New York, respectively. The authors have received valuable criticism of successive drafts from many persons and wish to acknowledge particularly suggestions from W. O. Jones, Kazushi Ohkawa, David Bell, W. Arthur Lewis, Richard Easterlin, Roger Gray, Arthur T. Mosher, and Philip M. Raup.

First, in virtually all underdeveloped economies agriculture is an existing industry of major proportions, frequently the only existing industry of any consequence. Typically, some 40 to 60 percent of the national income is produced in agriculture and from 50 to 80 percent of the labor force is engaged in agricultural production. Although large quantities of resources—chiefly land and labor—are committed to agriculture, they are being used at very low levels of productivity.

The other significant characteristic is the secular decline which occurs in the relative size of the agricultural sector [6] [39] [45] [27] [26]. The importance of this process of structural transformation and the size of the related capital demands place a great burden on agriculture to provide capital for expansion of other sectors. The economic transformation also has important implications with respect to the changing role of labor and capital and the choice of methods for developing agriculture.

Secular Decline of the Agricultural Sector: the "General Transformation Model." The two basic factors generally recognized as responsible for the structural transformation of an economy are: (1) an income elasticity of demand for food that is less than 1 and declining, and (2) the possibility of a substantial expansion of agricultural production with a constant or declining farm labor force.

A third factor that has received less attention is probably of considerable importance: by and large modern technology permits the most drastic reduction of costs in manufacturing industry, in power generation, and in long-distance transport. It is within these fields that investments in modern, power-driven machinery and the application of advanced technology lead to early and revolutionary reductions in costs so that price-elasticity and substitution effects reinforce differential income elasticities in changing the pattern of output and consumption.

The relative decline of the agricultural sector will not proceed as rapidly or as far in countries that have a marked comparative advantage in exporting agricultural products. But even countries particularly well suited by their resource endowment to emerge as major agricultural exporters can be expected to witness a substantial reduction in the share of agriculture if they achieve a sizable increase in per capita incomes. Denmark and New Zealand stand out as countries that have benefited greatly from their position as leading agricultural exporters; even so, less than 20 percent of their labor is presently engaged in agriculture.[1]

The reasons for the secular decline of agriculture and substantial expansion

---

[1] The Danish example is particularly striking. The country is conspicuously lacking in resources other than its excellent agricultural potential. More than 65 percent of total agricultural output is sold abroad, and despite considerable expansion of nonagricultural exports since World War II, agriculture still accounts for some 60 percent of total foreign exchange earnings [18, p. 7] [22, p. 114]. Note: Numbers refer to numbered citations given in the list of references at the end of this paper.

of manufacturing and other components of the nonagricultural sector have not been fully elucidated; but this type of structural transformation of an economy seems to be a necessary condition for cumulative and self-sustaining growth. A mere change in the product-mix available for consumption, obtainable up to a point entirely by means of international trade, is apparently *not* a sufficient condition.[2]

The Two-sector Classical Growth Model. The implications of the dynamic nature of the growth process have been elaborated most clearly in W. Arthur Lewis' two-sector model, which represents a special case of the "general transformation model" characterized above. Since, in densely populated countries, a considerable proportion of the rural labor force may provide an increment to production less than the requirements for its own subsistence, Lewis assumes in his model that there is a surplus of manpower in agriculture (subsistence sector);[3] and that the nonagricultural (capitalist) sector is the dynamic element which absorbs this surplus of manpower.[4]

Since the supply of labor available in the traditional sector is assumed to be in effect "unlimited," the transfer of manpower to the capitalist sector is determined by the demand for labor in that sector, which in turn is limited by the rate of capital accumulation. In the capitalist sector it will normally be necessary to pay a wage determined by the average product per man in the traditional sector, plus some margin dictated by transfer frictions, social views of minimum subsistence, trade union pressure, and other institutional forces.

This is, of course, a transitional phase. "When capital catches up with labour supply," as Lewis phrases it, the two-sector model is no longer

---

[2] Even Viner, who has been critical of using income from the agricultural sector to "subsidize uneconomic urban industry," does not really take issue with this proposition [48, p. 124]. His (reluctant?) concession is phrased in a double negative: "It is not my position that the path to economic progress is not, for many countries and even for most countries, by way of industrialization and urbanization." "The real problem," he continues, "is not agriculture as such or the absence of manufactures as such, but poverty and backwardness, poor agriculture, or poor agriculture and poor manufacturing. The remedy is to remove the basic causes of the poverty and backwardness" [48, p. 71]. Viner later suggests that if the masses of the population in underdeveloped countries were "literate, healthy, and sufficiently well fed . . . all else necessary for rapid economic development would come readily and easily of itself" [48, p. 131]. These factors are obviously important, but it seems highly questionable that shortcomings in literacy, health, and nutrition have been the sole obstacles, or even the major obstacles, to achieving rapid economic growth. Moreover, a static view of comparative advantage is an inadequate basis for determining what is or is not "uneconomic urban industry."

[3] For discussion concerning the physical conditions in which such a labor surplus will or will not arise and for empirical support, see [33]. Georgescu-Roegen [12] emphasizes that special institutional arrangements are required to make it possible for certain workers to "receive more than they earn." The most common of these institutional arrangements is the family farm in which the unit of production is also the unit of consumption.

[4] Strictly speaking, the subsistence and capitalist sectors of the Lewis model do not correspond exactly to agriculture and nonagriculture. The distinguishing feature of the capitalist sector is that labor is employed for wages for profit-making purposes and that substantial quantities of reproducible capital are used [30, p. 8] [29, p. 146].

relevant. However, in the short run, nonfarm job opportunities cannot be created sufficiently rapidly to move ahead of population growth in the countryside. Dovring has called attention to the fact that the farm labor force frequently does not decline in absolute numbers until fairly late in the process of development; the absorption of surplus labor from agriculture depends not only on the rate of increase of nonagricultural employment but also on the "weight" of the non-agricultural sector in the economy [8].

Lewis' treatment emphasizes the implications of the two-sector model for industrial development policy. So long as the conditions of this classical growth-model are relevant, factor proportions and productivities will and should be different in the two sectors and a different calculus is applicable to allocation decisions.

Resource Allocation in Agriculture. Since there may be discrepancies between private and social benefit or between private and social cost, the relevant concept in agriculture as elsewhere is the social marginal productivity of alternative investment projects [4, pp. 76–96] [9, pp. 56–85]. This concept, or the less sophisticated but often more operational technique of estimating cost-benefit ratios, is reasonably serviceable in appraising large-scale investment projects in the agricultural sector.

There are compelling considerations, however, which suggest that the most practical and economical approach to achieving sizable increases in agricultural productivity and output lies in enhancing the efficiency of the existing agricultural economy through the introduction of modern technology on a broad front. Of particular importance are expenditures for "developmental services" or "unconventional inputs" such as agricultural research, education, and extension that broaden the range of alternative production possibilities available to farm operators and strengthen their capacity to make and execute decisions on the basis of more adequate knowledge of agricultural technology.

Three considerations emphasize the need for a special approach in determining the level of resource allocation to agriculture and for establishing priorities within an agricultural development program. First, it is virtually impossible to quantify the schedule of increase in output or reduction in costs that can be expected as a result of expenditures for developmental services such as agricultural research or extension [1]. Even an *ex post* estimate is difficult, a fact brought out clearly in Griliches' interesting attempt to estimate the returns that can be attributed to the investment of resources in the development of hybrid corn [14].

The second factor is the importance of complementarities among agricultural inputs. It is necessary in designing a rational program of agricultural development to define a "package" of inputs—conventional and unconventional—that will be most efficient in increasing agricultural output.

The third difficulty concerns the need to discriminate between the use of scarce and relatively abundant resources. Investible funds, foreign exchange, and certain forms of entrepreneurial talent are in particularly short supply and are critical for industrial development. In contrast, many of the inputs for agricultural development are relatively abundant. In particular, agricultural labor will continue to have low opportunity cost for some time owing to the slow growth of demand for industrial labor. Use of shadow or accounting prices represents one technique for taking account of the abundance of these resources. However, explicit recognition of the special characteristics of the process of agricultural development is essential for designing a strategy for increasing agricultural output and productivity which will minimize requirements for the scarce resources indispensable for expansion of the capitalist sector.

Historical Experience. The proposition that a substantial rate of increase in agricultural production can be achieved largely through the more effective use of resources already committed to the agricultural sector and with only modest requirements for the critical resources of high opportunity cost is essentially an empirical generalization. Considerable support for the proposition is provided by the experience of countries in North America and Western Europe that have been successful in increasing agricultural productivity.[5] More pertinent, however, is the historical experience of Japan and Taiwan.

Labor productivity in Japanese agriculture approximately doubled over a span of 30 years, comparing farm output and labor inputs during the years 1881–90 with the decade 1911–20. The comparable increase in Taiwan appears to have been even larger—something like 130 to 160 percent over the 30-year span between 1901–10 and 1931–40 [23, pp. 499–500] [22, pp.23, 41, 78, 91]. A threefold expansion of sugar yields and a nearly twelvefold increase of output was a conspicuous element in the increase registered in Taiwan. This particularly rapid progress in sugar was favored by the spectacular world progress in breeding higher yielding varieties of cane during the first three decades of the present century and the fact that exportation to Japan provided an outlet for the rapidly expanding production. Similarly, the fivefold increase in cocoon production and sevenfold increase in output of raw silk in Japan was considerably more rapid than the overall growth of agricultural output. Technological progress resulting from research aimed at heavier yields of mulberry leaves, selection and breeding of superior races of silkworms, and improvements in practices ranging from the methods of feeding silkworms to the reeling of silk from the cocoons was the decisive

---

[5] Studies of the growth of agricultural productivity in the United States have underscored the importance of unconventional inputs and suggest that technological change has been about as important as the quantitative increase in conventional inputs in bringing about increased production [43]. Technical innovations were probably even more important in the impressive growth of agricultural productivity in Denmark; the average annual (compound) rate of increase between the 1880's and the decade of the 1930's was about 2 percent [22, pp. 102–4].

factor in the rapid growth in the sericulture industry. Here again, however, the availability of an expanding export market was a necessary condition for the rapid growth of output that was attained.

It is also clear that technological progress was the decisive factor responsible for the increase in productivity and output of rice and other basic food crops that accounted for the bulk of agricultural production in Japan and Taiwan. The three key elements were: (1) agricultural research leading to the development and selection of higher-yielding varieties; (2) increased application of fertilizers; and (3) activities that facilitated wide use of the most productive plant varieties and of improved farm practices. The high degree of complementarity among various agricultural inputs is clearly evident in the agricultural advance achieved in these two countries. The work of the plant-breeders was largely directed at developing varieties characterized by a strong response to increased applications of fertilizer; the gains achieved were the result of the joint advance in improving plant varieties and in raising the level of soil fertility by heavier application of chemical fertilizers. Changes in cultural practices also played a necessary part in realizing the full potential of new varieties combined with heavier fertilization.

Increase of crop area, largely through extending the area of double-cropping, and expansion of irrigation were more important in Taiwan than in Japan during the periods considered; development in those directions was already fairly advanced in Japan by the 1880's. Thus it appears that agricultural investment was a somewhat more important factor in Taiwan than in Japan, but to a large extent it was direct, non-monetary investment [22, pp. 77–81].

The expenditures in Japan and Taiwan for agricultural research, extension-type activities, and other developmental services were very modest in relation to the large increments in output obtained.

II. Agriculture's Contributions to Economic Development

The most important ways in which increased agricultural output and productivity contribute to overall economic growth can be summarized in five propositions: (1) Economic development is characterized by a substantial increase in the demand for agricultural products, and failure to expand food supplies in pace with the growth of demand can seriously impede economic growth. (2) Expansion of exports of agricultural products may be one of the most promising means of increasing income and foreign exchange earnings, particularly in the earlier stages of development. (3) The labor force for manufacturing and other expanding sectors of the economy must be drawn mainly from agriculture. (4) Agriculture, as the dominant sector of an underdeveloped economy, can and should make a net contribution to the capital required for overhead investment and expansion of secondary industry. (5) Rising net cash incomes of the farm population may be important as a stimulus to industrial expansion.

1. *Providing Increased Food Supplies.* Apart from autonomous changes in demand, presumably of limited importance, the annual rate of increase in demand for food is given by $D = p + \eta g$, where p and g are the rate of growth of population and per capita income and η is the income elasticity of demand for agricultural products [37].

Growth of demand for food is of major economic significance in an underdeveloped country for several reasons. First, high rates of population growth of $1\frac{1}{2}$ to 3 percent now characterize most of the world's underdeveloped nations, so that growth of demand from this factor alone is substantial. As a result of international borrowing of knowledge and techniques in the public health field and the availability of such powerful weapons as DDT, the sulpha drugs, and penicillin, the decline in death rates is frequently sharp. This, in combination with the slow decline in birth rates, has resulted in rates of natural increase substantially higher than those that characterized the presently developed countries during their "population explosion."[6] Moreover, there is now only a weak relationship between the factors mainly responsible for the rise in the rate of natural increase and the factors determining the growth of a nation's income.

Secondly, the income elasticity of demand for food in underdeveloped countries is considerably higher than in high-income nations—probably on the order of .6 or higher in the low-income countries vs. .2 or .3 in Western Europe, the United States, and Canada.[7] Hence, a given rate of increase in per capita income has a considerably stronger impact on the demand for agricultural products than in economically advanced countries.

The increase in farm output in Japan between the 1880's and 1911–20, which seems to have been of about the same magnitude as the growth of demand during that period, corresponded to an annual rate of increase in demand of approximately 2 percent. With current rates of population growth and a modest rise in per capita incomes, the annual rate of increase of demand for food in a developing economy can easily exceed 3 percent, a formidable challenge for the agriculture of an underdeveloped country. Moreover, as a result of the expansion of population in cities and in mining and industrial centers dependent upon purchased food, the growth of demand

[6] The rapid population growth now characteristic of underdeveloped countries reinforces the view stated earlier that structural transformation of an economy is a necessary condition for cumulative economic growth and substantial increase of per capita incomes. Such a transformation, with the accompanying urbanization, increase of incomes, spread of education, and changes in attitudes and incentives, is a precondition for reduction of birth rates to levels compatible with a sharply lowered death rate. It may be desirable in some countries to reinforce the indirect influence of economic and social transformation by direct measures to encourage reduction of birth rates; but there is no evidence to suggest that direct measures alone would be sufficient.

[7] These approximations relate to income elasticity with respect to food expenditure measured at the farm level, the concept most relevant to assessing the growth of demand for agricultural products. We have reviewed some of the evidence bearing on income elasticities in developed and underdeveloped countries in [21, p. 339].

for marketed supplies is a good deal more rapid than the overall rate of increase. Thus there are additional problems in developing transportation links and marketing facilities in order to satisfy the requirements of the nonagricultural population.

If food supplies fail to expand in pace with the growth of demand the result is likely to be a substantial rise in food prices leading to political discontent and pressure on wage rates with consequent adverse effects on industrial profits, investment, and economic growth. There is scant evidence concerning the price elasticity of demand for food in underdeveloped countries. At least in the case of an increase in prices as a result of demand outstripping supply, there is a strong presumption that the price elasticity for "all food" is extremely low, probably lower than in economically advanced countries. Cheap starchy staple foods—cereals and root crops—provide something like 60 to 85 percent of the total calorie intake in low-income countries, so there is relatively limited scope for offsetting a rise in food prices by shifting from expensive to less costly foods; and the pressure to resist a reduction in calorie intake is strong.

The inflationary impact of a given percentage increase in food prices is much more severe in an underdeveloped country than in a high-income economy. This is a simple consequence of the dominant position of food as a wage good in lower-income countries where 50 to 60 percent of total consumption expenditure is devoted to food compared with 20 to 30 percent in developed economies.

Owing to the severe economic and political repercussions of a substantial rise in food prices, domestic shortages are likely to be offset by expanded food imports, provided that foreign exchange or credits are available.[8] For some countries that are in a favorable position with respect to foreign exchange earnings this may be a satisfactory solution. But foreign exchange is usually in short supply and urgently required for imports of machinery and other requisites for industrial development that cannot be produced domestically. There is no simple or general answer to this question of import substitution that Chenery has described as "the most important and most

[8] Some underdeveloped countries have reacted to the social and economic problems resulting from food shortages and their inflationary consequences by instituting compulsory food collection, price controls, and rationing. It is easy to appreciate that considerations of social equity would lead to such measures in a low-income country; but from the standpoint of economic development the effects of an attempt to maintain such food distribution controls on a continuing basis are almost entirely unfavorable. Such programs tie up scarce administrative talent in a program of uncertain value that is usually ineffective as well; and they impede the growth of a market-oriented agriculture. Much higher returns are obtainable from a well-conceived program of agricultural development to expand total output rather than controlling its distribution. For an interesting discussion of experience in Pakistan see [46, pp. 121–26]. If short-run instability of food prices resulting from fluctuations in farm output is a real problem, there may be justification for establishing a food reserve, especially if U.S. surplus stocks can be drawn upon to provide the initial stock.

difficult aspect of development programming . . ." [5, p. 67]. In view of the potential that exists for increasing agricultural productivity it is likely to be advantageous to obtain the additional food supplies by increased domestic output rather than by relying on expansion of exports to finance enlarged food imports.[9] In any event, a static view of comparative costs may be misleading. The demand for imports of machinery and other items can be expected to increase as development proceeds, so the existing exchange rate is not likely to reflect the future demand for and supply of foreign exchange [5, p. 67].

The foregoing discussion has stressed the severe penalties attached to failure to achieve the "required" increase in output. This notion of a "required" increase in output should not be pushed too far; the price elasticity of demand for food is low but not zero and there is normally the possibility of adjusting supplies via imports. Nevertheless, it is noteworthy that the demand for food is a derived demand determined essentially by the growth of population and of per capita incomes; and this characteristic of the demand for food cuts in both directions. Not only does it mean severe penalties for failure to expand food supplies in pace with the growth of demand, but it also implies that the returns on investment in expansion of food crops for domestic consumption fall off sharply if food supplies increase more rapidly than demand.* There is thus a significant difference between the domestic demand for food products and the more expansible demand for agricultural exports (of a particular country) and for the miscellany of goods and services produced by "nonagriculture."

2. *Enlarged Agricultural Exports.* Expansion of agricultural exports is likely to be one of the most promising means of increasing incomes and augmenting foreign exchange earnings in a country stepping up its development efforts. A profitable export crop can frequently be added to an existing cropping system; the capital requirements for such innovations are often

[9] This is, of course, merely a presumption, and it does not alter the fact that it is important to maintain price competition between domestic and imported foodstuffs, nor the fact that it is advantageous to import foodstuffs that cannot be produced efficiently at home, wheat imports in tropical regions being an important example. The availability of large quantities of U.S. agricultural surpluses on favorable terms has the effect of somewhat reducing the importance of measures to increase agricultural productivity and output in a developing country; but there remains the question whether such windfall supplies will be available on a continuing basis in quantities sufficient to satisfy a rapidly growing demand.

* Subsequent analysis of theoretical and empirical data suggest that the price elasticities of demand for agricultural commodities may not be so inelastic. The concern with rising food prices remains great as stated on the preceding page. But, somewhat less inelastic demand removes some of the pressure resulting from lags in supply shifts and concurrently allows more scope for expansion of supply more than demand. For an elaboration of this modification, shared by both authors, see: J. W. Mellor, "Toward a Theory of Agricultural Development," in Herman M. Southworth and Bruce F. Johnston (eds.), *Agricultural Development and Economic Growth* (Ithaca, New York: Cornell University Press, 1967), pp. 21–61; and J. W. Mellor, *The Economics of Agricultural Development* (Ithaca, New York: Cornell University Press, 1966). (Footnote added in August 1968).

moderate and largely dependent on direct, non-monetary investment by farmers.

Development of production of export crops has a further advantage in catering to an existing market; and an individual country that accounts for only a small fraction of world exports faces a fairly elastic demand schedule. In view of the urgent need for enlarged foreign exchange earnings and the lack of alternative opportunities, substantial expansion of agricultural export production is frequently a rational policy even though the world supply-demand situation for a commodity is unfavorable.

There are, of course, disadvantages to heavy reliance on agricultural exports. And simultaneous efforts to expand exports of certain agricultural commodities in a number of underdeveloped countries involve the risk of substantial price declines, especially if the relevant price and income elasticities are low.

A longer-run goal is diversification which will lessen the vulnerability of an economy that depends heavily on export proceeds from one or a few crops. One of the rewards of the structural transformation associated with economic growth is the greater flexibility of a diversified economy. Of much greater immediate importance, however, is the fact that for most of the underdeveloped countries the introduction or expanded production of agricultural export crops can and should play a strategic role in providing enlarged supplies of foreign exchange.[10]

3. *Transfer of Manpower from Agriculture to Nonagriculture Sectors.* To the extent that the Lewis two-sector model with its assumption of a perfectly elastic supply of labor is applicable, it follows that manpower for manufacturing and other rapidly expanding sectors can be drawn easily from agriculture. On the other hand, if the rural population is sparse and there is a good potential for expanding output of profitable cash crops, it may be difficult to obtain labor for a rapidly expanding capitalist sector. In any event, the bulk of the labor for the expanding sectors must be drawn from agriculture in the earlier stages of development simply because there is almost no other source. The experience of Japan, where the conditions of the two-sector model were approximated, seems to indicate that the rate of

[10] As with so many of the policy issues that face a developing country there is no simple answer because intelligent decisions require a balancing of contradictory considerations. Agricultural exports are vulnerable to sizable price fluctuations, and there is a possibility of deterioration in a country's terms of trade if it is dependent on crops which experience a secular decline in price. It has been elegantly demonstrated that under certain assumptions expansion of exports can lead to "immiserizing growth," but we share Nurkse's skepticism concerning the concept of "output elasticity of supply" on which the demonstrations rest and agree with his conclusion that the pessimistic appraisals of the effects of trade really amount to demonstrating that an economy incapable of adapting to changed circumstances is at a disadvantage [36, pp. 58–59]. Much more important than a theoretical possibility of immiserizing growth is the fact that for the predominantly agricultural economy of an underdeveloped country, expansion of export crops is likely to offer a practical and economic means by which incomes and foreign exchange earnings can be increased. The gains are likely to be especially significant in relation to development in those instances in which the enlarged production of export crops depends primarily on the use of relatively abundant resources of low opportunity cost.

investment was the limiting factor and that transfer of labor to industry was not a major problem [22, pp. 51–73]. In view of the potential that exists for increasing agricultural output per man, it is to be expected that labor-supply problems in manufacturing and other growing industries will not be serious provided that intelligent and vigorous efforts are made to enhance farm productivity.[11]

4. *Agriculture's Contributions to Capital Formation.* The secular decline of the agricultural sector and the structural transformation of an economy that characterize the dynamics of growth underscore the importance and difficulty of the problem of capital accumulation in an underdeveloped country. This is probably the most significant implication of Lewis' two-sector model in which the rate of capital formation determines the rate at which employment can be expanded in the capitalist, high-wage sector of the economy; and the rate of expansion of employment in the capitalist sector relative to the growth of the total labor force determines how soon the surplus of rural labor will be reduced to a point where wage levels are no longer depressed by the low level of productivity and earnings in the subsistence sector.[12]

An underdeveloped country that is making determined efforts to achieve economic progress faces formidable requirements for capital to finance the creation and expansion of manufacturing and mining enterprises, for overhead investment in transportation and utilities, and in the revenue needed for recurrent expenditure for expansion of education and developmental services. These requirements are certain to outstrip the supply of funds available except in those countries which have large earnings from petroleum or mineral exports or particularly favorable access to foreign capital. The sheer size of the agricultural sector as the only major existing industry points to its importance as a source of capital for overall economic growth. This presumption is particularly strong during the early stages of economic growth inasmuch as reinvestment of profits, historically the major source of capital accumulation, cannot be significant so long as the capitalist sector remains a small segment of the economy.

Since there is scope for raising productivity in agriculture by means that require only moderate capital outlays, it is possible for the agricultural sector to make a net contribution to the capital requirements for infrastructure and for industrial expansion without reducing the low levels of consumption characteristic of the farm population in an underdeveloped

---

[11] Fleming has asserted that the ease with which labor can be transferred from agriculture to nonagricultural industry "has frequently been exaggerated" [10, p. 254]; but he largely ignores the significant potential that exists for raising labor productivity in agriculture.

[12] The difference between the rate of growth of total and nonagricultural employment, which Dovring has termed the "coefficient of differential growth," is a useful measure for comparing the speed of sector changes [8].

country. An increase in agricultural productivity implies some combination of reduced inputs, reduced agricultural prices, or increased farm receipts. Labor, being the abundant input in agriculture, is the principal input that will be reduced, and attention has already been given to agriculture's role as a source of manpower. Implicit in the earlier discussion of the need to expand agricultural production in pace with the growth of demand for food was the important proposition that stable or reduced agricultural prices can facilitate capital accumulation by preventing deterioration or even improving the terms of trade on which the industrial sector obtains food and other agricultural products.

Before considering the possibilities of securing a flow of capital out of agriculture, mention should be made of the ways in which the resource requirements of the agricultural sector can be minimized. The approach to agricultural development considered in Section III is one which minimizes requirements for scarce resources of high opportunity cost and which emphasizes the possibility of enhancing the productivity of the resources already committed to agriculture. It is also desirable for the capital requirements for agricultural expansion, including the increased outlays for fertilizers that are likely to be so important in this phase of agricultural development, to be financed as much as possible out of increased farm receipts that may accrue with the increase of productivity and output. Possibilities also exist for levying school fees, charges for land registration, and other fees that cover all or part of the cost of services provided for the farm population. But for many of the developmental services important to agriculture, it is *not* desirable to link services rendered with a charge to defray the cost. This is partly because individual farmers may not be able or willing to pay for such services, but more important is the fact that social returns to expenditures for research and extension to raise agricultural productivity may be much larger than the private benefits that can be appropriated by individual producers.

Japan is probably the clearest example of a country where agriculture contributed significantly to the financing of development. It was noted earlier that the impressive increase in farm output and productivity in Japan between 1881–90 and 1911–20 required only small capital outlays and but moderate increases in other inputs. Consumption levels of the farm population increased much less than the rise in productivity in agriculture, so that a substantial fraction of the increment in product in agriculture could be used to finance capital formation in the capitalist sector of the economy.

Since heavy taxes on agriculture were the principal device used to siphon off a part of this increase in productivity, it is possible to obtain some notion of the magnitude of this contribution in relation to total investment. Estimates of the division of the tax burden between agriculture and nonagriculture by Seiji Tsunematsu indicate that agriculture's share was some 80 percent as late as 1893–97 and was still about 50 percent during the years 1913–17 [22, pp. 53–57] [40, pp. 446–48].

Tax revenues from agriculture thus provided a large part of the funds that the Japanese government used in fostering development by constructing "model factories," by subsidizing the creation of a merchant marine and shipbuilding industry, and by strategic investments in overhead capital such as railroads, education, and research.

Rosovsky's estimates of investment in Japan throw light on the importance of government's role in investment. Even with allowance for the fact that his figures understate private investment, the data indicate that government investment, excluding military investment, exceeded 50 percent of total investment throughout the period 1895–1910 [42, pp. 354–57].

This heavy reliance on agricultural taxation appears to have been a conscious policy. The eminent economic historian Takao Tsuchiya has interpreted the policy in these terms; "The urgent necessity for protecting and fostering other industries compelled the government to impose a heavy land tax on the agricultural population to obtain the wherewithal to carry out industrial development programs" [35, p. 4].

Political and institutional problems frequently make it difficult to translate the increased potential for saving and capital accumulation, made possible by increased agricultural productivity, into an actual increase in investment. Recent experience in India and Pakistan, for example, gives rise to doubts as to whether capital accumulation and economic growth will proceed at a "satisfactory" pace. Despite the stress that has been placed on promoting economic development, agriculture's contribution to investment and revenue requirements for government expenditure for current services seems to have declined; or at least there is evidence that agriculture's relative contribution to tax revenues has declined appreciably. Wald reports that whereas land revenues in India provided more than 20 percent of total tax revenue in 1939 they accounted for only 9 percent of the tax receipts of India's central and state and provincial government in 1954 and only 5 percent of total tax receipts in Pakistan in 1952 [49, pp. 44n, 61–63].

The political difficulties in taxing the agricultural sector are often formidable, but it seems likely that insufficient recognition of the strategic role that agriculture can and should play in contributing to the capital requirements of economic development has been a factor in the failure to realize the potential for a higher rate of capital formation. Frequently, simple inertia and weaknesses in the tax system have been major factors: government revenues from land in the seven Part A states in India increased only 50 percent between 1938/39 and 1951/52 whereas the index of wholesale prices of major agricultural commodities increased 550 percent. On the other hand, inertia has contributed to high tax yields in instances in which tax revenues have been geared to rising world prices. The yield from the land tax in Burma declined from 40 percent of total government revenue prewar to 5 percent in 1952, but this was offset by the profits of the state agricultural marketing board which provided some 40 percent of total government revenue [49, pp. 54,

63]. The influence of the postwar rise in commodity prices was a particularly significant element in the large take of export taxes and marketing board surpluses in Ghana, Uganda, and other African countries.[13]

The conclusion suggested so strongly by both theoretical considerations and historical experience is that in underdeveloped countries, where agriculture accounts for some 40 to 60 percent of the total national income, the transition from a level of saving and investment that spells stagnation to one permitting a tolerable rate of economic growth cannot be achieved unless agriculture makes a significant net contribution to capital formation in the expanding sectors. If communist countries have an advantage in securing rapid economic growth, it would seem to lie chiefly in their ability to ride roughshod over political opposition and divert a maximum amount of current output into capital accumulation. And agriculture has been a prime target in squeezing out a maximum amount of surplus for investment. In the Soviet Union compulsory collection of grain at artificially low prices was used to siphon off the increment in output originating in agriculture and to facilitate the forced-march development of industry.[14] The rural communes in Communist China appear to be a device aimed not only at extracting the maximum possible surplus of capital from the countryside but a maximum labor effort as well.[15]

Societies which value individual freedom and which limit the arbitrary power of government are unable and unwilling to apply the sort of coercion and drastic reorganization of rural communities involved in the collectivization drive in the Soviet Union and in the creation of the Chinese communes. But this should not blind us to the hard fact that an essential element of economic growth is, in Lewis' phrase, "the process by which a community is converted from being a 5 percent to a 12 percent saver . . ." [31, p. 226]. In the earlier phases of development it is well-nigh certain that agriculture must play a major role in the process.

5. *Increased Rural Net Cash Income as a Stimulus to Industrialization.* One of the simplifying assumptions of the two-sector model is that expansion

[13] This is not intended as a blanket endorsement of export taxes and marketing board surpluses as devices for mobilizing funds for development. Nurkse and others have rightly emphasized that excessively heavy taxation can "kill the goose that lays the golden eggs," which seems to be an accurate description of Argentina's policies during the decade following World War II. It is also true that arguments for mobilizing funds by taxing the agricultural sector have a hollow ring if they encourage spendthrift government policies and expenditure on "public consumption goods," which Walker and Ehrlich believe to have been true in Uganda [50].

[14] For a brief description of Soviet experience and references to fuller treatments see [23, pp. 508–10].

[15] Recent reports indicate that the rural communes have encountered considerable difficulty in maintaining production efficiency because of some of the special problems of large-scale management in agriculture that are noted in Section III. See the summary of recent discussion of agricultural policy in the *People's Daily* and *Red Flag* by Jacques Jacquet-Francillon in *Le Figaro*, March 15, 1961, p. 5.

of the capitalist sector is limited only by shortage of capital. Given this assumption, an increase in rural net cash income is not a stimulus to industrialization but an obstacle to expansion of the capitalist sector.[16]

It is true, of course, that investment decisions may in fact be influenced not only by the availability of capital but also by demand conditions and estimates of the future profitability of additions to capacity. Nurkse has been especially emphatic in stressing the importance of *opportunities* for profitable investment as a strategic factor influencing the rate of capital formation, and Lewis himself emphasized in his report on industrialization in the Gold Coast that increased rural purchasing power is a valuable stimulus to industrial development [32]. Nurkse has given this concise statement of the problem:

> The trouble is this: there is not a sufficient market for manufactured goods in a country where peasants, farm laborers and their families, comprising typically two thirds to four fifths of the population, are too poor to buy any factory products, or anything in addition to the little they already buy. There is a lack of real purchasing power, reflecting the low productivity in agriculture [36, pp. 41–42].

There is clearly a conflict between emphasis on agriculture's essential contribution to the capital requirements for overall development and emphasis on increased farm purchasing power as a stimulus to industrialization. Nor is there any easy reconciliation of the conflict. The size of the market is particularly pertinent to investment decisions in industries characterized by economies of scale so that a fairly high volume of demand is needed to justify construction of a modern factory. But substitution of domestic output for imported manufactured goods often provides a significant addition to demand that does not depend upon an increase in consumer purchasing power. Furthermore, if capital requirements for developing infrastructure and capital-goods, or export industries are large relative to the amount of capital that can be mobilized, insufficient consumer demand is unlikely to limit the rate of investment.[17] Political considerations, of course,

---

[16] Lewis states that: "Anything which raises the productivity of the subsistence sector (average product per person) will raise real wages in the capitalist sector, and will therefore reduce the capitalist surplus and the rate of capital accumulation, unless it, at the same time, more than correspondingly moves the terms of trade against the subsistence sector [29, p. 172].

[17] It would appear that this was the situation that prevailed in Japan during the decades prior to about 1920. A provisional interpretation of developments in Japan during the years 1920–32 suggests that a low level of consumer purchasing power may have been more important than a lack of investable funds in limiting the rate of expansion of the capitalist sector. Even so, deflationary policies and an overvalued exchange rate appear to have been the principal factors responsible for the retardation in the expansion of the capitalist sector in Japan during this period [22, pp. 60–74]. It seems abundantly clear that Japan's remarkably rapid rate of economic growth since World War II has been stimulated by social changes that led to increased purchasing power among the farm population and industrial workers; but it is also true that by that time the existence of a sizable industrial base and a high rate of profits provided the funds which permitted an extremely high rate of investment.

also play an important role in this determination. Although this is another of the policy issues for which no general answer is possible, it will normally be appropriate to emphasize the capital contribution from agriculture in early stages of the structural transformation.

III. Resource Requirements and Priorities for Agricultural Development

It has been argued that a substantial rate of increase in agricultural production can be achieved largely through the more effective use of resources already in the agricultural sector and with only modest demands upon the scarce resources of high opportunity cost which are indispensable for industrial development.

The design and implementation of a rational program of agricultural development, however, is by no means a simple task. Although the experience of Japan, Taiwan, Denmark and other countries that have made notable progress in agriculture throws light on the type of approach that is likely to yield high returns, their experience can only be suggestive. Variations in soil, climate, and in human resources are of such importance that many aspects of agricultural development are specific to a particular country, region, district, and, ultimately, to an individual farm. Changes over time in the availability and relative prices of productive factors are also of great importance in influencing decisions concerning the choice of techniques of production and the combination of farm enterprises.

Agricultural Development Policies. Emphasis is given here to a particular type of strategy for raising the productivity of an existing agricultural economy. The low productivity of farm labor, land and other resources in the agricultural sector is largely due to the lack of certain complementary inputs of a technical, educational, and institutional nature. Under these circumstances a crucial requirement for devising an appropriate agricultural development program is to identify these complementary inputs, determine in what proportions they should be combined, and establish priorities among programs designed to increase their availability.

Such a policy for agricultural development, emphasizing measures to increase the efficiency of an existing labor-intensive agriculture and with chief reliance on technological innovations rather than large capital investments, is obviously *not* applicable under all conditions. It is therefore convenient, even at the risk of considerable over-simplification, to emphasize the changing position by defining three specific phases of agricultural development: Phase I: Development of agricultural preconditions. Phase II: Expansion of agricultural production based on labor-intensive, capital-saving techniques, relying heavily on technological innovations. Phase III: Expansion of agricultural production based on capital-intensive, labor-saving techniques.

The labor-intensive, capital-saving approach to agricultural development, appropriate to Phase II, requires an environment in which the possibility of change is recognized and accepted, and in which individual farmers see the possibility of personal gain from technological improvement. Phase I is defined as the period in which these preconditions are met.

Improvements in land tenure are likely to be the most essential requirement in Phase I since an unfavorable tenure situation may stifle the incentive for change even though the potential exists for large increases in output.[18] Rural attitudes toward change are also influenced by the attractiveness and availability of consumer goods, awareness of the possibility of technical improvements, availability of market outlets, and many other factors. If traditional group restraints and individual attitudes hostile to change seriously impede agricultural progress, considerable importance attaches to community development programs emphasizing adult literacy, self-help programs directed at the satisfaction of "felt needs," and similar activities that promote greater receptivity to change. There are probably relatively few underdeveloped areas where agricultural policies should be based on the assumption that the preconditions phase prevails.[19] But certainly there are situations in which deficiencies in the institutional environment or attitudes unfavorable to change are critical limiting factors; and in any event, continuing improvement in institutions and incentives can be expected to facilitate agricultural progress.

At the other end of the spectrum, the capital-intensive, labor-saving technology of Phase III typically represents a fairly late stage of development, especially for countries with a high population density. Japan, for example, is apparently just entering this stage. In this phase, the opportunity costs of most inputs, including labor, are high by past standards, and rising. Not only is the use of labor-saving farm machinery increasing but the use of many other urban-produced inputs is expanding as well. Hence the need for credit facilities becomes acute. Phase III is generally distinguished by the fact that a substantial amount of structural transformation has occurred so that agriculture no longer bulks so large in the economy.

---

[18] It is impossible to do more than call attention to this complex and important subject of land reform in this general treatment of agricultural development and its relation to over-all economic growth. Philip Raup has presented a persuasive statement of the economic importance of land tenure reform [41]. See also Doreen Warriner [51].

[19] With respect to the limitations on development that have been attributed to the allegedly irrational behavior of peasant agricultural producers, there seems to be a growing consensus that this view, espoused particularly by J. H. Boeke, is not borne out by the available evidence. Joosten, whose analysis of rubber exports in Indonesia refutes Boeke's notion of a perverse supply schedule, concludes that: ". . . a scrutiny of the facts shows that the peasant farms his land as rationally as possible under the social and economic conditions affecting him and within the limit of his opportunities as regard labour, land, markets, capital, knowledge and managerial skill" [25, p. 99]. Most of those who have given careful study to the problems of peasant agriculture would indorse that view (see for example [24]).

Agricultural Development Policies in Phase II. The emphasis in Phase II on increasing the efficiency of an existing agriculture by heavy reliance on technical innovations associated with labor-intensive, capital-saving techniques, is related to certain distinguishing features of this stage of development: (1) agriculture represents a large proportion of the economy; (2) the demand for agricultural products is increasing substantially, but the "required" increase in output of food for domestic consumption is fixed within fairly narrow limits determined by the rate of increase of population and of per capita incomes; (3) capital for the expanding industrial sector is particularly scarce; and (4) the distinction between resources of high opportunity cost and those which are abundant in agriculture and characterized by low opportunity cost is of considerable importance.

The design of an appropriate strategy for increasing agricultural productivity requires a high degree of judgment and intimate knowledge of the physical resources and agricultural characteristics of a particular region. Precise determination of an optimal production system, including optimal factor-factor and factor-product relations and operation of the various developmental services at optimal levels, is impossible. There is an inevitable and substantial margin of uncertainty in anticipating the returns likely to accrue from research programs and in forecasting the effectiveness with which knowledge of improved techniques will be disseminated and applied by individual farm operators. Moreover, the importance of innovations developed by individual farmers, an important feature of a progressive agriculture, is even more difficult to anticipate.

The essence of the problem is to identify those factors that are currently limiting increased production and to define a combination of inputs that will yield large returns in increased farm output and productivity. Although general presumptions may be of some value as a guide to research and analysis, there is no substitute for farm-level studies carried out in areas representative of the different types of farming situations that exist within a country or region. Such studies are needed to determine the nature of present input combinations and returns and ways in which efficient decisions and practices at the farm level are hindered by lack of essential inputs.

A number of attempts have been made to inventory the "nonconventional inputs" important for increasing agricultural productivity.[20] Four categories of complementary inputs or developmental services may be listed: (1) research to develop improved production possibilities; (2) extension-education programs; (3) facilities for supplying inputs of new and improved forms, particularly improved seed and fertilizers; (4) institutional facilities for servicing agricultural production, such as credit and marketing agencies, and rural governmental bodies for fostering collective action such as building

[20] See for example [13] [34].

feeder roads. These complementary inputs have a number of characteristics important to the agricultural development process:

First, they come from outside traditional agriculture. The individual farm operator makes the decision, for example, whether to use fertilizer or improved seed if those inputs are available. But whether the fertilizer or seed is available in a time, place, and form conducive to increased production is in large part determined by influences beyond the control of the individual farmer.

Secondly, all of these nonconventional inputs or developmental services include a large institutional component. Since agricultural research and extension-education programs offer tremendous external economies these functions are normally performed by governmental agencies. Under the conditions existing in low-income countries, it is also frequently desirable for government to encourage the creation of, or even to provide, the institutional facilities required to supply certain production inputs and credit and to process and market agricultural products.

Third, and most important, is the existence of important complementarities among the various conventional and nonconventional inputs. It is largely because of these complementarities that research and extension programs and making available fertilizers and other critical inputs can yield large returns in increasing productivity of the resources already committed to agriculture. Careful proportioning of the added inputs is also important. The interrelationship between the development of improved seed and increased use of fertilizer has already been stressed in reviewing the experience of Japan and Taiwan.

In addition to recognizing the desirability of economizing on resources of high opportunity cost, special attention needs to be given to concentrating resources on programs of the highest priority. Establishing a large number of objectives involves a twofold danger. An attack on items that are not currently of strategic importance obviously increases expenditure and lowers returns on investment. Perhaps even more serious, undue dispersion of effort reduces the effectiveness of critical programs because the shortage of competent administrative personnel imposes a severe limitation on the effectiveness of agricultural development programs.

This last consideration weighs heavily against price support and credit programs which require a considerable amount of high-level administrative talent.[21] The need to concentrate limited resources on priority programs

---

[21] It is sometimes argued (e.g. [13, pp. 25–28]) that it is necessary to shift risk and uncertainty from the innovating farmer to other persons. But the members of the farm population in an underdeveloped country are not at a common level of poverty, and there is usually a group controlling a substantial proportion of the land, with asset and income positions well above the average, which is capable of bearing the risk and uncertainty of innovation and investment. Improved credit institutions become a high priority need as the use of capital equipment becomes more important.

also makes it desirable to identify those geographical regions within a country that have high potential for large increases in production. Ability to supply the food requirements of expanding urban centers or a capacity for low-cost production of export crops with good market prospects are likely to be particularly pertinent considerations.[22]

For many countries the most critical components of an agricultural development program in Phase II are (1) research, (2) programs to make knowledge of improved technology available to farmers, (3) arrangements for supplying certain strategic new types of inputs, and (4) enlarged educational opportunities. Introduction of new crops may offer a potential for large increases in the value of agricultural output and frequently enlarged foreign-exchange proceeds as well. But this is dependent, in part at least, upon research to establish the suitability of possible crops to local conditions, to provide planting material, and to determine appropriate cultural practices.

1. *Agricultural Research.* The advances in scientific understanding, particularly during the past century, represent a possible windfall gain for a country launching a program of agricultural development today. It is largely because of the accumulated knowledge in such fields as soil science, plant nutrition, and genetics that there are the potential increments of productivity which provide the opportunity for taking up slack in a developing economy. Although an underdeveloped country can draw on the fundamental research and understanding that have been accumulated, the identification of promising avenues of progress and the testing and adapting of improved seed and cultural practices to local conditions are indispensable for realizing the gains that are attainable.

Mounting an effective agricultural research program is a long-term project that depends heavily on continuity of personnel. Shortage of qualified agricultural scientists is a critical problem which can be overcome only in part by employment of research workers from abroad.[23] So basic is an effective program of research to the other elements of an agricultural development program that it represents one of the few instances in which plans and budget allocations should err on the side of boldness, provided this openhandedness applies only within the limits of carefully determined research priorities.

---

[22] The Swynnerton Plan for accelerated development of African agriculture in Kenya is an important example of a plan and program that have given special attention to "lands of high potential" [7, pp. 9–15]. B. van de Walle's sketch of a plan for agricultural development of the Congo advocates concentration of resources on areas of high potential for export crop production or which possess locational advantages in supplying urban centers; the limited investments in other areas would be justified by social rather than economic considerations [47, p. 48].

[23] The cooperative program of the Rockefeller Foundation and the Ministry of Agriculture in Mexico owes much of its success to the continuity of service of the key scientists and the emphasis given to the training of young Mexican agricultural scientists [15].

2. *Extension-Education Programs.* The effectiveness of agricultural research is dependent upon an extension-education program which carries research findings to farmers and carries knowledge of farmers' problems back to the research staff. The extension techniques that have been effective in the United States are not necessarily appropriate in other countries. Japan achieved notable results without an extension service per se; extension-type activities were performed by local experiment stations, village agricultural associations, and in other ways. In Jamaica and Denmark a network of agricultural societies has provided an effective mechanism. Where farmer resistance to change is strong there may be a need for programs of supervised credit or subsidization of new inputs; and under some circumstances a government tractor-hire service might be justified in part as a technique for securing acceptance of improved practices or more productive farming systems. But the final success of a program to develop agriculture depends on training tradition-bound farmers to make economically sound decisions regarding new alternatives.[24]

A commonly recommended alternative to the slow process of training the mass of farmers to make their own decisions is to institute some form of large-scale farming using specialized management, such as collective farms and various types of cooperative farming. But economies of scale in agriculture do not continue for nearly as far out the scale line as in the case of other forms of production. The high degree of variability in agriculture poses problems of management and decision-making which cannot be centralized without considerable duplication of effort. Brewster has stressed particularly the large number of "on-the-spot supervisory decisions" that must be made in agriculture [3]. There is a basic difference between agriculture and industry in this respect because the biological nature of the agricultural production process means that the operations to be performed are separated in time and space. This increases the importance of these on-the-spot supervisory decisions and reduces some of the advantages of mechanization.[25] A further significant economic advantage of decentralized management and decision-making arises from the more direct individual interest in the outcome of the farm enterprise with consequent favorable effects on incentives, initiative, and upon what Raup has termed the

[24] For discussion of the problems and feasibility of a program of management assistance to farmers in low-income countries, see [20].

[25] An interesting study by G. K. Boon of conditions under which mechanization is economical in the construction of field trenches emphasizes that "labour-intensive methods in construction are characterized by the absence of some of the disadvantages which they usually imply in industrial processes"; for example, "substituting labour for machinery for construction processes does not involve larger factory buildings and other extra capital outlays" [2, pp. 11–12]. This sort of contrast is, of course, even more evident in the differences between agricultural and industrial processes.

"accretionary process of capital formation" that are of such importance in agriculture.[26]

Judging from the experience of collective farms and production cooperatives these considerations are of considerable importance; but they do not rule out the possibility of exceptions. It has been noted, for example, that plantations may facilitate the introduction of new export crops for which the capital and technical requirements are demanding, particularly if integration of production and processing is important for the control of quality [21, p. 342]. These advantages of large-scale production depend upon a high level of managerial skill; and they are likely to be temporary.[27] Similarly, some form of tractor-hire service or contract plowing provided either by the agricultural department, a cooperative, or private entrepreneurs, may be an economical arrangement, particularly if technical considerations such as deep or timely plowing are important.[28]

3. *Supply of Strategic New Types of Inputs.* Certain of the complementary inputs of critical importance to increasing agricultural production in Phase II are items such as chemical fertilizers that are new and must be supplied from outside the traditional village economy. Fertilizers and pesticides depend upon the establishment of new productive capacity or upon foreign exchange for imports; thus they compete directly for scarce resources of high opportunity cost. The returns on investment in those inputs, however, can be extremely high provided that the full range of complementary inputs is available—notably improved seed, knowledge of fertilizer response under various soil and cropping situations, and an extension organization capable of disseminating information to farmers.

The new inputs also require new institutional facilities to make them available at the farm level. In some countries fertilizer manufacturers have done this job effectively, but frequently in the earlier stages of development it is necessary for the government agricultural service or cooperatives to

---

[26] Raup stresses the influence of a suitable tenure situation and of the time-consuming character of production processes upon capital accumulation in agriculture. Both elements are important, for example, in the growth of livestock numbers and quality as a result of slow improvements in feeding levels and better management and disease protection [41, p. 14]. Likewise, he emphasizes the importance of "periodic unemployment" in agriculture when the opportunity cost of labor is measured only in the reservation price of leisure time. "An incentive system that will maximize the investment of this labor in the firm is one of the basic requirements for agricultural growth. In terms of capital creation that structure is best which creates the maximum likelihood that the farm family will elect to 'exploit' its own labor" [41, p. 22].

[27] In past years it was claimed that African smallholders could not produce high quality Arabica coffee in Kenya; but in the last ten years there has been a spectacular expansion of production by African producers. Problems of quality control have been difficult but by no means insoluble. This development has, of course, been supported by government research and extension programs and loans to facilitate the establishment of cooperative pulping stations.

[28] The highly successful Gezira Scheme in the Sudan exemplifies an interesting combination of labor-intensive and capital-intensive techniques [11, pp. 230–34].

perform this function. To make available supplies of improved seed requires intricate institutional arrangements for seed multiplication and distribution so as to insure a pure supply; and here again governmental initiative is likely to be essential.

Improvement of transportation facilities may also be crucial to farmer utilization of purchased inputs. Improved transportation also increases production incentives through higher farm prices and speeds the spread of innovation through improved communication.

4. *Education and Agricultural Development.* Virtually all aspects of agricultural development hinge on developing a broad range of educational institutions. The critical problems concern the use of the small nucleus of trained personnel to staff training programs and the financial burden arising from enlarged expenditures for education.

Despite difficulties of finance and lack of trained teachers, many underdeveloped countries today are committed to large-scale expansion of educational facilities. This increased supply of trained people can be turned to good account in agriculture since trained manpower is needed to remove the bottleneck to efficient utilization of the labor and land resources that are already abundant in this sector. This is in marked contrast to the situation in industry where the large requirements for capital equipment to be combined with labor constitute a bottleneck to rapidly expanding the utilization of trained labor.

Efforts aimed at developing local government institutions, increasing literacy, and instituting rural social changes by community development or other techniques can be commenced by personnel with slight initial training supplemented by continuing in-service training. Even in the case of agricultural extension, programs at the early stages can emphasize relatively simple production innovations such as fertilizer-seed combinations, introduction of improved tools, and efforts to raise the general standard of husbandry nearer to that of the better farmers. The spread of education among the farm population broadens horizons, provides necessary skills for keeping records and accounts, and strengthens the capacity of farmers to make rational decisions.

Agricultural development in Phase II is potentially a dynamic process characterized by continuing increase in agricultural productivity.[29] This is so, in part, because of differential rates of adoption of new technology, but it is also a consequence of the continuing stream of innovations generated

---

[29] Higgins argues incorrectly that "with the labor-intensive techniques of small-scale peasant agriculture the opportunities for technological improvement are extremely limited" [16, p. 422]. His assertion seems to be based on the erroneous view that agricultural development at this stage is a one-shot proposition—shifting from "bad" seed and practices to "good" seed and practices—and that a dynamic process of agricultural development is impossible until "the discontinuous jump to more extensive and more mechanized agriculture" can be made [16, p. 442].

by an effective research program. This continuing growth of farm productivity depends on a large number of changes which individually give relatively small response but collectively add up to a large response. It requires continued improvement in incentives and in the institutions serving agriculture, including further refinement in the operation of the research and extension organizations, and the establishment or strengthening of institutions of higher education to provide the needed professional and administrative personnel.

IV. Conclusions

In this examination of agriculture's role in the process of economic development, an attempt has been made to emphasize features that have a high degree of generality. But diversity among nations and the variety that is so characteristic of agriculture inevitably limits the validity of a condensed, general treatment. The density of the rural population and the stage of economic development that has been reached stand out as having a particularly significant bearing on the importance of some of the factors examined in this paper.

Despite these qualifications, it is believed that the general thesis advanced has wide relevance: rural welfare as well as overall economic growth demand a transformation of a country's economic structure, involving relative decline of the agricultural sector, and a net flow of capital and other resources from agriculture to the industrial sector of the economy. Agriculture's contribution to the requirements for development capital is especially significant in the earlier stages of the process of growth; it will not be so crucial in countries which have the possibility of securing a sizeable fraction of their capital requirements by export of mineral products or in the form of foreign loans or grants.

Policies that take account of this process of secular transformation and its implications are in the long-run interest of the farm population as well as the country as a whole. Reduction of the farm labor force is a necessary condition for establishing factor proportions that yield returns to labor in agriculture that are more or less in accord with returns to labor in other sectors. More concretely, insufficient movement out of agriculture will perpetuate, or lead to, excessively small farms and serious underemployment of labor as the proximate causes of substandard farm incomes.

Although this paper has stressed the importance of agriculture's role in development, we part company with those who draw the inference that agricultural development should precede or take priority over industrial expansion. Sayigh, who can be taken as representative of that view, asserts that "deep progress cannot be achieved on both these fronts simultaneously" [44, p. 448]. It is our contention that "balanced growth" is needed in the sense of simultaneous efforts to promote agricultural and industrial development. We recognize that there are severe limitations on the capacity of an underdeveloped country to do everything at once. But it is precisely this consideration which underscores the importance of developing agriculture in such a way as to both minimize its demands upon resources most needed for industrial development and maximize its net contribution to the capital required for general economic growth.

REFERENCES

1. D. E. Bell. "Allocating Development Resources: Some Observations Based on Pakistan Experience," in *Public Policy—A Yearbook of the Graduate School of Public Administration, Harvard University 1959.* Cambridge, 1959.
2. G. K. Boon. *Alternative Techniques of Production, A Case Study of a Construction Process—Field Trenches.* Netherlands Economic Institute, Progress Report No. 5, Pub. No. 2060. Rotterdam, 1960.
3. J. M. Brewster. "The Machine Process in Agriculture and Industry," *Journal of Farm Economics,* Vol. 32 (February 1950), pp. 69–81.
4. H. B. Chenery. "The Application of Investment Criteria," *Quarterly Journal of Economics,* Vol. 67 (February 1953), pp. 77–96.
5. ———. "Development Policies and Programmes," *Economic Bulletin for Latin America,* Vol. 3 (March 1958), pp. 51–77.
6. C. Clark. *Conditions of Economic Progress.* London, 1951.
7. Colony and Protectorate of Kenya. *A Plan to Intensify the Development of African Agriculture in Kenya.* Nairobi, 1954.
8. F. Dovring. "The Share of Agriculture in a Growing Population," *FAO Mo. Bull. Agri. Econ. and Stat.*, Vol. 8 (August–September 1959), pp. 1–11.
9. O. Eckstein. "Investment Criteria for Economic Development and the Theory of Intertemporal Welfare Economics," *Quarterly Journal of Economics,* Vol. 71 (February 1957), pp. 56–85.
10. J. M. Fleming. "External Economies and the Doctrine of Balanced Growth," *Economic Journal,* June 1955, pp. 241–56.
11. A. Gaitskell. *Gezira, A Story of Development in the Sudan.* London, 1959.
12. N. Georgescu-Roegen. "Economic Theory and Agrarian Economics," *Oxford Economic Papers,* N. S., February 1960, Vol. 12, pp. 1–41.
13. Government of India, Ministry of Food and Agriculture. *Report on India's Food Crisis and How to Meet It.* New Delhi, April 1959.
14. Z. Griliches. "Research Costs and Social Returns: Hybrid Corn and Related Innovations," *Journal of Political Economy,* Vol. 66 (October 1958), pp. 419–31.
15. J. G. Harrar. "International Collaboration in Food Production," Address before the Agricultural Research Institute, National Academy of Sciences—National Research Council, Washington, D.C., October 4, 1954.
16. B. Higgins. *Economic Development: Principles, Problems, and Policies.* New York, 1959.
17. Indian Cooperative Union. *Rural Development and Credit Project, Evaluation Report.* New Delhi, 1960.

18. Institute of Farm Management and Agricultural Economics. *Technical and Economic Changes in Danish Farming, 40 years of Farm Records 1917–1957.* Copenhagen, 1959.
19. E. Jensen. *Danish Agriculture: Its Economic Development.* Copenhagen, 1937.
20. S. E. Johnson. "Management Assistance in Farming," *Indian Journal of Agricultural Economics,* Vol. 14 (October–December 1959), pp. 27–32.
21. B. F. Johnston and J. W. Mellor, "The Nature of Agriculture's Contributions to Economic Development," *Food Research Institute Studies,* Vol. 1 (1960), pp. 335–56.
22. B. F. Johnston, "Agricultural Development and Economic Transformation: Japan, Taiwan, and Denmark." Paper prepared for an SSRC Conference on Relations Between Agriculture and Economic Growth, Stanford, November 1960.
23. ———. "Agricultural Productivity and Economic Development in Japan," *Journal of Political Economy,* Vol. 49 (December 1951), pp. 498–513.
24. W. O. Jones. "Economic Man in Africa," *Food Research Institute Studies,* Vol. 1 (May 1960), pp. 107–34.
25. J. H. L. Joosten, "Perverse Supply Curves in Less Developed Economies?," *Netherlands Journal Agricultural Science,* Vol. 8 (May 1960), pp. 98–102.
26. S. Kuznets. *Six Lectures on Economic Growth.* Glencoe, Ill. 1959.
27. M. Latil. *L'evolution du revenu agricole.* Paris, 1956.
28. H. Leibenstein. *Economic Backwardness and Economic Growth.* New York, 1957.
29. W. A. Lewis, "Economic Development with Unlimited Supplies of Labour," *Manchester School,* Vol. 22 (May 1954), pp. 139–41.
30. ———. "Unlimited Labour: Further Notes," *Manchester School,* Vol. 26 (1958), pp. 1–32.
31. ———. *The Theory of Economic Growth.* Homewood, Ill., 1955.
32. ———. *Report on Industrialization and the Gold Coast.* Gold Coast Government, Accra, 1953.
33. J. W. Mellor and R. D. Stevens. "The Average and Marginal Product of Farm Labor in Underdeveloped Countries," *Journal of Farm Economics,* Vol. 38 (August 1956), pp. 780–91.
34. A. T. Mosher. *Technical Cooperation in Latin-American Agriculture.* Chicago, 1957.
35. H. G. Moulton. *Japan: An Economic and Financial Appraisal.* Washington, D.C., 1931.
36. R. Nurkse. *Patterns of Trade and Development.* Stockholm, 1959.
37. K. Ohkawa. "Economic Growth and Agriculture," *Annals Hitotsubashi Acad.,* Vol. 7 (October 1956), pp. 46–60.
38. K. Ohkawa and H. Rosovsky. "The Role of Agriculture in Modern Japanese Economic Development," paper prepared for the Carmel Conference on Urban-Rural Relations in the Modernization of Japan, August 1959; published in a shorter version in *Economical Development and Cultural Change,* Pt. II, Vol. 9 (October 1960), pp. 43–67.

39. E. M. Ojala. *Agriculture and Economic Progress.* London, 1952.
40. G. Ranis. "The Financing of Japanese Economic Development," *Economic History Review*, Vol. II (April 1959), pp. 440–54.
41. P. M. Raup. "The Contribution of Land Reforms to Agricultural Development: An Analytical Framework." Paper prepared for an SSRC Conference on Relations Between Agriculture and Economic Growth, Stanford, November 1960.
42. H. Rosovsky. "Japanese Capital Formation: The Role of the Public Sector," *Journal of Economic History,* Vol. 19 (September 1959), pp. 350–73.
43. V. W. Ruttan. "Agricultural and Non-Agricultural Growth in Output per Unit of Input," *Journal of Farm Economics, Proceedings,* Vol. 39 (December 1957), pp. 1566–76.
44. Y. A. Sayigh. "The Place of Agriculture in Economic Development," *Agricultural Situation in India*, Vol. 14 (New Delhi, 1959), Annual Number, p. 445.
45. T. W. Schultz. *The Economic Organization of Agriculture.* New York, 1953.
46. F. C. Shorter. "Foodgrains Policy in East Pakistan," in *Public Policy—A Yearbook of the Graduate School of Public Administration, Harvard University 1959.* Cambridge, Mass., 1959.
47. B. van de Walle. *Essai d'une planification de l'économie agricole congolaise.* INEAC Sér. Tech. No. 61. Brussels, 1960.
48. J. Viner. *International Trade and Economic Development.* Glencoe, Ill., 1952.
49. H. P. Wald. *Taxation of Agricultural Land in Underdeveloped Countries.* Cambridge, Mass., 1959.
50. D. Walker and C. Ehrlich. "Stabilization and Development Policy in Uganda," *Kyklos*, Vol. 12 (1959), pp. 341–53.
51. D. Warriner. *Land Reform and Economic Development.* National Bank of Egypt, 50th Anniversary Commemorative Lectures. Cairo, 1955.

22 An "Agricultural Surplus" as a Factor in Economic Development*[1]

WILLIAM H. NICHOLLS†

> When by the improvement and cultivation of land . . . the labour of half the society becomes sufficient to provide food for the whole, the other half . . . can be employed . . . in satisfying the other wants and fancies of mankind.
>
> ADAM SMITH.

I. INTRODUCTION

In the present article, I shall define (with occasional modifications) an "agricultural surplus" as the physical amount by which, in any given country, total food production exceeds the total food consumption of the agricultural population. This concept might appear to be too simple and obvious to warrant serious consideration. Unfortunately, what was obvious to Adam Smith in 1776 is easily overlooked amid the agricultural affluence of today's advanced countries. As a consequence, Western economists have tended to ignore or seriously underestimate the importance of an agricultural surplus both in the earlier economic history of today's developed countries and in those countries which still remain at or near the bare subsistence level of food consumption.

My own reading of economic history, developed at length elsewhere,[2] has led me to the conclusion that, "until underdeveloped countries succeed

---

* *Journal of Political Economy*, Vol. LXXI, No. 1 (February 1963), pp. 1–29.

† Vanderbilt University, Nashville, Tennessee.

[1] This paper is a major revision of the J. S. McLean Memorial Lecture which the author presented at the Ontario Agricultural College, Guelph, in January, 1962. That lecture was distributed in limited numbers by Ontario Agricultural College in processed form, under the title, "The Importance of an Agricultural Surplus in Underdeveloped Countries." Since the present paper has corrected some errors of logic or exposition contained in the Guelph lecture, while more effectively treating the international-trade aspects of the problem, the author would prefer that this paper be cited insofar as the two sources deal with common subject matter.

[2] William H. Nicholls, "The Place of Agriculture in Economic Development," to be published by Macmillan (London) during 1963 as part of the *Proceedings* of the Round Table on Economic Development, with Particular Reference to East Asia, which the International Economic Association held at Gamagori, Japan, during April 2–9, 1960.

in achieving and sustaining (either through domestic production or imports) a reliable food surplus, they have not fulfilled the fundamental pre-condition for economic development." Kuznets reached a similar conclusion on the basis of his comparative studies of economic development: "an agricultural revolution—a marked rise in productivity per worker in agriculture—is a pre-condition of the industrial revolution in any part of the world."[3] If Kuznets and I are correct, much mischief has resulted from the fact that most Western policy-planners and theorists have misread the Law of the Declining Relative Importance of Agriculture, tending to emphasize the existence of a *labor* surplus in agriculture while taking a surplus of *food output* (except in a very long-run context) for granted. They have thereby reinforced the predilections of economic planners in the underdeveloped countries for all-out emphasis on industrial development.

Few theorists have incorporated the production side of agriculture into their models. Insofar as policy planners have done so, they have largely proposed means of raising agricultural productivity, notably mechanization and land consolidation, which require drastic structural changes in agriculture and presuppose the massive absorption of surplus agricultural labor by prior industrialization. Thus, in theory and policy, economists have largely neglected the *initial* importance of the production side of agriculture, which they try to make the cart behind an industrial horse. Fortunately, those so oriented are now finding that history is catching up with them. The current news from Communist China, India and Pakistan, Turkey, Russia, and even Argentina and Brazil offers mounting evidence that agriculture cannot be so easily dismissed as they had once supposed.

With this jeremiad off my chest, let me turn to my principal objective—the development of some partial analytical models which give greater precision to the concept of an "agricultural surplus." I shall give special attention to determinants of the size, and potential contributions to economic growth, of the agricultural surplus under various conditions of population pressure and under different systems of land tenure. I shall particularly emphasize the opportunities for, and limitations of, making agriculture a positive generating force instead of a needless drag on general economic development.

II. THE BASIC TOOLS

For present purposes, my graphic techniques may easily be confined to those familiar with elementary production theory. However, it is well to make explicit at the outset my basic assumptions and the special definitions of particular curves which will hold throughout the entire analysis which follows.

---

[3] Simon Kuznets, *Six Lectures on Economic Growth* (Glencoe, Ill.: Free Press, 1959), pp. 59–60.

Let us assume that (1) all agricultural land is of homogeneous quality; (2) agricultural techniques are given; (3) only food crops are grown, industrial crops (if any) being treated as a separate part of the agricultural sector; (4) food output is produced by a large number of identical production units each of whose acreage of land is the optimum amount (small) for the given level of techniques (primitive); (5) a constant proportion of the agricultural population participates in the farm-labor force; (6) per capita food consumption is given and identical for all individuals in any given agricultural population; and (7) labor and land are so combined that any given agricultural population maximizes its food output. If assumptions (5) and (7) are inconsistent with each other, as they may be under special circumstances, we shall abandon (5) in favor of (7).

Under these assumptions, the product curves would take the following form. The annual total product curve (TP_1 in Fig. 1, *A*) will follow the path $OMQQ'$, the linear portions OM and QQ' following from our maximizing assumption (7). This means that all agricultural land will be *in actual use* only for populations of OA_2 or greater. As population increases from nil to OA_2, land is brought under cultivation (and the number of identical farms increased) in the same proportion as population is increasing, so that total food output increases along OM proportionately with population. For a population of OA_6, total product will be at its maximum A_6Q, which level will presumably be maintained for still larger populations by avoiding further increases in the amounts of labor *actually used* in production. With TP_1 so defined, the average product curve (AP_1 in Figure 1, *B*) will be $N_4RT'T$ and the marginal product curve (MP_1 in Figure 1, *B*) will be $N_4RS'SA_6A_8$.

On the *consumption* side, the annual total consumption curves (TC_S and TC_F in Figure 1, *A*) depend upon the levels of food consumption which prevail. Let us suppose that per capita food consumption may vary from a minimum biological subsistence level (say, 2,000 calories per day) to a maximum, "fully fed" level (say, 3,000 calories per day). In Figure 1, *B*, let ON_1 and ON_2 measure (on an annual basis) these two extremes of per capita food consumption, as represented by the average consumption curves AC_S and AC_F, respectively. The vertical levels of these AC curves then determines the slopes of the corresponding linear total consumption curves of Figure 1, *A*.

The slope of each of the several annual total wage curves (TW_1 to TW_4) in Figure 1, *A* is similarly dependent upon the relevant annual wage rate (ON_1 to ON_4) as determined by the intersection of the supply and demand curves for labor in Figure 1, *B*.[4] In the latter figure, the various vertical

[4] As we shall see later, wages need not be separately considered under a system of owner-operated farms, but become highly relevant where the agricultural land is owned by rent-maximizing landlords who hire their farm workers.

lines beginning at A_1, A_2, etc., may be considered the shifting short-run supply curves of labor. For populations up to OA_5, the demand curve for labor will correspond to the marginal product curve $N_4RS'S$. Thus, the real annual

FIGURE 1

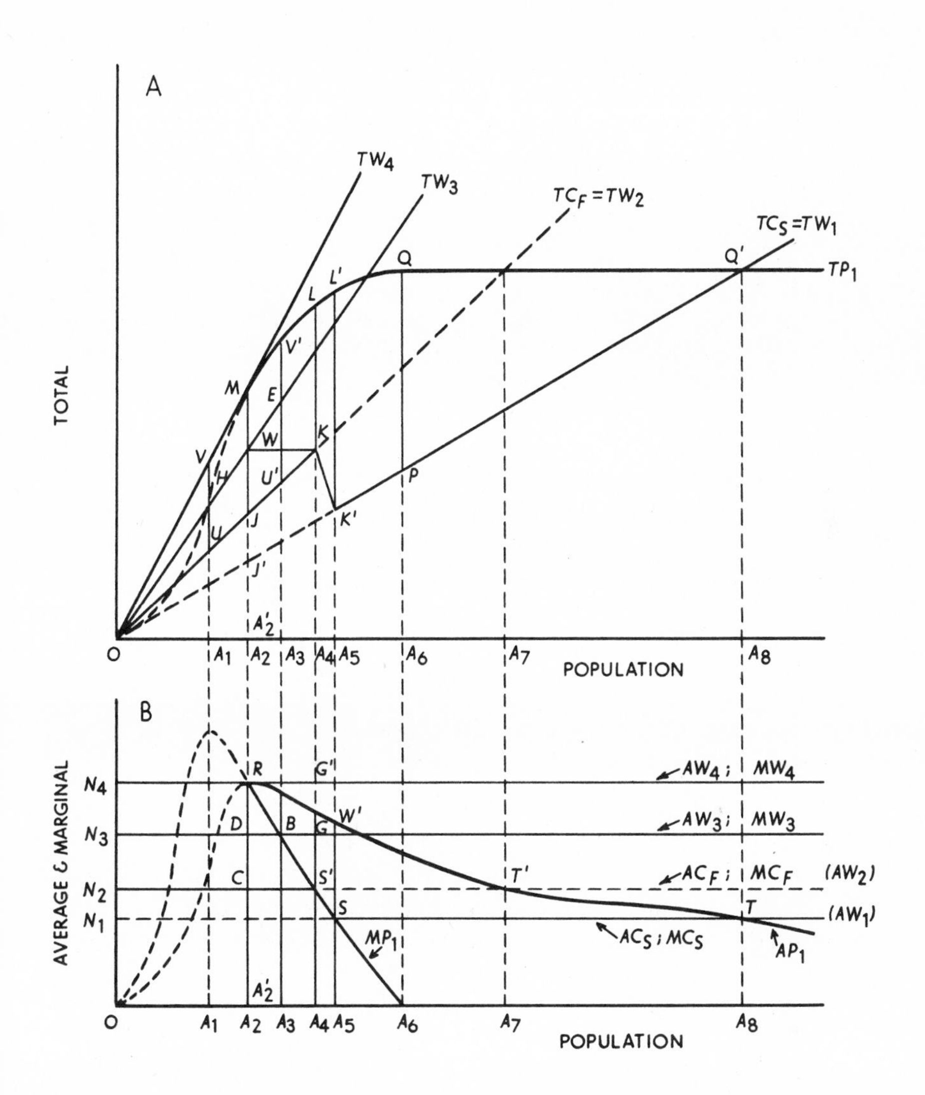

wage rate will be ON_4 for all populations up to OA_2 and ON_3 for a population of OA_3. When population reaches OA_4, the annual wage (ON_2) will be just sufficient to provide a "fully fed" diet. Hence, any further increase in population A_4A_5 must mean not only a fall in the wage rate to ON_1

but a deterioration in the diet itself to the subsistence level.[5] Thus, AC_S represents the minimum (subsistence) annual wage. For any population in excess of OA_5 (for which $MP_1 = MC_S$), some farm workers must receive more than their specific contribution to food output ($MC_S > MP_1$) in order to survive. Agriculture having thus become "overpopulated," the phase of the MP_1 curve SA_6A_8 loses all relevance as a factor in wage determination, social necessity forcing the abandonment of all efforts to maximize anything but total food output.[6] We shall therefore assume that, for the entire range of possible populations, the average consumption curve is $N_2S'ST$ (Figure 1, *B*) and the total consumption curve $OKK'Q'$ (Figure 1, *A*).

We now have all the tools necessary to determine the *agricultural surplus*. The annual (total) agricultural surplus is the vertical difference between the total product curve (TP_1) and the relevant total consumption curve (TC_F or TC_S)—VU for a population of OA_1, KL for a population of OA_4, $K'L'$ for a population of OA_5, and PQ for a population of OA_6. The agricultural surplus will entirely disappear only when population reaches its maximum level—OA_7 for a "fully fed" population ($TP_1 = TC_F$), OA_8 when the diet is at the subsistence level ($TP_1 = TC_S$). Thus there will normally be some range of population (such as OA_8) within which there are annual agricultural surpluses of varying but positive magnitude.[7] Each surplus will also be subject to various alternative uses, some of which will promote economic development more than others. To this problem we now turn, first considering conditions of *under*population, then conditions of *over*population.

In the section which immediately follows, we shall limit ourselves to that range of agricultural populations (OA_5) for which the marginal product of farm labor equals or exceeds the subsistence wage rate. Countries whose agricultural population is so large (greater than OA_5) that the marginal product of farm labor falls below the subsistence wage will be considered "overpopulated" and analyzed in a later section.

III. "AGRICULTURAL SURPLUS" IN AN UNDERPOPULATED COUNTRY

Let us first consider the case of an "underpopulated" country—that is, one in which land is initially so relatively abundant that it is a "free good."

---

[5] We ignore the possibility that, for any given level of population, food output would fall because workers will have lower energy levels as they become less adequately fed. Otherwise, for populations in excess of OA_4, the total product curve would be lower than that indicated by TP_1.

[6] Nicholas Georgescu-Roegen, "Economic Theory and Agrarian Economics," *Oxford Economic Papers*, N.S., Vol. 12 [1960], pp. 1–40 demonstrates convincingly on both empirical and theoretical grounds why this is normally so. Here, out initial assumptions (above) being in conflict, we retain assumption (7) while dropping assumption (5).

[7] We shall, however, have occasion later to recognize the possibility that some or all of a particular country's agricultural land might be so infertile that TP would coincide with, or lie entirely below, the TC_S curve (cf. n. 24).

We shall analyze the economic development of such a country and the role an agricultural surplus can play in that development. We will consider two types of agriculture—that consisting of one sector (food production only) and that having two sectors (food and industrial crops).

A. A One-Sector Agricultural Economy

Let us assume a newly settled country whose entire population is engaged in food production. Suppose further that there is an agricultural surplus—that is, more food production than the existing population needs for its own subsistence—but no opportunities for international trade. Since the food surplus would then have no alternative value in the form of imported consumer or producer goods, it would be extremely difficult if not impossible to develop a domestic nonfood sector beyond the handicraft stage. Under these circumstances, any population of less than OA_7 would be surfeited with food and there would be a maximum incentive for population growth. Thus, starting with a relatively small population of (say) OA_2, one might expect population to follow an equilibrium adjustment path (Figure 1, *A*) along TP_1 from *M* to the intersection with the TC_F curve.[8] Up to this point ($TP = TC_F$), at which population was OA_7, there would also be no incentive to improve farming techniques. If the population grew beyond OA_7, the path would (unless techniques were now improved) move horizontally along TP_1 to Q' as the *TC* curve gradually swung down to its minimum level TC_S. With $TP_1 = TC_S$, an absolute maximum population of OA_8 would have been reached.

Fortunately, such "new" countries as those of the Americas and Australasia were born after channels of international trade had been well developed. Let us therefore assume instead that any food surpluses produced in our newly settled country may be freely and profitably exchanged for foreign-produced goods under constant terms of trade. The relatively high levels of living which such exchangeable food surpluses (over and above complete satisfaction of food needs) make possible would then probably become habitual, thereby favoring voluntary restraints on population growth in order to enjoy further material progress. By what process might such material progress take place? Since our analysis depends in part on the land-tenure system assumed, we shall consider separately the situation in which all farms are owner-operated and that in which farm workers do not own the land they cultivate.

---

[8] This particular adjustment path follows from our initial assumptions (5) and (7). The assumption that labor is a constant fraction of population is somewhat awkward, however, given the significant time lag before newly born children can become part of the labor force. If we recognize such discontinuities in the adjustment of the size of the labor force by dropping assumption (5), the adjustment path might alternatively run horizontally from *M* to the TC_F curve, vertically to the TP_1 curve, horizontally to the TC_F curve, and so on, until $TP_1 = TC_F$.

A System of Agricultural Freeholders. Let us assume in this section that the "new" nation has a liberal and equalitarian land-settlement policy, distributing all available "free land" in units of family size so that the prevailing system of land tenure is one of owner-operated farms. Each farmer, being at once landlord and laborer, will then seek to maximize his total returns from land and labor combined. This means that he will maximize his *average* (not total) agricultural surplus. For any population up to OA_2, farming techniques remaining constant, the average agricultural surplus (AP_1–AC_F) will be at a maximum RC (Figure 1, B). Per capita real income (which may be measured by the heights of AP_1 since the economy is entirely agricultural) will also be at its maximum level RA_2. Hence, OA_2 may be considered the optimum population, for the given technology, in a nation of agricultural freeholders.[9]

There is no reason to assume, however, that population growth will cease when it has reached OA_2. To be sure, agricultural freeholders—having become habituated to a high real level of living and mindful of the dangers of their landholdings becoming fragmented through inheritance—might be expected to impose considerable voluntary restraints upon further population growth. However, even a moderate increase in population from OA_2 to OA_4 would significantly reduce the per capita agricultural surplus if nothing is done to raise agricultural productivity or to create nonagricultural employment. For, while the *total* agricultural surplus would continue to increase from MJ to LK, the *average* surplus would fall from RC to GS'. Thus, if the entire current agricultural surplus is consumed (presumably in the form of imported consumer goods), it must be at the expense of lower per capita real income as population grows beyond OA_2.

This need not happen, however, if part of the agricultural surplus is accumulated and directly or indirectly invested in essential types of social overhead, in a domestic nonagricultural sector, and in improved agricultural

[9] Any population smaller than OA_2 will surely grow to that level since (given constant international terms of trade) population increase costs nothing in per capita real terms. Strictly speaking, there will be certain necessary social overhead costs associated with population growth. An important example is investments in transportation, since the available land is "free" only after it and its product have been made accessible. Similarly, the population will probably not reach OA_2 (at which all "free" land has been taken up) before agricultural techniques are improved. Indeed, each farmer—having all the land he needs but being unable to hire farm workers at a wage below their maximum average product (RA_2)—can increase his real income *only* by improving his techniques. In both instances, however, accumulation and direct or indirect investment out of agricultural surplus will probably pay off handsomely by way of the growth in the size of that agricultural surplus. In addition, with the concomitant growth in the size of the domestic market, increasing opportunities for development of an industrial sector (again financed initially out of agricultural surplus) will probably already have been seized before the population reaches OA_2. For reasons of convenience, however, let us assume that, at a population of OA_2, TP_1 reflects the effects of any prior investment in social overhead and in agricultural techniques and that the non-agricultural sector employs a negligible part of the total population.

techniques. More specifically, farm owner-operators need not become progressively worse off as population grows from OA_2 to OA_4 (1) if A_2A_4 jobs can be created in the nonagricultural sector, the *agricultural* population remaining constant at OA_2; (2) if, through investment in better agricultural techniques, farmers can raise the total product curve (TP_1) sufficiently to permit an agricultural population of OA_4 to enjoy an average product of at least A_4G' ($= A_2R$); or (3) by some combination of the two. Given an initial agricultural surplus of MJ, the initial financing for one or both of these alternatives (and associated social overhead investments) can be found.

Let us look first at social overhead investment since, if wisely made, it may contribute significantly to both industrial development and agricultural improvements. A nation of agricultural freeholders, producing a substantial agricultural surplus, is in an unusually favorable position to minimize the role of government. To a very large extent, the achievement of an optimum allocation of the agricultural surplus among nonfood consumption, nonagricultural investment, and agricultural investment can be left to the voluntary decisions of private enterprise. Nonetheless, an agriculture of equalitarian structure is likely to be particularly aware of the need for certain public services which individual farm families cannot provide for themselves satisfactorily if at all. At the same time, an equalitarian agriculture will probably be associated with a democratic socio-political environment in which government is responsive to demands for the public services which a majority of small landowners want and are willing (through taxes) to pay for.

Hence, at a minimum, government will probably be called upon to assume the role of assuring an optimum rate of direct or indirect public investment in transportation, education, agricultural research and extension services, banking and credit institutions, and other types of social overhead. To provide such social services for any given population, government will presumably tax away some part of the agricultural surplus. To that extent, the funds immediately available for imported consumer goods and private domestic investment will be reduced. However, subsequent returns on private investment in either agriculture (whose TP_1 curve will rise, increasing the agricultural surplus for the given population) or the nonagricultural sector will presumably be higher.

Let us now consider more generally the contributions which an initial agricultural surplus can make to both nonagricultural development and to agricultural improvements. For analytical purposes, let us incorporate social overhead and government into our model by the following assumption—any given investment is allocated between tangibles (plant and equipment) and intangibles (social overhead) in such a way as to maximize the response in terms of productivity, the sources of that investment—whether private (voluntary savings) or public (taxes)—being in the proportions consistent with its optimum allocation.

It seems reasonable to suppose that, as population grows to OA_2 and beyond, there will be an increasing number of opportunities for profitable investments in a nonagricultural sector. This is particularly likely under our assumption of an equalitarian land-ownership pattern, the equitable distribution of incomes favoring the development of a demand for a broad range of goods and services. While initial opportunities will lie primarily in the residentiary industries (retail and wholesale trade and other services, and the manufacture of bulky goods too costly if imported from afar), the growing size of the domestic market will increasingly permit import-substituting manufacturing enterprises to achieve an efficient scale of operations.

Suppose then that, with an entirely agricultural population of OA_2, enough of the initial agricultural surplus MJ is shifted from consumption to nonagricultural investment to provide nonfarm employment for a small increment of population A_2A_2 at a real wage of A_2R. Insofar as this initial investment goes into industrial *fixed* capital, an equivalent part of the food surplus will now have to be exchanged for imported industrial producer goods instead of imported consumer goods. In addition, part of the initial investment will take the form of advances of a major component of industrial *working* capital—the food needed to feed the nonfarm population. As the consequence of such investment, exports will fall as food is diverted from the export market to domestic consumption. While initially small, this loss of export revenue will become increasingly significant as the nonagricultural population grows towards A_2A_4, at which level WJ of the constant agricultural surplus MJ will be consumed as food by the nonagricultural sector.

Declining food exports need cause no problem, however, if farmers shift their expenditures for industrial consumer goods from foreign to domestic sources in step with the shifts in the market for food from foreign to domestic outlets. Thus, by the time total population reaches OA_4, OA_2 farmers may meet the nonagricultural sector's needs for WJ food by purchasing an equivalent amount of domestic industrial goods, the exchange having to that extent become internal rather than international.[10] By such import replacement, the agricultural population can also provide the nonagricultural sector with a major part of the market needed for its growing output of industrial goods. In addition, the investment in the nonagricultural sector will have generated income which—whether accruing to manufacturers and industrial

[10] Farmers will have no reason voluntarily to avoid such import replacement if the prices and qualities of domestic industrial goods are the same as those of foreign origin and if the domestic product mix corresponds to farmers' preference patterns. However, if domestic manufacturers can produce profitably only with tariff protection, internal terms of trade will turn against agriculture and encourage its premature contraction at the expense of the agricultural surplus and food exports. While there will be a considerable incentive on the demand side for the industrial sector to produce the product mix desired by farmers, comparative advantages within the industrial sector may favor a somewhat different product mix. In this case, however, parts of the nonagricultural sector will have to find sufficient export markets to earn the additional exchange which that sector needs for purchasing its residual food needs from the domestic agricultural sector.

workers or (as nonfarm investment income) to farmers—will presumably not only maintain but increase the effective demand for industrial goods, domestic or foreign.

Unless the "new" nations' natural endowment for agricultural production is exceptionally poor, however, it is unlikely that a population increase from OA_2 to OA_4 would be entirely absorbed in the nonagricultural sector. More likely, at some intermediate point if not at the outset, the relative returns on capital investment in agricultural improvements would exceed those on nonagricultural investment. This being so, suppose that part of the

FIGURE 2

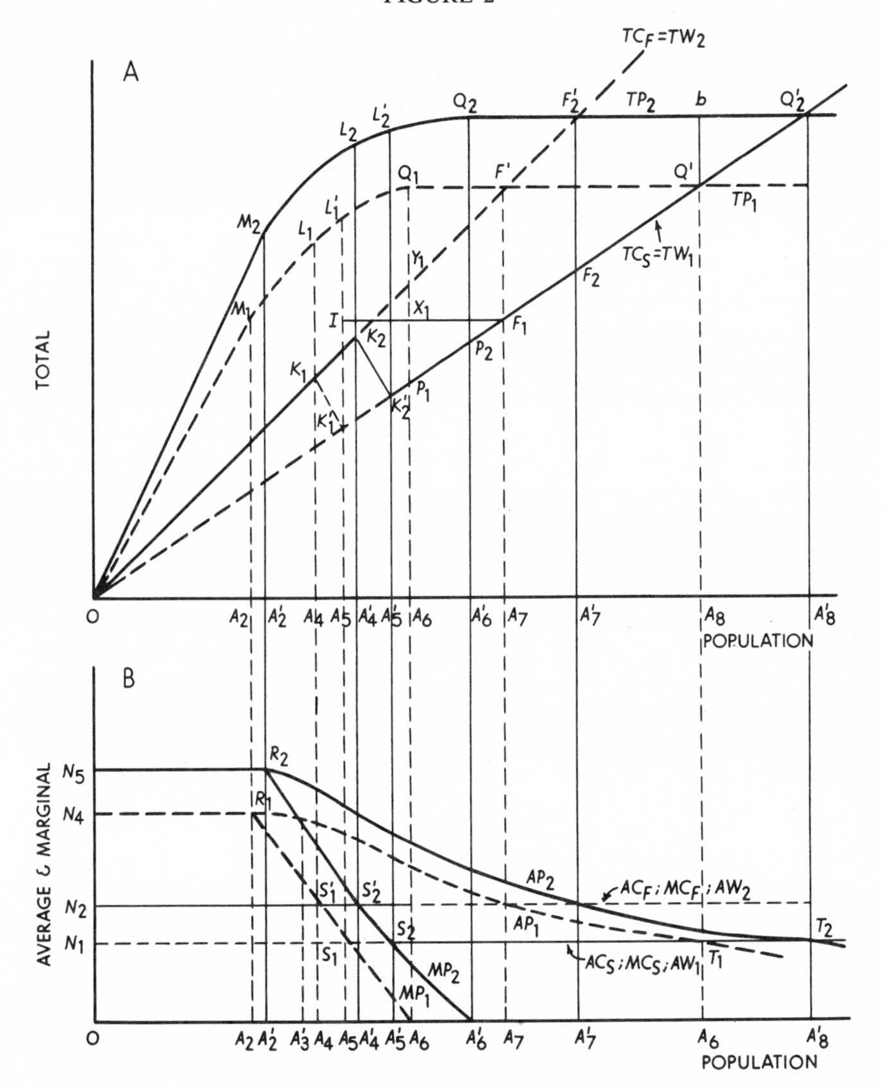

export revenue derived from the agricultural surplus is invested in the agricultural sector, raising the total product curve of agriculture from TP_1 to TP_2 (Figure 2, *A*). The optimum agricultural population would then increase from OA_2 to OA'_2,[11] its per capita farm income at the same time increasing from R_1A_2 to $R_2A'_2$ (Figure 2, *B*). In this case, of the assumed increment of total population A_2A_4, $A_2A'_2$ would find profitable employment in agriculture, reducing to A'_2A_4 the number of farm people who would have to find nonfarm employment in order to prevent per capita income in agriculture from declining along AP_2.

Whether any given agricultural surplus would be sufficient to provide the nonagricultural investment needed to employ a given number of people (such as A'_2A_4) at a *given* wage ($R_2A'_2$) cannot be determined a priori. However, the chances of doing so would have been considerably improved as the result of the agricultural improvements assumed, since the size of the agricultural surplus (and food exports) would have substantially increased. Hence, greater resources than before would be available for nonfarm investment and further agricultural investment. In any case, a population of OA_4 (even if entirely in agriculture) would be better off than was the smaller farm population OA_2 before the agricultural improvements were made.

However, achievement of an optimum allocation of the agricultural surplus might be prevented by certain institutional factors. Thus, the equalitarian structure of agriculture might tend to favor excessive investment in agricultural improvements, since farmers would have a particularly strong interest in improving their own land, while perhaps lacking full knowledge of alternative investment opportunities in the nonagricultural sector. On the other hand, if a political majority can be won for public policies which uses taxes, import duties, direct public subsidies, or inflation to provide funds for nonagricultural investment, there may well be excessive investment in the industrial sector. An agrarian democracy would presumably be in the best political position to prevent unduly heavy taxation of agriculture to promote industry. However, commercial-industrial minorities have historically shown surprising success in winning sufficient political support from agriculture—through appeals to national pride, considerations of national security, and persuasion of farmers to ignore their own immediate economic self-interest[12]—to establish such public policies at an early stage.

---

[11] This would correspond with the empirical fact that, in the earlier stages of economic development, the agricultural population continues to grow absolutely but not relatively.

[12] The willingness of the corn and wheat farmers of the United States Midwest to adhere for more than a century to high-tariff policies, despite their heavy dependence on export markets, is a classic example. Regional differences in comparative advantage and consequent economic interests; the greater political and cultural leadership of coastal regions and capital cities which earliest experience commercial, industrial, and urban development; and disenfranchisement of illiterates and slaves (which works to the political disadvantage of rural areas) have also been historically important factors favoring industrial interests in largely agricultural countries.

By such means, "infant" industries may be created before they are yet profitable enough to attract adequate private funds in the absence of public protection and subsidies. If so, the short-run effect will be a shift in the terms of trade against agriculture, a decline in the level of voluntary savings by farmers out of a given agricultural surplus, discouragement of investments in agricultural improvements, and a slower rate of expansion (perhaps even a reduction) in food output and the size of the agricultural surplus. Hence, unless the "infant" industries are capable of rather quickly becoming self-sustaining, the potential contributions of the agricultural surplus to general economic development may not be fully realized, food exports falling more rapidly than their equivalent in terms of import replacement.

Despite this danger, a system of agricultural freeholders would appear to be most favorable to the establishment of a process of "balanced" growth, during which excesses of investment in either agriculture or industry are largely avoided. In such a favorable politico-economic environment, an initially large and growing agricultural surplus can serve as the principal means of getting industrial (and general) development under way.

International terms of trade remaining constant, the extent to which it will continue to pay to allocate investment to agriculture will, of course, depend in considerable part on the richness of the nation's natural endowment. If this endowment is sufficiently rich (as in the United States or New Zealand), agriculture's *TP* curve will continue to respond satisfactorily to further investment in improved techniques until very late in the development process. In nations with a less rich endowment (England or Japan), agriculture's initial role may be no less important. However, relatively larger allocations of investment to the industrial sector will be warranted at an earlier stage of development, such nations perhaps ultimately even becoming net importers of food. If the international terms of trade shift in favor of food products, any given *TP* curve for agriculture, while constant in physical terms, will be shifting upward in value terms, encouraging greater relative emphasis on agriculture. The opposite will be true if the terms of trade move against food products, particularly if the given country becomes a sufficiently large food exporter that, by its own increased exports, it lowers the world price.

While agriculture's physical productivity (*TP*) can be progressively raised only by capital investment, the form which such investment should take will vary with the changing relative scarcities of the several productive factors. Once all available land has come under cultivation, investments in land-saving improvements will immediately become appropriate. Whether early capital investments in agriculture should also be labor-saving will depend upon whether agriculture's capital stock or its population is growing more rapidly. At the outset, population may be outpacing capital, in which case capital investments which are labor-saving should be avoided since the result would be the creation of a redundant labor force and enforced (unwanted) leisure in the absence of sufficient alternative nonfarm job opportunities. As economic progress brings a faster rate of capital accumulation than of population growth in agriculture, however, investment in that sector can take on a progressively more labor-saving character, this tendency being greatly accelerated once the nonagricultural sector has developed so far that the *absolute* agricultural population beings to fall. Only at that stage will the size of farm (in terms of land) begin to increase, opening the way for full-scale mechanization of farming operations. Similar principles hold for the nonagricultural sector.[13]

A System of Landlords and Tenants. How will our previous analysis be affected if we assume that individual farms are operated by renters or hired workers rather than by their owners? Given a landlord-tenant system, landlords would seek to maximize the returns (rent) on their land (the vertical difference between TP_1 and the relevant TW curve in Figure 1, A) for any given agricultural population by equating MP_1 and the going wage rate.

Let us first note, however, that—given a society of free men and an equalitarian land-settlement policy—a landlord-tenant system could be established in an "underpopulated" country only under special circumstances. Given constant agricultural technology, an agricultural population of OA_2 or less would result in a real wage so high (AW_4) that the corresponding TW_4 curve would coincide with the TP_1 curve along OM and landlords would receive *no* rent. Land would be too plentiful to have any scarcity value, so that the entire agricultural surplus would accrue to farmers as workers ($AP_1 = AW_4$) even if they did not own the land. Not only would there be no economic incentive for the creation of a separate landlord class but, at the same time, agricultural workers would certainly not be available for hire, since they could freely acquire land of their own.

Once a system of freeholders had thus been established, it could be *generally* displaced by a new landlord class only if some special group (domestic or foreign) had superior access to the knowledge, capital, and markets needed to raise agricultural productivity substantially, particularly by achieving certain potential economies of scale. Presumably owner-operators would be willing to sell their land only if they were offered a price which would give them a stream of discounted future annual incomes greater than that based

[13] As William Fellner (*Trends and Cycles in Economic Activity* [New York: Henry Holt & Co., 1956], chap. 8) has shown, under conditions in which capital has begun to grow more rapidly than labor as well as land, uninterrupted growth requires that cost-saving innovations in both agriculture and industry be sufficiently plentiful to absorb all new savings without permitting the yield on the growing stock of capital in the two sectors to fall below some necessary minimum level of return. The form which such improvements take must also change in order to be compatible with changing relative scarcities. In the absence of government interference which prematurely promotes the adoption of labor-saving types of improvements, however, forms of improvements are likely to be *induced* which are compatible with a fairly constant rate of return on investment and continuing full employment at *rising* real wages.

on their current return (the vertical difference between AP_1 and the appropriate AW) on the land by a premium sufficient to compensate them for their loss of satisfaction when they give up their status as landowners. Thus, for any given agricultural population, would-be landlords would have to anticipate having TP and AP curves which were higher than TP_1 and AP_1 by at least the amount of this premium if they were to be able to offer a price sufficient to persuade owner-operators to give up their land. This premium would presumably be greater, the greater the agricultural population, for population growth would bring increasing rewards for land ownership and declining labor income, with a consequent enhancement of the social status associated with working one's own land.

Let us pursue this matter further by supposing that a landlord class could achieve a total product curve of TP_2 while owner-operators (lacking equal access to the means of achieving such agricultural improvements) continued to produce according to TP_1 (Figure 2, *A*). For populations of less than OA'_2, there would be no incentive (apart from possible speculative motives) for a landlord class to establish itself in the absence of a bonded labor force (indentured workers, peons, or slaves). In a free labor market, wages would rise from R_1A_2 to $R_2A'_2$ (Figure 2, *B*), absorbing all the gains in productivity which the landlord tenant system was capable of achieving.[13a] If the population increased beyond OA'_2, however, wages under the new system would fall below $R_2A'_2$ and landlords could anticipate some rent insofar as former owner-operators had not captured part of this rent as a premium for selling their land.

For purposes of further analysis, let us assume that AP_1 includes this

---

[13a] For agricultural populations of less than OA'_2 the major problem facing would-be landlords would be a scarcity of wage labor, not land. Land would be no less "free" to them than to the original owner-operator class unless application of their superior techniques required landholdings larger than some prevailing legal ceiling on the size of settlement unit specified in the nation's public land policy. In the latter case, they might have to resort to land purchase from earlier settlers (cf. n. 14 below), even though unsettled land was still available to others and was not of a quality less than that of settled land. In any case, if those having access to superior techniques could also meet their labor requirements from their own families, two separate classes of owner-operators (operating at sharply different levels of technique and productivity) might emerge. However, if the class with superior techniques had the desire or necessity of hiring much or all of its farm labor force, the profitability of its doing so in a free labor market would depend upon the level to which it bid up wage rates.

At best, would-be landlords could hire former owner-operators at slightly above their opportunity cost of R_1A_2; at worst, they would force the wage rate up to its maximum level of $R_2A'_2$. Initially, the number of hired workers demanded might be so small a proportion of the agricultural population that the wage rate would be only slightly above R_1A_2, permitting partial replacement of the owner-operator system on a profitable basis. However, in the text, we suppose that the would-be landlords' demand curve for labor would be shifting to the right sufficiently more rapidly than the supply curve of labor (population) so that the wage rate would quickly rise to and remain at its maximum level of $R_2A'_2$, thereby bringing such displacement to a halt long before it had become general.

necessary premium for each agricultural population. Then OA'_3 becomes a critical level of population at which the wages (MP_2) which can be earned by working the landlords' land are just sufficient to compensate for the loss of wages, rent, and status (AP_1) which could be earned under the less productive owner-operator system. For populations between OA'_2 and OA'_3, workers would be better off under a landlord-tenant system than if they operated their own farms. Therefore, within this range of populations, the purchase of land by would-be landlords would be facilitated by the fact that sellers would enjoy a wage premium, as a result of which the extent of their encroachment (via the selling price of land) on the landlords' rental income would probably be reduced. If the owner-operator system remained intact until the agricultural population had grown beyond OA'_3, however, the increasing gap between AP_1 and MP_2 would have to be compensated for by increasing land prices. Thus, for populations in excess of OA'_3, the landlords' rent would be restricted to the vertical distance between TP_2 and TP_1, lessening the opportunities for the more productive landlord class to establish itself.

We may conclude that, for any given difference in productivity (level of TP) assumed for the two systems, the opportunities for a change to a landlord-tenant system would be best when the agricultural population had grown slightly beyond OA'_2, particularly if the owner-operators showed less foresight than the would-be landlords about the consequences of further population growth. A change to landlordism would also be more likely, the greater its superiority in terms of productivity, since the more TP_2 exceeded TP_1, the greater the initial wage premium and the greater the range of populations (the farther right A'_3) within which it would pay owner-operators to sell their land.

Finally, it is worth noting that, under certain special circumstances, a landlord-tenant system might replace an owner-operator system even for populations of less than OA'_2. If one allows for some differences in the quality (including locational advantages) of the land, it might be easier for landlords to persuade certain freeholders to sell their land while they still have the opportunity of moving with an advancing "frontier," where they can again set themselves up as owner-operators on still available "free land."[14] However, the landlord class would still have to solve the problem of labor scarcity, since the free agricultural work force on the older lands would decline as former freeholders (except for the impecunious) either re-established themselves elsewhere in agriculture or used their newly won capital

---

[14] This actually happened in the Southern Piedmont during 1830–50. Tidewater cotton planters bought and consolidated the land of small, largely subsistence freeholders (who had settled the Piedmont in the latter part of the previous century), the latter moving west where they could take up "free" land once more. This process might not have been possible —in spite of the high profitability of cotton at that time—if the planters had not been able to bring their labor supply (slaves) in with them.

to establish nonagricultural enterprises. Thus, even if the opportunities for agricultural reorganization were very large, the partial displacement of a system of owner-operators for populations of less than OA'_2 would probably be possible only if accompanied by the introduction of a system of indenture, peonage, or slavery.

Insofar as the initial freeholders succeeded at an early date in winning public investments in social overhead (which would help to equalize differences in knowledge, foresight, site value, and the like), the original freeholding system would probably be preserved unless potential economies of scale in agriculture were considerable. There are few types of food production for which economies of scale are so great as to require such an outcome. If an increasingly unequal distribution of land ownership ultimately grew out of initial equality in the food-producing sector, it would therefore be largely the cumulative result of actual differences in the quality of land, social-overhead investment, etc., which we have assumed to be absent. On the other hand, certain industrial crops may be of such a nature that large-scale production on a landlord-tenant basis may produce substantial economies. In an "underpopulated" country well suited for such industrial crops, therefore, agriculture might ultimately take on a dual character, with one sector producing food on family-sized farms under a freeholding system and another sector producing industrial crops on large-scale plantations, whose many workers did not own their own land. We shall return briefly to this case of a two-sector agricultural economy in a later section.

But what if the original land-settlement policy was oligarchic rather than equalitarian? For example, assume that, as in much of Latin America, most of the initially unsettled land was granted by the Crown to a few favored individuals. Such a situation would probably tend to lead to an agricultural structure characterized by a very few landlords, renting many operating units to an equal number of worker families who supply all of the farm labor. Before analyzing this important special case, we must make certain special assumptions if the curves of Figure 1 are to be as valid for a landed oligarchy as for a system of agricultural freeholders. First, if we define the agricultural population as the total of the landlord and tenant populations, the landlord population must constitute a negligible proportion of the whole.[15] Second, there must be no difference in the productivity of renters (workers) and owner-operators, so that TP_1 is equally valid for either. Finally, let us assume that the landlords either hire their workers for the lowest possible wage in kind or achieve the same effect by rent charges (whether in cash or crop shares)

---

[15] A more general solution would require drawing a negative coordinate to the left of O in Figure 1, A measuring the landlord population to the left and only the worker population to the right of the origin. Then, the subsistence of the landlord population being a fixed charge on the economy, the TC_F (or TC_S) curve would begin at the (negative) point representing the landlord population, with the same slope ($= MC_F$ or MC_S) as before.

for use of the land which net the tenant an equivalent to the going wage.[16]

Given oligarchic control of all land from the outset of settlement, the few landlords might be able to extract considerable rent for populations well below OA_2. Thus, they might exploit their monopoly of land by releasing it for use by would-be settlers in only that quantity which would maximize their rent, using private armies or other devices to protect unused land against squatters and interlopers. Given the settlers' derived demand curve for land, suppose that a settler population of OA_1 would maximize total rents at VU (Figure 1, A). That low level of population would then net as wages only ON_2 instead of ON_4, the difference accruing to the oligarchy as rent.[17] The total agricultural surplus available for purchase of foreign industrial goods would initially be considerably smaller (VU instead of, say, MJ) than under a "free"-land policy. However, because of the highly unequal distribution of income, the landlord class could already live in comparative luxury if it chose to do so.

Nonetheless, insofar as population grew beyond OA_1 without the necessity of increasing the wage above ON_2, the landlords' total rents would (up to a population of OA_4) be increasing. Hence, the oligarchy might find it profitable to introduce a positive recruitment program to shift the supply curve of settlers (hence the demand curve for land) to the right. Given more time, the same result might be achieved through natural increase, either that of the original settlers, or that of more heavily populated countries, increasing the numbers who would be willing to migrate to the new country at the given wage rate.

But suppose the landed oligarchy were unable to attract the desired number of free immigrant workers (perhaps in part because its efforts to bar

---

[16] This assumption means that, even if land is rented on the basis of crop shares (that is, a fixed proportion of the total output for any given population), the landlords can exact an increasing share as population increases—at least so long as the residual left to the tenant is above the subsistence level ON_1. Such an assumption appears to be eminently reasonable, particularly in a new country in which noneconomic factors would be least likely to have caused the establishment of "traditional" shares unrelated to market conditions.

Even so, however, suppose that for some reason a customary landlord's share of $1/k$ was established which was constant regardless of population. Whatever the value of k, tenants would (like owner-operators) prefer an agricultural population of OA_2 or less, since they would then be best off per capita; but the landlord class would prefer that tenant population (OA_6 in Figure 1, A) which would maximize $1/k$ of TP ($= 1/k$ of A_6Q), hence TP. However, k remaining constant, population cannot exceed that level at which $(1 - 1/k)$ TP falls below TC_S. If this critical level of population is less than OA_6, the landlords would have to settle for a total income less than the maximum. The smaller the value of k (the larger the landlord's share), the more likely this outcome would be. Alternatively, if the tenant population grows beyond the critical level, the threat of starvation might generate social pressures or force which would reduce the landlord's share, thereby permitting the larger population to persist at the expense of the landlord's income.

[17] For purposes of this analysis, we assume that the supply curve of land coincides with the horizontal axis up to the point at which all land is in use, where the supply curve becomes vertical. Assuming as before that there is a constant ratio of labor to land for

squatters were not wholly successful) and were too impatient to depend upon the natural increase of the initial settlers? Alternatively, it might find it possible to reduce any indigenous labor to peonage or might import slaves, turning such artificially cheap sources of labor (at the minimum possible wage AC_S) to the production of a larger agricultural surplus. For example, for a peon or slave population of OA_2, they might win for themselves MJ', even larger than the agricultural surplus MJ which the same number of owner-operators (preferring a more generous diet) would choose to produce. Even if the peons or slaves were less productive than free men, so that TP_1 were lower, the landlords would probably retain a considerable part of the lower agricultural surplus, none of which they could capture if they had to hire an equivalent number of unbonded settlers at the necessary market wage A_2R. Insofar as the indigenous population proved to be a passable labor force, as in Mexico or Peru, such a *latifundium* system might well be ended only by revolutionary methods. However, insofar as slavery was the preferred source of agricultural labor, the system might gradually die out, through a tendency for the cost of slave labor to rise toward the alternative of hiring free men—in the United States and Brazil, the historical trend well before abolition was toward rising import prices of slaves (as an increasing demand faced an increasingly restricted supply).

In any case, let us now assume that, by the time the agricultural population actually reaches OA_2, the landlord class must (for whatever reason) man its agricultural operations with completely free labor hired at the going market rate A_2R. Whatever their previous success in exacting income by means which made land artificially scarce and labor artificially cheap, the landlords can now regain their advantage only if the agricultural population grows further. Should the population grow to OA_3, the real wage will fall from AW_4 to AW_3 and the rent will rise from nil to $V'E$. For a still larger population, the real wage will decline to AC_F (= AW_2) and the rent will increase to KL.

---

populations less than OA_2, we can measure settler population as well as quantity of land horizontally, so long as all land is not in use. Furthermore, the marginal product of land will be constant over the same range. The settlers' demand curve for land can be derived from this constant gross product by subtracting from it vertically the supply curve of settlers, which presumably must cut the vertical axis at a wage equal to at least the subsistence wage ON_1. (The example in the text implies that a higher wage ON_2 is required to attract OA_1 settlers.) Unless this supply curve of settlers is completely elastic, the demand curve for land will be falling. If this demand curve cuts the horizontal axis at or to the left of the point at which all land is in use, it will determine the number of settlers who will be attracted by a "free"-land (no-rent) policy. Given oligarchic land ownership, however, the amount of land (hence number of settlers) would be sharply restricted to the point at which *marginal* (not average) revenue equals zero. Only if the supply curve of settlers were very elastic, so that marginal revenue equaled zero to the right of the point at which all land had been released for use, would it pay landlords to cease their restrictive practices. If the population grew sufficiently beyond OA_1, whether due to the increasing ease of attracting immigrants or to natural increase, this would in any case be the ultimate outcome as the demand curve for land shifted to the right.

The size of the agricultural surplus for any given population will be the same (assuming TP_1 constant) as under an owner-operator system, the only difference being in how the surplus is distributed. For a population of OA_2, the workers will capture the entire surplus MJ. For an intermediate population of OA_3, the surplus will be $V'U'$, of which the landlords will receive $V'E$ as rent and the workers EU'. For a population of OA_4, the entire surplus KL will accrue to the landlords.

Thus, unlike either owner-operators or agricultural workers, the landlord class will benefit from an increase in the agricultural population beyond OA_2 because it has a strong interest in cheap labor and dear land. Such an increase in the worker population, unless accompanied by the creation of an equivalent number of nonfarm jobs, must mean a rapidly increasing concentration of agricultural income in the hands of the few landlords. Under these circumstances, is an agricultural surplus of equal magnitude likely to serve with the same effectiveness in contributing to non-agricultural development and agricultural improvements, hence to general economic growth?

Let us begin with social overhead investment. At a population of OA_2, since the agricultural workers command the entire agricultural surplus, they are as able as the same number of owner-operators to finance such investment. Hence, if the worker class is equally cognizant of the advantages to itself of public outlays for the general welfare, it may be quite willing to pay the necessary taxes if government is responsive to its wishes. It is possible, however, that the landed oligarchy (while currently deriving no *economic* advantages from land ownership) will dominate the political process. If so, the landlords as politicans will be happy to tax away part of the initial agricultural surplus enjoyed by the worker class. But they will probably direct the resulting public revenues largely toward those types of social overhead which primarily benefit the landowner and toward subsidies for the establishment of importing firms, agricultural trading and processing enterprises, and banks which they themselves dominate. They will probably see little advantage to themselves in public investments in the education of the masses of workers. Insofar as they are able to gain control of the marketing and banking process, they may even be able to squeeze out part of the (real) agricultural surplus for themselves by paying abnormally low prices for the workers' products and charging the workers abnormally high prices for imported merchandise and for credit.

If the worker population of OA_2 is unable to overthrow such "taxation without representation," when its economic power is greatest, its chances of breaking out decline rapidly as its numbers grow beyond OA_2. As this happens, the economic power of the landlord class quickly increases at the expense of the workers. Increasingly the principal source for financing social overhead, the sociopolitically dominant landlord class will rarely be willing to tax itself in order to support such public services as education and agricultural extension. Hence social overhead investments are likely to lag far behind the levels which a democratic society dominated by agricultural freeholders would be able to achieve.[18]

To what extent might the workers be able to avoid such an outcome by financing investment in nonagricultural enterprise out of the agricultural surplus? At a population of OA_2, the worker class would capture the entire surplus. If the landed oligarchy were willing to sell its land,[19] the workers might give first priority to using the surplus to enable them to become owner-operators, in which case the analysis of the previous section would become appropriate. However, if we assume that land purchase is not possible, one might expect the workers to be particularly interested in non-agricultural investment since they have no incentive to invest in permanent improvements in land which they do not themselves own. Such investment would give them protection against exploitation by any trading monopolies controlled by the landlord class and, initially at least, there would be the same effective demand for a broad range of goods and services as under an owner-operator system.

The barriers to such investment by agricultural workers would be considerably greater, however. First, the landlord class might use its political power to bar their direct entry into nonagricultural enterprise and its economic power (through control of the banking system) to frustrate their choice of the nonagricultural investments best serving their own needs and interests. Second, the workers' initially favorable economic condition would be more likely to encourage a higher rate of natural increase (at the expense of accumulation) than if they owned the land they cultivated. Third, given their lower social status and lesser educational advantages, they might be less aware of nonagricultural investment opportunities and less self-reliant, venturesome, and foresighted.

Given such barriers, they would probably be less successful than owner-operators in preventing the agricultural population from increasing beyond OA_2. If their numbers did increase they would have much less financial staying power for creating enough nonfarm employment to keep their real wage from falling, since their share of the agricultural surplus would decline rapidly. Any nonagricultural investment they might have made at the outset would have to have been sufficiently profitable to become almost immediately self-sustaining. For they probably could not long maintain at initial levels the investments out of their rapidly falling annual farm income, even if this

[18] The author argued elsewhere that this actually happened in the United States South (see his *Southern Tradition and Regional Progress* [Chapel Hill: University of North Carolina Press, 1960], pp. 106–13).

[19] At a population of OA_2, the landlords might be expected to be most willing to sell their land since it produced no rent. If they had accumulated sufficient wealth from the past, however, they might choose to hold on to their land in anticipation of a rapid rise in land values as population increased beyond OA_2 or, if significant population growth was not expected, they might see opportunities for investing in agricultural improvements which would produce rents at a population of OA_2 or slightly more.

income were supplemented by some nonfarm investment income. Furthermore, their original nonagricultural investments could easily prove to have been misdirected in view of the rapidly growing concentration of income in the hands of a few rich landlords, who would presumably want a very different product mix than the masses of workers. For such reasons, nonagricultural enterprises based on investment and consumption by agricultural workers might easily die aborning.

If, then, the agricultural population grows well beyond OA_2, the key factors determining whether or not the given country enjoys economic growth or stagnation are the attitudes and motivations of the very small but rich landlord class. If the landlords choose to invest their increasingly great wealth in industrial development and/or agricultural improvements, a process of economic growth may get under way. Where this has happened historically, it has usually been because the landlord class abandoned long-held agrarian (and often hedonistic) values in response to some competing value system whose growing acceptance threatened the landowners' traditional dominance. In both eighteenth-century England and nineteenth-century Japan, a new value system—oriented toward concepts of thrift, efficiency, and profit and largely industrial-urban in both origins and objectives—broadly affected the aspirations of the landed oligarchy and enlisted its powerful backing for both agricultural improvement and industrial development.

Here, however, we are primarily concerned with the more typical case in which landed oligarchies are a strong restraining force on economic development. At a population of OA_2, they would have the greatest incentive to invest in agricultural improvements but, because they receive no rent, lack the resources to do so unless they have previously accumulated wealth. If agricultural population grows from OA_2 to OA_4, their incentive to invest in agricultural improvements will probably decline because, without any effort or sacrifice on their part, their rental incomes will be burgeoning. Furthermore, even if investments in agricultural improvements would increase their incomes (as well as those of their workers) further, they may already be so rich that they are insensitive to such opportunities. The same may be true for investments in the non-agricultural sector, particularly since the landlords may view industrial development as a threat to their socioeconomic power and (because it would raise the cost of agricultural labor) to their economic well-being as well. In addition, the opportunities for developing domestic industrial enterprises will be greatly limited by the fact that the worker class has few if any resources with which to purchase off-farm goods and services.

Under such circumstances, the landlord class will have little incentive to invest in domestic enterprises other than plantation-based agricultural processing or export-import agencies which facilitate the exchange of their large food surplus for foreign industrial goods, mainly luxuries for their own consumption. Otherwise, they may invest largely in "safe" bonds and shares in more developed countries, exporting most of the benefits of the increasing income from food exports to other countries. There will be little or no internal multiplier effect by which the export base might be broadened, the size of the domestic market expanded, and the growth of complementary and subsidiary industries encouraged. The neglect of investment in social overhead (especially education) will impose another important barrier to economic growth.[20]

In such a static situation, it is quite conceivable that an originally "underpopulated" country can slip over into a condition of "overpopulation." The crucial question here is what happens during the phase of population growth A_4A_5. The landlord class may even view favorably the further growth of agricultural population from OA_4 to OA_5, since total land rents will become even larger (growing from LK to $L'K'$) as the workers' diet is squeezed down to the bare subsistence level AC_S. Even so, such a view will prove to be shortsighted from the standpoint of the landlords' own self-interest. First, the deterioration of the workers' food intake may affect worker energy and productivity, lowering the TP curve. Second, once the agricultural population has reached OA_5, any further increase will mean that the marginal productivity of labor (MP_1) falls below the subsistence wage AC_S. At this point, social pressures for "make-work" and dangers of worker revolt will probably cause nonmarket forces to take over, reducing the landlords' agricultural surplus in proportion as population grows.

Hence, as agricultural population grows beyond OA_4, a prudent landlord class would be moved to bestir itself at last to seek ways of developing nonagricultural employment for an otherwise redundant labor force and of improving agricultural techniques. While it will now have maximum resources for investing in both domestic industry and its own agriculture, it may well have delayed too long. Given past neglect of opportunities for investing in human capital, for developing necessary economic, social, and political institutions, and for preventing increasing inequalities of income distribution which narrow the domestic market, the pattern of demographic behavior and the whole sociocultural framework may make a transition to a condition of "overpopulation" more probable than achievement of a successful turnabout at this late date.

We must therefore conclude that, with rare exceptions, a landed oligarchy will not be conducive to turning an initially large agricultural surplus into a primary generating force in getting a process of self-sustaining economic growth under way.

---

[20] Cf. Douglas C. North, *The Economic Growth of the United States 1790–1860* (Englewood Cliffs, N.J.: Prentice-Hall, Inc., 1961), chap. 1, esp. pp. 4–7 and 9.

B. A Two-sector Agricultural Economy

Thus far we have assumed that the agriculture of the given country is entirely engaged in food production, any agricultural surplus consisting only of food. Let us consider briefly an alternative situation in which the agriculture has two sectors—one engaged in food production (largely for domestic consumption) on small owner-operated farms, the other producing industrial crops (largely for export) on large-scale, highly capitalized, well-managed, and highly productive plantations.[21]

In countries in which a sector of the latter type has become important, it has typically been based on foreign capital and management, freeing its initial development from dependence upon domestic financing out of an agricultural surplus in the food-producing sector. However, we need not preclude the possibility that the large-scale sector was developed by a domestic landed oligarchy which was initially able, on the basis of peon or slave labor, to squeeze out a considerable agricultural surplus in the form of industrial crops (sugar, cotton, tobacco, or coffee) which were readily and profitably exchangeable for any necessary food imports. We might further suppose that the oligarchs lacked sufficient control (or the will to enforce it) over the entire land supply to prevent settlement by owner-operators on the residual unutilized lands. We shall here treat industrial-crop production as if it were part of the nonagricultural sector, centering our attention once more on the food-producing sector. To simplify our analysis, let us assume that the large-scale sector of agriculture produces no food of its own.[22]

In this new situation, we may take the curves of Figure 1 as representing only that part of agriculture that is engaged in food production on owner-operated farms. Since the large-scale sector has ample resources for meeting its food needs by imports, the food-producing sector need not be more than self-sufficient. For example, suppose that the subsistence wage were ON_4 instead of ON_2 in Figure 1, *A*, so that TC_S (now TW_4) coincided with TP_1 over the phase OM. Then, any food-producing population up to OA_2 could produce enough barely to subsist. Suppose instead that ON_3 represented the subsistence diet and ON_4 the "fully fed" diet, so that TW_3 became TC_S and TW_4 became TC_F. Then, a food-producing population of OA_2 or

---

[21] The analysis which follows would be equally applicable if the large-scale sector produced primary products of nonagricultural origin, such as petroleum or minerals.

[22] In large-scale agriculture, this assumption is often approximated in fact because (1) the use of land for industrial-crop production is usually much more profitable; (2) unskilled gang labor of the type used in producing most industrial crops is usually unsuitable for efficient cereal and livestock production; and (3) subsistence food production by workers on plots assigned them by the landlord may, in the latter's view, unduly divert them from their obligations to work at producing the major cash crop. Where the use of such plots is a major part of the total compensation to workers, however, it may be viewed as essentially the equivalent of a subsistence wage, although the quality of the workers' diet would probably be higher than if all food needs had to be met by off-farm purchase.

less could enjoy an optimum diet unless it chose to squeeze that diet in order to acquire a minimum amount of nonfood goods by exchange. Any population growth beyond OA_2, however, would have to be at the expense of a poorer diet.

Even if such low productivity in the food-producing sector is due to primitive techniques rather than to an inherently poor natural endowment, the large-scale sector might not be inclined to use any of its resources to improve the situation. To be sure, if TP_1 were raised sufficiently, the large-scale sector would be able to meet its food needs more cheaply through domestic exchange than through imports. Then, by three-way trade, it would (wages remaining constant) command more foreign industrial goods than before, while the food-producing sector could now also import some industrial goods for its own consumption. However, the small-scale structure of the latter sector would in any case discourage direct private investment by the large-scale sector. Furthermore, since wages in the large-scale sector would depend upon the alternative returns which its workers could earn by cultivating their own land, it might consider agricultural improvements in food production unfavorably because they would raise its labor costs. For this reason, it might be reluctant to support (through taxes) *public* investment in the food-producing sector.

The possibility that part of the surplus of the large-scale sector of agriculture will be voluntarily directed into domestic industrial development may also be rather remote. If the large-scale sector is foreign-based, it may be an important adjunct of the colonial policy of the mother country, which may explicitly discourage industrial development of its colony. Even if the large-scale sector is dominated by *indigenous* capital and management, however, the difficulties of mobilizing its surplus for industrial development may be equally great, for the same reasons as those already discussed in the previous section on oligarchic food production. In either case, this sector may make certain important capital investments in irrigation works, railroads, warehousing, docks, and other valuable assets which directly facilitate its operations. But such investments may be too specialized to provide broader benefits to the economy at large. Indeed, such a large-scale sector of agriculture is usually so little integrated with the domestic economy that it is only nominally indigenous rather than foreign.

However, one important exception might be noted. If the particular industrial crop becomes less profitable—because of soil exhaustion, plant disease, falling export prices, or otherwise—indigenous capital and management in the large-scale sector will probably seek better alternative domestic investment opportunities elsewhere. This possibility is especially likely if the country produces so large a part of the world supply of the given crop that, by its own expansion, it causes the world price to fall. Such a turn of events may (perhaps in combination with production controls) encourage the strongly profit-motivated entrepreneurs of the large-scale sector to shift resources either into food production or into nonagricultural enterprises.

With this possible exception, effective mobilization of the surplus of large-scale agriculture for general economic development must usually await such political reforms as the winning of national independence or the broadening of the electorate. Only then is it possible to capture through taxation, tariffs, exchange controls, and other political devices this surplus for purposes of general economic development. When this happens, however, there is a strong danger that the effectiveness of the highly productive large-scale sector in earning foreign exchange will be seriously impaired by nationalization (accompanied by inefficient indigenous management), by enforced division into small properties, or by political harassment of foreign capital and management. Even if such a dissipation of the large-scale sector's surplus is avoided, there is a further danger that it will be too largely allocated to industrial development, cutting food imports sharply without sufficient offsetting investment in the domestic food-producing sector. There are probably few countries in which—taking international comparative advantage and alternative domestic investment opportunities fully into account—it will not pay to invest part of the surplus produced by the large-scale agricultural sector in means of raising the food-producing sector's *TP* curve. In the absence of such investment, the food-producing sector can easily become a serious bottleneck, interrupting a smooth process of industrial-urban development.

Given these problems of mobilizing the surplus of a highly productive, large-scale agricultural sector for general economic development, a country which also has from the outset a relatively productive and equalitarian food-producing sector is indeed fortunate. For then the agricultural surplus of the food-producing sector can play the same active role as that already discussed in an earlier section, serving as the principal source for financing both agricultural and nonagricultural investments and providing a broad market for domestic manufactures. Initially, the large-scale sector of agriculture would itself play a passive role in getting economic development under way, little if any of its own large surplus being directed voluntarily into agricultural improvements in food production or into the establishment of domestic manufactures. Politically, its influence would probably be negative as it actively opposed public policies which would provide social overhead for the benefit of the food-producing sector and promote industrial development.

However, the coexistence of an equalitarian sector of agriculture would provide an important political offset to such oligarchic tendencies. As a consequence, it might prove possible politically to establish public policies by which the large-scale sector's surplus would be partially mobilized (albeit involuntarily) for general development purposes. As the food-producing sector and domestic manufactures developed, the large-scale sector might gradually become integrated into the national economy, increasingly meeting its need for both food and manufactures from domestic rather than foreign sources.

We may conclude that even a substantial exportable surplus of industrial crops, produced by the large-scale sector of agriculture, can usually be effectively mobilized for general economic development only by political means. Hence, the political environment must be such as to permit the capture of part of that surplus for developmental purposes, while avoiding its dissipation, misallocation, or destruction. Perhaps most favorable to such an outcome is the coexistence of a productive and equalitarian food-producing sector, whose agricultural surplus can be the prime generating force for developing and integrating the national economy, and through whose moderating democratic political influence, constructive rather than disruptive public development policies can evolve.[23]

---

[23] In his analysis of the early economic development of the United States, North (*op. cit.*) concludes that the oligarchic South's highly profitable export trade in cotton was the prime generating force, but only because of the spread of the internal market economy by interregional trade among the plantation South, the equalitarian midwestern food sector, and the industrial Northeast.

Application of my own analysis to the same case would require giving greater credit to the Midwest food sector as an initiating economic and political force. As the Midwest's rich natural endowment came under exploitation, its increasing agricultural surplus quickly condemned to near extinction the agriculture of New England. The latter region was thereby forced to concentrate even more on trade and manufacturing, in which its comparative advantage was strong, in the process creating an important political bloc favorable to industrialization. Thus, the Midwest and Northeast complemented each other in ways favorable to balanced economic growth of "the North." While interregional trade undoubtedly had an accelerating effect on all three regions, the South from an early date was inclined toward economic, political, and cultural separatism. While resisting politically many public policies favoring the development of other regions, it bought New England (rather than English) manufactures largely because the hated tariffs forced it to, and bought midwestern foods because they were then the world's cheapest. The Civil War offers the ultimate proof that interregional trade had not sufficed to mobilize adequately the South's agricultural surplus for national economic development or to integrate it fully into the national economy (cf. my *Southern Tradition*, esp. chap. 2).

Brazil's economic development offers an interesting comparison. Historically, the Brazilian economy was largely dependent on the production for export of sugar, coffee, and other industrial crops on a large-scale basis. Until recent decades, probably little of this large agricultural surplus found its way into the development of either efficient food production or manufacturing. After 1929, with public policies directed toward maintaining the incomes of coffee planters in the face of heavy overproduction, the latter's interests first began to turn toward direct investments in urban real estate and industrial enterprise. Only after 1947, however, did the national government—through large-scale deficit financing, high tariffs, and a system of multiple exchange rates which discriminated against domestic coffee planters—begin to capture much of the coffee sector's surplus for use in promoting industrial development. Under such stimuli, southern Brazil has recently enjoyed considerable industrial (and general) development. Meanwhile, however, its older sugar- and cotton-exporting northeast region has remained feudal and backward, in part because it has never been adequately integrated with the food-producing and industrializing South, and in part because the latter proved to be more efficient even in those major industrial crops produced in the Northeast. Even in the South, the historical lack of an equalitarian food-producing sector is only very gradually being overcome through public investments in social overhead and the use of taxation to discourage large landholdings. Despite these recent advances investment in Brazil's food-producing sector clearly appears to be lagging behind the optimum level needed for achieving a maximum rate of economic growth.

IV. "AGRICULTURAL SURPLUS" IN AN OVERPOPULATED COUNTRY

Let us now consider the situation of a country which suffers serious overpopulation. For this purpose, let us return to Figure 2, once more assuming in turn an agricultural structure of owner-operator farms and one of landlords and tenants. We need not this time distinguish between one-sector and two-sector agriculture since we shall analyze food production under a landlord-tenant system in a way that is equally applicable to food production under a two-sector situation.

We have already defined "overpopulation" for the level of agricultural technique represented by TP_1 as any population greater than OA_5, at which MP_1 equals the subsistence wage AC_S. Let us suppose that our particular country is initially suffering from maximum possible overpopulation, with OA_8 people in the food-producing sector. At this level, the entire food output ($A_6Q_1 = A_8Q'_1$) is required to feed the people at a bare subsistence level ($AP_1 = AC_S$ at T_1 and $TP_1 = TC_S$ at Q'_1). Under these circumstances, A_6A_8 of the agricultural population would be redundant in the sense that it could be removed from agriculture without lowering total output, TP_1 being constant and MP_1 zero.[24]

Would there then be any agricultural surplus out of which to finance economic development? If we continue to define (1) the agricultural surplus as the excess of food output over the food needs of the agricultural population, *including those who are redundant*; and (2) the TP_1 curve as including the share paid to landlords (if any), the answer is "No." We shall, however, have occasion to modify these definitions.

A. The Case of a Peasant Agriculture

Suppose first that there are no landlords, all farms being owned and operated by peasant families. Then, by the time the agricultural population reaches OA_8, the entire agricultural surplus will have been exhausted by the peasants' own food needs. However, if we classify the population from the point of view of productive activity as distinct from place of residence, we might as accurately consider the redundant portion A_6A_8 to be *nonagricultural* population. So viewed, the agricultural population having been redefined as OA_6, an agricultural surplus of P_1Q_1 might be said to exist.

---

[24] This principle of maximizing total output under conditions of overpopulation might, under the assumed circumstances, also warrant the cultivation of a second class of land so much less fertile than that (homogeneous) land assumed in Figures 1 and 2 that its TP curve lay below its TC_S curve for all possible populations. Rather than keep the entire redundant population A_6A_8 on the better land and the poorer land idle, it would pay to divert redundant workers to the poorer land so long as their marginal productivity was greater than zero, even though none of the diverted workers produced enough for his own subsistence.

Certainly the existence of a food surplus which will at least feed the redundant population—should ways be found to use it in initiating agricultural improvements or the production of non-agricultural goods—has considerable potential value. However, this surplus will be insufficient to provide any investment funds for importing (or otherwise obtaining) industrial production goods. Hence, nonagricultural and industrial-crop sectors being here assumed absent, the given country has (apart from birth control) few routes for escaping stagnation: depopulation resulting from disaster, the mobilization of redundant labor for direct capital formation through sheer muscle power, and the receipt of private philanthropy or public grants-in-aid from abroad. Let us consider these several alternatives briefly.

Suppose that a sudden disaster reduces the population from OA_8 to OA_7. The redundant population would then become smaller (A_6A_7), requiring only P_1X_1 of the agricultural surplus for its food needs and freeing as much as Q_1X_1 for investment in production goods. However, this potential gain could easily be wiped out entirely if the smaller population increased its food consumption to the maximum ($F_1F_1' = Q_1X_1$) or to a lesser level, spending the difference on nonfood consumption; or if natural increase restored its numbers to their former level OA_8. In the event of such a disaster, therefore, the government would be fully warranted in trying to prevent either eventuality by taxing away the full agricultural surplus P_1Q_1 and devoting it to the reemployment (in industry or agriculture) of the redundant population A_6A_7. However, in today's world—where famine relief and public health services can be so quickly mobilized internationally—unplanned disasters are much less likely to occur than formerly. Furthermore, few countries (Stalinist Russia and Communist China may represent partial exceptions) would willingly engage in *planned* disaster as a solution to overpopulation.

On the other hand, the potential of "bootstrap" operations as a means of creating fixed capital is far greater than commonly believed. Unused or underutilized labor represents a stupendous waste. If properly organized and motivated, such labor can be turned to direct capital formation. Communist China appears to have recognized this opportunity by making extensive use, especially in construction, of a considerable volume of unpaid or underpaid labor on a largely involuntary basis; by its emphasis on labor-intensive methods of expanding production; and by the development of small-scale rural industries.[25] However, China's recent difficulties in maintaining agricultural output suggest that its coercive methods of labor recruitment and its excessive zeal in diverting labor from agriculture have done much to undermine the motivations of its once energetic, resourceful, and individualistic peasantry.

---

[25] Wilfred Malenbaum, "India and China: Contrast in Development Performance," *American Economic Review*, Vol. 49 (1959), esp. 303–7.

The Chinese experience offers both a challenge and a lesson to other overpopulated countries which seek to develop within a democratic rather than totalitarian framework. The challenge lies in finding democratic organizational techniques for recruiting redundant rural labor effectively on a voluntary basis. One can find in most overpopulated countries isolated situations in which, usually due to the accidental emergence of outstanding local leadership, such techniques have been found and effectively applied. But few if any overpopulated countries have found democratic means of generalizing such favorable local experiences, in large part because of the inadequacies of public investments in education, agricultural research and extension services, and the like.

The lesson of the Chinese experience is that, for good or ill, the motivations of the peasantry are important. Hence, given appropriate organization and leadership, the problem is how to enlist these motivations as a positive factor in expanding productive activity. From this standpoint, despite all the disadvantages of small-scale farming units, a system of peasant owner-operators has, under conditions of severe overpopulation, much to recommend it. Having accepted the principle that *all* family members will share and share alike in the distribution of the total output, the family will have the maximum inventive both to save instead of consuming any fortuitous surplus which it may produce, and to forego leisure in favor of investing otherwise redundant labor in private and community capital projects which add (however little) to productivity.[26] By just such a slow accretionary process of investing small annual increments of savings and larger amounts of underutilized labor, peasant families can gradually raise the stock of agricultural capital substantially, to the lasting benefit of agricultural productivity.

If full advantage is to be realized from such favorable private motivations, however, social overhead investment becomes essential, both to speed the process of making agricultural improvements and to prevent population growth from dissipating any initial gains. Hence, insofar as a poor and overpopulated country is able to attract foreign aid, it will usually be wise to direct a major part into such public services as agricultural research and extension, farm credit, and marketing improvements. Suppose now that, through some combination of "bootstrap" operations and foreign-financed

[26] Even in the poorest countries of the world, there is probably a small, largely invisible agricultural surplus which is too widely dispersed among cultivating families to be captured through normal taxation procedures (cf. P. G. K. Panikar, "Rural Savings in India," *Economic Development and Cultural Change*, Vol. 10 [1961], pp. 64–85. If such funds are to find their way into capital formation at all, therefore, they will probably do so in the form of minor improvements in the peasants' own land or (given effective local leadership) in community projects which require cooperative effort but convey considerable private benefit (cf. Philip M. Raup, "The Contribution of Land Reforms to Agriculture: An Analytical Framework" [presented at a conference of the Social Science Research Council's Committee of Economic Growth at Stanford University in November 1960].

social overhead investment, the total product curve in Figure 2 is raised from TP_1 to TP_2. The given agricultural population OA_8 will now produce the larger total food output A_8b instead of $A_8Q'_1$. While still formidable, the redundant population at least will have been reduced from A_6A_8 to A'_6A_8.

Population remaining constant at OA_8, Q'_1b of agricultural surplus will now be available as a potential source of investment funds for either creating nonfarm jobs or achieving further gains in agricultural productivity. Unfortunately, this entire surplus could quickly disappear as a result of diet improvement or the growth of the agricultural population to OA'_8, at which no one would be better off than before. Hence, insofar as possible the government must tax away the entire gain Q'_1b. Since such a tax policy would seriously weaken peasant incentives to make further agricultural improvements, however, certain offsetting tax credits should also be offered to farmers who adopt approved farming practices, accept effective methods of birth control, and the like, so that what they retain from the agricultural surplus (including more food) will be used to maximum advantage.

B. The Case of a Landlord-Tenant System

But what if the structure of the food-producing sector is such that the cultivators do not own their own land, instead renting the land from a relatively few landlords? In previous analysis, we assumed that TP_1 *includes* the landlords' share and that, once the agricultural-worker population exceeds the level OA_5 at which the agricultural surplus is maximized, the landlords will have to give ground to noneconomic considerations by abandoning the marginal principles of distribution followed in a market economy. Then further population growth beyond OA_5 will have to come out of the landlords' share (the entire agricultural surplus) since workers receive *only* the subsistence wage.

If we continue to make these assumptions, the landlord (like the owner-operator) will now take as his objective *maximum total output*, not maximum agricultural surplus. He will therefore also choose, for populations of OA_6 or greater, to use labor until its marginal product is zero.[27] For example, if the total worker population which landlords must feed is OA_7, they will prefer to use OA_6 rather than OA_5 workers since the increment of labor input A_5A_6 (Figure 2) will, while producing less than the subsistence wage, *add something* to total food output ($AC_S > MP_1$ but $MP_1 > 0$). Therefore,

[27] Georgescu-Roegen (*op. cit.*, pp. 24–25) insists that, even under a system of landlords, overpopulation requires capitalistic principles to give way to "the feudal system of distribution," in which some workers are paid more than their specific contribution to output. According to him, "Striking historical evidence of this aspect of feudalism is provided by the gleaners, who received a share greater than the quantity of corn gleaned. In contrast with this, capitalism has no place for gleaners."

the residual (IL'_1) accruing to landlords from the maximum agricultural surplus $L'_1K'_1$ produced by OA_5 labor will be less than the residual (X_1Q_1) which they can capture from the smaller agricultural surplus P_1Q_1 produced by OA_6 labor.

Carried to their logical conclusion, however, these assumptions would mean that, when the worker population reached OA_8, the landlords' share would be completely exhausted. That this should happen in spite of the ever increasing scarcity of land relative to population hardly seems credible. Let us therefore assume instead that, for populations of OA_5 or greater, the landlords receive as rent a crop share which is a certain percentage of any given total output. At a population of OA_5, the landlords could exact a crop share of $L'_1K'_1/L'_1A_5$ (slightly over half as the curves of Figure 2 are drawn). If the landlords were willing and able absolutely to enforce this share, it would be impossible for the worker population to grow beyond OA_5. This barrier to further population growth would not be fully effective, however, if the landlord class (as is not improbable) gave ground (motivated by paternalism or fear) as an alternative to permitting some of their workers to starve as their numbers increased. Insofar as they did, the landlords' percentage share would have to be reduced. Let us assume that this happens as the population grows to OA_8 but—redefining the TP_1 curve to represent only the sharecroppers' *net* product—suppose that even at OA_8 the landlords' share is significantly positive.[28]

If the landlord population is relatively small, virtually all of its total share rents representing agricultural surplus, a source of investment funds for economic development will exist in spite of the subsistence level of the great masses of the agricultural population.[29] Suppose first that the landlord class decides voluntarily to invest a major part of its surplus in nonagricultural development (which would reduce the redundant agricultural population for a given level of techniques) and/or in improvements in food-producing techniques. Suppose it does the latter, so that gross productivity increases, raising the sharecroppers' net-product curve from TP_1 to TP_2 in Figure 2. For a population of OA_8, the agricultural surplus (entirely at the disposal of the landlords) would then be further increased by Q'_1b. With so large a redundant population, the landlord class would not have to share any of this gain with its farm workers. However, it might find that it paid to divert this

[28] As we saw earlier (n. 16), this maximum population will be larger, the smaller the landlords' percentage share, while, whatever the latter share, landlords will also maximize their rents by maximizing total output. It is also worth noting that, if we took the subsistence requirements of landlord families into account, the greater their numbers relative to sharecropper families, the greater the landlords' percentage would have to be.

[29] In the remainder of this section, the analysis will in general be equally applicable if one substitutes "the management class of the large-scale industrial-crop sector" for "the landlord class" and—assuming once more that the food-producing sector consists of owner-operated farms—considers that the *TP* curves represent *gross* output and that all redundant population is in the latter sector.

increment of surplus (or even more) to workers in the form of incentive payments by which they would be encouraged (through an improved diet or the adoption of better practices) to produce more food and fewer children, raising the total product curves further. By such a process, they might overcome some of the motivational disadvantages normally associated with cultivators who did not own their own land. By becoming willing to devote its accumulation to domestic investment rather than to lavish living, a landed oligarchy *could* provide out of its agricultural surplus the stimulus for helping an overpopulated country to move from a state of initial stagnation into one of ultimately self-sustaining economic growth.[30]

However, for the various economic and political reasons already considered, the landlord class is not often likely to play this important role voluntarily. This is unfortunate since, where it does not, an overpopulated country can usually escape from stagnation only by the more difficult and initially disruptive route of sociopolitical revolution. Given such a revolution, the landed oligarchy's surplus can at last be taxed away; or (by agrarian reform) its land can be expropriated and operated collectively by the state or redistributed to small owner-operators.

Where private landholdings have been very large and inefficiently managed, as here assumed, a good case can be made that collective farming (as in Mexico) is a more efficient method of providing agricultural workers with social overhead investment and of capturing the agricultural surplus than land redistribution on a private basis. On the other hand, particularly given the temptation to mechanize agriculture prematurely on state collective farms, the problem of redundant population is likely to plague even the collectives, while the superior motivations of small owner-operators (especially in livestock production) are largely absent.[31] If large landholdings are

---

[30] According to Gustav Ranis ("The Financing of Japanese Economic Development," *Economic History Review*, 2d Ser., Vol. 2 [1959]), the Japanese landlord, far from being "Ricardo's wastrel type," from 1868 on devoted himself to agricultural improvements and (shunning the diversion of his respectable surplus to high living or speculation) invested a large part of his surplus in nonagricultural industries as well (p. 447). Beginning its modern period in "a classic Malthusian situation," Japan quickly found ways of tapping previously underutilized reserves of productivity with a minimum need for additional investment. It centered its initial efforts on agriculture, raising yields per acre as well as per man remarkably without disturbing the very small size of cultivating unit. Having raised agricultural productivity substantially, however, Japan effectively channeled most of the gains into nonagricultural development. Ranis further says of the Japanese agricultural worker: "Before 1868 he supported the feudal ruling classes in the cities; after the Restoration he became the prime source of developmental capital. Good returns to be obtained from the soil—through his labor—were gathered up by means of high rents and the tax on the land" (pp. 444–45). (Cf. the similar findings of Bruce Johnston, "Agricultural Productivity and Economic Development of Japan," *Journal of Political Economy*, Vol. 59 [1951], pp. 498–513.)

[31] Much the same arguments apply to large-scale, mechanized state farms built up (as in Russia) by collectivizing small owner-operated units. This latter procedure is almost certain to meet greater political resistance (and have a more deleterious effect on worker incentives) than one by which government simply displaces the private large landlord in

broken up in favor of small owner-operated units, however, the latter motivations can be effectively mobilized only if the government supplies the small holders (through public research, extension, credit, and marketing facilities) with the managerial and financial assistance which the private landlord class had formerly failed to provide.[32]

V. CONCLUSION

In view of the diversity of population and land-tenure situations with which I have dealt in this paper, I will not attempt to summarize my findings. Let me only express the hope that, by its very diversity, this analysis has demonstrated the almost universal importance of having a substantial and reliable agricultural surplus as the basis for launching and sustaining economic growth. Admittedly, I have passed over lightly or taken for granted the several important allocative criteria that would have to be applied in assessing properly the relative merits of agricultural and industrial development in any particular instance. Among these criteria I would particularly specify the relative dynamic (accelerating) character, relative marginal productivities of capital, and relative international comparative advantages of the two sectors. I would insist as much as the next economist that, insofar as information permits, such criteria should be applied faithfully in policy formulation for underdeveloped countries. However, in actual practice, judgments and guesses must often be substituted for nonexistent facts and empirical knowledge. Where this is done, I believe that usually agriculture is unduly undervalued.

The undervaluation of agriculture is particularly likely to occur within the *short-run* context of the next several five-year plans of most of today's overpopulated countries. This outcome would be unfortunate for three reasons. First, even if agriculture is in fact more traditional and static than industry, plans which fail to do anything about it can quickly bring any initial growth of the industrial sector to a halt as further natural increase, compounded by a high income elasticity of demand, turns a modest food surplus into a food deficit, with concomitant inflation and diversion of scarce foreign

---

an otherwise unchanged large-scale agricultural structure. The Soviet Union's current agricultural difficulties—with 45 percent of its labor force still in agriculture and its farm-labor productivity scarcely 10 percent of the United States—hardly recommend collectivization of small holdings. The striking agricultural progress of Japan, and, more recently, of Poland, suggests that the alleged advantages of collectivization of small-scale private operating units are easily exaggerated.

[32] Nationalization or division of large-scale agricultural organizations engaged in industrial-crop production is, however, likely to have serious effects on the size of the agricultural surplus. Since such commercial enterprises are often well financed and efficiently managed, while serving as a major source of foreign exchange, their potential contribution to economic development can easily be destroyed before equally satisfactory finance and management can be provided from alternative public or private sources—an example is Cuba's sugar industry at the present time.

exchange. Second, because their agricultural techniques are typically still so primitive and productivity so low, the overpopulated countries still have tremendous opportunities to increase food output by relatively moderate injections of capital into small-scale operating units, taking supplies of agricultural land and labor as given. Finally, for such countries, international comparative advantage is far more likely to rest initially in agriculture (especially in industrial crops) than in manufactures.

Within a sufficiently long-run context, of course, the policy objectives of today's underdeveloped countries *must be* substantial industrial-urban development, a smaller agricultural labor force, and larger-scale, mechanized farms. In the process, these countries may ultimately become major customers, on a strictly commercial basis, for food produced by nations now plagued with large agricultural surpluses. In the interim, however, they cannot hope to offset their entire food deficit by imports, whether purchases or gifts, even if they are willing and able to do so. First, the food deficits they face in the near term are of a magnitude far beyond the physical (if not fiscal) capacity of the advanced countries to cover out of either present huge stocks or annual surpluses. Second, until they have taken up the great slack in their own underutilized national endowment, the overpopulated countries have a substantial potential for increasing their food supply on an economic basis. Under these circumstances, the most that the current food surpluses of the United States and other advanced nations can do is to tide the overpopulated countries over until they can put their own agricultural houses in order. Beyond this immediate necessity, the advanced countries primarily need to supply such countries with the resources (other than land and labor) for producing food, rather than the food itself. The sooner this is done, the sooner will public foreign-aid programs make their optimum contribution to the achievement of sustained economic development in the world's overpopulated countries.[33]

---

[33] Cf. Earl O. Heady, "Food for Peace—Boon or Bane to the Economy of the United States" (unpublished paper presented at a symposium of the Ohio State University Land-Grant Centennial in early 1962).

Part VII Agricultural Policy

23 The Bureau of Agricultural Economics under Fire: A Study in Valuation Conflicts*†

CHARLES M. HARDIN‡

There is no end to the manifestations of the drama of politics; but two useful analytical concepts are valuation-struggles and power-struggles. Power struggles are involved in the effort by the Navy to remain outside a department of national defense. Both struggles over power and, more importantly, struggles over valuations are present in the controversy over control of nuclear research: Should it be civilian or military? Within agriculture there are power struggles; the fight in the North Central region between the Agricultural Adjustment Administration and the Farm Bureau in 1943, and the present issue between the Soil Conservation Service and the Farm Bureau are examples of struggles which are chiefly for power. But the attack on the Bureau of Agricultural Economics heavily involves valuations.

"Valuations" is used in Gunnar Myrdal's sense—see *An American Dilemma.*[1] Myrdal has followed the Negro problem to its roots in "a struggle for the soul of America." He discusses conflicts over social policy with reference to relationships of such policy toward *beliefs* and *valuations.*

* *Journal of Farm Economics,* Vol. XXVIII, No. 3 (August 1946), pp. 635–68.

† While assuming full responsibility of authorship, the writer wishes to thank those who generously commented on this article in manuscript, although revision in the light of comments proved impossible. Especial appreciation is due Professors T. W. Schultz, Economics, and L. D. White, and Avery Leiserson, Political Science, of the University of Chicago. The writer also wishes to begin the acknowledgment of a great and general debt to Professor John D. Black, of Harvard University. The author continued his study of the BAE to 1953 when the agency was dissolved and also noted certain criticisms of the methodology employed in the original article. See Charles M. Hardin, *Freedom in Agricultural Education* (Chicago: The University of Chicago Press, 1955), Chap. xiii and xv.

‡ University of California, Davis, California.

[1] (2 vols.; New York: Harper & Bros., 1944.) See Vol. 1, Introduction, and Chapter 1, Vol. 2, Appendix 1.

Beliefs are ideas about the nature of reality: *what things are.* Valuations are ideas about obligations, morale and otherwise: *what things ought to be.* "Beliefs concerning the facts are the very building stones for the logical hierarchies of valuations into which a person tries to shape his opinions."[2] But valuations equally influence what is believed.

In the kind of free-wheeling society, a measure of which we have enjoyed in the United States in the fairly recent past, valuation struggles, while important, have been glossed over somewhat by recurring prosperity. But prosperity now seems no longer automatic. It is engineered. The regulatory state, the promotional state, is at hand. When the state, to paraphrase Lasswell, tells the farmers who can grow "what, when, and how," conditions change. It is no longer equally possible to submerge valuations and beliefs, which, instead, must be hauled out of intellectual attics and examined.

To make this perfectly clear, some of the valuation and belief conflicts that will appear in the following pages are as follows. *First,* differences over economics and economic policy. There is a tendency for farm-bloc Congressmen[3] and agricultural pressure group leaders to think in classical economic terms.[4] Their *belief* here is in the free market; the market really is honest, they think, in distributing economic rewards among men according to their contributions—so long as there is no interference with its (the market's) operations. This *belief* is related to *valuations:* first, that a man ought to get what he is worth, and, second, that he ought to get this reward from his own efforts: therefore, there should be no government subsidy. As farm leaders put it, "The farmer should get a fair price in the market place." This statement is offered by farm leaders as descriptive of the result of the present agricultural adjustment (and related) programs which rig the market in favor of the farmer but leave enough of the old forms to support the fiction: "a fair price in the market." Now, how does the conflict come in? Economists in the Bureau of Agricultural Economics (henceforth: BAE) are not so inclined to *believe* in classical economics; in this they are no different from many, if not most, professional economists. This does not mean that these economists are all "Keynesians" or members of any other school; rather, it means that their *belief* is not an automatic free market. If the market is imperfect, what *valuation* emerges? What *ought* to be done? *The government ought to work out programs to correct the imperfections of the market*—there is the valuation. The reader may argue that both *belief-valuation* chains lead to the same result: positive agricultural programs. But there is a great difference. BAE can frankly admit the government's policy-making role; it can freely examine subsidies, for example, as possible alternatives to price-guarantees. But for the

[2] *Ibid.,* Vol. 2, p. 1030.

[3] The writer will feel free to generalize for purposes of exposition without attempting to do justice to nuances of belief.

[4] This statement may sound absurd in the face of the evidence of regulatory farm programs; but reflection will convince the reader that it is at least strongly arguable.

farm Congressmen and Farm Bureau leaders even to consider subsidies means that they must deny their *belief* that there is a fundamental economic order in the universe which results—or would result—in a fair distribution of goods and services and their *valuation* that a man *ought* to get these goods and services by his own efforts.

Another example is offered of *belief-valuation* conflicts, in which the reader will note a relationship to that conflict pointed up above (for, as Myrdal shows, beliefs and valuations tend to form systems). Here many of the farmer's Congressmen and group leaders have a *belief* that heredity is more important than environment in determining what individuals become. "Blood will tell; you can't make a silk purse out of a sow's ear." Men in BAE are more likely to *believe* that environment is more important than heredity; they accept the Irishman's exclamation when told that one man is as good as another; "Yiss, and dom sight better, too!" These *beliefs* are related to *valuations* concerning *equality*. Both groups would assert that men *ought to be* accorded equal treatment. But for Congressmen and group leaders, this ideal is realized through equal treatment before the law; a man either has the stuff of success in him or he has not. If he has, he will make his own opportunities, given a fair field and no favors. If he has not, nothing much can be done for him. Acceptance of this *belief-valuation* chain enables men to accept and support the present farm programs regardless of their unequal effects. For such inequality merely recognizes the natural inequality among men; if one farmer has a larger historical base than another, he ought to have a larger allotment under the program. Contrarily the BAE. Its members, emphasizing environment over heredity, argue that men ought to be given *equality of opportunity*. They believe that many men, given health and medical care, food and education, now beyond their means, given also an easier access to resources than at present, can rise in productivity, in social worth, and in their self-appraisal.

Other conflicts could be added. For example, take the belief that the farmer is more moral and more righteous than the urbanite—that he is the "salt of the earth," as Earl C. Smith, ex-president of the Illinois Agricultural Association, puts it. This *belief* supports the *valuation* that the farmer ought to have special treatment economically and otherwise. For example, the "greater nobility" of farmers is held to justify their heavy over-representation in state legislatures. This *belief-valuation* chain arouses levity among those urbanites to whom farmers constitute the bucolic plague. But reaction in the BAE is different. Some of its members are probably agricultural fundamentalists, too. Others in BAE project a less circumscribed but similarly optimistic faith in human nature beyond the farmers alone to include humanity. City-dwellers, they think, are created as much in the image of God as farmers—or as farmers' representatives who, after the manner of Thomas Wolfe's successful "Joiners" have generally "gone to town!"

It is hoped that the foregoing discussion will clarify the approach of this paper.[5] And it is hoped that the paper will afford some insight into the nature of the struggle now going on within agriculture. *We must assert the gravity of the issues upon which Congressmen and administrators differ.* Howard R. Tolley is wrong when he says that it is merely a question of "understanding each other."[6] He is wrong because some of the misunderstandings arise from conflicts in *belief-valuations—conflicts that can only be resolved if these beliefs and valuations are brought to the surface.*

This is the prologue; the stage will now be set and the actors introduced.

THE BUREAU OF AGRICULTURAL ECONOMICS

The reorganization of the Department of Agriculture of 1938 made BAE the "arm of the Secretary" for program formulation: it was, as a staff agency, to give preference to policy-making rather than to research. Here begins the real story of the conflict over power and, especially, over valuations with which this paper is concerned. Powerful "action" agencies within the Department have sought to limit BAE's policy-making role that their own possibilities in this field might remain undiminished. The American Farm Bureau Federation has attacked the BAE as part of its general effort to bring all agricultural policy formulation and administration under its own domination or that of what it considers its handmaiden: the Extension Services of the Land-Grant Colleges and Universities. A handful of strategically placed Congressmen[7] have pursued a policy of attrition, culminating in 1946 in appropriation cuts which threaten to reduce BAE to an insignificant role. In addition, BAE has been cut down both by the Secretary's reorganization and the Secretary's practice.[8] Actually, remarks of Secretary Anderson strongly

---

[5] The reader is urged to turn to Myrdal for a full treatment.

[6] House Hearings, fiscal 1947, p. 293, January 17, 1946.

[7] The term "Congress" will be used sparingly in these pages; it would be misleading to do otherwise. A few strategically placed Congressmen are arbiters of BAE's fate. Since 1938 the appropriation item has been subject to very little debate on the floor of the House; to none in the Senate. There have been three House votes, none of record, with the largest participation in any single vote at 131 (1942). It would be a fair question to ask how many of these members could write a page of critical evaluation regarding BAE's work. The few Congressmen whose names recur in these pages operate on the subcommittee level, upon the floor at times, and in conference. Four years, fiscal 1942 through 1945, saw four conference committees on agricultural appropriation bills. There were 51 places on these committees, of which 39 were held by 11 men: Cannon, Tarver, Lamberston, Dirksen, and Plumley for the House; Russell, Hayden, Bankhead, Nye, McNary, and Tydings for the Senate.

[8] Secretary's Memorandum No. 1139, Dec. 12, 1945, includes the provision, effective Jan. 1, 1946:

"5. The responsibility for leadership in general agricultural program planning, including direction of the interbureau committees and working groups both in Washington and in the field, is hereby transferred to the office of the Secretary. . . ." See House Hearings, fiscal 1947, p. 182, Jan. 15, 1946. (Since many citations will be made to the hearings of agricultural subcommittees of Congressional Committees on Appropriations for various fiscal years, this method of citation will be used consistently.)

suggest that the staff-work and advisory function in policy formation have been transferred, not to his office, but to the research divisions of the national farm organizations, chiefly the American Farm Bureau Federation.[9]

Briefly, the BAE was organized in 1922, and economic and statistical work was gathered under its aegis. The original three divisions had grown to eleven in 1945. Creation of the BAE was only one of the manifestations of the rise of farm problems in terms of national political economics in the 1920's. Controversy over the agency's activities is not new. The Outlook Service, designed as a major part of the program of "assisted laissez faire" to give farmers information for their individual adaptations to the market, was begun in 1923. In 1927 the Outlook accurately predicted a fall in cotton prices; by Congressional direction such predictions as to cotton were—and are still—proscribed. In 1931 the Outlook contradicted President Hoover's opinion that the debt moratoria would be beneficial in its effect upon the wheat market; by Presidential order BAE was prevented from further use of the future tenses in such announcements.[10]

Because of such restrictions, conservative leadership, and the tendency for "action" agencies to do their own economic research and planning, BAE's role was somewhat circumscribed in these years. The Federal Farm Board assembled its own strategic and economic staff. The early Agricultural Adjustment Administration had within it, as a mark of the concern of Henry A. Wallace and his associates over possible misdirections of agricultural policy, a Land Policy Section. But the futher creation of other action agencies, dealing separately and directly with individual farmers, and the great droughts of the middle thirties brought home the need for coordinated governmental approaches to agriculture's problems.

The Office of Land Use Coordination was created in 1937. The following year at the Mount Weather (Virginia) Conference, representatives of the Land Grant Colleges and Universities and of the Department of Agriculture agreed to a method of cooperative policy considerations designed (a) to provide overall program formulation with respect to operations of the federal Department and state agencies affecting land-use, (b) to establish a means for Departmental collaboration with the Land Grant Colleges, and (c) to bring to life the cherished "two-way" democratic concept of M. L. Wilson and others by enlisting the active cooperation of farmers. The BAE was made the federal partner in this effort. Howard R. Tolley, who had become administrator of the agricultural adjustment program with Chester C. Davis's retirement early in 1936, became Chief of BAE.

---

[9] House Hearings, fiscal 1947, pp. 20–21; January 18, 1946.

[10] For the BAE consult John M. Gaus and Leon O. Wolcott, *Public Administration and the United States Department of Agriculture* (1940), index; Arthur W. MacMahon and John D. Millett, *Federal Administrators* (1939). See especially pp. 365–372 and p. 72 for the career of Howard R. Tolley. See also John D. Black, *Agricultural Reform in the United States* (1929). Persia Campbell, *American Agricultural Policy* (1933).

THE PROGRAM OF ATTRITION

The process of cutting down the BAE has been going on for some time. The cooperative federal-state land-use planning program was the first to suffer. The conflict resulting in its demise was essentially over power. Of late issues over *valuations* and *beliefs* have sharply emerged. Some statistical showing can be offered that this last statement is true. Work in BAE is divided into (a) "economic investigations," and (b) "crop and livestock estimates." The latter is supposed to be "objective"—men can count the number of sheep in a field and get the same result, be they Democrats, Republicans, Socialists, Marxists, or whatever. Moreover, this sort of "research" yields tangible results that appeal to "practical men" as eminently worthwhile.[11] But "economic investigations" especially when used as the basis for formulation of controversial policy are quite another matter. As the table shows, "economic investigations" have borne the brunt of the attrition, whether power-based or for reasons of conflicting *belief-valuations,* against BAE.

TABLE 1
APPROPRIATIONS FOR ECONOMIC INVESTIGATIONS AND CROP AND LIVESTOCK ESTIMATES, BAE, 1941–1947

	Economic Investigations	*Crop and Livestock Estimates*
1941	$3,908,602	$1,122,200
1942	3,322,490	1,374,043
1943	2,392,519	1,220,626
1944	2,475,636	1,571,720
1945	2,375,236	1,735,000
1946	2,420,000	1,737,000
1947	1,994,607 (House Bill)	2,037,000

Source: Senate Hearings, fiscal, 1945, p. 126 (April 19, 1944), table showing BAE appropriations, 1941 through 1944. Senate Hearings, fiscal, 1946, p. 34 (April 5, 1945). House Hearings, fiscal, 1947, p. 92 (January 18, 1946); 92 *Cong. Rec.* 2116, March 8, 1946 (Daily Ed.).

At one time Congress was more sanguine regarding the economic investigations of BAE. The Agricultural Appropriation Act for fiscal 1940 (passed in 1939) gave the bureau extremely broad authority. The following wording has enabled H. R. Tolley to assert that Congress accepted Henry A. Wallace's action in making BAE the arm of the Secretary:

"Economic investigations: For acquiring and diffusing useful information among the people of the United States, and for aiding in formulating programs for

[11] Congressman Taber (N.Y.): " . . . that is the only activity they have which is of value to the farmer." 92 *Cong. Rec.* 2117, March 8, 1946 (Daily Ed.).

authorized activities of the Department of Agriculture, relative to agricultural production, distribution, land utilization, and conservation *in their broadest aspects,* including farm management and practice, utilization of farm and food products, purchasing of farm supplies, farm population and rural life, farm labor, farm finance, insurance and taxation, adjustments in production to probable demand for the different farm and food products; land ownership and values, costs, prices, and income in their relation to agriculture, including causes for their variations and trends, $839,100: *Provided,* that the Secretary may transfer to this appropriation from the funds available for authorized activities of the Department of Agriculture such sums as may be necessary for aiding in formulating programs for such authorized activities, . . . "[12]

In 1939, Congressman Taber (R., N.Y.) vigorously objected to the wording on grounds that it constituted legislation in an appropriation bill. The categorical denial made then by Congressman Clarence Cannon (D., Mo.) is of some significance when one considers the tenor of Congressional charges in 1946 that BAE has outstripped its authority:

"This entire paragraph provides for investigation and research and is fully authorized under the organic law, which provides that the Secretary of Agriculture shall acquire and diffuse among the people of the United States information on subjects connected with agriculture, 'in the most general and comprehensive sense of that word'."[13]

BAE escaped controversy in 1940; but in December of that year the American Farm Bureau Federation framed a general attack upon the manner of policy formation and execution in agriculture. The Farm Bureau proposed that there be created in the Department of Agriculture a five-man

"nonpartisan board . . . representative of the Nation's agriculture . . . independent . . . with respect to other bureaus and agencies. . . . It should cover the administration of the Agricultural Adjustment Administration and Crop Insurance, the Soil Conservation and Domestic Allotment Act, Surplus Marketing and Disposal, including the Stamp Plan, Commodity Credit Corporation, the Soil Conservation Service, and the planning activities now in the Bureau of Agricultural Economics."

---

[12] Italics supplied. The transfer from other agencies was in recognition of BAE's rôle in program formulation. The procedure has been for Congress to authorize such budgetary transfers. BAE desired that appropriations be made to it direct rather than by transfer, a step recommended in 1941 by the Office of Budget and Finance, U.S. Department of Agriculture, and by the Bureau of the Budget, Office of the President. Reason advanced for the shift: to expedite Departmental and BAE book-keeping. Another reason may well have been that BAE desired more security against powerful action agencies (such as the Agricultural Adjustment Administration, the Soil Conservation Service, the Farm Security Administration, the Forest Service). In other words, what happened here is another manifestation of the power struggle within the Department. Congressmen did not probe to this possible underlying reason. They doubted that the proposed increases for BAE would be matched by equal reductions in appropriations for planning agencies. As Cannon (D., Mo.) said to Mr. Tolley: "We prefer to have you keep the books." House Hearings, Fiscal 1942, pp. 277–282, January 9, 1941.

[13] 84 *Cong. Rec.* 3307. The chair ruled against Taber's point of order.

On the state level, such programs so far as practicable and including the "State-wide planning program of the Bureau of Agricultural Economics," were to be administered by state committees composed of men appointed by the five-man Washington board from nominees submitted annually by state Extension Directors who previously had consulted with "State-wide membership farm organizations. . . ."[14]

The entire Farm Bureau proposal was not accepted, but Congressmen did cut the BAE by $500,000.[15] In reporting the bill to the House, Mr. Cannon said that the Department should have discretion as to where the cut should be applied; but it was later stated by Senator Bankhead that the argument against the land-use planning activities had "influenced to a large extent the reduction."[16]

The Farm Bureau feared then and still fears the development of farmer committees by any agencies in the Department of Agriculture. Remembering that sponsorship by Extension gave tremendous impetus to the early Farm Bureau movement, leaders of the Farm Bureau do not want to see history repeat itself and a new farm organization emerge from the land-use planning committees, soil conservation district supervisors, or any other source. The kind of issue involved is essentially over power; the struggle is less over the ends involved, and inherent valuations, and more concerning the means: "Who is going to operate?"

Also for reasons involving power, the Farm Bureau was probably aided in its attack upon BAE by the Soil Conservation Service and (although there is less evidence for this) by the Agricultural Adjustment Administration. Although both agencies were playing Machiavelli's game, neither could have read Chapter 3 of *The Prince,* where the warning is given to avoid unison with strong states to crush weaker ones. "He who is the cause of another's greatness is himself undone. . . ." Even at the time, S.C.S. and Farm Bureau were bitter antagonists, as they are today; and in 1943 the struggle between the Farm Bureau and the A.A.A. raged throughout the north central states.

The Soil Conservation Service may have felt that it would have a stake in the future of agricultural planning if soil conservation districts rather than counties could become the local vehicle. In 1941, Congressmen Terry (Ark.) and Collins (Miss.), both members of the sub-committee for agricultural appropriations, were critical of the planning program as encroaching upon, or duplicating, or taking credit for, the work of the Soil Conservation Service.

---

[14] House Hearings, fiscal, 1942, Part II, p. 417; February 11, 1941.

[15] The cut was made in the appropriation bill for fiscal 1942. The Department of Agriculture recommended $5,714,000 for BAE's economic investigations. The Bureau of the Budget cut this by $2,500,000. The House, on recommendation of the Committee on Appropriations, cut the figure to $2,620,000. The Senate restored this last decrease, but the conference committee returned to the House figure. 87 *Cong. Rec.* 2881 and 5400; April 2 and June 20, 1941.

[16] 87 *Cong. Rec.* 1671, March 3, 1941; and Senate Hearings, fiscal 1943, p. 120; April 21, 1942.

Terry asked H. R. Tolley: "Now you are claiming credit for the work that is being done by the Soil Conservation Service?"[17] Both these men were among the House Managers on the conference committee, who prevailed upon Senate Managers to accept the House cut.[18]

The BAE had criticized the Agricultural Adjustment Administration's program in a manner perhaps not favorably received.[19] But again the issue, as the writer became aware of it, was essentially over power. Henry A. Wallace was followed by Claude Wickard as Secretary, and Mr. Wickard had come up through the Triple-A. Nor was this the only bit of evidence that the A.A.A., with perhaps two thirds of the Agricultural Department's appropriations, was, in effect, rapidly becoming the Department. In 1941, with war increasingly imminent, more coordination became necessary in agricultural programs. Conversations were held as to proper mechanisms, and it was remembered that in World War I, there had been state and county War Food Boards in which (especially on the county level) representatives of Extension had played important roles and solidly built the reputation of what was then a new agency.

But in July, 1941, the Defense Boards (later, War Boards) were created by Secretary Wickard *around the machinery of the A.A.A. even down to the county level.* The announcement shocked the Land Grant Colleges. The Extension Committee on Organization and Policy was reported marshalling its forces. One Extension Director told the writer: "We've got our back up now; we are going to fight."

But fight against whom? With what allies? There is a strain of Hamlet in Extension, and the A.A.A. knew how to exploit it. At the critical moment, a story was circulated through A.A.A. channels that Howard Tolley was using the Land-use Planning Committees to create a new farm organization to replace the Farm Bureau—with which, remember, Extension is allied formally or otherwise in many states. This was the same Tolley who was held responsible in Land Grant College minds for the "divorce" of A.A.A. from Extension in 1936. So Extension Directors hesitated to back the only alternative they had against Secretary Wickard's War Boards—the Land-use Planning Committees; and the opportunity was lost.

It should be said, however, that the Extension Directors responded earlier in an effort to save the $500,000 cut in BAE appropriations. The most impressive demonstration in favor of the planning program was that of Extension Director L. R. Simons, Cornell, who was also Chairman of the

---

[17] House Hearings, fiscal 1942, January 9, 1941, pp. 280, 286–87.

[18] Other House Managers were Cannon (Mo.), Tarver, Leavy, Lambertson, Dirksen, and Plumley. 87 *Cong. Rec.* 5400. In 1942 Dirksen was the chief individual factor in wiping out the remainder of the planning program. Lambertson is traditionally for economy (cf. his remarks in Congress, June 8, 1940, 85 *Cong. Rec.* 5762). Leavy and Tarver were apparently favorable to the BAE planning program at this time.

[19] *Report* of the Chief of the BAE, 1940, pp. 65–68.

Extension Committee on Organization and Policy.[20] Simons's appearance before the Senate group was unavailing, however, as noted.

In 1942 the planning program[21] was done away. Congress added to the item for "economic investigations" as shown above the proviso:

> "That no part of the funds herein appropriated or made available to the Bureau of Agricultural Economics shall be used for State and county land-use planning."

This restrictive language marked the success of a continued attack by the American Farm Bureau Federation. President O'Neal's prepared statement on the appropriation bill commended Congress for "effecting a substantial saving in the administration of the land-use planning program" for fiscal 1942. He proposed complete elimination of the program, saying "we have not had a single protest from any farmer with respect to the elimination of this appropriation. . . ." He praised research functions of the BAE, for which "here in the city of Washington" adequate funds should be provided.[22]

Nevertheless, the House Appropriations Committee did not recommend the death of the planning program. In reporting the bill for fiscal 1943, Congressman Tarver (D., Ga.) said:

---

[20] Senate Hearings, fiscal 1942, March 20, 21, 1941, pp. 360 ff. Director Creel was well-informed and extremely favorable in his remarks. He described the Mount Weather conference of 1938 and a follow-up meeting at Roanoke, Virginia, September, 1940. At Roanoke there was general agreement among representatives of state Extension Services that the work was progressing satisfactorily; the only criticism he could recall was that the program was perhaps being pushed too rapidly. He informed Senators of a special committee of the Extension Committee on Organization and Policy which had reported favorably on the planning program, the report of which had been received by the appropriate committees of the Association. Furthermore, Simons had wired state Extension Directors, asking that they communicate their attitudes to Congress. He received wires from 37 Directors favoring restoration of the $500,000 cut. Only four Directors opposed the program, and these included three from states which had signed no memorands of understanding with BAE (apparently Pennsylvania, Illinois, and California). A few Directors, such as D. W. Watkins, South Carolina, approved the program but urged its transfer to the Extension Service. The telegrams to Simons (printed, *ibid.*, pp. 379–91) are for the most part highly commendatory, although a few, such as that of R. K. Bliss (Iowa) were rather negative. Simons also presented favorable letters from the New York State Conference Board of Farm Organizations, made up of eight farm organizations, including the New York Farm Bureau, the State Grange, the Grange-League-Federation, and the Dairymen's League; the New York State Grange had resolved separately in favor of the program. A number of North Dakota officials also attempted to help BAE, including Governor Moses. President Talbott, North Dakota Farmers Union, also favored BAE. *Ibid.*, pp. 217 ff.

[21] In January, 1942, there were 1891 counties in the program and more than 8000 communities. Nearly 125,000 farm men and women served on county and community committees and another half-million attended open community meetings. Some 18,000 federal, state, and local governmental employees participated. BAE maintained representatives in land-use planning in 47 states. Pennsylvania was never in the program. For further detail see H. R. Tolley, *The Farmer Citizen at War,* New York, 1943; Annual Reports of the Chief, BAE, 1940 through 1943; House Hearings, fiscal 1942, pp. 258–77, January 9, 1941. For a critical appraisal: Neal C. Gross, "A Post-Mortem on County Planning," Journal of Farm Economics, August, 1943.

[22] House Hearings, fiscal 1943, February 6, 1942, p. 620; cf. Senate Hearings, fiscal 1943, April 28, 1942, p. 730.

"The committee is very favorably impressed with the prospect for beneficial results from the activities of this organization."[23]

Congressman Dirksen, from the heart of rural Illinois, the strongest Farm Bureau State, led the fight against the planning program. On March 3, 1942, he was eloquent in his praise of Tolley:

"The Bureau of Agricultural Economics is a planning organization. They have one of the headiest, one of the finest, and one of the most able men in the United States in charge of its activities. That is Howard Tolley. He could make far more money in private business than he does working for the Government, but notwithstanding all that, I am inclined to believe that we are almost planning some of our farmers out of existence."

He then proceeded to detail the "seven broad phases" of BAE work, on each of which he gave a curious interpretation.[24]

Dirksen proposed an amendment in the Committee of the Whole to cut the BAE by $1 million, saying, in effect, that he was carrying out the wishes of the American Farm Bureau Federation.[25] He charged that the BAE had "set up area offices in the country, they have set up regional offices, and they have made an attempt to set up county offices. . . ."[26]

Congressman Tarver, chairman of the subcommittee on agriculture, House Committee on Appropriations, vigorously opposed Dirksen's amendment. No one should vote for this amendment, he warned, unless he had read pages 312–316 of the committee hearings.[27] The subcommittee had listened to the Farm Bureau's point of view for two days, he informed the House; the Farm Bureau had offered valuable suggestions which were adopted, but not all their points had carried. "I do not believe the Congress would be justified in

---

[23] 88 *Cong. Rec.* 1890, March 3, 1942.

[24] *Ibid.*, p. 1895 and cf. pp. 1992–93. For example, Dirksen discussed *war production goals*. His comment was to give the farmer a fair price and he will produce. A return argument might fairly cite the importance of the pattern of farm prices in determining *what* farmers would produce as well as the degree to which farm prices had, by Congressional direction, become governmentally administered by this time. Again, other than prices, production goals involved consideration of fertilizer, machinery, and labor shortages as well as problems involved in shifting crop rotations, problems of storage, transportation, and the like. *Attaining required production*—Dirksen attacked this by citing the wheat referendum of the Agricultural Adjustment Administration ascertaining whether farmers desired to reduce wheat production; it may be fairly asked what the BAE had to do with the routine performance by AAA of functions directed by the Agricultural Adjustment Act of 1938.

[25] 88 *Cong. Rec.* 1993; at other points, in answer to Members' queries, Dirksen was wont to quote the attitude of the Farm Bureau, pp. 1995 and 1997.

[26] To put it in its most kindly light, Mr. Dirksen was at least misinformed on these issues. While BAE had set up regional offices, it had not created "area" offices within the states, as both Farm Security Administration and Soil Conservation Service had done. Nor could it fairly be said that BAE had made an attempt to set up county offices. Extension Directors of the several states generally were chairmen of State Land-use Planning Committees; Extension County Agents were frequently chairmen of county committees. Nowhere was a BAE employee assigned to work permanently with a county planning committee.

[27] These pages contain the formal written presentation of its work that BAE made to the committee.

writing an appropriation bill based solely on the opinions of representatives of the Farm Bureau Federation."[28] Recalling Dirksen's praise of Tolley, Tarver also commended the Chief of the BAE. Dirksen's rejoinder acknowledged that there were elements of valuation as well as power at issue. Rexford Guy Tugwell was an able man, he declared, but Tugwellian policies were anathema. Involved here also was a question of the direction of policy.[29]

The planning program was allowed to die without objection. Energies of the Land Grant Colleges were directed in 1942 to fighting off a threatened reduction in appropriations for Extension work. With the exception of Extension Director H. J. Haselrud, North Dakota, no state college official testified one way or the other regarding the planning program.[30] Remember that the BAE had been cut for the fiscal year then current by $500,000, most of which had been used to contribute to the salaries of 308 employees in the Extension Services of cooperating states. Supposedly, BAE could have reduced elsewhere and saved these cooperative employees.[31] To do so might have meant to recruit the aid of the Land Grant Colleges in 1942; but to do so would also have meant to relinquish nearly the entire program to the states. For these "cooperative employees," although BAE paid as much as three fourths of the salaries of some of them, were responsible to State Extension Directors.[32]

ATTRITION CONTINUES: CLEAR EMERGENCE OF ISSUES OVER VALUATIONS

The introductory pages of this paper now become particularly germane. The attack on the planning programs, culminating in its destruction, turned largely upon power questions, although attention may be directed again to Dirksen's interesting strictures against the *kind* of policies he suspected Tolley of advocating. Since 1944, the issues have been more and more clearly over valuations. House Members were critical in that year of the BAE and the

---

[28] 88 *Cong. Rec.* 1997. Before the Senate subcommittee on agricultural appropriations, H. R. Tolley attempted to show how important American Farm Bureau Federation influence had been in the action of the House. He desired to read a statement from the Farm Bureau *Official News Letter* of March 24, 1942. Senator Bankhead interrupted him, saying that he was uninterested in anything that had not occurred on the floor of the House. "Regarding the House cut of $1 million, I don't care anything about what was back of it." Senate Hearings, fiscal 1943, p. 120; April 21, 1942.

[29] Tarver thought that Tolley and Tugwell should not be mentioned in the same breath. His opposition to Dirksen was supported by Hare, Barden, and Leavy. Cannon of Missouri stated that he had voted against the amendment but after further study believed the cut could be made. Dirksen's supporters were May and Jennings. The House accepted Dirksen's amendment, 76 to 55. The Senate restored $500,000 of the reduction but in Conference the restoration was halved so that BAE wound up with a slice of $800,000 for economic investigations, $750,000 of which was derived from Dirksen's amendment. See 88 *Cong. Rec.* 1993, 1997, 4183, 5057, 5061, 5624.

[30] E. J. Haselrud, Director of Extension, N.D., Senate Hearings, fiscal 1943, p. 127,

Department for not acting vigorously enough in the interests of the dairy farmers. Secretary Wickard was stating that farmers' incomes were higher than they ever had been. Yet, said Judge Tarver, look at the plight of the dairy farmers! Auditors had examined the books of dairy farmers in Georgia and had proved that such farmers were showing operating losses.

The Secretary of Agriculture, Tarver said, drew upon Tolley and the BAE for advice upon which to base his statements. When Tolley offered to examine the records to which Tarver referred, the latter said he would be glad to accord Tolley all the time necessary, if the latter would go to the O.P.A., or Marvin Jones, or Fred Vinson, tell them on the basis of Tarver's facts whether the dairy farmers were going broke, and "try to influence them to grant relief of a character that would enable these folks to stay in business."[33]

The writer suggests that if the issue here is probed, it will yield elements of the *belief-valuation* description. Tarver appears to believe in the peculiar worthiness of farmers; hence the *valuation* that farmers ought to get more money. He also appears to believe in the genuine worth to society of the lawyer's conception of ethics; Tarver, like many Congressmen, is a lawyer.[34] Lawyers believe in advocacy. Everyone is entitled to his day in court and to the benefit of counsel. The common law is hammered out by judges case by case in adversary proceedings of "right and wrong, between whose endless jar justice resides." This *belief* in the way justice emerges in the legal field is projected to the political field where the farmer, too, is seeking collective "justice." The *valuation* that a *lawyer* ought to be an advocate is in turn projected to the *economist* and others: the economists in the Department of Agriculture, "the farmer's department," ought to present "the farmer's side" of the "case."

So we have Tarver, with his accustomed forthrightness, laying it down that BAE ought to conceive its role as providing an economic rationale on the basis of which further claims of agriculture may be supported.

April 21, 1942. See also the favorable testimony of Glenn J. Talbott, President, N.D. Farmers Union, pp. 913 ff. and an editorial from *Wallace's Farmer,* March 21, 1942, entitled "Don't Put a Blindfold on Farmers," *ibid.,* p. 125.

[31] The cut of $500,000 for fiscal 1942 was followed by a decrease from $573,000 to $150,000 for cooperative employees.

[32] On February 17, 1943, in response to a question from Mr. Tarver as to whether the BAE had received complaints from farmers or others about the discontinuance of this program, Mr. Tolley replied: "Mr. Chairman, at the beginning of the fiscal year, when . . . we served notice upon the people with whom we had been working that we would not be able to work on it any more, a great many from the colleges, directors of experiment stations, and farmers on the State and county committees expressed to us their regret that we would not be able to work with them any more. They gave us oral and written statements—there were many of them—as to how valuable the work has been and how valuable a part the Bureau of Agricultural Economics had played in it; and in a considerable number of States and counties they are carrying on the work as best they can." House Hearings, fiscal 1944, p. 168.

[33] House Hearings, fiscal 1945, p. 153 and *passim;* February 8, 1944.

[34] See Roland Young, *This Is Congress* (1943), p. 173.

In his oral report to the House on the committee bill, Tarver referred to a difference of opinion among committee members regarding BAE. Admitting the vital need of its economic investigations "if properly conducted," Tarver said, emphasizing that he spoke for himself alone, that "while the information it furnishes should, of course, be accurate," the BAE

"is supposed primarily to be working for the benefit of agriculture and of the farmer and . . . too much of its effort has been devoted to an attempt to prove that the condition of the farmer is satisfactory, and that he is being accorded a fair deal in comparison with other classes. . . ."

Tarver thought this wrong. If the farmer was disadvantaged, then BAE should show it. " . . . and I, therefore, feel that it has not been wholeheartedly the servant of agriculture it should have been." If the committee were sure the BAE would mend its ways, he added, it might feel justified in asking for an increase in appropriations for economic investigations.[35]

In 1945 Mr. Tarver again was critical of BAE's analytical work. Tarver pointed out that although farmers' net income had risen in 1944 over 1943, his share of the national income had fallen from 9.2 to 8.5 percent. He scored BAE for having no better counsel to offer for the farmers' relief than subsidy payments.[36] Yet Tarver successfully opposed the efforts of Congressmen H. Carl Andersen and Rich to reduce by an additional $210,000 the appropriation for economic investigations. The result was a bill which cut economic investigations $100,000.[37]

Senators were somewhat unhappy about this reduction, and a few remarks will indicate at least Senator Russell's consciousness of a possible attrition policy against the Bureau.

Senator Russell. "Dr. Tolley has not fared any too well for some reason for several years, and I guess they thought that was a good reason to cut his appropriation this year."

Senator Reed. "I want to say as I said before of the Bureau of Agricultural Economics, there is no agency in the District of Columbia or in the United States for that matter, that responds more courteously or more efficiently or is more dependable in regard to requests from me than the Bureau of Agricultural Economics."

Senator Bankhead. "They have always been very courteous to me."[38]

---

[35] 90 *Cong. Rec.* 2941; March 22, 1941. Again the Senate attempted to increase the appropriation item and partially succeeded. The House had provided $2,325,326 for economic investigations; the Senate made this $2,475,236. The conference committee provided $2,375,326. *Ibid.*, p. 4575.

[36] House Hearings, fiscal 1946, p. 182, *passim;* February 13, 1945.

[37] This cut was probably due as much to Dirksen as to anyone. It was predicated upon the five-year census of agriculture, it being stated that "because . . . information developed by the impending farm census will render unnecessary the collection of many types of statistics which have . . . been collected" by the BAE. 91 *Cong. Rec.* 2548, 2680–81. Mr. Dirksen was the only member of the subcommittee to raise the issue in the hearings. House Hearings, fiscal 1946, p. 216; February 13, 1945.

[38] Senate Hearings, fiscal 1946, p. 90; April 6, 1945.

1946

So we arrive at the present year. When Clinton P. Anderson replaced Claude M. Wickard as Secretary of Agriculture, there followed the customary reorganization of the Department, reorganization in which eventually BAE's formal role was to be reduced. Meanwhile, two issues over valuations have arisen. One of them is the recurring disagreement over BAE's proper role. The skepticism of Congressmen as to BAE's usefulness, and even its integrity, in the service of agriculture has grown to a critical point. When this issue is considered, readers will recognize its historical relationship to past attacks against BAE; the policy of attrition has become a major offensive.

The second issue will be discussed first. It involves certain reports prepared by BAE for administrative use, one of which is held by Congressmen to raise the racial issue in the South. The problem here is a profound one, and is directly concerned with relative valuation systems. In fulfilling its broad role as a research agency, BAE has concerned itself, in the spirit of the act of 1862, in acquiring and diffusing "among the people of the United States useful information on subjects connected with agriculture, in the most general and comprehensive sense of that word." But the basic act was written when the easy assumption was made that social problems were amenable to solution through research, study, and education: all men if properly enlightened, would agree on policy. Sweet reasonableness was the universal solvent. Such was the creed of liberalism; but about the turn of the century, there was a recrudescence of doubt as to whether human beings are as rational as pictured —or, at least, are rational in quite the same way.

The writer feels that it is very important to an understanding of contemporary agricultural politics that issues of beliefs and valuations be raised. Governmental agricultural policy is almost completely different today from that of 20 years ago. Today such policy has effects growing in profundity, reaching further into the rural social structure, and tending toward a greater degree of inflexibility and irreversibility. We cannot refuse to consider all the possible effects of this new partnership between the government and farmers. *To assume that there is no Negro problem and that agricultural policy has no effect upon it is not to escape our responsibilities.* It is, rather, to accept one set of valuations rather than another. Right here the issue over relationships between politicians or statesmen and administrators emerges in its most important form. Is it possible for government to maintain research and policy-formulating agencies, subject to the direction, of course, of responsible officials, but capable of objective, sustained, and thorough examinations of rural society, or of labor relations, or of any other sector of the economy? We cannot even address ourselves to the real issue of this kind of administrative politics unless we are prepared to haul our beliefs and valuations into the open. Readers are enthusiastically referred to Myrdal, Volume 2, Appendix 2,

Section 2: "Methods of Mitigating Biases in Social Sciences." Now to return to the trials of the BAE.

We cannot ascertain what the effect of the racial issue raised by the BAE report on Coahoma County, Mississippi, had on BAE appropriations. On the floor of the House, Whitten (Miss.) implied that this report was the chief cause of a reduction of nearly $500,000 in funds for economic investigations in fiscal 1947.[39] But apparently the Department of Agriculture and certainly the Bureau of the Budget had already recommended a reduction in funds for BAE that fully covered surveys of this kind. Specific questions on this point were asked and answered in the hearings. Therefore, either the racial issue was used as a beachhead for a general punitive expedition against the BAE through a reduction many, many times the amount spent for the one offending investigation in Mississippi; or some other purpose motivated Congressmen in recommending the large decrease.[40]

What happened was this.[41] In July, 1944, the BAE initiated a series of studies of 71 counties in the United States. The Report of the Chief of the BAE for fiscal 1945 states:

"The regional field staffs have conducted studies on current and anticipated rural migration problems in 71 counties representative of the major type-of-farming regions of the country. These studies are being summarized into regional and national reports. Studies of the economic and social problems of veterans returning to agriculture and changes in farm-family expenditure patterns are being carried on in this 71-county sample." (p. 12; compare 1944 report, p. 6.)

The approximate total cost of the project was $17,795, according to a statement submitted by the BAE to the appropriation subcommittee.[42]

One of the counties was Coahoma County, Mississippi, located in the northern delta of the Mississippi River. Frank D. Alexander prepared a report entitled "Cultural Reconnaissance of Coahoma County, Mississippi," December, 1944. Thirty-five copies of the report were dittoed, of which 16 were distributed: 9 in the Department of Agriculture; 3 to Congressmen Abernethy, Whittington, and Winstead of Mississippi, upon request; and 4 to persons outside the Department for review and criticism.[43]

These facts are as stated; but the record is scanty, perhaps by intention. As Congressman Whitten of Mississippi said:

---

[39] 92 *Cong. Rec.* 2117, March 8, 1946 (Daily Ed.).

[40] House Hearings, fiscal 1947, p. 284; January 17, 1946.

[41] Unless otherwise noted, all material here is drawn from House Hearings, fiscal 1947, pp. 234–242, 282, 286. January, 1946. Thus 18 of 130 pages of Hearings upon BAE appropriations are concerned with this issue; in addition, there are one or two indirect references on the floor of Congress.

[42] The suggestion on the floor of the House was that the cost of the surveys was much more than these figures indicate. 92 *Cong. Rec.* 2117, March 8, 1946, Daily Ed.; cf. remarks of Abernethy and Whitten.

[43] In addition, some excerpted paragraphs were more widely circulated by someone outside the BAE.

"Again, I have not put these matters in the record because I did not want to spread an indictment of fine folks, regardless of the types and character of folks that may have made it, or the motives they may have behind them in this report."

The "fine folks" were the people of Coahoma County, whom Whitten and Tarver thought slandered by the report. In addition to the alleged slander, the charge was raised that the report was published; when Tolley denied this, the dittoed copy was waved in his face. When he sought to explain that the copies were for administrative use, Whitten termed the reports "secret documents" and suggested "ulterior motives" behind the collection of the material. Whitten asked:

"Do you think that would be doing the American farmer any good if we were by leglislation, if necessary, to put your Bureau back to gathering agricultural statistics and take you out of the socialization field and the accumulation of claimed data and the printing of such vicious attacks on the county and its people, as is done by your Bureau in the case before us."

When Tolley asserted that BAE was a "public agency," Whitten agreed that it should be, but "I do not see how you can say you are, fairly and frankly." Whereupon Tolley stated:

"I say we should be a public agency, we should conduct ourselves, and what we do and what we find out in such a way and in such a manner that it will be available to the public at all times, and we should at all times welcome the public to know what we are doing. We should be glad to tell them what we are doing, why we are doing it and how we are doing it, and what we have in mind. I think that this line of work is quite valuable in enabling the Bureau . . . to keep abreast of the agricultural situation and the status of the agricultural situation and its people in this country."

Now what was in this document? That we shall probably never know. Whitten and Tarver both were skeptical of its purposes, or rather, the purposes of the 71-county study, as Tolley stated them.[44] Tolley himself repudiated the paragraphs "on the matter of the race question" which had been excerpted from the report by someone for circulation—"which I think personally were unfortunate, and no reason for them being in there. . . ." Tolley maintained that this part of the report comprised only 3 or 5 percent. Tarver and Whitten thought it comprised 40 to 50 percent. The only excerpts were read into the hearings by Tarver, as follows:

" 'At present the militant Negro leadership in urban centers of the North is making its opinions felt on the rural Negroes of Coahoma County, for a number of

---

[44] When Whitten asked if the document was to "raise the race question and make it something of a problem," Tolley said. "No: with respect to the matter of population and . . . the matter of returning veterans, with respect to the matter of what use farmers will make of their wartime savings, if any. That is part of our general effort to keep a running picture of the agricultural situation. . . ."

them subscribe to northern newspapers which do not hesitate to emphasize injustices done Negroes'."[45]

and:

" 'The city of Clarksdale has a highly rated white school system and a junior high school for Negroes. The municipal swimming pool for whites is located on the campus of the white high school. The school system maintains a free kindergarten for white children of preschool age. The superintendent of the white school is strongly opposed to employing Negro teachers who come from the North or who have been educated in northern schools'."

Setting aside Mr. Tolley's repudiation of such paragraphs, both of those reproduced here seem to report observations "subject to empirical verification."[46] Prospective dwellers in Coahoma County, veterans looking for farms, for example, might or might not want to know such "facts" before making their final decisions. Presumably, there are some Negro veterans.[47] Finally, the reader may judge in the only way he can, subjectively, as to the inflammatory quality of these paragraphs.

BAE AND THE MIND OF THE SECRETARY

It would be seriously wrong to construe the current attack upon the BAE as simply a manifestation of the racial situation. Nor are the only valuation issues—or even, in all probability, the most important valuation issues—involved in the Coahoma County report.

Earlier illustrations have been offered to show a growing Congressional suspicion that BAE does not properly view its role as the farmer's advocate and that BAE has poorly understood and falsely pictured the farmer's real position. Two issues will set forth the situation as it now stands. The first issue is concerned with the *belief-valuation* conflict over economic facts and economic policy that was set forth in the beginning of the paper. It is illustrated by two examples. The first is the conflict over the policy, which certain Congressmen and pressure group leaders heartily dislike, of letting prices of farm products fall to their natural levels and making up the farmers' income

---

[45] This paragraph caused Tarver to remark:

"I think that the treatment accorded Negroes in industrial centers of the North is much worse than that which is accorded Negroes in the agricultural sections of the South in which they are dealt with, on the whole, with sympathy and understanding. Therefore, this is very probably entirely without justification, untrue, and shows an incorrect statement of the situation. It stresses the importance of leadership, so-called militant northern Negro leadership, which in my judgment is a most unfortunate thing and which is doing a greater injury to the Negroes of the South than anything else when it comes to the handling of racial problems which exist in the South, problems which in the main are stirred up by these northern agitators, who seem to take every opportunity of stirring up things of this character. . . ." Hearings, p. 241.

[46] This is a widely accepted criterion for the ascertainment of "social facts"; see Talcott Parsons, *The Structure of Social Action* (New York: McGraw-Hill Book Co., 1937), pp. 41–42, "Note on the Concept 'fact'."

[47] For a discussion of the "Southern Plantation Economy and the Negro Farmer," see Gunnar Myrdal, *An American Dilemma* (New York, 1944), Vol. I, chap. ii.

to some determined level by governmental payments. Secretary Anderson made some speeches which appeared to endorse this heresy. But, since Secretary Anderson was recently a Congressman, although never in the charmed circle of that body so far as agriculture is concerned, it is hard for former colleagues to suspect him of apostasy. Moreover, Congressman Tarver pointed out that Secretary Anderson cannot really know much about cotton since he does not come from a cotton-producing section; therefore, he can be exonerated for accepting bad advice and the blame can be placed upon his advisers. Another example of the first issue here is found in the action of the Secretary with respect to the announcement by O.P.A. of the intention to fix price ceilings on raw cotton.

The second issue concerns both the same *belief-valuation* chain, and in the writer's judgment, another that was introduced early in these pages. The second belief-valuation chain involves a conflict that is obscured but needs to be hauled out. In another manifestation, the writer has attempted to bring it out as regards the tobacco program.[48] It concerns the conflicting beliefs about heredity and environment, and it is buried pretty deep. But it can be smelled out in the conflict over BAE's effort to broaden its investigations of farmers' incomes and expenditures.

It should be stated clearly that the elaboration of the *belief-valuation conflicts* also offer data of importance to the student of administration *per se*. Indeed, a most important administrative problem is the relationship of professional, career administrators and civil servants to the political arms of the government; executive or legislative. The experience of BAE in its relationship to the secretary and to Congressmen suggests the great importance of the *belief-valuation* analysis in this context.

THE SECRETARY, THE BAE, AND PRICE POLICY FOR AGRICULTURE

Price policy in agriculture has long been controversial. Students outside the Department of Agriculture have offered their criticisms of present policies.[49] The Farm Economic Association sponsored a contest in 1945 on price policy for agriculture which called forth many critical essays.[50] These outside critics have been denounced by agricultural politicians,[51] but when

[48] See the writer's forthcoming article, The Tobacco Program: Exception or Portent?

[49] See, e.g., Report of the Committee on Post War Agricultural Policy of the Ass'n of Land Grant Colleges and Universities, October, 1944; John D. Black, *Parity, Parity, Parity* (1942); and *Food Enough* (1943); T. W. Schultz, *Redirecting Farm Policy* (1943); and *Agriculture in an Unstable Economy* (1945).

[50] See *Journal of Farm Economics*, November, 1945.

[51] House Hearings, fiscal 1947, pp. 18–19; January 18, 1946. Compare remarks of Earl C. Smith, annual address to the Illinois Agricultural Association, who regarded the "prize winning essays as a challenge to the Departments of Economics of *our* Land Grant Colleges to offer proposals that recognize the fundamental importance of a sustained, contented and prosperous agriculture . . . " November 28, 1945, Chicago, pp. 23–24; italics supplied.

the BAE as part of the "farmers' own Department" presumes to suggest a critical note, the politicians have available more effective weapons than denunciation: they can punish the agency through its annual appropriations.

Secretary Wickard proposed a plan for cotton in December, 1944. This was followed in April, 1945, by a mimeographed analysis of BAE further exploring alternative approaches to the cotton program.[52] In both these statements, the alternative program given strongest support would involve drastic redirection of present policies. Not long after Secretary Anderson's incumbency, he was making speeches in the South which strongly suggested his acceptance of the more drastic alternatives discussed by his predecessor, particularly for cotton.

Strategically-placed Congressmen have become increasingly concerned about such official criticism of the farm program. In the Hearings upon the Department Appropriation Bill for 1947 repeated efforts were made to pin the formulation of the new proposals for agriculture on BAE, but Mr. Tolley steadfastly refused to admit a larger function than that of gathering facts, making analyses, reaching conclusions, and—*if called upon*—offering recommendations.[53] His interpretation means that whatever recommendations BAE makes upon request are, for policy-making, i.e., political purposes, accepted, rejected, or modified on the responsibility of the Secretary and on his responsibility alone. In addition, Tolley insisted that recommendations were presented as alternatives, a practice which, of course, would strengthen the interpretation that the Secretary alone is responsible for choice of policy.

What actually happens may not be subject to such classical interpretation. The relationship problems between "amateur" political heads of departments and their technical staffs have been frequently canvassed in the literature of

---

[52] Secretary Wickard's statement, "Post War Problems of Cotton," was presented to the Special Committee of the House Committee on Agriculture on Post-War Farm Programs. The BAE analysis is "A Conversion Program for the Cotton South," mimeo., for administrative use.

[53] See Tolley's remark: "The Bureau of Agricultural Economics does not decide upon the volume of production of the various commodities that will be asked for in the years ahead, nor do we decide upon the price policy, or the price support policy of the Department." House Hearings, fiscal 1947, p. 184; January 15, 1946. When Tarver pressed him as to whether a "recommendation" had not been made in favor of the let-prices-fall policy, Tolley replied: "If I may answer precisely, we suggested that consideration be given to that possibility." Whereupon Tarver: " . . . I wish to express my own opinion . . . that in fostering the promulgation of such a policy, in my judgment, your Bureau is doing a disservice for agriculture . . . " p. 187.

Compare pp. 248 ff., colloquy with Dirksen and others probing where the authority lay. References were made to speeches of Secretary Anderson. Authority of the Department under present legislation, particularly Section 303 of the Agricultural Adjustment Act of 1938 (parity payments) and the "intent of Congress" were canvassed. Dirksen remarked that the Treasury Department goes "on the theory that there is no such thing as Congressional intent and that it is for them to fashion what it is their fancy to have been the

political science. Only one aspect of such relationship problems, that of alleviating administrative bias, can be touched upon here. Roscoe Pound, Justice Holmes, and others attempted to educate the jurists of an earlier day as to the importance of conflicting *belief-valuation* systems.[54] For other disciplines a considerable literature has likewise emerged which, first, calls attention to the inevitable presence of "biases," "prejudices," and, second, seeks to develop some methodology for the approximation of objectivity. Hence it may be stated that *properly* qualified social scientists—operating in the presence of the critical professionalism that obtains today—are well-aware of the importance of bias in any analysis. But the real rub comes when one asks whether any particular group of scientists is "properly qualified"—there is no litmus paper test. Are BAE Social Scientists "properly qualified?" One could compile laudatory references on the part of fellow scientists outside BAE but capable of professional judgment. One could list the impressive number of honors and other items of recognition accorded BAE staff-members.

But would Congressmen accept this kind of evidence? Congressmen grant the ability of BAE members; the very attack on BAE is proof enough: intimidation is the severest form of flattery. But Congressmen would probably not accept the "proper qualification" of BAE members in the sense employed above.

The upshot is that Tolley might make all manner of denial without avail. The rumor was being spread that certain members of the BAE were "writing the secretary's speeches for him." And Congressmen were certain that the BAE poisoned the mind of Secretary Anderson by selling him the "let-prices-fall" policy. After three days of Tolley's testimony, Tarver said to Secretary Anderson that Tolley favored the "let-prices-fall" policy.

"I do not know that he made any unequivocal admission of that type

---

intent at some anterior date. It is really amazing how they do that." Whereupon, Tolley: "Economists are not supposed to be experts on the intent of Congress." Dirksen was also concerned as to whether any alternative to the policy that he liked to characterize as "letting prices dribble down to a world level." Tolley said: "No . . . the consequences of prices supported by act of government is being given just as serious consideration. One is being weighed against the other . . . " (see especially, p. 259).

The extent of the questioning on this point may be indicated by a colloquy between H. Carl Andersen of Minnesota and Tolley. Andersen inquired why he should vote for a BAE appropriation or have any confidence in its work if all it had to offer was a proposition of putting farmers "on the same level with farm labor throughout the world . . . " Tolley said:

"I do not know whether it would be worthwhile to further answer. You have heard all this . . .

"Speaking of the entire work of the Bureau . . . , it has been pointed out here repeatedly that facts and statistics with reference to agriculture, and a summarizing and analysis of those facts and statistics, make up a great part of the work that we do. It is for people in positions such as yours to judge as to how much, if any, of those they want." *Ibid.*, p. 264; January 16, 1946.

[54] In *Lochner* v. *New York*, 198 U.S. 45 (1905), Holmes dissented: "general propositions do not decide concrete cases. The decision will depend on a judgment or intuition more subtle than any articulate major premise."

because the doctor does not make unequivocal admissions of any type."[55] Tarver understood that speeches of the Secretary indicated his approval of the policy.

Secretary Anderson stated flatly that this was not correct. He is "not attracted in any way to the proposal that we allow prices to drop to the world level, whatever it may be, or whatever the domestic level may be, and then fill out the difference with a payment from the Treasury." He had so informed his staff. As to the parity, which had been "a fine thing for the farmer," the formula needed reexamination. But proposals to change the formula "would have to come from the farmers themselves and from the farm organizations."[56]

The Secretary's position was acceptable to Congressmen. H. Carl Andersen stated on the floor of the House:

"Mr. Chairman, in fairness to the Secretary of Agriculture, I want to state that he personally has refuted any intention of foisting any such program upon the American farmer. I fear, however, that he may be over-ridden by certain men who have more authority in policy making than he has in this administration.

"We must have for agriculture, not a defeatist program as seriously studied by the Bureau of Agricultural Economics, but a constructive forward-looking program,

---

[55] Tolley certainly came close to such an "admission." In doing so he gave credence to either of two beliefs. First, that the "innermost convictions" of supposedly objective social scientists necessarily color their findings and that in turn these findings are foisted upon ingenuous policy-makers. Second, that, given the nature of present and prospective agricultural programs, an important part of an agency charged with "program formulation" is to be able to look squarely at the eventualities any course of policy may entail. Tolley said:

"The point I want to make . . . is that holding the price at which cotton moves into the world market away above the world price is going to do two things. One of them is to dry up the export market, unless we have export subsidies or something like it. The other is to dry up part of the domestic market on account, on the one side, of competition from substitutes, and on the other side just the economic fact that the higher the price the less the market will take. So, to have a market for cotton, what we can produce and what we should produce in this country, and to have a market mechanism so that cotton will clear the market and not get piled up and *make it necessary for us to have strict and rigid production control, cutting down the amount of cotton that is produced in future years,* it seems to me that serious consideration should be given to letting the going market price of cotton be at or near the price that will clear the market, both domestically and foreign; that loan operations and all other operations should be in that way, and that the difference between what a farmer gets for his cotton or other commodities and what has been determined to be the parity return should be made up of payments, if you please, in the way they were made up in 1933, 1934, 1935, 1936, and 1937." House Hearings, fiscal 1947, p. 226; italics supplied. Compare pp. 230, 231, 255.

[56] House Hearings, fiscal 1947, pp. 19–20, 33, and 50–58. January 18–19, 1946.

Much was made of the fact that the let-prices-fall policy had no authoritative political sponsorship. Tarver asked Tolley: "So far as you know . . . no farm organization, no farm leader, no State commissioner of agriculture has suggested this plan of yours with reference to allowing agricultural products to be disposed of at world prices and making up the difference between that and parity prices from the Federal Treasury." None that he had seen, Tolley replied. House Hearings, fiscal 1947, p. 261; January 16, 1946; cf. Tarver's remarks in the House, 92 *Cong. Rec.* 2048; March 7, 1946; (Daily Ed.).

which will hold up farm commodity prices, union labor wages, and give a decent scale of living for all of us here in America."[57]

Thus do Congressmen reach over the heads of "responsible" Secretaries to smite their wicked advisers. Note that the objection is even to giving "serious study" to any program that might be an alternative to that already become sacrosanct.

BUREAU OF AGRICULTURAL ECONOMICS, THE SECRETARY, AND OFFICE OF PRICE ADMINISTRATION CEILINGS ON COTTON

The BAE was attacked because Chester Bowles, while Administrator of O.P.A., had announced raw cotton ceilings. The press stated that this was done with Secretary Anderson's approval and Tarver assumed that the Secretary acted upon the advice of the BAE. Tolley and O.V. Wells, Assistant Chief, were queried on this point. Wells interpreted the action in the sense of legal conformance. The Secretary of Agriculture, according to law, is required to state that price ceilings on agricultural commodities, as announced, will return parity to the farmer. Wells described the calculation whereby it was determined that the minimum announced ceiling would do so.[58] The Secretary of Agriculture would have an opportunity later, according to Wells's statement, to decide on the advisability of promulgation of ceilings. Mr. Tolley emphasized that the BAE had not been consulted on the matter, although granting, of course, that BAE statistics had been used. This is part of Tolley's effort to delineate a public servant's functions; his analyses and conclusions are available to his superiors. Many of them are available to the public; his *recommendations,* however, are available only to his superiors and then only upon request.

This policy satisfied neither Tarver[59] nor Whitten.[60] Tarver thought it might be BAE's duty, even if not specifically requested, to advise the Secretary of Agriculture as to what price ceilings would mean to cotton farmers. Tolley said that, not having been asked, he did not know what statement he would make in this regard. Tarver thought this an "indefinite statement" from one in Tolley's position "upon whom I think the farmers . . . have a right to rely to exert his full influence and ability on their behalf. . . ."

He would propound the question to Tolley; he, Tarver, was trying to ascertain whether appropriations should be granted. Was Tolley really

---

[57] 92 *Cong. Rec.* 2106, March 8, 1946 (Daily Ed.); cf. Tarver's remarks, *ibid.,* p. 2048, March 7, 1946.

[58] House Hearings, fiscal 1947, pp. 191–203, 225–234; January 15, 1946.

[59] Hearings, pp. 202–203.

[60] For Whitten, compare p. 225. "Actually you just drift along and do not care to get into conflict with Administrator Bowles . . . with the Labor Department nor with the CIO or the labor organizations, and for that reason you just do what you are called on to do, and let it go at that . . . "

fighting for the farmer or had he the consumers' interests and the high salary levels of his Bureau in mind? Then:

"Just what can you say, or will you say, regarding this problem of the cotton farmer which to him is a matter almost of life or death? Have you any opinion about it? If so, will you express such opinion as you have? Just where do you stand?"

This gave Tolley an opening that he exploited fully:

"That is a different question. I am very glad to talk. You have asked me how I feel toward the farmer and how I feel about the welfare of the farmer."

Mr. Tarver. "We all feel kindly toward the farmer. I was more specific than that."

Mr. Tolley. "I have said this afternoon that I personally feel that the farmer should have an opportunity to have a level of living equal to other classes in the United States. . . . That is the basis of the analysis and the research done in the Bureau. . . . That is . . . my personal philosophy and the way that I try to run my job."

Mr. Tarver. "I am trying to find out—"

Mr. Tolley. "That is my philosophy."

Mr. Tarver. "I am trying to find out—"

Mr. Tolley. "Now, you asked me about cotton in the South."

Mr. Tarver. "No; I did not ask you that particularly. I asked you about this action of the Office of Price Administration. Have you any opinion about it? Is it fair to the cotton farmer? If . . . not, why . . . not? . . . Do you have any opinion? Say so if you have."

Mr. Tolley. "I think that it is in line with the legislation that the Congress has enacted."

Mr. Tarver. "And you think that it is fair?"

Mr. Tolley. "I did not say that. First of all, I think it is in line with the legislation that Congress has enacted. Now, has Congress enacted legislation that is fair to cotton farmers? I think that Congress has enacted legislation that has helped cotton farmers."

Mr. Tarver. "I do not want your opinion of the legislation enacted by Congress. You have not been asked for that."

Touché! It is not often that the bureaucrat turns on his tormentors; nor is it often that principles of administrative responsibility are set forth with as much wit.

Digging further into the question of cotton prices, one finds the fundamentally different beliefs about what exists and valuations as to what public officials ought to do, both interrelated. Congressmen thought that if industrial labor was to be guaranteed 75 cents an hour, so should cotton farmers. Cotton, therefore, should sell for 75 cents a pound, since, it was argued, it took approximately an hour's labor to produce a pound of lint. Judge Tarver set out the one hour-one pound figure, and Sherman Johnson, Assistant Chief, BAE, gave some appearance of approving Tarver's statement. Later, however, Johnson declared that labor for the country over averaged half an hour per pound of lint cotton. To this Tarver retorted: "I think it is a very generally accepted fact that the statement you made on yesterday (i.e., one hour-one pound) is more accurate."[61]

But Sherman Johnson could not agree. His previous estimate had been too high. Tables were printed showing hours of direct labor per pound of cotton and income from cotton on family operated cotton farms in various regions. A glance at these tables will convince readers of the difficulty of the Piedmont, from which Tarver hails, in the light of the comparative advantage of the Southwest. In Piedmont two-mule farms, 1940–44, some .52 of an hour were required per pound of lint; in the Southern plains (e.g., the Texas Panhandle) the figure was .12 of an hour. Consequently 1944 figures for return for an hour's labor show 28 cents on such Piedmont farms but 88 cents in the Southern Plains.[62]

But Congressmen were dissatisfied with BAE's method of calculation. What labor should be included? Should labor to produce feed for mules to work the cotton be shown as labor directly for cotton production or separately? Tolley and staff desired to consider typical farms as units and to compare different combinations of enterprises on typical farms as to the total costs involved, including labor, and total incomes received. Congressmen Whitten and Tarver apparently wanted to single out cotton specialty farms, show all labor on such farms as incident to cotton production, arrive at a figure of the time consumed in producing a pound of lint under such circumstances—*and then take this figure as a general one for cotton's labor requirements: thus indicating what the price per pound should be for cotton.* Both Congressmen are lawyers; this approach naturally would enable counsel to make the best possible case for his client. BAE, then, was requested to provide an economic rationale for cotton prices high enough to recompense farmers for labor, the necessary amount of which Congressmen had predetermined. Any failure on BAE's part so to perform brought the prompt charge of "consumer-mindedness," O.P.A.-mindedness, or of having "an innermost attitude of mind" that twisted the evidence against the farmer. No respect was shown for the integrity of Dr. Sherman Johnson, a man with one of the brightest reputations in the profession. It is no wonder that Tolley felt compelled to defend the honesty of his staff![63]

Later Secretary Anderson told the subcommittee that he had refused to join in the press release with O.P.A. on cotton ceilings. Absent from the Department when the request came from O.P.A. to agree to the legality of the announcement of the intention to place ceilings on raw cotton, Anderson himself had not signed the approval. " . . . I certainly would not go back on that approval, because we cannot put ourselves in the position of saying we would not ever approve a ceiling on cotton if cotton got completely out of

---

[61] Hearings, *op. cit.*, pp. 189, 260 ff.
[62] *Ibid.*, pp. 277–78.
[63] *Ibid.*, pp. 288–96.

hand." He further assured Congressmen that actual establishment of a ceiling "will require the approval of the Department of Agriculture." Congressman Tarver asserted that even in contemplation cotton ceilings were having unfavorable effects upon the price. He invited the Secretary to issue a statement in the immediate future as to whether he would accord approval to ceilings if finally proposed to become effective. When the Secretary wished to comment, Tarver informed him:

"There was today a meeting of some 100 or more Representatives from the South to discuss this question, and they appointed a committee to wait on you, on Mr. Bowles, and on the President to discuss this general subject. . . . So I do not want you at this time, unless you feel inclined so to do, to give any positive expression of your views . . . until you have heard . . . the committee."

The Secretary obeyed this injunction.[64] On the floor of the House, Tarver stated that the Bureau of Agricultural Economics was largely responsible for the "perfectly senseless and ridiculous proposal" of O.P.A. to place ceilings on raw cotton.[65]

FARM INCOME AND EXPENDITURE INVESTIGATION

The second issue which reveals the problem of valuations in its bearings upon the politics of agricultural appropriations has an importance that no amount of discussion here can accord full justice. We have a planned agriculture; and Congressmen want it that way. So, among pressure groups, does the American Farm Bureau Federation.[66] Critics have noted the regressive income effects of the program as it has developed: the tendency to give "to him that hath" and take away from him that has little, even that little which he has.[67] True, there has been some palliative modification of the program. But the operative principle remains the historical base.[68] As to its effect (as well as that of other factors which help determine farm incomes) we have the almost incredible admission by O. V. Wells, as knowledgeable of agricultural programs as any one:

"We know very little about the distribution of . . . income between farm families."[69]

---

[64] House Hearings, fiscal 1947, p. 50; January 18, 1946.

[65] 92 *Cong. Rec.* 2048; March 7, 1946 (Daily Ed.).

[66] See the list of fifteen basic laws "To Stabilize Agriculture," *The Nation's Agriculture,* October 1945.

[67] See T. W. Schultz, *Redirecting Farm Policy* (1943), pp. 20, 66.

[68] For the way this works, see the writer's articles in John D. Black, ed., "Nutrition and Food Supply; the War And After," *The Annals of the American Academy of Political & Social Science,* January 1943, pp. 191 ff., and "The Tobacco Program: Exception or Portent?" *Op. cit.*

[69] House Hearings, fiscal 1947, pp. 279–82 for all citations in this discussion; January 17, 1946.

In short, we are plunging ahead with regulatory programs which tend to freeze a pattern of income distribution among farmers without really knowing what the actual distribution is, and what the real effect on individuals is likely to be—and we have been going merrily along in this fashion for nearly 13 years.

Wells also said:

" . . . there is at the present time, in the Department of Labor, a rather well conceived program of finding out as much as possible about the income and living conditions of laboring people. I believe the Congress of the United States . . . directed the Bureau of Labor Statistics to calculate a minimum cost budget for the American working family, for the average American workman in cities. Such a minimum cost budget will . . . be used to compare with the income of those laboring people.

"Now we have done a great deal of work in the Bureau of Agricultural Economics on agricultural income . . . (and) on parity prices. However, parity price and overall income do not in my opinion, adequately measure the living conditions that American famers either now have or expect."

But, in addition, he had stated:

"We also know very little about the total amount of income received by farmers and farm people from work off the farm, although of course we are well aware that it is rather substantial."

And it was this and similar utterances upon which Tarver seized:

"If I judge correctly . . . , one of the purposes is to show that the farmer has a better income than he has been supposed to have."

And, brushing aside attempts at explanation, he continued:

"The trouble about it in my mind is that I used to be a very strong advocate of the work of your Bureau. I resisted efforts to decrease an appropriation some years ago, and have always thought that sufficient funds ought to be provided for you; but during the last year or two a suspicion has grown up in my mind that you may not be working for the farmer; you may be working more for the consumer of agricultural products; and if I interpret part of your testimony correctly, one of your purposes here is to gather information which will show that the farmer's income is not so deplorably low as has been heretofore represented from the sale of agricultural commodities, but that in addition he has some kind of mythical income from work that he is supposed to do off the farm. I am just not convinced in my own mind that your purpose is to help the farmer."[70]

There is no question of Tarver's strategic support of the BAE, as shown above. He was to come to its rescue again in 1946 when Congressman H. Carl Andersen attempted to slash the funds for economic investigations by another $300,000 on the floor of the Committee of the Whole.[71] But the

[70] House Hearings, fiscal 1947, pp. 279–82; January 17, 1946.

[71] 92 *Cong. Rec.* 2116–2117; March 8, 1946 (Daily Ed.). Andersen's effort lost by eight votes.

appropriation for investigating income and expenditures has not been granted. We shall continue to operate in a manner beneath the aspirations and technical pride of democracy by enforcing regulatory programs without at the same time making the fullest effort possible to ascertain their effect upon differently situated individuals.

Part of our failure here may well be due to the refusal or inability to examine the *belief valuation* issue involved. To restate the issue as it appears to the writer, we have adopted regulatory programs for agriculture which entail the assignment to individual farms of quotas and some control both over entry into farming and also over increases of various enterprises in farming. Quotas are assigned largely on a rule-of-thumb, the "historical base." The entire program is rationalized as an effort to get "economic justice" (parity) for the farmer. But, in general, results are tested by comparing *general* ratios of prices received and paid by farmers, of farmers' and others' incomes. The assumption must be that the general returns to farmers break down acceptably to individual farmers. That there is some difficulty, politically at least, in making this assumption is shown by the various efforts to improve the A.A.A. allotments in the interest of the small farmer.[72] Why is the assumption made? In the early days of the A.A.A., rules of thumb had to be employed. But to have maintained the assumption for 13 years suggests that it accords with some *belief valuation* chain. The *belief* that helps explain the easy acceptance of the way the program works is that men are naturally unequal in farming ability as in other things and that heredity plays a strong part in passing on special ability from father to son. The *valuation* is, of course, that rewards *ought* to be in accordance with ability. If these *belief valuation* chains are held, one can accept the historical base as resulting in rough justice for individual farmers.[73] When such *belief valuations* are challenged, either openly or, as with the BAE, tacitly, a conflict on a very profound level results.[74]

CONCLUSION

The story of attrition against the BAE has offered insight into the power struggle, especially as regards the formidable American Farm Bureau Federation which turns its fire, now on this agency, now on that one, through its Congressional spokesmen, such as Dirksen. Recently one Land Grant College official expressed doubts to the writer whether BAE can survive under present leadership since "Ed O'Neal no longer has any use for Tolley."[75]

[72] Such adjustments in allotments in favor of small farmers are frequently palliative in nature. See "The Tobacco Program: Exception or Portent?" *Op. cit.*

[73] Other *belief-valuation* chains are involved; e.g., the hardy belief in automatic laws of economics.

[74] Similar conflicts over valuations frequently occur between the Farm Security Administration and other agencies or farm organizations. FSA's rural rehabilitation program flies in the face of the *belief-valuation* chain analyzed above.

[75] This was before H. R. Tolley's resignation.

That O'Neal and the Farm Bureau carry great weight in the downfall of BAE is strongly suggested both by what appears in foregoing pages and by the new restrictive wording of the appropriation item added in 1946 by the House.[76] Before the subcommittee, O'Neal urged that BAE be confined to statistical and fact-finding research.

"*It should be prohibited from conducting social surveys,* agricultural planning and promotion, and opinion polls (except bona fide factual marketing studies and surveys of consumer attitudes and preferences with respect to the consumption of agricultural commodities). All funds for this type of work should be eliminated. *The regional offices should also be eliminated* as this is a needless expense." (Italics supplied.)

The BAE item in the appropriation bill, with the Committee cut of $485,543 below the Bureau of the Budget recommendations, which the House accepted, contains new restrictions as follows:

"*Provided further,* That no part of the funds herein appropriated or made available to the Bureau of Agricultural Economics shall be used for State and county land-use planning [to this point, language is the same as that added in 1942; then]: *or for the maintenance of regional offices, or for conducting social surveys.*" (Italics supplied.)

The chief focus of this paper, however, is the *belief valuation* conflict. If "everything includes itself in power," then appetite may well make "an universal prey." If it is possible to go further, we cannot afford to rest on power analyses alone. The *belief valuation* approach should be helpful in permitting a more profound understanding of the nature of the issues which divide us.

Meanwhile, what is to be done about BAE? Considering the nature of modern agricultural programs, is there no need somewhere for organized consideration of their effects? Congressman Hope of Kansas has charged that the tobacco program provides not merely a closed shop, but a closed shop with a closed union.[77] There is a tendency for separate programs to be developed for all important agricultural commodities: where are they leading the country? Are we not at least going to inquire? If we retain any pretensions whatsoever to rationality, what are we to do about the available agency for such inquiry, the BAE?

---

[76] House Hearings, fiscal 1947, pp. 1644, 1653–55; 92 *Cong. Rec.* 2116, March 8, 1946 (Daily Ed.). It should be added that in none of the years, 1941–1946, was the BAE the chief target of Farm Bureau criticism. In 1941, the main emphasis was upon acceptance of the sweeping AFBF proposals, as noted, and the shortcomings of FSA and SCS. Both these agencies have figured prominently in AFBF criticism in each succeeding year. An all-out attack was leveled at FSA in 1942; in 1943, chief emphasis appears to have been upon reforming the AAA; in 1944, AAA, FSA, SCS, and departmental information offices were chief subjects of criticism.

[77] See the writer's "The Tobacco Program: Exception or Portent?" *Op. cit.*

To do anything about the plight of the BAE is, as these pages show, extremely difficult. A handful of strategically situated Congressmen have BAE at their mercy. Their control is tightly held; for BAE appropriations stimulate by no means the wide Congressional interest that the issues over parity payments, Commodity Credit Corporation loan rates, the organization of agricultural credit, the food-stamp plan, and other matters arouse. The greater the general Congressional indifference, the more vulnerable is BAE to the strategic few. But where can this Bureau, which Congressman Sheppard of California called "the heart pulse of the operation" of the Department, find support? In the Land Grant Colleges? Remember the record in 1942. Unless the Colleges get cut heavily in on the appropriations, they are not interested. In the Secretary of Agriculture? The record of 1946 returns a negative answer: the BAE is made the scapegoat for secretarial policy determinations. It becomes increasingly difficult to accept the idea of the Secretary as the responsible political chief of the Department.

Since this paper was written, H. R. Tolley has dramatized the issues it attempts to analyze by resigning as Chief of the BAE. O. V. Wells has been appointed to succeed him. The writer hopes that his argument will have convinced readers that this shift in personnel is no solution to the problem. The nature of the problem is such as to involve, among other things, conflicts over beliefs and valuations. In the future as they have in the past, such conflicts will affect the determination of agricultural policy and relationships between politicians, pressure group leaders, administrators, and civil servants. Whoever leads the BAE, unless that organization becomes merely a recording angel, is going to be concerned with the substance of policy. He is going to need continuous and intelligent criticism. If he is to neutralize biases among his staff, attain a degree of objectivity, and *still carry the analysis down into the belief valuation conflicts,* he must have support—continuous, intelligent, and critical, nevertheless, *support.*

24 Agricultural Policy and Farmers' Freedom: a Suggested Framework*†

DALE E. HATHAWAY‡

Students of American agricultural policy spend much time and effort in attempting to rationalize the apparently irrational value systems of the American farmer and his representatives as displayed in their political actions and attitudes. We are confronted with a group who seem to place the highest value on individual freedom and yet periodically vote into effect controls that put rather stringent restrictions upon their freedom to determine the amount of a crop they may plant or sell. Some explanations of these actions have been attempted, but as yet none has been completely successful. It is suggested that none is likely to be that is cast within the popularly accepted theory of social values,[1] and that there is a sound theoretical framework somewhat akin to that used in economic theory[2] which will provide a much more useful approach in our analysis of social values and political policy.

This matter is of more than academic interest at the present time. After twenty years of agricultural policy which often has been cited as a menace to farmers' "freedom" we have a new administration in power, one which

---

* *Journal of Farm Economics,* Vol. XXXV, No. 4 (November 1953), pp. 496–510.

† Journal Article No. 1557 of the Michigan Agricultural Experiment Station. This paper is adapted from a paper presented by the author to the Social Science Seminar on Freedom held at Michigan State College during spring term 1953. The author is indebted to many of his colleagues for their helpful comments, and especially to Dr. Glenn Johnson and Dr. James Shaffer who made many helpful suggestions throughout the development of the paper. The author, of course, assumes the responsibility for any errors.

‡ Michigan State University, East Lansing, Michigan.

[1] See Gunnar Myrdal, *An American Dilemma* (New York: Harper & Bros., 1944), especially pp. 47 and 48 and Appendix I.

[2] See J. R. Hicks, *Value and Capital* (New York: Oxford University Press, 1948), chap. i, or M. W. Reder, *Studies in the Theory of Welfare Economics* (New York: Columbia University Press, 1947).

wishes to make certain that the farmers' "freedom" is maintained. Yet it appears that farmers may not be as anxious to maintain this freedom as some have thought, if the political reactions of farm-state congressmen are any indication of farmers' attitudes on the subject. At the time of this writing farmers have been asked to choose between further restrictions on one of their "freedoms" or drastically lower price supports for wheat, and they chose less freedom. Other such decisions are likely to face them in the near future. Will this be an indication that farmers have abandoned their freedom in order to get higher prices, thus completely reversing the position that the leaders of the two largest farm organizations have supported so strongly from 1946 through 1952? It is suggested that the answer is no. These apparently erratic fluctuations of our agrarian society can be explained within a rational framework. An understanding of this framework is necessary at a time when new policies are being formed.

A WORKING DEFINITION OF FREEDOM[3]

In order to discuss the concept of freedom in relation to agricultural policy an attempt must be made at some definition of freedom. First, it should be recognized that no one is completely free, and therefore "absolute" freedom is not meaningful to this discussion. There must be some method of evaluating whether a particular policy leads to a reduction of freedom or an increase in freedom. For this particular discussion we shall be concerned about the state of freedom of the individual farmer in the operation of his farm.

To begin this definition of freedom it is suggested that an individual is free when he is able to do an act or not to do an act. Notice that this concept of freedom implies both his *ability to choose* to do an act or not to do the act, and the actual *ability to carry out* that act if he should choose to do it or not to do it. Certain restrictions may be placed on an individual's freedom, and freedom is reduced or removed if these restrictions are present in a given policy. A common restriction is the loading of the consequences of doing an act or of not doing an act in such a manner that it will cause a person to choose a course of action that he would not otherwise choose. Accepting this broad definition means that the consequences of all acts are loaded in a price system since any price loads the consequence of doing or not doing an act involving production. It seems an unrealistic assumption to say that all prices are a restriction on freedom; and therefore, it is suggested that the consequences are not loaded unless there has been a conscious attempt by

---

[3] The author has drawn upon ideas developed by Professor H. S. Leonard, Head of Department of Philosophy of Michigan State College, in a paper presented to the Seminar on Freedom, and Frank H. Knight, *Freedom and Reform* (New York and London: Harper & Bros., 1947), especially chap. i.

individuals or groups to apply coercion to specifically influence an act under consideration.[4]

Another restriction on freedom of the individual may result because he lacks knowledge of all the alternatives which are open to him or knowledge of the consequences of all these alternatives. However, it is obvious that full and complete knowledge is impossible. Therefore, everyone has certain restrictions on freedom and it is necessary to modify the definition so that it becomes meaningful. For this purpose it is suggested that the individual is free if he has a knowledge of the important alternatives that face him and the consequences of these alternatives relevant to the rational formation of that particular decision. With this somewhat oversimplified definition of freedom, let us proceed to a discussion of freedom and agricultural policy.

Just as there is no such clearly definable concept as complete freedom, neither is there any meaning unless we are discussing a specific freedom to do something. Since most of the discussion of freedom and agricultural policy seems to revolve around the relationship of the federal government and the individual farmer, this discussion will be primarily concerned with the policies of the government as they have affected or may affect the individual farmer *in the operation of his farm.*[5]

At this point in the discussion it is useful to stop and point out that there are a number of other social values held in our society which have entered in the formation of agricultural policy and which may come in conflict with freedom.[6] In the field of agricultural policy the more important values that might be listed are family farm ownership; equality, which may at times be called justice and has come to be known at present as parity, but which is essentially a concept of real farm income; and the value that we place on economic efficiency. Another value which has become more prominent and which probably should be added to the list is the value of stability or security. At various times different public programs attempt, or are developed in an attempt, to increase or improve the attainment of these social values. Sometimes the attainment of several of these values coincide and any one program may increase or help achieve a fuller attainment of a number of these values. At other times a program designed to attain one of these values may conflict with other values, and in many cases such programs may conflict with the freedom of the farmer to operate his farm.

The idea that there are a number of values which conflict with freedom is not a new one; however, it does seem that there has been a lack of clarity

---

[4] Under this definition penalties for overplanting marketing quotas that reduce acreage below intentions to plant are restrictions on freedom, but actions of traders on the grain market would not be unless they attempted to corner the market.

[5] This rules out of this discussion the effects of a tight monetary policy or progressive taxation, although the same theoretical framework seems applicable with some alterations.

[6] See the article by D. E. Hathaway and L. W. Witt, "Agricultural Policy: Whose Valuations," *Journal of Farm Economics*, August 1952.

regarding the point at which these values conflict. It has been pointed out that there is no such thing as absolute freedom, and this is true of all of the other values under discussion. In order to be meaningful, we should realize that we are discussing these values in marginal terms only. This is extremely important for several reasons.

The first reason is the relationship of marginal social values to the political compromise. Our political parties are famous for the marginal compromise they make in order to gather the support of minority groups, to the dismay of the advocates of programmatic parties. Perhaps to some these compromises may not appear marginal, yet neither major party would ever admit that they had drastically reordered their principles to collect the groups that make up their parties. If we were dealing with absolute values, political compromise would be unlikely if not impossible unless major portions of society were willing and able to reorder their entire value systems in a relatively short time.[7] This is probably impossible under a rational democratic system of government and would probably result in revolution over numerous issues if it were necessary. In fact, we have seen one instance in our history when the value conflicts involved such large marginal increments of so many values that a major portion of society would have been required to drastically reorder their value systems to live within a new national policy. They refused to do this and a civil war resulted.

Another reason that social values must be considered in marginal terms is directly related to the first. If discussions are in terms of absolute values and their conflicts it becomes important to determine the ordering that an individual places on these values and aggregation becomes difficult if not impossible. Then if people seem to desire programs that conflict with this ordering it is assumed that there must be either a group of conflicting absolute values which persons fail to recognize in their conscious activities or that there is a continuous and frequent reordering of the various social values. This has been a favorite subject of many authors who accept the first assumption as true. It is suggested that neither assumption is necessary and that the use of the marginal concept is much more useful and meaningful.

By using the marginal concept it can be perfectly rational for an individual to hold freedom as his highest value, even above life itself, and still be willing to sacrifice some small portion of his freedom in order to achieve more security. This involves only marginal rates of substitution between the values and easily serves to explain why persons make different choices at different times without the confusing problem of trying to explain why there were changes in the total value systems of a society.

Viewing these conflicts between values as marginal conflicts has another

[7] Most authors say either that this is true or that there exist higher values to which persons turn when value conflicts occur, but these higher values are rarely defined. Neither explanation seems satisfactory and both can be avoided if we abandon our concern regarding the ordering and conflicts in absolute terms.

usefulness in light of our discussions of agricultural policy. It seems that two or more of these values which may conflict when considered in an absolute sense are probably complementary for certain ranges at their margins. Thus we can have programs which increase both freedom and security within certain ranges, which if carried to extremes would result in a decrease in one or the other.

FIGURE 1

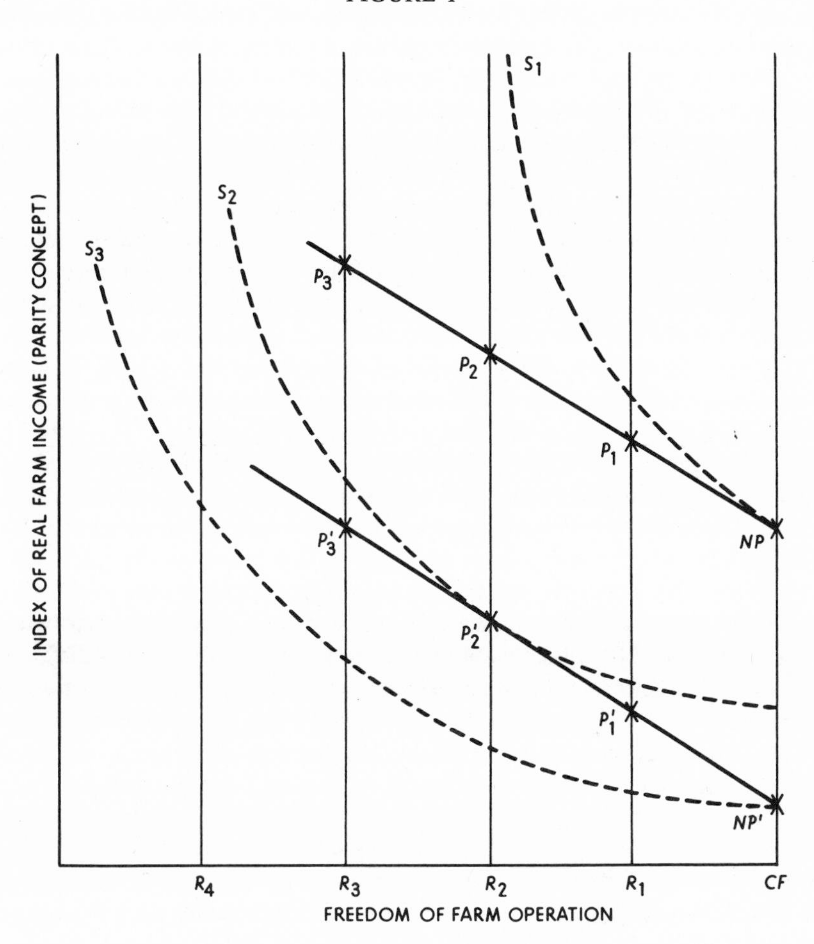

The framework of marginal substitution of social values not only seems to avoid confusion in discussion, but the concept also has the advantage of diagrammatic expression.

In Figure 1 let the horizontal axis represent the freedom under discussion, in this case the freedom of farm operation. At point CF the farmer has complete freedom from government interferences in the operation of his farm and points R_1, R_2, R_3, and R_4 represent successively greater government restrictions on the freedom of the farmer in the operation of his farm. On the vertical axis let us have a scale representing an index of real income to be expected from the crop under discussion, which is closely related to the farmers' concept of parity and equality.

Now let us add a series of curves which indicate the pattern of the marginal rate of substitution that a farmer has between the value he places upon freedom of farm operation and his real income position in society. For lack of a better name, these are called "satisfaction" curves and the individual farmer is more satisfied on curve S_1, than S_2 or S_3. However, the level of satisfaction which he may attain regarding the two values under discussion is determined in large part by forces beyond his control, i.e., the market for his product and the possibilities of market manipulation via government intervention.

Thus, at point NP there is no program and the farmer has complete freedom of farm operation, at point P_1 there is some restriction of freedom and the income position is higher, at P_2 there are even more restrictions on freedom and a higher income position, and at point P_3 there would be greater loss of freedom of farm operation and a somewhat higher income. Given the income possibility line just described the farmer would receive the most satisfaction with no government program since he could attain satisfaction curve S_1 from the free market. This situation undoubtedly represents the position of most farmers in the early post-World War II period. At that time no support program offered to farmers could improve their income position enough to get them to accept the accompanying controls.

Now let us turn to a market condition illustrative of the 1953 wheat market. The market price in the absence of a government program would result in income NP′ which would place the farmer on the lower satisfaction curve S_3, but the farmer knows or believes he can improve upon this position by accepting control program P_2' which places him upon satisfaction curve S_2. Thus, farmers may vote a control program into effect for a commodity *without any change in their social values regarding freedom,* merely because their income or total welfare possibility line has moved sharply to the left due to changing economic conditions. Where at an earlier time he was willing to sacrifice very little freedom to receive increased income, he now is ready to sacrifice some freedom of farm operation to improve his income position.

It can be readily seen that the characteristics of the income possibility curve and the satisfaction curves are extremely important in the formulation and acceptance of agricultural policy. Regarding the income possibility curve, it can be reasoned that the slope of that line would be closely related to the price elasticity of products under discussion. This, of course, seems to explain why products for which there is a relatively inelastic demand would come under control programs at an earlier time than would those with a more elastic demand, since the slope of the income possibility line would be greater and thus the point of tangency with a satisfaction curve involving some loss of freedom would come earlier, unless the satisfaction curves are very flat.[8] The amount that the income possibility curve shifts with changing economic conditions depends, of course, upon the income elasticity of the products being discussed.

There is less to indicate the shape of the various individual farmer's satisfaction curves that represent the marginal rates of substitution between these social values. Obviously, some persons place an extremely high marginal value on freedom of farm operation regardless of economic conditions and would have very steep curves, while others are willing to sacrifice some freedom to gain greater income regardless of how high incomes are at the time and would have very flat curves. It appears likely that the lower curves would tend to become flatter for all farmers.

Given the income possibility curve and the satisfaction curves for the individual social values, a program will be adopted (or desired) whenever the income possibility curve is tangent to a higher satisfaction curve of a majority of the farm population than the satisfaction curve they might attain without such a program.[9, 10] Thus two conditions could bring about sharp shifts in farmers willingness or desire regarding certain types of programs. One would be due to a shift in the income possibility line, due either to changing economic conditions or to the advent of a new program that gives greater incomes with the same restriction of freedom. Another shift could result because of a change in the satisfaction curves (marginal rates of substitution) of farmers who had become irritated with government controls or because of a basic change in their value systems due to the impact of new ideas or facts. However, it would seem that the latter type of changes would occur slowly and that our apparently rapid changes in

---

[8] The elasticity of demand for the product is also closely associated with another major value sought by government programs, the value placed upon income stability. A third value cannot be shown on our diagram, but the complete determination of the individual's satisfaction surface depends upon the simultaneous solution of a system of equations representing the marginal values of all of the social values concerned in a given program.

[9] This assumes that the political processes work well enough to establish such equilibrium. If the political leaders do not correctly appraise the situation, they may be changed. In the meantime the income possibility curve may move even further to the left as conditions get worse. Thus a mild control program at one time might make a stricter program at some later time both impossible and unnecessary.

[10] This seems to avoid the problem of aggregating individual orderings of these social values which has been discussed at length by Kenneth J. Arrow in *Social Choice and Individual Values* (New York: John Wiley & Sons, Inc., 1951). In general our voting processes consist of two phases. In an election we vote "yes" or "no" for an individual and attempt to vote yes for the one that we believe has approximately the same rates of marginal substitution between social values as we have. A congressman voting in a committee or an individual farmer voting on wheat marketing quotas votes yes or no on a specific proposal. The farmer does so in regard to his own satisfaction surface and the congressman does so in line with his estimation of the satisfaction surfaces of a majority of his constituents.

farmers' attitudes consist of changing income possibility curves relative to fairly stable satisfaction curves.

It is suggested that this type of framework can also be useful in understanding attitudes and political actions toward other phases of agricultural policy than price supports and production controls. This would require some redefinition of terms and relabeling of axes for the diagram, and will be impossible due to the lack of space in this discussion. Let us turn now to the history of the 1920's and 30's to see if this theoretical framework helps to explain the political action of farmers and their organizations.

AGRICULTURAL POLICY AND FARMER'S FREEDOM—1920–40

Numerous discussions are available on the reasons for the problems that beset agriculture starting in the 1920's. These will not be covered again since it has been stated that the effects of the price system on agriculture are not regarded as constituting a restriction on freedom of the individual farmer. To view the price system as a restriction on freedom of farm operation makes the whole idea meaningless, and as mentioned before prices will be viewed as a restriction on freedom only in cases where there has been concentrated coercion to specifically drive down individual farm prices. A farmer's lack of knowledge that a specific price decline is coming may be a restriction on freedom, but no more than is his lack of knowledge of a forthcoming price rise a restriction on freedom. For this reason, low farm prices in relation to other prices is viewed as an income equality problem in most cases.

In the early 1920's the problem was not of agricultural freedom, but one of achieving equality of income for agriculture. It is interesting to note two other developments of that time. The first was that throughout the 1920's many agrarian groups were clamoring for equality, for protection of the family farm, and suggesting restrictions on the freedom of the individual farmer in the form of production controls. At that time the executive branch of government refused to interfere with the freedom of the individual farmer in the operation of his farm. In fact, the only programs that the executive branch seemed willing to carry out were those that would increase the freedom of the farmer through the extension of knowledge, more research and discussion of better marketing methods. Thus, we had two major policy making groups within our society with sharply differing marginal rates of substitution between these social values. The executive branch of the government apparently regarded freedom of individual farm operation very highly and refused to restrict it regardless of the effects that the lack of a positive policy was having on the other values held by farm groups. At the same time some farm organizations and many other representatives of farmers, including many congressmen from the so-called farm bloc, were demanding government programs that would increase or help achieve equality for farmers at the sacrifice of some of their freedom.[11] The result of this conflict was a long period of inaction during which agriculture suffered a great deal.

Conditions in the early 1930's became much worse,[12] and starting with the advent of the New Deal there was action, a great deal of action, for a number of reasons. One reason was that the new leaders that came into power in the executive branch of the government were those whose estimates of the relationships between the various social values more nearly coincided with those of a majority of the public at that time. Secondly, the economic and social conditions of the great depression had altered the income possibilities from the unsupported market so drastically that policies which previously had no possibilities of acceptance were readily adopted. With a major portion of our resources unemployed efficiency became of little or no concern, even among economists. Thus, in agricultural policy there was action as inequality became greater, family farm ownership was threatened, and the security of agriculture was impaired. At that time a policy to achieve these values was complementary, and there was no widespread protest from the agricultural sector of the economy when freedom of farm operation was restricted and production control for agriculture was inaugurated on a widespread basis.[13] Of course, this phenomenon was true throughout the economy in general, and we found that the early programs of the New Deal were largely those which attempted to increase income equality and security, and many reduced individual freedom without a great deal of protest from any segment of society.

In the area of agricultural policy the restriction of the farmers' freedom came primarily via the loading of the consequences of producing certain crops. These consequences were loaded by the making of or withholding of certain types of payments by the government. This type of activity was found unconstitutional and was replaced by another activity under the Soil Conservation Act of 1936, which essentially was still a loading of the consequences of growing certain "soil depleting" crops.

In the Agricultural Adjustment Act of 1938, certain provisions were established which could be severe restrictions on the freedom of farmers in the operation of their individual farms. Again these activities take the form of the loading of the consequences of growing or of not growing certain crops. The mildest form of these restrictions is the acreage allotment, in which the consequences are loaded by the withholding of government

---

[11] Another reason for the divergent attitudes may have been different opinions as to the income possibility line with no government intervention or with various types of programs.

[12] Primarily because the income possibility for agriculture was so poor without government intervention.

[13] It is entirely possible that conditions were bad enough that the income possibility curve became concave to the lower areas of the income and freedom scales on the diagram shown in Figure 1.

support prices from the farmer who fails to comply with his acreage allotment. If the price support program in operation is very effective, these consequences may not be at all severe since the market price may approach the support price of the government program. However, the Agricultural Act of 1938 also included provisions for marketing quotas, which may be a severe restriction on the freedom of the individual farmer, since it puts rather substantial cash penalties on the production of crops on acreage in excess of the farmer's allotted acreage. Both of these forms of restriction of farmers' freedoms were used for several crops between 1938 and 1942.

It is doubtful that these severe restrictions on the freedom of the individual farmer in the operation of his farm could have been written into our agricultural policy at that time without the consent and approval of the major farm organizations. This does not suggest those organizations had lost their high regard for the freedom of farmers during that period. However, they were willing to sacrifice some freedom of farm operation in order to gain more of other values.

It should be pointed out that these severe restrictions on farmers' freedom (marketing quotas) can only be put into effect after the affirmative vote of two-thirds of the eligible farmers who vote. If the Secretary of Agriculture should request marketing quotas and the eligible farmers fail to approve the quotas, the support price on the crop in question is lowered drastically or removed entirely. Thus, by this vote farmers are essentially asked to choose between a promise of higher incomes and more security, or more freedom. Since the authorization of marketing quotas in 1938, the tobacco producers have voted affirmatively on marketing quotas in every year except one. This seems to be a definite indication that this group places a higher value on what they believe to be an increase in security and equality of income than they do on the increased freedom they might gain from an unsupported market. Recent research by Glenn Johnson[14] indicates that they have been quite successful in achieving their desires since the program has apparently resulted in real gains to the producers over a free market.

The 1938 Act also authorized the use of other restrictions on the freedom of farmers and marketing agencies; namely, marketing orders and agreements. These load the consequences of marketing certain classes of products. Like the marketing quotas they require an affirmative vote of the producers or marketing agencies dealing with the commodities. These devices have been used widely on a number of perishable commodities, providing many examples of where a majority of the persons involved have been willing to sacrifice some freedom for what they thought might be additional equality or security.

Thus, as we moved through the 1930's, there seemed to be a tendency

---

[14] *Burley Tobacco Control Programs*, Bulletin 580, Kentucky Agricultural Experiment Station, February 1952.

to evolve agricultural policies that authorized greater and greater restrictions upon the freedom of the individual farmer in the operation of his business. The major value that farmers and their representatives seemed to be seeking to achieve during those years was equality for agriculture. Throughout this period farmers sacrificed freedom in an attempt to achieve higher prices because through these programs they could achieve a higher level of satisfaction than was offered by the uncontrolled market.

FREEDOM AND POSTWAR AGRICULTURAL POLICY

By the end of World War II the problem of equality of income for American agriculture or at least for the commercial farmers had been solved by high farm prices. At the same time the capital structure of commercial agriculture resulting from these prices was such that they had made rapid gains in efficiency of production. The status of the family farm was well established and most commercial family farms had never known a state of prosperity as good as that in the postwar period. This meant that the market was satisfying, to a large extent, most of the major values that are desired by the important groups in the agricultural society. Most farmers were willing to sacrifice very little freedom in order to gain any more security, because the income possibilities from the free market placed them far to the right on their indifference maps and additional security or equality from government programs could not improve their position.

During this postwar period the leadership of the largest farm organization, the American Farm Bureau Federation, came to men who believed that equality, efficiency, and freedom came through a free price system. Thus the weight of the organization was behind a rate of substitution that placed an extremely high marginal value on the freedom of the individual farmer to operate his farm, and there came strong demands for more freedom for farmers and a willingness to take lower price supports to achieve their goal. The leadership of the political party in power at the time was a man who apparently placed an extremely high marginal value on equality, and the Secretary of Agriculture, a major force in the formulation of new agricultural policy, also seemed to think farmers would be willing to sacrifice some freedom to get additional security and income.

The greatest clash of these two conflicting views came over the Brannan Plan, which was proposed by Secretary of Agriculture Brannan in 1949. The controls that Secretary Brannan proposed were the ones that had been written into law in 1938. He did not propose any new controls and said he wished to avoid the use of these controls as much as possible. Not only did the law contain no new controls, but it is doubtful that even the high level price supports which Secretary Brannan proposed would have required any more production control at the present time than the lower level of price supports required during the 1930's. Thus, it is suggested that the

Brannan Plan was not any more serious threat to the freedom of the farmer than were many of the programs that were actually in operation during the great depression. However, due to the drastic differences in the income possibility position of farmers and the resulting changes in the marginal rates of substitution between these values among farm people and their leaders between 1938 and 1949, freedom appeared a more important value by 1949 and there was a great hue and cry over the farmers' loss of freedom under the Brannan Plan, The Agricultural Act of 1949, and recent amendments to that Act. Thus, we find ourselves at a time when there is a widespread discussion of farmers' freedom in agricultural policy, and the relationship between high supports and strong production controls.

The increased emphasis on freedom in our present policy discussions does not appear to be the result of an attempt to impose new and invidious forms of government control upon the farmer. Rather, it is the natural result of a sharp clash between groups which have differing ideas as to the marginal value of freedom and the other social values. It is not surprising then that the new Secretary of Agriculture in his first policy statement, of three and a half pages, mentioned the word "freedom" *six* times and "free" *five* times, while his opponents in Congress and some of the farm organizations demand higher supports to guarantee farmers "fair" prices and incomes.

If the recent vote on marketing quotas for wheat and the political pressure brought to bear upon Secretary Benson regarding price supports for butter and beef are to be judged as representative, there are strong indications that farmers' positions regarding government controls and government aid are again changing as their income possibilities change. Thus we may be confronted with the interesting spectacle of two successive Secretaries of Agriculture who are plunged into political hot water by the shifts in farmers' marginal rates of substitution between these social values. On one side was Secretary Brannan who offered an income possibility line at a time when the market placed farmers on a satisfaction curve so far to the right that no program containing production controls could reach it and be acceptable, and now Secretary Benson who wants to withdraw from such activities when the market places many farmers on a much lower satisfaction curve and when farm people know there are possible programs which they would accept to maintain farm prices. Oh what a popular figures these men might be were their positions reversed!

EMPIRICAL INVESTIGATIONS AND POLICY IMPLICATIONS

At this stage of generalization the author, at least, is willing to conclude that this theoretical framework does seem to offer a rational explanation of social values and political actions of our farm groups. In addition, however, it seems to be useful in another way in that it appears that the positions of these curves and income possibility lines is within the realm of possible empirical verification, an attribute not easily found in the present framework.

To suggest some of these possibilities and what they might entail let us turn again to the diagram, Figure 1. This discussion will be much like the first, only it shall be in terms of a specific problem. For that problem let us tackle the problems of support programs for wheat and the control programs that seem an inevitable accompaniment.

On the vertical axis let our scale be in terms of the real income to be realized from wheat production. Let the horizontal scale be some measurement of the farmer's freedom to operate his farm, pertaining specifically to the production of wheat. At point CF the farmer has complete freedom to plant all or none of his farm to wheat, to use any production practices, sell any amount he wishes, within the uncertainty of free market prices for wheat. At the other end of the scale, R_4 is the point where the farmer is given a bushel allotment of wheat he can sell and the use of excess acreage is controlled; this representing about the greatest restriction on freedom of farm operation that can be visualized under our present programs. Between these two extremes are three other possible points that represent varying restrictions on freedom of farm operation: acreage allotments without any penalty other than loss of full support guarantee, R_1; marketing quotas which merely enforce acreage allotments but allow improved production practices, R_2; and marketing quotas in bushels which prevent the use of improved practices, R_3. The relative position of these points along the line would be determined at the same time as the program possibility line and would be somewhat variable for individuals because of rotations, feasible alternatives, and individual preferences; but in general their relative positions would be highly dependent upon the physical acreage or bushels reduction necessary to achieve the desired gain over free market incomes. In the aggregate this depends, of course, on supply-demand analysis of given conditions.[15]

The present methodology in agricultural economics research has advanced to the point that the empirical determination of the income possibility lines for various agricultural commodities is now possible. At present very little of this type of analysis has been done, at least for presentation to the general public of farm operators who are forced to make important policy decisions on the basis of little or no information regarding the true income possibility lines. Certainly the farmers are to be blamed less than the professional economists if the farmers vote programs into effect that reduce their freedom

---

[15] For a program such as the tobacco program to work as well as it does administratively, approximations of this analysis must be made each year, at least on an informal basis. Of course, if we assumed that the government would continue high-level supports without production controls there would be no loss in freedom to the farmer in the context we are using, in fact there might be a gain from the added price certainty. Unfortunately (or fortunately) our present programs call for production controls, and unless our policies undergo some rapid changes these controls are likely to continue.

of farm operation because they have incorrect or no information regarding their true income possibilities under other alternatives. There is certainly much to be achieved before the profession has fulfilled its role in aiding farmers to achieve their maximum satisfaction position from agricultural policy. To claim that farmers have the wrong marginal rates of substitution between social values is not the answer!

The determination of the satisfaction curves of the farmers is important and depends on carefully conducted interviews with farmers. If farmers were asked a series of questions—"Would you vote for marketing quotas on wheat which reduced your acreage———percent in order to get——— cents per bushel higher than the free market price?"—for each type of controls, a series of points on that individual's satisfaction curve at that time could be approximated.[16] Thus at any given time it would seem possible to determine from a sample of farmers whether a given program would be acceptable to farmers, giving us among other things some measurement of how well our normal political processes are functioning in the development of agricultural policy. Such investigation might also help isolate some of the factors influencing the different marginal rates of substitution of social values between individuals, certainly an important addition to our understanding of agricultural policy and its formation.

To return to practical policy, it appears that Secretary Benson faces a tremendous problem in his attempt to change the direction of our agricultural policy during a period in which the income possibility line for farmers is shifting rapidly and bringing forth different marginal rates of substitution for these social values among farmers. A change in policy in the face of declining agricultural prices may not be possible immediately, but it is important that our policy-makers understand what must be done to have a new policy accepted.

Above all, it seems important that we do not accuse farmers of having traded their birthright for a "mess of pottage" until we know more about their basic value systems and satisfaction surfaces and ways to bring these substitution rates more nearly in line with those of our society as a whole.

---

[16] If the individual had a zero marginal value for freedom of farm operation this should approximate a constant income curve. It is assumed that this would not be the case, although such a curve might be a good point from which to start.

25 Economic Preconceptions and the Farm Policy*

J. K. GALBRAITH†

On farm policy, in recent times, there has been a remarkable divergence between the weight of scholarly recommendation and the course of practical action. In the years since World War II, it seems clear, the policy of providing firm price guarantees for farm products has gained markedly in political favor.[1] As recently as five years ago it was widely assumed that this policy would be discontinued as soon as the psychological transition to peacetime conditions had been completed and the opposition of some intransigent friends of the so-called "high and rigid" supports had been overcome. The policy can no longer be viewed as temporary. It has won the advocacy of a body of legislators of both parties who are formidable both in numbers and power. They clearly have on their side an important sector of farm opinion despite the formal opposition, so far, of two of the three national farm organizations.[2] During the presidential campagin of 1952 both candidates committed themselves, for the immediate future, to price

* *American Economic Review,* Vol. XLIV, No. 1 (March 1954), pp. 40–52.

† Harvard University, Cambridge, Massachusetts.

[1] Under legislation expiring in 1954, support of prices at 90 percent of parity is mandatory for six so-called basic commodities—corn, cotton, wheat, tobacco, rice and peanuts. Support is also mandatory but within a price range below 90 percent of parity for a few more products, of which the most important are dairy products and wool and mohair. Other farm products may be supported at the discretion of the Secretary of Agriculture, and under this authority, which of late has been used rather sparingly, a limited number of other products (principally feeds and vegetable oil products) have been receiving formal support.

[2] The American Farm Bureau Federation and the National Grange have, so far, opposed the inflexible support prices at 90 percent of parity. Only the smaller and more regional Farmers' Union supports the policy. However, it has been evident for some time that the Farm Bureau, especially in the South, does not have the full concurrence of its state units on this issue, and presidents of State Federations have appeared before Congressional committees in opposition to the position taken by the national organization.

supports at present levels and to the extension of protection to products not now covered. The popularity of price supports has clearly impressed a Secretary of Agriculture who has not concealed his personal distaste for the policy and his hope that it might be abandoned.[3]

In sharp contrast with the growing popularity of the policy has been the position of the economists who have spoken on this subject. Criticism of the policy would hardly be remarkable. What is remarkable is the unanimity with which this policy has been condemned by the professional students who have spoken on the subject. There have been almost literally no expressed partisans of the fixed guarantees. In the current climate of professional attitudes approval of the present farm policy, one senses, would be not alone exceptional but eccentric.

It follows that the literature in opposition to the present policy is nearly coextensive with the writing on agricultural policy. Thus toward the end of the war a committee designated by the Association of Land Grant Colleges and Universities urged the liquidation of wartime price guarantees, the precursors of the present support prices.[4] Such fixed price guarantees were almost uniformly criticized and rejected by the prize-winning essays in the contest on postwar farm price policy conducted by the American Farm Economic Association.[5]

More recently, in a strongly argued brief, the present policy has been unequivocally condemned by a committee of thirteen distinguished agricultural economists which included the present and seven past presidents of the American Farm Economic Association.[6] The economists find the present policy inconsistent with general economic welfare, specifically damaging to low-income consumers and, among other faults to be mentioned presently, a threat to the freedom of decision of farmers. They urge its total abandonment and the re-establishment of "flexible prices based on open market demand and on free competition, not price controls."[7]

---

[3] In his first press conference, in what may not have been the happiest choice of words, Secretary Benson expressed the belief that price supports should be used only to protect the farmer from "undue disaster." Amplifying this later at St Paul, he said, "Price supports should provide insurance against disaster and help stabilize national food supplies. But price supports which encourage uneconomic production and result in continuing heavy surpluses and subsidies should be avoided."

[4] Committee on Postwar Agricultural Policy, *Postwar Agricultural Policy*, October 1944.

[5] Published in the *Journal of Farm Economics*, Vol. 27 (November 1945), pp. 743–902.

[6] *Turning the Searchlight on Farm Policy*, hereafter cited as *Searchlight* (Chicago: The Farm Foundation, 1952). The authors were O. B. Jesness, University of Minnesota; George H. Aull, Clemson Agricultural College; M. R. Benedict, University of California; E. L. Butz, Purdue University; T. K. Cowden, Michigan State College; F. F. Hill, Cornell University; Asher Hobson, University of Wisconsin; L. J. Norton, University of Illinois; T. W. Schultz, University of Chicago; Henry B. Arthur of Swift and Co.; Frank L. Parsons of the Federal Reserve Bank of Minneapolis; Edwin G. Nourse; and Frank J. Welch of the University of Kentucky.

[7] *Ibid.*, p. 80. This last comment provoked a dissent from Dean Welch in such terms as would indicate substantial reservations in his case on other conclusions.

I. THE CASE AGAINST THE POLICY

The economists who have spoken on the subject have not only been nearly unanimous in their objection to the present farm policy, but they have also been comprehensive in their criticism. The policy is credited with few or no good effects. To it is attributed a variety of unfavorable consequences all of them extremely serious.

The most common and probably the most telling criticism of the policy is that of its assumed effect on resource allocation and therefore on the efficiency with which economic resources are employed.[8] There are two parts to this indictment: first, the support prices interfere with price movements and therewith, it is held, in a damaging way with optimal resource allocation within the agricultural industry; and, second, they are condemned for interfering with the movement of resources between agriculture and nonagricultural enterprise and, in particular, for holding unneeded labor in farming. The effect on resource allocation within agriculture is regarded with particular alarm, an emphasis that may be attributed, at least in part, to the persuasive work of Professor Theodore W. Schultz. He has shown that price influences may not be dominant in the distribution of labor and capital between agricultural and nonagricultural enterprise[9] and that "The movement of workers in and out of agriculture has been inconsistent with our economic *rationale* as to what people do (in the short run) in adjusting to changes in relative prices of products."[10] But he has compensated for this seeming slight to the price system with a powerful exposition of the role of relative prices in adjusting resource use within agriculture. "Income-stabilizing programs are too heavy a burden for the pricing system to bear if it is to function efficiently in guiding agricultural production."[11] However, alarm over the effect of support prices on resource movement in and out of agriculture has by no means disappeared. The committee of economists above cited (rather curiously with Schultz's concurrence) states that the subsidy, inherent in the use of support prices, inhibits the movement of resources and the equalization of factor returns between agricultural and nonagricultural enterprise[12] and that "a support program above real market prices tends to tie down resources that should be moving out to nonagricultural uses. . . ."[13] The consequences are clearly deemed to be grave.

---

[8] This criticism will be recognized as implicit in the commonplace assertion that support prices prevent or retard needed adjustments in agriculture or stop desirable production shifts. *Cf.* the quotation from Secretary Benson above.

[9] *Agriculture in an Unstable Economy* (New York, 1945).

[10] *Ibid.*, p. 89.

[11] Schultz, *Production and Welfare of Agriculture* (New York, 1949), p. 80. This is a theme to which Professor Schultz returns throughout the volume.

[12] *Searchlight*, p. 34.

[13] *Ibid.*, p. 64. See also D. Gale Johnson, "High Level Support Prices and Corn Belt Agriculture," *Journal of Farm Economics*, Vol. 31 (August 1949), pp. 509–19.

Next to its effect on allocative efficiency, the most sharply articulated criticism of the present farm policy concerns its relation to foreign trade policy. For export crops, the support of prices above world levels must be offset by subsidies if the crop is to continue to move in international trade. Furthermore, the effect of support operations may be to attract imports which means in turn that foreign producers are sharing in the subsidies by the United States government to its domestic producers. Tariffs and quotas will almost inevitably be urged and quite likely be invoked to prevent what would otherwise be an international distribution of domestic largesse. The prima facie inconsistency of such export subsidies, tariffs and quantitative restrictions with the professed goals of American foreign economic policy has been developed at length by Professor Johnson,[14] and has commanded the attention of other scholars.[15] Recent administrations, it is held, have promoted a liberal trade policy with one hand and in the farm policy have laid the foundation for economic nationalism with the other.

A third criticism of the policy is that the support prices contribute to a reduction of consumer welfare by restriction on the aggregate of resource use. For example, the economists hitherto cited assert that "A high-price program involving restriction of production hurts consumers, particularly in the lower-income groups, because they cannot satisfy their wants as adequately as they could if productive resources were used more fully."[16] Similar allegations have been frequent. Thus, in addition to distorting the pattern of resource use, it is also charged that the policy results in an absolute withdrawal of resources from use.

While damaging the public at large, the gains to farmers from this policy are held to be transitory or illusory. Thus, while finding monopolization of resource use damaging to consumers, the above-cited economists also warn farmers that ". . . monopolistic restrictions on farm production are much less effective than [they] have been led to suppose . . ." and that "This conclusion is based both on logic and the last three decades of agricultural experience."[17]

The policy is also condemned as a cause of inflation and as a brake on recovery when deflationary forces are dormant. The above-cited economists conclude that it is dangerous on both of these grounds.[18] Support prices "are among the factors which tend to put agriculture 'on the bandwagon'

---

[14] D. Gale Johnson, *Trade and Agriculture, A Study of Inconsistent Policies* (New York, 1950).

[15] For example, Lawrence Witt, "Our Agricultural and Trade Policies," *Journal of Farm Economics*, Vol. 32 (May 1950), pp. 159–79. Schultz, *Production and Welfare of Agriculture*, pp. 216 ff.

[16] *Searchlight*, p. 65.

[17] *Searchlight*, p. 56.

[18] On the inflationary effects of the policy two of the economists, T. W. Schultz and T. K. Cowden, entered a dissent. *Searchlight*, pp. 50 and 70.

of a general inflationary movement" and "freemarket clearing prices are likely to do a better job of pulling the economy out of business depression." Professor Brandt has been even more vigorous in his condemnation of the inflationary tendencies of the policy,[19] while with considerable, although perhaps declining frequency, other scholars have held that, in seeking to stabilize farm prices, we may succeed only in unstabilizing the economy at large.

Finally, and beyond the range of economic values, the present policy is held to have the effect of destroying the freedom of choice, political independence, and moral character of the farmer. Thus the above-cited economists, in a passage italicized for emphasis, agree "that the evolution of national farm policies has now brought agriculture into a position of undue reliance on public financial assistance, on efforts to restrict market supplies, and into undesirable political involvement." Brandt has stated that "Our agricultural policy is now involved in the broad economic issue of western political democracy," and that "When millions of able [farm] entrepreneurs have regained the self-confidence to operate without the social harness of bureaucratic guidance and universal risk insurance, it is an event that may amount to a decisive victory in the free anticollective world."[20] It would seem to follow that political democracy both in the United States and abroad has been placed in jeopardy by the present farm policy.

If the economists who speak with the greatest authority on this matter are to be taken at their word—and it would be improper to do otherwise or to suppose that they are engaged in the poor scientific method of seeking emphasis through exaggeration—then our present farm policy profoundly threatens our national well-being. Inefficiency, economic isolation, monopolistic exploitation, inflation, depression, and the economic serfdom and political debasement of farmers are all abetted by the policy. The prospect, if all these tendencies are advanced, is disenchanting. Yet the policy which portends these afflictions is one on which Congress is launched and with increasing determination. If the economists are right, then we must brace ourselves for an unpleasant time for there is nothing in the present trend of affairs to suggest that their counsel will be heeded in time. The prospect is alarming unless, the seeming unanimity notwithstanding, there is a chance that the economists are wrong.

II. THE SETTING OF THE CRITICISM

It is the function and discipline of social scientists to concern themselves with consequences that lie beyond the eye of the politician. In the early thirties, with similar unanimity, the economists concerned with trade policy

---

[19] "Agricultural Policy During Rearmament," *Journal of Farm Economics*, Vol. 34 (May 1952), pp. 192 ff.

[20] *Op. cit.*, pp. 194–98.

attacked the political advocacy of higher tariffs. In the later view, few would have argued that the politicians who, nonetheless, proceeded to enact the Hawley-Smoot tariff were following the course of wisdom. This may be the present case.

Yet, when any group of scholars finds itself strongly at odds with the current of practical policy it would seem important that it be sure of its case. This is especially true in the present instance for the farm policy under attack has now been in effect, in war and peace, for some thirteen years. Disaster or, at a minimum, grievous disorder has been predicted for much of this period. Yet during this time agriculture has shown, by common consent, a vigorous technological and managerial improvement and, on purely prima facie grounds, would seem to have conformed to high welfare criteria. As Brandt, in a statement that should be contrasted with his depressing view quoted above, has said:

> During the last few decades, a breath-taking technological evolution has been opening new frontiers in agriculture, and the progress has been most spectacular in the United States and Canada. Not only did it assist greatly in winning World War II, but it also kept millions of people in Europe and Asia alive after the war, while providing us at home with a better diet and lifting a large proportion of our farmers to a new level of income.[21]

Moreover, there is a question whether the economists who have been speaking on farm policy have been bringing to bear all of the data which are relevant to a policy judgment. Without exception, the economists herein cited are offering recommendations for practical action. Such recommendations must be shaped not alone by economic and moral criteria, both of which have been liberally invoked, but also by the attitudes and desires of those who are affected. To assume that the economist should recommend only what farmers want or believe they want would reduce him to the role of a poll-taker. But to fail to take account of the farmer as a political entity, while making essentially political recommendations, can be an equal and opposite error. The theorist who, having reached the conclusion that such would be a socially meritorious course, urges union members to disband their organizations and to support the government in legislation to this end is not likely to have either a large influence on labor legislation or even a large reputation for political perspicacity and realism. Should he proclaim his desire to end all unions, willy nilly, he would appropriately be considered somewhat authoritarian in his attitudes. It seems possible that kindred recommendations are not only being made but are a commonplace in regard to farm policy.

If this is so, one antidote is a fuller appreciation of the history of the farm movement in the United States. By a fortunate accident of timing, the product of the mammoth labors of Professor Murray R. Benedict of the

---

[21] *Op. cit.*, pp. 185, 186.

University of California has recently become available. This is the first comprehensive history of agricultural legislation in the United States and of the organization and agitation which gave rise to it.[22] Benedict shows in a wealth of detail how long the present policy has been in the making. It is a story of much diversity in method and much inconstancy of both leaders and followers. Yet it also mirrors a remarkable and continuing determination by farmers to gain some control over market forces. The reader is left in little doubt that for a half century or more the free market has had little more appeal to the farmer than the unorganized labor market to the worker —or, for that matter, than an industrial market of atomistic purity would have for the modern corporation executive. Yet the free market is what is being urged on the farmer. Anyone is privileged to advocate revolution. He is perhaps better for knowing when he is a revolutionary.

III. RESOURCE ALLOCATION

Farm policy may still be a commitment to manifold disorders and disasters, and no less so because the commitment is deep. And even though the disasters have been predicted with increasing urgency for a decade or more without appearing, they may still be ahead. But it is possible that the analysis on which the prediction is based is incomplete or in error. This possibility also needs consideration in any re-examination of the grounds on which the economists' condemnation is based.

There is evidence that the analysis is at least partly in error. As noted, the most persuasive indictment of the farm policy to the economist is the effect of the policy on resource use efficiency. If prices must be a vehicle for sustaining income to farmers, they cannot be an efficient instrument for guiding resource use. For if prices are fixed they no longer command the movement of resources within agriculture or between agriculture and industry in accordance with the dictates of consumer choice.[23]

Obvious though this may seem, further examination shows that some of the concern is ill-founded and more of it is subject to serious, if unconscious, exaggeration. As a broad tendency—to which I concede numerous exceptions —the support prices will be effective during times of low aggregate demand or depression. It is then that prices generally will be resting on the supports. At times of high demand—when the latter is sufficient to sustain high or "full" employment—some or most of the prices of supported commodities are likely to be above the support levels.[24]

---

[22] *Farm Policies of the United States, 1790–1950, A Study of Their Origins and Development* (New York, 1953).

[23] *Production and Welfare of Agriculture*, pp. 20 ff.

[24] This has been the general postwar experience although during part of 1952 and most of 1953, mainly as the result of the rapid shrinkage of foreign demand, this has not been true. I discuss this case presently.

When prices are above support levels there is no direct impairment of allocative efficiency as the result of the existence of these noneffective supports.[25] But when prices are at support levels as the result of a general deficiency in demand their effect on allocative efficiency is, to say the least, ambiguous. In this context—that of some degree of depression—some resources are idle. The use of resources in the "wrong" place may then be the alternative to no use at all. In any case, their use in one place need not deny resources to another employment since, by definition, there are idle resources on which those other uses may draw. This would appear to have been overlooked by Schultz, for example, who has stated:

> . . . during a depression, when consumer's purchasing power shrinks and prices drop . . . measures that keep farm prices from falling below the support price will disrupt both internal and external trade, unless it should happen that measures employed by the government create enough additional demand to equilibrate the supply at a price at least as high as the support price.
> . . . there are two primary objectives that appear to be appropriate in pricing farm products: (1) to improve the allocation of resources in agricultural production, and (2) to maintain farm income. . . .[26]

The "disruption" of which he here speaks is plainly a disruption in resource allocation.

If support prices do not impair allocative efficiency within agriculture in periods of full employment and they do not worsen it in periods of unemployment, then apparently they do not impair it at all. And we have the impressive testimony of Schultz himself to show that relative prices and rewards to factors are a secondary consideration in the movement of resources between agriculture and other enterprise and specifically that labor tends to move from agriculture to industry in times of high relative income rather than low.[27]

However, I do not wish to overprove my case. Because the prices established by the parity formula are arbitrary and bear no necessary relation to equilibrium levels for individual products at full employment demand and because shifts in demand and supply schedules (of which the recent decline in exports and the recent growth in oleomargarine use provide notable examples) can sharply reduce consumption of particular products, price

---

[25] There is a possible indirect effect through the reduction of uncertainty in price expectations. This, however, may have long-run investment consequences which would be generally approved. See below, p. 50.

[26] *Production and Welfare of Agriculture,* p. 96. *Cf.* also my comments, this *Review,* Vol. 40 (June 1950), pp. 460–63. These views were expressed nearly four years ago, and it is my impression, based on conversation and correspondence, that Schultz, while still insisting on the absolute importance of free price movements for allocative efficiency (*Cf. Searchlight,* p. 50, footnote) might now be less insistent on the point in a depression context.

[27] *Op. cit.* Also Walter W. Wilcox, "High Farm Income and Efficient Resource Use," *Journal of Farm Economics,* Vol. 31 (August 1949), pp. 555–57.

supports may be effective for some products even when aggregate demand is sufficient to sustain full employment. The conditions necessary for a distortion of resource use are then present.

However, here also an amendment to the conventional criticism is in order. In regard to allocative efficiency it seems plain that much comment is decidedly nonquantitative. If inefficiency can be demonstrated, it is *pro tanto* intolerable. There are no degrees of damage; a death sentence on the policy that produces it follows automatically. There is no need to inquire whether the loss of efficiency is serious—whether it warrants the desperate alarm that it induces.[28] Moreover, an examination might, in fact, reveal a rather small cost. Under the relevant conditions—peacetime demand at full employment levels but with some support prices effective—the usual situation, at least in superficial view, tends to be one of fairly general abundance. The obvious manifestation of short-run inefficiency in resource allocation would be shortages and high prices for some products, while the supported products were impounding labor and other resources. This has not been obviously the case to date. At most, price supports have checked the movement of resources from production where the marginal utility of product, *e.g.,* for storage, is very low to others where marginal utility is also low or at least not spectacularly high. Thus a prominent alternative use for resources now held by supports in dairying would be in beef cattle production where there are no supports but where not all concerned would insist on the urgency of increased production.

It is possible, although by no means certain, that the supports have inhibited secular shifts, as from cotton to dairying in the South. Proof would require, however, a showing of the effect of the policy on long-run price relatives which is presently lacking. There seems to be little doubt that the tobacco programs have changed the ratio of land to fertilizer inputs. Even here, however, a case could be made that the distortion has been caused not by the support price but by the form of the resulting control.

IV. FARM AND TRADE POLICY

At first glance the inconsistency of the present support policy with a liberal trade program seems inescapable. Moreover, the desirability of such a trade policy—unlike the absolute importance of unimpaired allocative efficiency—is something which I am not disposed to question. Further, while the welfare consequences of an inefficiency in resource use are hardly matters of observation, the tariff adjustments and quotas that are required by the policy and their incongruity with our proclaimed trade policy are wholly visible.

---

[28] This question has recently been asked by Willard W. Cochrane. *Cf.* "A Theoretical Scaffolding for Considering Governmental Price Policies in Agriculture," *Journal of Farm Economics,* Vol. 35, No. 1 (February 1953), p. 4.

Yet here again some qualifications, not commonly emphasized in attacks on the policy, are important. The products presently receiving the 90 percent mandatory supports are either export crops or crops where there are normally no important imports. The general effect of the support prices is to create a market in the United States which would not otherwise exist. The quantitative restrictions and tariffs, to mention the most ostensibly illiberal consequences of the policy, thus protect a market which would not be attractive except for the support prices. Some qualifications are necessary with respect of certain qualities and staple lengths of cotton. There are more important qualifications with respect of wheat and competitive feed grain imports from Canada. (The impact of these restrictions is overwhelmingly on Canada.) But the general rule holds. The policy restricts imports that have first been made artificially attractive.

This is not a complete extenuation nor is it intended to be. As noted, the posture and integrity of American trade policy is inevitably weakened by any restrictions on imports and also by the counterpart subsidies on exports. On the other hand, there is surely a difference between a restrictive measure which offsets an increase in imports induced by another policy and one—like the classical tariff—which has the single aim and effect of inhibiting imports. To the extent that the farm policy is attacked as an original onslaught on a liberal trade policy rather than an unfortunate compensation the critics are not on strong ground.

V. RESTRICTIVE AND CYCLICAL EFFECTS

A measure of ambiguity or internal inconsistency has already been noted in the other common criticisms of the policy. In objecting to price supports both as a restraint on resource use and hence damaging to the consumer and also as a self-liquidating form of monopoly, the economists above cited have apparently contradicted their own arguments. It would be, however, that they have also drawn attention to a possible difference between the short- and long-run effects of the farm policy. During the years that the present policy has been in effect there has been a substantial expansion in farm output accompanied by a seemingly favorable rate of technological change. Stability in price expectations would normally be thought favorable to this expansion and change and to the requisite investment. Thus reduction in price fluctuations as the result of some monopolization in particular years *could* be the basis for a larger production and lower prices in the long run. Such considerations have played little part in the technical and scientific criticisms of the policy.[29] The exclusion of price expectations as a factor

---

[29] Cochrane (*op. cit.*, p. 5) has suggested that in specific instances (tobacco, with regard to which he cites the investigations of Glenn Johnson in Kentucky, and similar work on potatoes in Minnesota) the price support programs have accelerated technological innovation and investment. Schultz has repeatedly emphasized the importance of reducing the amplitude of year-to-year price fluctuations in agriculture.

in production responses (except only to show that they defeat monopolistic aims of farmers) would seem to be poor scientific method.

The attack on the policy as inflationary in inflation and deflationary in deflation also involves problems of internal reconciliation. Further, during the periods of acute postwar inflation the supports were effective only in rare instances for particular commodities.[30] Meanwhile there were counter-inflationary effects from the liquidation of previously accumulated inventories. As one example, wartime and postwar cotton textile prices would have been far higher, both in the United States and abroad, had it not been for the large inventory carried over from the depression years of the thirties. It seems impossible that those who charge inflation against this policy have measured their argument against this history.

The argument that the supports accentuate or perpetuate deflationary tendencies is also weak. In the economists' report hitherto mentioned the case depends partly on the assertion that the restriction incident to the policy in time of declining demand introduces an "unstabilizing factor."[31] It also rests partly on the claim that "free-market clearing prices" are more likely to arrest or reverse deflation than supported prices and associated production controls.[32] Both of these propositions are coupled with the statement that for "many" farm commodities the price elasticity of demand is greater than unity so that to obtain a given increase in income a more than proportionate cutback in output is required.[33]

These contentions do not stand scrutiny. The statement on price elasticity is flatly in conflict with the evidence.[34] Indeed it is difficult to believe that the available information on the elasticity of demand for farm products could have been reviewed by the economists with markedly more care than a political advocate would normally bring to bear. But even more important, in the practical operation of the support policy in a period of declining demand, the control of production lags well behind—sometimes does not even follow—the pegging of prices. Income, accordingly, is maintained at the volume given by the support price times the full output. If no companion provision is made for taxes, the effect of government expenditures to maintain such income is surely counterdeflationary. In the approximate year and a quarter (to October 31, 1953) that farm prices have been at or near support

[30] In 1946 and 1947, the years of most rapid increase in prices, the parity index averaged 113 and 115, respectively.

[31] *Searchlight*, p. 69.

[32] *Ibid.*, p. 70.

[33] *Ibid.*, p. 70. Schultz, in a related comment, appears to disagree with his colleagues' views on the price elasticities as, indeed, he has elsewhere.

[34] Karl A. Fox, "Factors Affecting Farm Income, Farm Prices, and Food Consumption," Bureau of Agricultural Economics, *Agricultural Economics Research*, Vol. 3 (July 1951), pp. 65–82, George L. Mehren, "Comparative Costs of Agricultural Price Supports in 1949," *American Economic Review, Proceedings*, Vol. 41 (May 1954), pp. 717–46. These and other data on price elasticities are summarized by Schultz in *The Economic Organization of Agriculture* (New York, 1953), pp. 186 ff.

levels, the Commodity Credit Corporation has committed 2.5 billion dollars to maintain income. There is at least a presumption that these expenditures have had an important effect in limiting the deflationary effects of the heavy decline in farm exports. Here again, the professional objection to the policy is on highly debatable grounds.

I shall pass quickly over the noneconomic objections to the policy. Whether the farmer has, in fact, been debauched or fettered is a matter of opinion, although it involves opinions that social scientists, when speaking professionally, should doubtless render with caution. On the most frequently cited charge—that policy threatens the farmer with a "substantial restriction [of their] freedom of choice," to quote the dry language of the economists above cited, or that they have placed him in "the social harness of bureaucratic guidance" in Brandt's more colorful figure—one observation must be made. This is a loss of freedom which is, by all appearances, much more disturbing to philosopher friends of the farmer than to the farmer himself. And it would be odd were men of some repute both for their intellectual alertness and their political determination, to have lost their freedom without more awareness and without protest.

VI. CONCLUSION

The foregoing is not intended to be a general exculpation of the present farm policy. On the contrary, the policy seems to me to have serious faults. The present price (parity) standards in my view are arbitrary. The discrimination in policy between the so-called basic commodities which are subject to mandatory support and the remainder of agricultural production—which is subject to the same market conditions and is of greater aggregate value—is impossible to defend. The present policy incorporates a design for acquiring large government stocks but none for their management and disposal. It benefits least the income of those farmers who receive least.

A strong case can also be made, if a given farm income is to be guaranteed, that the technique of supporting prices by loan and purchase operations is inferior, for many commodities, to measures which would allow prices to find their own level in the market and provide direct payments to sustain income at the guaranteed levels. Such a technique would go far to reconcile the agricultural with the national trade policy, and it would also elide many of the inventory and disposal problems inherent in the present policy by the admirable device of not acquiring the stocks in the first place. It is interesting that such a policy, in broad contour, has recently replaced fixed price guarantees in the United Kingdom.

Such proposals are not, however, the concern of this paper. Its purpose was to examine the present remarkable divergence between scientific prescription and practical farm policy. That some aspects of the latter are ill-conceived is hardly surprising. This is an area where imperfection is in the nature of things. But the standards of the scientist are less tolerant. He should, to cite the rules the afore-mentioned economists have laid down for themselves, "have technical competence to discover and explain the consequences of given economic actions" and he "should not be [among the] special pleaders for any group or any cause."[35] Examination of the present criticism of farm policy leads me to question whether it is technically above reproach and also whether its weakness may not derive in part from predilections for a cause, which is not the less a cause because its goal is a seemingly traditional arrangement of economic life. If these are the reasons that economists in this field have lost touch with the present current of farm policy and are failing to influence its course there could be none more disturbing.

[35] *Searchlight*, p. 61.

26 Some Observations of an Ex Economic Advisor: or What I Learned in Washington*

WILLARD W. COCHRANE†

President Johnson (D. Gale, that is) asked me to develop a paper recounting my experiences in Washington from July 1960 to July 1964, and what I learned from those experiences that might be of interest to fellow agricultural economists. For my part, this seemed like a good idea; it provided me with the excuse to set down on paper, in an organized way, my thoughts on that interesting, sometimes exciting and often frustrating experience. If, then, you will excuse the use of the first person singular in the story that follows, we will turn to that story.

THE ASSIGNMENT

My assignment divides neatly into two periods: first, as agricultural advisor to then Senator John F. Kennedy, July to November 1960, and second as economic advisor to Secretary Orville L. Freeman, and Director of Agricultural Economics in the USDA, January 1961 to July 1964. The first period was the most exciting experience of my life; I observed the making of a president firsthand, and I participated in it firsthand.

It is, however, the part of the overall assignment that I would most like to do over. Not because I now feel that my advice was poor or wrong, because I don't. I still read with pride the two major campaign statements of John F. Kennedy on farm policy in which I had a hand: The Sioux Falls, South Dakota, plowing contest speech, and the "White Paper" entitled, "Agricultural Policy for the New Frontier."[1]

---

* *Journal of Farm Economics,* Vol. 47, No. 2 (May 1965), pp. 447–61.

† University of Minnesota, Mineapolis, Minnesota. The responsibility for the views and ideas in this paper is the author's alone.

[1] The text of the plowing contest speech and the statement "Agricultural Policy for the New Frontier" are both to be found in *The Speeches of John F. Kennedy: Presidential Campaign of 1960* (Final Report of the Committee on Commerce, U.S. Senate, 87th Cong., 1st sess., September 13, 1961).

I would like to do it over because of my political ineptness in that first period. As a political operator, I was green as grass, and I made some mistakes that were whoppers. If I had it to do over, I believe that I could be a more effective political economist—a more effective advisor to that wonderfully keen and human man, John F. Kennedy.

It is not easy, however, to be a successful advisor on the subject of farm policy to a man campaigning for the presidency. You are expected to give advice which will simultaneously correct the farm problem, or problems, and capture a majority of the rural vote, farm and nonfarm. As a farm advisor, you are responsible for the small town vote as well as the farm vote, and if you fail anywhere, it is better to fail on the solution to the farm problem than on the size of the vote favorably disposed toward your candidate. I did not appreciate these distinctions as fully in 1960 as I do now. In any event, it was a great experience, and I would not have missed it for all the tea in China.

The remainder of this paper, which means most of it, will be concerned with the implications and lessons of the second part of my assignment—with the period in the USDA from January 1961 to June 1964.

REORGANIZATION OF THE ECONOMICS WORK

Shortly after Orville L. Freeman was designated the next Secretary of Agriculture, he asked me to go to Washington and recreate or reestablish the old BAE, and then to head that organization. In the latter capacity, he asked me to serve as his principal economic advisor and program planner. Now there were many problems involved, large and small, in the above assignment, but none with respect to convincing Secretary Freeman that the economics work of the Department of Agriculture should be grouped into one agency. He had that objective in mind before he asked me to join his staff.

It is interesting to note that he acquired that organizational objective from an individual (not me) who fought strenuously against the dismemberment of the BAE in 1953. Thus, the position taken and efforts made by the American Farm Economic Association with regard to the dismemberment of the BAE in 1953 were not in vain. They contributed significantly to the reestablishment of an economic research agency in the USDA in 1961.

The BAE was not recreated in the exact form and name that existed prior to 1953 for a number of reasons. First, the major administrative groupings in the department were no longer called bureaus; they were now called services. Second, the name BAE was an anathema to certain key congressmen. Third, many agencies in the USDA were not enthusiastic about turning the principal planning function back to "a" BAE. Fourth, we wanted to emphasize the new look in crop reporting and centralize the statistical work in Washington into one agency. And fifth, we wanted the man who headed the economics and statistical work in the department to report directly to the Secretary of Agriculture.

To achieve the objective of the Secretary of Agriculture with regard to concentrating all of the economics work of the department into one agency, and to accommodate that organizational objective to the many and varied pressures that were involved in 1961, an Agricultural Economics grouping was established in the department. The structure of that grouping was and continues to be (as of December 1964) as follows. The grouping is headed by a Director of Agricultural Economics who operates at the assistant secretary level and reports directly to the Secretary. This idea was borrowed from the Republicans who created the post of Director of Agricultural Credit in March 1953 to head a grouping of credit agencies within the department. And it parallels the organizational structure of the Department of Agriculture in which services with related missions are grouped together and report to an assistant secretary or a director.

Two services report to the Director of Agricultural Economics: the Economic Research Service and the Statistical Reporting Service. The work of the ERS is divided into two major segments: a domestic segment comprised of four divisions, Economics and Statistical Analysis, Farm Production Economics, Resource Development, and Marketing, and a foreign segment comprised of two divisions, Development and Trade Analysis and Foreign Regional Analysis. It should be noted at this point that the "old BAE" did not deal with foreign economic research; prior to the organization of ERS, foreign economic research work was done in the Foreign Agricultural Service. The work of the Statistical Reporting Service falls into three divisions: the Agricultural Estimates Division, the Field Operation Division and the Standards and Research Division.

One further unit was created in the Agricultural Economics grouping. It is the Staff Economists Group (SEG). It is a small unit of five or six professionals, each of whom reports directly to the director. This unit was created to assist the director in his role as economic advisor to and program planner for the Secretary, and to divorce, to the extent possible, policy staff work from the ongoing research and statistical work of the two services. Members of the Staff Economists Group extend and support the role of the Director of Agricultural Economics as a policy advisor and program planner.

Some members of our profession have argued that the Director of Agricultural Economics cannot serve effectively as both the general director of a large economic research and statistical gathering organization, and as the principal economic advisor and program analyst of the Secretary. Those members may be correct, if your view of the economic research and statistical organization of the USDA is identical with that of a good economic research organization in a great university or foundation.

But they are not the same and cannot be the same. This does not mean that the economic research in the USDA is biased, slanted or incorrect. It does mean that the economic research and statistical work of the USDA is mission oriented. So long as the USDA undertakes major resource adjustment programs, price support and income protection programs, credit programs, and marketing and distribution programs, it must have the basic intelligence and research to operate those programs rationally and efficiently. The intelligence must be reliable and relevant and the research must be informative and relevant. Both should be excellent in quality, but both must be oriented to the needs of the decision makers.

In this view the entire Agricultural Economics grouping may be viewed as a staff organization servicing the needs of the decision makers of the operating programs, of which the Secretary is the chief decision maker. The Statistical Reporting Service collects and refines the basic price, income, production, stock and resource data needed to make intelligent decisions regarding the operating programs by the administration, the congress and the general public. The Economic Research Service analyzes that data and develops the important and relevant relationships for the use of all concerned —the administration, the congress and the general public. The Staff Economist Group takes the research results and develops them into policy analyses that show the consequences of alternative courses of action. It does the final staff work—organizing and presenting the data in ways that narrow down the judgment areas and facilitate rational decision making.

The Director of Agricultural Economics is responsible for this entire process: responsible for the collection of relevant and reliable data, responsible for the development of informative and reliable research results, and responsible for the presentation of analyses and appraisals of existing and alternative programs in ways that contribute to rational decision making. In this view, in this sense, the Director of Agricultural Economics serves both as director of research and as a policy advisor at one and the same time, and must serve effectively in both roles if the decision-making process is to be effective.

Certainly all economic organizations should not be viewed in this mission oriented manner. But I really believe that the economic research and statistical work in the USDA cannot be viewed in any other manner, if we want effective program operations.

Further, in an administrative sense the Director of Agricultural Economics operates no differently than say, the Assistant Secretary for Rural Development and Conservation, or the Assistant Secretary for Marketing and Consumer Services. These assistant secretaries are administratively responsible for the agencies in each of their groupings, and each is the Secretary's principal advisor in the subject matter areas of his grouping. So each assistant secretary and director is simultaneously an administrator in the chain of command, and the advisor to the Secretary on subject matter specialties that fall under his jurisdiction. In other words, the Agricultural

Economics grouping is organizationally comparable to other groupings in the USDA.

How has the organization worked in practice? I may be too intimately involved, too close to it, to judge the results objectively, but I believe that it has worked extremely well in practice. Certainly the *esprit de corps* of the economic researchers has improved under the organization. Certainly the methodological improvement program in statistical collection has continued and is reaching the payoff stage. Certainly economic analysis has made an important contribution to the decision process within the department and in the White House staff agencies. The effective work of the Staff Economist Group in this connection was noted a year or so ago in a letter of commendation from the Bureau of Budget to the Secretary of Agriculture. And certainly the quantity and quality of economic research in the foreign field has improved under the reorganization.

In sum and in short, statistical intelligence and economic analysis were made an integral part of the decision process in the USDA in the past four years, the morale of the staff has been lifted to a high level, and I know that the quality of research and statistical work has improved in some areas, and I believe that it has generally. As you can see, I am proud of the achievements of the Statistical Reporting Service, Economic Research Service and the Staff Economists Group over the past four years.

But this pride of achievement does not blind me to some difficult and continuing problems in connection with the Agricultural Economics grouping in general and the Economic Research Service in particular. The work of the Statistical Reporting Service is not so vulnerable to the cutting and slashing discussed below as is the Economic Research Service, because it (SRS) has strong constituent support in the form of state departments of agriculture and many commodity groups.

Turning now to problems of economic research and economic staff work, we must recognize first of all that it is hard, extremely hard, to get money for economic research. The Kennedy-Johnson administration was always generous with economic research in the administrative budget, but congress is a different matter. Lacking strong pressure group support and faced with the fact that many congressmen are afraid that the research results will not turn out "right," economic research has "rough sledding" in the appropriation committees.

The budget difficulty is not going to lessen in the near future, and it could get worse. Secretary Freeman, Under Secretary Murphy and the White House were consistently sympathetic and helpful with respect to the budget for economic research in agriculture during the past four years. President Kennedy is gone, Freeman and Murphy will leave some day, and when they do, it could happen that their successors will be less enthusiastic about economic analysis. In such an event, the budget cutting could begin in the adminstration and continue right through the congress.

There was something to the O. V. Wells' theory that you should hide economic research in the big operating agencies to protect its budget. Now we have economic research out in the open, in its own agency, hence it is vulnerable to budget cutting in the drawn-out budget process from the too numerous enemies and "fair weather friends" of economic research.

Second, there are more than a few active empire builders in the USDA who would love to carve up the Economic Research Service and add a branch or division or even a service to their respective empires. By this action the acquisitive bureaucrat gains budget and bodies, which is the true test of empire. And his ego is also inflated by having his own private economic analysis unit. Of course, this carving up process would all be done in the name of some good cause such as "improved administrative efficiency."

But Secretary Freeman and Under Secretary Murphy believe in effective economic staff work at the office of the Secretary level, hence they believe in a strong and independent economic research organization. Thus, the bureaucratic wolves have been held at bay—the ERS carcass has not been torn apart. The Secretary and the Under Secretary have protected their principal intelligence agency, even when it served up unpleasant intelligence.

But again, the present Secretary and Under Secretary will not always be around to protect the Economic Research Service. What happens then to this staff agency without pressure group support? First, we can hope that the next Secretary of Agriculture, whenever that might be, will understand and appreciate the importance of a strong economic staff agency to his office. Second, we can do our best to inform that Secretary, whoever he may be, of the importance to himself and to the effective operation of the USDA of a strong economic research organization. But if the Secretary does not really believe in good economic research you could well see the second dismemberment of the BAE, ERS, call it what you will, by the big, strongly supported agencies of the department.

Third, to the extent that the Director of Agricultural Economics and his Staff Economist Group serve as the Council of Economic Advisors to the Secretary of Agriculture, doing all kinds of staff work that involves the subject areas of the operating agencies, this leads to tension and frictions at best, and real trouble at worst. These frictions and tensions can be held to a minimum by good communications and responsible staff work, as I believe they have been during the past four years. Nonetheless, it does lead to difficult and strained relations; there is no avoiding this unless each piece of staff work is a "whitewash" job.

So here we have another source of trouble for the Agricultural Economics grouping. The Secretary needs something akin to the Council of Economic Advisors to advise him on the consequences of new programs and the operations of old ones. And the Staff Economists Group is in an excellent position to provide the Secretary with this service—that really is its reason for being. But in providing that service—the service of planning and appraising other people's programs—it often finds itself in a strained position, to say the least.

I am not prophesying the demise of the Agricultural Economics grouping in general or the Economic Research Service in particular. If the Director of Agricultural Economics is prudent and works diligently in support of his services, Secretaries of Agriculture come along who understand, or learn in time, the worth of good economic staff work based in turn upon reliable and relevant economic analysis and statistics, and this profession supports the Agricultural Economics grouping in the USDA with vigor and wisdom, then it will survive. But it will not survive unless it is carefully tended and cared for; like a rose garden in Minnesota, without wise and loving care, the elements and the predators will kill it.

THE POLICY EDUCATION OF THIS EX ADVISOR

Level of Price Support. In the 1960's the level of farm prices cannot be raised by purposive governmental action. This means that the general level of farm price support cannot be raised above its present level; individual commodity price supports may be raised modestly, particularly where that action does not convert directly into increased food prices, but not the overall level.

The reason is simple. This is now an urban society, and food prices are one of the most politically sensitive items in the cost of living. Any conscious, purposeful action by government to raise farm prices and thereby raise food prices brings a flood of protests down upon the one man elected by all the people, the president. Thus, a politically sensitive president, as Eisenhower was, as Kennedy was, and as Johnson was, will not permit his administration to raise the level of farm price support and thereby raise food prices.

A conscious policy of raising food prices is considered political suicide. And that is what raising the level of price supports amounts to. I learned this in the fiery furnace during the 1960 campaign, and my colleagues and I in the USDA relearned it on several occasions between 1961 and 1964.

This dictum does not apply with such vigor to the use of payments to farmers. Payments to farmers found increased use first in the Eisenhower administration, and second in the Kennedy administration. The Bureau of Budget, other members of the White House staff and city congressmen always oppose the increased use of payments, hence greater budget expenditures, to farmers, but not with the complete inflexibility that they oppose actions that increase food prices. However, I happen to be one who believes that we have reached the end of the rope with respect to budget increases for farm programs, too. We now live in an urban society, and each year the congress and the pressures operating on congress come one step closer toward recognizing that fact.

Farmers and Controls. It is perfectly clear that farmers will not accept effective, mandatory controls. They might if those controls were permitted to result in much higher prices; but, as we have already observed, that is not politically possible. Farmers will not, however, except in a few commodities, accept mandatory controls as a means of effectively limiting production at a minimum cost to the government.

On the other hand, we know that farmers do like and will accept voluntary control programs with payments, such as the feed grain program. Voluntary programs, in essence, provide them with an additional farm option which they are free to choose if it is to their advantage. In summary, farmers will not accept collective, mandatory control programs that have the purpose of reducing program costs; but they are happy with a voluntary type program, where they are free to choose the option of reducing production if it's to their personal advantage.

Program Costs. Everyone would be completely happy with voluntary control programs if it weren't for one little item—program costs. With voluntary programs, you get exactly what you pay for. If payment rates are low, you get few acres out of production, because few farmers see it to their advantage to choose that option. If payment rates are higher, you get more acres out of production. And if payment rates are high, you get a lot of acres out of production, but program costs are also high.

Further, with constant prices, and increased yields per acre, payment rates must increase to buy the same number of acres out of production. And, where yields per acre are increasing, an increased number of acres must be diverted from production to hold total output constant, or in line with a slowly growing demand. Thus, with rising productivity, program costs must, or are likely, to increase for two reasons: Payment rates per acre diverted from production must increase, and the number of acres diverted are likely to have to be increased. So voluntary programs lead to increased program costs—this is their limitation.

Attitudes versus Program Mechanics. We know what the nature of the commercial farm problem is—it is too many productive resources producing a little too much year after year. It is the production year after year of 5 to 10 percent more total product than the commercial market will take at the present level of prices. Now there are an infinite number of program mechanics, or combination of program mechanics, for dealing with this chronic excess capacity problem. Each one has certain advantages and certain disadvantages: Some cost more, some less; some raise farm income, some reduce it; some control on acres, some on bushels and pounds; and some restrict individual decision making and some enhance it. And between 1961 and 1964 the Kennedy-Johnson administration ran through the relevant numbers—costs, prices, acreages, production, stocks, exports—on a very large number of these alternatives.

The problem is not one of not knowing the myriad of alternative program mechanics that are available for dealing with the excess capacity problem. And it is not one of searching until one perfect program mechanic is found; there is no such thing as a perfect solution. The problem is one of having the courage, the attitude, to place in operation a program which has the capacity, the power, to eliminate excess productive capacity in farming.

Basically, the problem confronting the nation with respect to excess capacity in commercial farming is one of attitude, not of program mechanics. Many different program mechanics are available to deal with the excess capacity problem; what is lacking is the courage on the part of politicians, farm leaders, farmers themselves and farm economists who serve as advisors to place in operation any one, or combination, of the alternatives that has the capacity, but which hurts someone, to cope with the excess capacity problem. Rather than face the issue, those concerned keep searching for the perfect solution which they know does not exist, or have deluded themselves into believing does exist. Farm leaders and farm experts have tended to become alchemists, but instead of trying to turn lead into gold, they are trying to turn excess production capacity into higher farm incomes, lower government program costs, lower food prices and less production control. Frankly, I find those multiple objectives impossible of simultaneous achievement.

International Lessons. Those people who find it impossible to face the real issue of chronic excess capacity at home, turn increasingly to the never-never land of the export market. Somewhere in some far off place there must be hungry people "dying" to receive food packages from the United States, or there must be a dollar market that has not yet been found. Now, as we all know, there are millions of undernourished people in the underdeveloped countries, and the commercial export markets are expanding with rapid economic growth in Western Europe, Japan and to some extent the Soviet Bloc.

But we are moving now all the food under P.L. 480 that the recipient countries will take, either as a matter of national policy or as a matter of handling, storage and transportation facilities. Further, we are working the commercial export markets with all the skill and diligence that this government and private traders can muster. This is not to say that a different administration or another set of private traders might not expand exports somewhat more rapidly than present parties. But it is to say that there are no great "rat holes" overseas that have been overlooked, down which American farm surpluses may be poured without end.

If any country in the world needed more food in 1964, it was India. But we could not move more grain into India because of handling and storage bottlenecks. You cannot move food to hungry people if the means does not exist to get it there. And Americans have not faced the issue of improving and expanding the handling, storage and transportation facilities in the recipient countries, as well as providing food aid.

The European Common Market countries need to import more feed grains to produce the more meat that their consumers are demanding with their increased incomes. But whether more or less feed grains will be exported to the Common Market depends in large measure on the Common Agricultural Policy decided upon by the EEC countries. We can try to be influential in that decision, as we have been doing, but whether that great market for American feed grains develops as it has the potential to do, depends primarily on policy decisions made in Western Europe not in the United States.

The Economic Literacy of Farmers. The economic literacy of farmers generally is distressingly low. In the wheat referendum of 1963, there were farmers who actually believed that wheat prices would rise with the elimination of price support or the reduction of price support to 50 percent of parity for that commodity. Most livestock producers, and many of their leaders, have no conception whatsoever of the indirect price and income support provided producers of animal products through the support of feed grain prices. Most producers do not understand the differential effect on their income from an output increase on their particular farm resulting from a technological advance, and from an aggregate output increase resulting from the industry-wide adoption of a new and improved technology. And the implications of farm technological advance for the average size of farm and the number of farms and farmers are just not considered.

I believe that the economic literacy of farm people generally was higher in the 1930's than it is in the 1960's. The typical commercial farmer of the 1960's, is a better, much better, technologist than his father, but on economic matters extending beyond his own farm or his own community he is terribly blind. He does not see the industry-wide interdependencies; he assumes that what is good for his farm is good for the industry; and on intercommodity substitutional relationships he is lost.

Economic illiteracy is not critcally important in a laissez-faire situation. But when farmers as a whole are involved in the management of their economy, that illiteracy is terribly important. A managed economy, and that is what we have in agriculture, like it or not, cannot be run either effectively or smoothly if the managers do not comprehend the consequences of their decisions.

IMPLICATIONS OF THESE LESSONS FOR ECONOMICS

A Division of Labor between USDA and University Economists. There is a natural division of labor in the work of USDA economists and the work of university economists, and this division should, in my opinion, be recognized. The USDA is best equipped by reason of budget and facilities to do the basic economic intelligence work of agriculture. Further, effective administration of the operating programs of the USDA requires a constant inflow of basic economic intelligence regarding crops, prices, incomes, production, stocks and so on. Universities and foundations cannot compete with the USDA in crop and livestock reporting, in the issuance of Situation Reports, and in the periodic issuance of basic information publications such as *The World Food Budget, Farm Costs and Returns,* and the *Balance Sheet of Agriculture*; and they should not try. In general, I believe, that the USDA does an excellent job of this basic intelligence work, and where it is weak, it should be advised of that weakness in a constructive way.

The USDA is also best situated by reason of its large staff, familiarity with program operations and immediate access to the necessary data to formulate the many alternative program mechanics and crank through the quantitative results of those alternatives. The cost, price, income, production, stock consequences of one, or several, program alternatives can be cranked through the USDA in a week, where it might take a year or two to complete that job in a university.

There is a problem here, I grant, with respect to the publication of the quantitative results of alternative program mechanics during the decision phase by an administration, and sometimes a question with respect to the objectivity of the results if they are published. This problem could be minimized, however, if the division of labor in this policy area were fully recognized and the USDA expected to make public the quantitative results of its studies of alternative programs, and it was requested to do so by legitimate groups and organizations.

Actually, we are not too far from this situation at the present time; the congressional committees often request, receive and publish analyses of the USDA showing the quantitative results of program alternatives. Further, I would say that an administration that consciously deceives itself and the public with regard to the quantitative results of alternative program mechanics will soon find itself in serious trouble. And as I shall point out in a moment, one important role for university economists should be that of constructive criticism of the estimating work of the USDA.

This leads me to the lines of work that the university economists are best suited to do in the division of labor under consideration. I would suggest that university economists have a comparative advantage in three areas, or categories, of work relating to national policy questions.

The first area is—creative analyses and methodological studies that take time, involve new relationships and methods and lead to needed new and improved estimates. I have in mind such studies as the Brandow study, *Interrelations Among Demands for Farm Products and Implications for Control of Market Supply,*[2] the Working study, *Demand for Meat,*[3] and the Griliches study, "The Demand for Inputs in Agriculture and a Derived

---

[2] The Pennsylvania State University, Agr. Expt. Sta. Bul. No. 680, August 1961.
[3] Institute of Meat Packing and the University of Chicago, 1954.

Supply Elasticity."[4] The results and conclusions of studies such as these reduce the judgment area in policy decisions and they improve the estimating procedures of the USDA. But they take time, and time is what the worker in the USDA does not have when he is meeting a deadline for one of his intelligence reports or is a part of a department-wide team estimating the results of a program alternative. And if I understand what universities are in business to do, these kinds of studies fit into their mission perfectly; these studies are creative, they probe the unknown and hopefully turn up with a new idea, or concept or estimate.

Second, the university economists should perform as constructive critics—appraising and evaluating ongoing action programs, the research results of the USDA with respect to alternative program mechanics and the basic intelligence work of the USDA. In general, university economists have performed well in this role over the years, but the role could be improved and enlarged upon. And, I believe, that regularized channels of communication could be established for the making of and the acceptance of constructive criticism if this role were fully recognized by both the USDA and university economists and statisticians.

The third area involves—assistance to farmers and the general public in understanding the important and relevant policy problems growing out of the developing farm economy, and the economic and social consequences of different general approaches to those problems. This line of work is necessary to help farmers and the general public understand reality and confront it—rather than moving in a dream world. One of the best examples of work in this area that I can think of, is the work that Iowa State University has done showing the general consequences of a free market approach.

More of this work needs to be done. Not more free market studies, but more in the way of helping farmers understand the nature and the causes of the problems that beset them, and realistic approaches for coping with those problems. University economists must assume the responsibility of helping farmers maintain contact with reality—the conceptualization of the real problems that confront them and the real relationships and forces that are involved in those problems.

The lines of work suggested here for university economists, on one hand, and the USDA economists and statisticians, on the other, do not represent any important breaks with the past. But the delineation does suggest, I believe, a rather natural division of labor in the work of these different groups of economists. And an understanding and recognition of this division of labor would help some individuals to find the right niche for themselves. I know it took me a long time to recognize that there are some things that you can and should do in the government with regard to policy work and other things that you cannot. And, I believe, as I look around me, that the

[4] *Journal of Farm Economics,* May 1959.

implications of this division of labor are not as yet fully clear to all of my colleagues.

The Economic Literacy Problem. It was argued earlier that the general state of economic literacy among farmers was in bad repair. If this is true, which I believe it to be, agricultural economists generally, but university economists in particular, must assume the blame. Why this is true I am not completely clear. But I have a theory or two.

First, agricultural economists engaged in the dual capacity of teaching and research have shortchanged their educational role and stressed their research role. Resident economists in agricultural colleges have been more concerned with exotic model building, than they have been with presenting and enlarging upon the important and relevant, although perhaps obvious, economic relationships in food and agriculture. Thus, we have dazzling theoretical spatial equilibrium models, but few economists explaining to farm leaders the effect of feed grain prices upon livestock production, hence upon livestock prices. And we have elegant theoretical welfare functions, but few economists explaining to farm leaders the implications of technological advance for farm incomes, sizes of farms and number of farmers.

Second, the extension economists in the state universities have been willing to carry intrafirm theory and practice to farmers. Hence, many farmers have become good practicing production economists. But extension workers generally have not, for one reason or another, carried interfirm theory and practice to farmers. Hence, farmers almost to the man do not understand and appreciate the aggregate, or industry-wide, implications of individual firm and consumer actions.

The time has come, and long since past, to do something about this economic literacy problem. Unless farmers understand the basic economic relationships of their industry, there is no way to confront them with reality with respect to the problems of their industry. Thus, it seems to me that each extension director, each head of a department of agricultural economics and each agricultural economist who thinks of himself as a leader, must give this problem very high priority in his thoughts and actions.

And more is involved here than presenting and extending "the facts." Farmers are barraged with facts. The problem is one of assisting farmers to gain a working knowledge of the important and relevant economic relationships involved in their industry. Somehow, some way farmers generally must gain this understanding.

The Future of Farm Policy. It is not the purpose of this final section of this paper to make predictions of things to come. It is the purpose, however, to describe what I believe to be a collision course in commercial farm policy, and to discuss the implications of that prospective collision.

Farmers generally have made it clear, as of the middle 1960's, that effective, mandatory controls are unacceptable to them. They do, however, appear to actually like voluntary control programs in which they are paid to remove acres from production. The program costs of voluntary control programs are high, and for reasons already discussed such costs are likely to increase with increased productivity per acre. But with the increased urbanization of the American society, and the unhappiness of the urban voter with farm programs, there must be some limit to farm program costs that the urban electorate will accept. And I believe that we are now at that limit or very close to it. Thus, the objective of farmers to have price and income support coupled with voluntary controls runs squarely into the budget limitation objective of urban people with regard to farm programs.

With a rate of increased agricultural productivity, which pushes total farm output continuously ahead of demand, such as we have experienced for the past 10 years, the collision is inescapable. The beginnings of the collision might well have been heard in 1965, except for two things: the poor crop in 1964 throughout the Middle West, and the heavy vote by farmers for President Johnson. These two very different developments could delay the collision for a year or two or three. But barring a major catastrophe such as a hot shooting war or an intensification and enlargement of the present spotty drought conditions, increased agricultural productivity is going to drive farm program costs, under voluntary control programs, into direct collision with the budget limitation objectives of the urban voter within the next 3 to 10 years. A crisis in commercial farm policy is in the making.

I am aware of the fact that the literature is full of "years-of-decision" and crises with respect to farm policy that have never materialized, and this paper may turn out to be simply another of those dire but incorrect prophecies. But I don't think so; the forces involved here are too general and too powerful. This does not mean, however, that I, or anyone else, can predict the timing of this crisis, the incidents leading up to it, the exact form that it will take, or its results. The forces at work are there to be seen by anyone who cares to take a careful look, but the timing and nature of the collision requires omniscience.

Any number of things could happen. To bring to a halt the rise in farm program costs, and possibly reduce budgetary expenditures, the administration might itself slowly reduce the level of farm price support. This would be a painful decision indeed, but it could happen. Or congress could do a number of things. It could simply place a budget ceiling on farm programs of price and income support and direct the administration to formulate programs that operate within that ceiling. Or it could simply not reenact all or some part of the wheat, cotton, and feed grain commodity legislation, in which case the program for each commodity reverts to a disaster type program where either the Secretary is directed to lower the level of support in accordance with certain specified criteria, or the level of price support declines automatically. Or it is even possible that farmers might rethink their production control position, and accept controls that keep supplies in balance with demand at lower levels of government costs.

But if this collision course argument is correct, then one thing is certain. The urban voter must give way with respect to budget objectives, or the farmer must give way with respect to the present level of price support under a system of voluntary controls. For 10 years the urban voter has been beating a Fabian retreat with regard to farm program costs. But I for one believe that the retreat is about over. Thus, I believe that farmers will be forced, in the next 3 to 10 years, to accept some major changes in the present policy of price and income protection.

This is the really big lesson that I learned in the past four years.

27 The Decline of the Agricultural Establishment*

JAMES T. BONNEN†

> "Woe to him that is alone when he falleth; for he hath not another to help him up."
>
> *Ecclesiastes* 4:10

What is the present state of agricultural policy? Understanding the present state of affairs always involves knowing some previous state. What policy decision makers are doing today is not only conditioned but also predetermined in a major degree by the successes and failures of time past—as well as by the changing structure of our political, economic, and social institutions. I want to look at each of these matters in turn. But first, where are we today and how did we get there?

Clearly we are at another node in agricultural policy. Over the decade ending in 1963 two alternative approaches to the farm problem were attempted. Both failed for lack of political acceptance. During the Eisenhower years, Secretary Benson made a valiant attempt, as he would put it, to return the farmer to the free market. Following that, the Kennedy Administration attempted to implement a system of government-run supply management using mandatory controls. Both of these approaches are now denied us. What is left?

---

* Originally titled "Present and Prospective Policy Problems of U.S. Agriculture: As Viewed by an Economist," published in *Journal of Farm Economics,* Vol. 47, No. 5 (December 1965), pp. 1116–29.

† Michigan State University, East Lansing, Michigan. The author is indebted to James D. Shaffer and Charles M. Hardin for several very helpful suggestions, and to a number of colleagues who generously provided critical responses to some of the arguments of this paper when they were presented in seminars and speeches over the past 18 months. Any errors of fact or judgment are the author's. The responsibility for the views and ideas of this paper is solely his. This paper is a further development of the research into the changing form and function of rural institutions begun five years ago. See James T. Bonnen, "The First Hundred Years of the Department of Agriculture—Land Grant College System: Some Observations on the Organizational Nature of a Great Technological Payoff," *Journal of Farm Economics,* Vol. 44 (December 1962), pp. 1279–94.

One must look at the successes of these two administrations to answer this. The Eisenhower Administration presided over the creation of PL 480, the Soil Bank, and a great enlargement of domestic supplemental and special food programs. The Soil Bank was not an unalloyed success, but it was the experiment from which we have learned much of what we know today about how to withdraw land from farm production. The Kennedy Administration passed an emergency feed grain bill in 1961 which is genuinely popular with farmers and which contains several ideas since extended to wheat and now extended to cotton in the 1965 Omnibus Farm Bill. Briefly the feed grain program, as fully developed, 1) requires farmers to divert some minimum acreage in order to be eligible for price supports, 2) provides payments for diverting the minimum acreage and for the voluntary diversion of additional acreage, and 3) prohibits the use of diverted acreage for planting to other major crops. This weds price supports to land withdrawal and keys acreage diversion to a specific commodity acreage allotment.

The price-support payment and the diversion-payment techniques tend to separate the income-support operation from the pricing mechanism. This gives one a fighting chance to maintain farm income while cutting surplus stocks and letting prices move toward a level that reduces the incentive for overproduction and allows the farmer to compete in world markets without export subsidies.

The final innovation of the Kennedy years was the application of the two-price certificate plan to wheat, which transfers part of the program cost from taxpayers to consumers.

These successful innovations of the past decade will be important pieces of any answer to the problems we now face.

POLICY PROBLEMS AND ALTERNATIVES

In the short run our choices amount to an economic and political dilemma. With voluntary programs, the unrelenting pressure of significant annual increases in yields means that budget costs go up each year—even if you are only maintaining the same level of farm income. Each year politicians are faced with a "Hobson's choice" between greater budgetary costs or higher prices to the consumer (via certificate-type systems), and—failing increases in either budget or prices—lower total farm income. If in the process of making political choices it is decided that farm-program budgets must be reduced, then total farm income (though not necessarily average per-farm income) must fall as a direct consequence, unless the costs of these programs can be transferred to the consumer. This is the economic dilemma. It is also a political dilemma, since each of these variables—budget, consumer costs, and farm income—involves politically potent interests.

Over the longer run we are faced with additional problems and alternatives. In trade policy shall we focus exclusively on our domestic markets and continue to play the role of the world market's high-priced residual supplier or shall we lower our prices to the level of the world market, negotiate some changes in the rules, and compete?

The future growth in world food and fiber markets will be that generated primarily by the economic growth of the developing nations.[1] Yet many of these nations are now apparently losing in the race between population growth and food production.[2] Crisis or no, under grossly inconsistent political demands, we allow PL 480 to fritter away its potential trying to be all things to all men. Should we continue to use PL 480 as an instrument of trade expansion, hardening the terms of aid until it becomes trade? Should we in agriculture continue to look at PL 480 as a "rat hole" down which to shove farm products or should we assume some responsibility for tying it to economic development in a more meaningful manner?[3]

When are we, in program design, going to face up to the asset-inflation-income paradox with its implications for the soundness of the farm financial structure, the process of intergenerational transfer of farms, the question of factor returns and the ownership and organization of the factors of production?[4]

Related is the question of when we are going to do something about the problems of people in rural life. As T. W. Schultz has pointed out repeatedly, the behavior of rural people, their representatives, and their institutions implies a materialistic bias in favor of plants, land, and animals and against people.[5] Our farm programs are specifically designed to do things to improve the value of plants, land, and animals. Even from the point of view solely of the farmers' welfare—to say nothing of the rest of the rural community or society as a whole—we have underinvested in rural health, education, and the other social services which develop the potential and productivity of people. It is hardly surprising that the primary result of our rural public-investment policy has been an inflation in farm-asset values while the returns

---

[1] Arthur B. Mackie, "Foreign Economic Growth and Market Potentials for U.S. Agricultural Products," USDA ERS For. Agr. Econ. Rep. 24, April 1965.

[2] Lester R. Brown, "Increasing World Food Output," USDA ERS For. Agr. Econ. Rep. 25, April 1965.

[3] The intertwined problems of trade, aid, and development policy are legion. Many of these are identified in the AFEA Presidential Address of D. Gale Johnson, "Agriculture and Foreign Economic Policy," *Journal of Farm Economics,* Vol. 46 (December 1964), pp. 915–29. See also W. W. Cochrane, "Some Observations of an Ex Economic Advisor: Or What I Learned in Washington," *Journal of Farm Economics,* Vol. 47 (May 1965), pp. 453–56.

[4] Walter E. Chryst, "Land Values and Agricultural Income: A Paradox?" *Journal of Farm Economics,* Vol. 47 (December 1965), pp. 1265–73, and Mason Gaffney, "The Benefits of Farm Programs: Incidence, Shifting, and Dissipation," *Journal of Farm Economics,* Vol. 47 (December 1965), pp. 1252–63.

[5] T. W. Schultz, "Underinvestment in the Quality of Schooling: The Rural Farm Areas," in *Increasing Understanding of Public Problems and Policies: 1965* (Chicago: Farm Foundation, 1964), pp. 26–29, and "Changing Relevance of Agricultural Economics," *Journal of Farm Economics,* Vol. 46 (December 1964), pp. 1007–8.

to the human factor in rural life have fallen further and further behind those to the urban community.

Will we continue to ignore the mounting problems and social ills associated with race, with rural poverty—with hired farm labor including migratory labor?

All of these matters are involved in some degree and manner in the public policy choices which commercial agriculture will be asked to make over the next few years in farm programs. They also are related to the choices with which the USDA and the colleges are faced in deciding the focus of their research.

The reason we have many of our present problems is that commercial farmers, their leaders, the USDA, the colleges, and other rural institutions have done very badly in making these choices. In part they have not always faced the facts of life honestly. But the real explanation lies in a single-minded pursuit of self-interest made lethal by inaccurate perception of where self-interest lies.

I wish to devote the rest of this article to the behavior of these institutions. I shall argue that the key problem of U.S. agriculture, present or prospective, is its own behavior, which is distorting and disordering the decision-making processes in which it is intimately involved.

THE DECISION-MAKING STRUCTURE OF AGRICULTURE

Four developments dominate any realistic description of the policy scene today.

1. The general power structure of this society has been transformed. But the political leadership of agriculture has either not awakened to this fact or it is trapped by its own past policies and mythologies, unable—even unwilling—to adapt organization, policies, and tactics to be effective in the new *realpolitik*.
2. The commercial agricultural power structure has reached a state of extreme organizational fragmentation, and its leadership is so engrossed in internecine warfare that these fragmented elements of commercial agriculture are themselves contributing greatly to a general erosion of the political power which together they exert.
3. The entire web of rural organizations had an original common goal of the economic development of American agriculture. Thus, no matter how diverse in origin they may have been, as a result of having a common general goal, they evolved into an *interdependent* set of organizations. Today this underlying complex of *interdependent* commercial, governmental, political, and educational organizations in the service of agriculture is changing, and no longer is as effective as once it was in identifying and solving the problems of rural life. The organizational system in agriculture is becoming socially disfunctional.

4. With few exceptions, in any direction you look, there are rising levels of conflict, destructive tension, and mounting evidence of what can only be described as a spectacular failure of leadership combined with "organizational dry rot." The generation of individuals who now man as well as lead these organizations do not understand their dependence one upon another; nor do they perceive the changing situation of their sister institutions well enough to be able to relate themselves in a manner that avoids unnecessary conflict. They are thus led into mutually self-destructive patterns of behavior.

The vitality of these rural institutions should be a matter of concern not just for its contributions to farmers or to rural life but for its continued potential contribution to the growth of the economy and the welfare of the American consumer.

I shall call this web of rural institutions the Agricultural Establishment.[6]

THE DISINTEGRATING SYSTEM

Over the last half of the nineteenth century and the first quarter of this century, we built a series of institutions to serve and transform agriculture from a traditional subsistence farming to a technologically progressive production process capable of sustaining higher levels of rural and national welfare. The functions of some of these institutions are now at least partially obsolete; others are so completely realized that the institutions, in order to survive, are looking for new roles. In other cases, where the old role may still be viable, the environmental facts of life have changed so greatly that the institution is under pressure to perform new functions (some not even related to rural life); and, finally, many of the old organizational forms are no longer effective. As a consequence, while the institutions survive the system is failing.

The land grant colleges and the USDA were created as research and educational organizations for the purpose of generating and extending new technologies to farming and generally aiding rural people in attaining higher level of living. Originally their organizations were strikingly similar. Today both have changed. The primary role of the USDA has been entirely transformed. Its research functions now account for less than 4 percent of its budget; about 85 percent of its budget is now devoted to gigantic programs of farm income support, conservation, and credit.[7] As a consequence, it now is organized very differently and its decision-making structure is no longer dominated by researchers and academically oriented people. Thus, it no longer behaves (nor is it free to behave) as the university-like organization it

---

[6] Schultz, "Underinvestment in the Quality of Schooling," p. 27.

[7] U.S. Congress, House of Representatives, Subcommittee of the Committee on Appropriations, *Hearings, Department of Agriculture Appropriations for 1966 Part 1* (89th Cong., 1st sess.), p. 346.

was until the late 1930's—but many land grant universities complacently presume on their relationship with the USDA as if nothing had changed and as if the USDA were a large philanthropic foundation on the banks of the Potomac devoted to being kind to friendly and deserving colleges of agriculture. Needless to say, the USDA has failed to act in this image and the level of tension and misunderstanding between the colleges and USDA has risen greatly.

The land grant university has changed also. It was once exclusively devoted to the affairs of rural life and farming. Now, however, it is under the most intense pressure to become a full-scale, high-quality institution of higher learning. It is in the process of extending its teaching, research and public service functions not only to the rest of our society but into the international area as well.

Caught in the middle of this transformation of his university, the Dean of Agriculture finds his college beleaguered within the University by these new growing and competitive functions, abused and often abandoned by his clients and allies in agriculture, and in many ways less able to control his college's destiny than at any time since the early unsettled days of the land grant system. But the USDA, and farm people, and their representatives resent and do not understand the causes of these changes in the role, and therefore, the behavior of "their college."

Let me provide a few examples of specific attitudes and behavior that are destroying the fabric of the relationship between the USDA and the colleges of agriculture.

1. Many department heads and professors in the agricultural colleges willingly take any USDA money, if it supports their programs, but have such a negative attitude toward the USDA as a scientific environment that they would encourage their better students to seek employment in almost any place rather than the Department. Yet without the high quality national research program of the USDA and its many services, these agricultural college professionals and their departments would have only a fraction of their present capacity.
2. Similarly, many USDA research administrators frequently express deep resentment that any of "their money" goes to the colleges, most of which they view as competitive and generally inadequate research organizations with high overhead costs. Indeed, many have come to believe that scientific progress will be achieved only by the establishment of large specialized USDA-operated laboratories. Yet many of these same administrators expect the agricultural colleges to "produce" for them high-quality, well-trained talent to man the research and action organs of the Department. They refuse to believe they have any responsibility for the human investment process from which they draw much of their trained personnel.
3. Most Secretaries of Agriculture tend to view Extension as their personal

field staff for *selling* new policies and action programs. Since Extension must (or should) maintain the politically neutral position of an educational agency, this expectation can only lead to frustration and recrimination.

4. There is another set of attitudes that is eroding the once close relationship of the colleges and the Department. Originally the Extension Services of the land grant colleges were intimately associated with their state Farm Bureaus. In more recent decades in practically all states this direct linkage has been broken or substantially weakened. At the same time agricultural politics has become polarized and the American Farm Bureau has aligned itself with the conservatives on all issues and with the Republican Party on most political matters. The USDA, however, whether run by Democrats or Republicans, continues generally to regard the colleges as a monolith of conservatism and often the personal property of the Republican Party. The general farm organizations share this attitude toward the colleges, and the more liberal organizations either refuse to support or directly attack the colleges of agriculture. While this characterization of the colleges is accurate for some states it is not true for the system as a whole. Rarely do the farm organizations or the USDA recognize that changes have occurred or that the states and their colleges vary in their behavior, nor do they bother to test the colleges' current patterns of behavior. This attitude has had unfortunate effects on many actions of the Department. Where the colleges and their extension services actually commit themselves to a partnership with any political party or even to a distinct political philosophy, they discredit themselves and destroy the national character of the Extension system.

One could go on at length to other attitudes and behavior which are eroding the relations between the colleges and the USDA, in mutually self-destructive patterns. I do not mean to imply that these attitudes do not reflect some real problems, but, because of a mutual failure to understand the other's situation, we are letting them become destructive of the fabric of our institutions. These examples are only symptoms of the problem—which is that *the roles we play have changed.*

I submit that if these two very interdependent organizations, the colleges of agriculture and the USDA, do not understand each other's modern roles and behavior any better than this, then they cannot really understand their own very well. The same kind of evidence of mutually destructive behavior is to be found in the relationships of practically all rural institutions: the colleges, the USDA, local rural community organizations both public and private, and the many organizations that attempt to represent the various interests of the farmer including the agricultural committees of Congress.

The land grant university is no longer linked exclusively to rural institutions at either the state or the federal level. Research, teaching, and extension funds come from many sources today and not even the federal relations of the college of agriculture are predominantly or exclusively with the Department of Agriculture and the agriculture committees of Congress. The land grant university is broadening its old functions of education and service to rural America, to service and education for the whole of society. The USDA has been forced to narrow its function to service for commercial agriculture alone. The colleges of agriculture, whether they like it or not, are being forced to move in both directions simultaneously and are having a very bad time of it.

The USDA, to an even greater degree than the college of agriculture, is no longer the master of its own house to the extent that it was in the 1920's and 1930's—when it was primarily a research and educational institution. Now that it is an action agency dispensing vast sums of money which directly affect the incomes and welfare of farmers, the agricultural committees of Congress, acting as agents of the commercial interests of agriculture, have taken over a substantial portion of the Department's executive function. Until very recently the committees exercised these functions with little concern for the desires of the Secretary of Agriculture or even the President of the United States.

No Secretary of Agriculture in modern times has really had effective control of the Department of Agriculture. This frustration of the Secretary's function is a consequence of the near monopoly of power in agriculture exercised by commercial agricultural interests (including nonfarm interests allied with farming) and focused primarily in specialized commodity organizations and the grass roots farmer committee structures which extend to the Washington level. Operating through the committees of Congress, they have badly mauled the Department of Agriculture in the past when it has not behaved solely as the agent of the commercial and business interests in agriculture. This severely limits the Department's capacity for public consideration of broader rural interests or even the public interest in agriculture. That the USDA is made to behave so it injures not only the Department, but commercial agriculture. It tends to give the USDA and agriculture an image in government, and in the rest of the society, of little more than that of a powerful but narrow and badly behaved vested interest.

The agricultural colleges look a little better only because they do not run commodity programs. For the colleges, too, under somewhat similar pressures, have tended to narrow their focus *in agriculture* predominantly on the interests of commercial agriculture. Thus, it can be said that the Land-Grant–USDA System has lost its dedication to the welfare of the *entire* rural community. We long have talked about doing something for the noncommercial and the nonfarm sectors—the problems of rural communities and the poor—but we never really seem willing to put "our money where our mouth is." We have missed many opportunities. For example, issues in market organization and bargaining power are being posed with urgency and obvious relevance today. There is also an urgent need to take program action on the multiplex aspects of poverty. Yet in neither case have the colleges or USDA put enough resources into research in these areas to provide the analytical base. The problems have been identified for decades but little research done. In the case of poverty, this is because it does not benefit the power structure in agriculture and it also diverts resources from the research interests of commercial agriculture. In the case of market organization, this is because the research results almost invariably upset some politically potent part of the market structure. So now we must make decisions and take action without adequate knowledge.

Yet the Department of Agriculture when it focuses on the problems of commercial agriculture generally performs with more imagination, polish, and expertise than all but a few small parts of the rest of the federal executive. No executive department has *the capacity* for objective problem solving and for administration of complex programs which the Department of Agriculture has.

No executive department is as badly abused by those it serves as the Department of Agriculture.[8] No other member of the President's Cabinet is subjected to the demeaning, public as well as private, political vituperation that is the daily fare of the Secretary of Agriculture—heaped upon him by the people he serves. His political usefulness is eroded in the vindictive cross fire leveled by the conflicting elements of the farm policy arena. He is held politically responsible for the design and execution of all policies by the very same brawling set of commercial agricultural interests who simultaneously attempt to deny him an effective role in the design of the same policies.

The result is that, in its efforts to limit or destroy the Secretary politically, commercial agriculture is destroying itself politically. This is not politics. Politics is the art of the possible—the compromise of conflicting interest. But in agriculture, many have forgotten what compromise is and are now engaged in a war, each to obtain his own ends, with no quarter given or expected and apparently with no concern for the long-run cost to agriculture —or to rural life, or to the Nation. Like the god of antiquity, Saturn, agriculture is devouring its own.

THE CHANGING POLITICAL POWER STRUCTURE OF COMMERCIAL AGRICULTURE

What has been the effect of the successful economic development of farming upon the political structure of commercial agriculture? In the process of increasing their productivity, farmers specialized in the production of one or a few commodities. The farm supply and farm product marketing systems have become highly specialized. Similarly, entire farming regions became specialized. Thus there have developed within agriculture many narrow and often conflicting economic and political interests. The conflicts grew so great

[8] The only exception, in my judgment, might be the Department of Justice.

over time that it became increasingly difficult for the general farm organizations to develop a national policy position, particularly on specific commodity legislation. The old farm bloc of pre-World War II days broke up and the specialized commodity organizations began to assume the initiative and control over much of agricultural policy, particularly as it related to commodities. Other specialized farmer county committee structures, created during the 1930's in the price-support, conservation, and credit areas, developed national organizations to reflect more directly their special interests in the political process. This fragmentation of the political organization of agriculture has transformed agricultural policy from reasonably consistent legislation, with broad social purposes generally supported by the society, into a hodge-podge of narrow special-interest legislation, the value of which is increasingly questioned by society.

Agricultural policy has come to mean commodities and little else other than a slight seasoning of conservation and credit. Through commodity and other specialized farmer organizations, the larger successful commercial farmers have come to dominate if not monopolize the political power structure of agriculture. And in the pursuit of their own interests practically all other concerns have been sacrificed—including most prominently the interests of the many small struggling commercial operators and the more than a million even smaller noncommercial operators whose prospect for earning a better living from farming is quite limited. Forgotten also are the problems and concerns of the better part of the rural population, which as a result of the development of agriculture are no longer a part of farming. In ignoring these and other public claims for its concern and support, commercial agriculture has injured its own interests.

The specialized commodity groups continue to brawl incessantly with each other. But the composition of these groups is changing and their power in the aggregate is now declining. This decline appears to be due to two things. The first is the increasing fragmentation of producer interests. For example, in cotton the producers themselves cannot agree on what they want. For years they have been fragmented into the Southeast, Mississippi Delta, Texas, and California–Arizona areas. Today even these groups are seriously fragmented. The other cause for the decline in power lies in the increasing voice of interests other than the producers in any commodity decision-making process. In cotton, for example, ginners and handlers, textile mills, cotton brokers and exporters, and the cotton exchanges all have an effective political voice in the decision-making process. In addition, rural community banking and commercial interests, the manufacturers of farm inputs, and even organized labor have an influence on what happens. As a consequence, the level of conflict and disorder is so great at present that it is almost impossible to get agreement within agricultural committees on legislation for many specific commodities.

Because of this disorder, the power of political decision making for agriculture is already in the process of drifting or is being transferred from the agriculture committees to other places in the Congress and to the Executive Branch. The disorder not only makes it nearly impossible to get a major decision in an agriculture committee but now makes agricultural legislation so politically expensive that legislation cannot be pushed through Congress without a political brawl or a major assist from the White House or both. Indeed, agricultural legislation of the present social outlook has grown to be the single, most politically expensive part of the legislative program of any President and his party. Political capital used to push the farm program through represents a reduction in the amount of political capital available to push the rest of the program through. It would be remarkable in such a situation if the majority party and the White House did not desire a reduction both in budgetary and political costs of farm legislation.

AGRICULTURE AND THE CHANGING POWER STRUCTURE OF THE SOCIETY

But before farm legislation can be made more acceptable and thus lower in political cost, the leaders of farm organizations and commercial agriculture will have to do a better job of relating themselves to the present power structure of this society. The political power structure which rural America helped to create many decades ago is gone forever. Gone, too, are the days of rural dominance in the political affairs of national, state, or local government. Rural leadership shows little sign even yet of understanding that it no longer leads a political majority. If rural people and their organizations are to have any continuing major role in determining agricultural and rural policy, their minority position must be faced honestly and they must learn how to work with and influence the new power structure.

AGRICULTURE'S POLITICAL LIFE STYLE

A minority must develop leverage far beyond its own direct impact if it is to exercise any effective political power. In the U.S. political structure, minority groups have the greatest potential advantage *today* in the political process that focuses on the capture of the executive organs of government. Holding or losing the political support of minority groups can mean the difference in a party's success or failure in capturing the executive branch. Thus, to maximize their power, minority groups must focus on the political party, the instrument that focuses on the capture of the executive branch. Rural people and their leaders will have to involve themselves actively in the partisan political process, and in both parties, if they are to generate enough political power to insure a continuing major role in agricultural and rural public-policy problems.[9]

---

[9] Dale E. Hathaway, "Problems Facing Rural America," *Journal of Cooperative Extension,* Vol. 3 (Fall 1965), pp. 165–72.

Farm-organization leaders and rural politicians, to be effective, must back away from their traditional hard-nosed Neanderthal style and from their prepackaged ideologies to combine in a politically pragmatic manner with whomever they can. Unlike a majority group, a minority to succeed must be prepared to recognize the most urgent or reasonable objectives of others. Majority groups tend to respond only to the demands of other majority groups or coalitions, and do not need to concern themselves greatly with the claims of minorities or even with the public interest. Rural and agricultural leaders must be so concerned if they are to survive. It is the obstinate refusal of the Agricultural Establishment to accommodate itself to the major and urgent problems of urban life that has generated the present intense hostility toward all things rural or agricultural. This hostility is most evident in the urban press and the political behavior of labor, among the frustrated political leaders of the urban metropolitan complexes, and in the intellectual community of scientific and professional people, many of whom are not only opinion makers, but also integral members of the present power structure.

The Rise of Urban Fundamentalism

It is almost cosmic irony that just as rural fundamentalism is clearly losing its influence outside rural life, an urban fundamentalism of equal irrationality and virulence has risen to replace it.[10] It now infests the seats of power like rural fundamentalism before it, disordering and distorting private, political, and bureaucratic decision-making processes. By urban fundamentalism, I understand a closed attitude of mind which asserts that urban society, its culture, and its values are intrinsically superior and should be the dominant mold in which all society is cast and the measure against which all social decisions are made. This disdain of everything outside of metropolitan urban culture, like its mirror image, rural fundamentalism, is predicated on a contemptuous ignorance—a disdain for and a fear of what is not understood or not experienced. Urban fundamentalism is the result of the increasing incidence of an exclusively urban cultural experience reinforced by fifty bruising years of urban intellectual and political frustration with the political and cultural imperialism of rural life. The Agricultural Establishment has been casting its fundamentalist bread upon the waters for decades. It is now being returned, multiplied many fold.

CONCLUSION

The entire web of rural institutions, which I have called the Agricultural Establishment, had an original common goal of the economic development of American agriculture. Thus, no matter how diverse in origin they may have

---

[10] On rural fundamentalism see Joseph S. Davis, "Agricultural Fundamentalism," in *Readings on Agricultural Policy* (Philadelphia: Blakiston Com., 1949), pp. 3–17.

been, as a result of having a common general goal they evolved into an *interdependent* set of institutions. To be interdependent is to depend in a mutually constructive tension one on another for continued effectiveness and even existence. This common goal of the economic development of agriculture has now been substantially obtained. As a result of the effect of this success and the impact of the economic and social forces generated by an industrializing society, this interdependent web of institutions

1. is now developing multiple goals, many of which are in conflict;
2. is becoming ineffective in the pursuit of its goals as a result of its failure to adjust rapidly enough to the realities of its new nature and new environment;
3. is failing to understand its basically interdependent nature, and thus is in serious danger of destroying itself as an effective instrument of rural public life; and finally
4. the odds for failure are even longer for there is the clear evidence that we are in the middle of a general failure of leadership, which while common to all institutions is *particularly critical in commercial agriculture,* where the power of political decision has been vested in the recent past. The leadership in moving their own institutions today must contend with professionalized bureaucracies that show growing signs of rigidity and organizational dry rot.

The *system* of organizations in the service of agriculture is disintegrating because of a lack of breadth and flexibility of view. This system was once reasonably self-contained. It is not now. It is now dependent upon, and must now be related to, a broad range of social and economic institutions and problems that go well beyond the experience and immediate interests of commercial agriculture.

Despite many changes leading toward conflict, the fundamental institutions of agriculture are still bound together in a common destiny. This system still has great potential. However, the leaders as well as the members of these institutions have failed to understand each other's changing situation and roles, and now abuse each other for failing to behave in the old patterns. The people and institutions of agriculture—whether farmers, their organizations, the colleges, the USDA, the agriculture committees and members of Congress, and our state legislatures, or others—must learn to tolerate multiple goals in the institutions with which they must cooperate. They must accept a looser sort of partnership in working toward their goals. They must learn to be more pragmatic. They must combine on those matters where they can agree. They must not refuse to cooperate to one end just because they cannot agree on another.

The role of leadership in agriculture has grown to be nasty, brutish, and frustrating—whether one speaks of the Secretary of Agriculture, the dean of the college of agriculture, the head of a farm organization, the chairman of a congressional agriculture committee, or any other agricultural leader. This fact of life is not well appreciated even in these leaders' own organizations. Even so, the major conclusion one must draw from the self-destructive behavior of the Agricultural Establishment is that there has been a general failure of leadership in the institutions underlying the policy process.

Rural leaders have isolated themselves from the present power structure and have yet to learn that they must adapt their own position to that of various groups in the power structure if successful coalitions are to be formed and if they are thus to obtain farm or rural minority objectives in the public and private decision-making processes.

The recent Omnibus Farm Bill passed Congress in part because of the support of labor, which was obtained by the Northern rural congressmen who voted for labor's major 1965 legislative objective, repeal of Section 14b of the Taft-Hartley Act. Rural leaders and politicians will have to have the support of just such groups if rural problems are to be solved in the future in a manner generally acceptable to rural people.

It is in the self-interest of the Agricultural Establishment not only that it change its political style of life, but also that it face its past errors honestly and subject its organizational form and programs, which are increasingly difficult to rationalize or defend, to the searching gaze of objective analysis and intelligent adjustment. It is already late. If the Agricultural Establishment fails to face the facts of its existence honestly and with intelligence, many of the institutions of agriculture will continue down their present unconscious path toward social irrelevance and oblivion. If the Agricultural Establishment continues, as it often has in the past, to prevent or discourage its educational and research arms from fully servicing this function of objective analysis, or if the land grant colleges and the USDA do not have the courage to fulfill this role, the Establishment will be finished as a socially useful system in a few years in any case. And the individual institutions, while surviving any of us here, will live out their organizational lives in socially diminishing roles of rising frustration and futility. The time that remains to put agriculture's house in order may not be long.

I like the way John Steinbeck described one of his characters as possessing "a fine steel wire of truthfulness—that cut off the heads of fast traveling lies." The great strength of the Agricultural Establishment in prevailing in the policy process in the past depended not only on political power but also on a dedication to the broad objectives of society and on the Land-Grant–USDA System's capacity to "cut off the heads of fast traveling lies."

As the direct political power of the Agricultural Establishment declines or becomes diffuse, it must increasingly depend on such "fine steel wires" and a clear recognition that, to survive, it must exhibit far more relevance to the broader objectives of society.

If the Agricultural Establishment cannot develop the leadership that is capable of seeing the situation as it really is and adjusting to it, it not only will fail to survive in any systemic and socially meaningful form but the system will deserve its death. And the headstone erected by an urban society will read:

THE AGRICULTURAL ESTABLISHMENT OF THE UNITED STATES:
ITS PROMISE EXCEEDED ITS PERFORMANCE,
AND FALLING INTO SOCIAL IRRELEVANCE
IT TOOK ITS OWN USELESS LIFE.
R. I. P.

Index of Names

Index of Names*

* In the Editors' Introduction there are many references to leading agricultural economists and their publications, mostly of dates prior to 1945; these references are not included in the Index of Names. The article by Charles M. Hardin, "The Bureau of Agricultural Economics Under Fire" (pp. 423–52), contains a great many references to congressmen and other public figures who were involved in the politics of agriculture during 1938–46. Most of these references are omitted from the Index of Names to maintain its emphasis on persons who have contributed to agricultural economics on a scientific level.

O

P

R

S

This book has been set in 10 and 9 point Times New Roman, leaded 2 points. Part numbers are 18 point Times New Roman; part and reading titles are 14 point Times New Roman; reading numbers are 24 point Times New Roman. The size of the type page is 27 by 45½ picas.